HETEROGENEOUS REACTIONS: ANALYSIS, EXAMPLES, AND REACTOR DESIGN

Volume 2

HETEROGENEOUS REACTIONS:
Analysis, Examples, and Reactor Design

Volume 2: Fluid-Fluid-Solid Reactions

L. K. DORAISWAMY

Director
National Chemical Laboratory
Poona, India

M. M. SHARMA

Professor of Chemical Engineering
Bombay University Department of Chemical Technology
Bombay, India

A Wiley-Interscience Publication

JOHN WILEY & SONS

New York / Chichester / Brisbane / Toronto / Singapore

Library of Congress Cataloging in Publication Data:

Doraiswamy, L. K. (Laxmangudi Krishnamurthy)
Heterogeneous reactions.

Includes indexes.
Contents: v. 1. Gas–solid and solid–solid reactions—
v. 2. Fluid–fluid–solid reactions.
1. Chemical reactors. 2. Chemical reactions.
I. Sharma, M. M. (Man Mohan) II. Title
TP157.D67 1983 660.2′99 82-19968
ISBN 0-471-05368-6 (v.1)
ISBN 0-471-05367-8 (v. 2)

Printed in the United States of America

10 9 8 7 6 5 4 3 2 1

Preface

The first major book on the design of certain classes of chemical reactors appeared in the late 1940s as Volume 3 of the now classical *Chemical Process Principles* by O. A. Hougen and K. M. Watson. This was followed by several books in the 1950s and 1960s: J. M. Smith's *Chemical Engineering Kinetics*, Octave Levenspiel's *Chemical Reaction Engineering*, G. Astarita's *Mass Transfer with Chemical Reaction*, P. V. Danckwerts' *Gas–Liquid Reactions*, H. Kramer's and K. R. Westerterp's *Elements of Chemical Reactor Design and Operation*, and K. Denbigh and J. C. R. Turner's *Chemical Reactor Theory*. Each book had as its main theme one or two classes of reactions, such as gas–solid (catalytic), gas–liquid, or homogeneous. The 1970s saw a series of books, again on practically the same systems, but with greater emphasis on analysis and mathematical modeling. Among these may be mentioned the books by J. J. Carberry; J. Szekely, J. W. Evans, and H. Y. Sohn; G. F. Froment and K. B. Bischoff; J. B. Butt; and Y. T. Shah. With the exception of *Chemical Reactor Analysis and Design* (by G. F. Froment and K. B. Bischoff), the strong point of almost all these books is largely analysis and/or design, with but a few examples interspersed to illustrate the theories. Particularly noteworthy books are the entirely theoretical *Chemical Reactor Theory*, edited by L. Lapidus and N. R. Amundson, the two practically oriented volumes of H. F. Rase, and the introductory text of C. G. Hill, Jr. All these books have many commendable features.

Industrially important reactions are predominantly heterogeneous, and the notable absence of a comprehensive and connected discussion of such systems provided the basic motivation for knitting them into a coherent theme in a single presentation. Further, we were struck by the preponderance of hypothetical and arbitrary examples in many current books; since such examples lack the impact we intend for our readers, we decided at the outset to incorporate, as far as possible, real and industrially relevant examples, both qualitative and quantitative. Thus the two volumes were conceived and written. We believe that this attempt is unique and hope that it fulfills our objectives and meets the requirements of a wide cross section of readers. We also believe that this is one of the few sets of two volumes in which threads of analysis have been assiduously woven into a web of design and examples. Taken as a whole, they have no counterpart at present.

We have been acutely conscious that these volumes have taken an unusually long time to write, and have undergone revisions during which their contents have seen drastic changes, including realignment of chapters. These changes were a result of newer knowledge that became available as well as the increasing store of research, industrial, and consulting experience of the authors. Our keen desire to include information concerning the translation of laboratory data into commercial plants, albeit in a limited way, has also contributed significantly to the writing time. During this period both of us have had the pleasure of contributing research papers and state-of-art reviews in just about all the subjects that we have covered in the 35 chapters that make up the two volumes.

The main theme of these volumes is: how to dissect the often complex problems relating to the interaction between diffusion and chemical reaction into tractable parts through a systematic analysis and a rational process-design strategy. To buttress this approach we have given a surfeit of qualitative and quantitative examples.

More than ten heterogeneous systems have been considered in these volumes. Volume 1 deals essentially with systems in which a solid phase appears either as catalyst or as a reactant; the second reactant is a gas or a solid, but one case of a system in which the second reactant is a liquid (the immobilized enzyme system) has also been included, in view of the similarity of approaches. Volume 1 comprises 21 chapters, of which 17 pertain to gas–solid (catalytic) reactions. The eighteenth chapter includes some special reactors such as those for supported liquid-phase catalytic systems, polymer-bound catalytic systems, and immobilized enzyme systems. The next two chapters are devoted to gas–solid (noncatalytic) reactors and the one following is concerned with solid–solid reactions.

Volume 2 is concerned essentially with systems in which a liquid is involved as one of the reactants. The second reactant is either a gas or a liquid. In some systems the solid phase also appears, either as the second or third reactant or as a catalyst along with gas and liquid (slurry or trickle-bed reactors). Volume 2 covers practically all systems in which the liquid phase appears as a reactant. The structure adopted is as follows: fluid–fluid reactions (Chapters 2–3); consecutive reactions (Chapter 4); one gas, two reactants (Chapter 5); simultaneous absorption and reaction of two gases (Chapter 6); reaction in both phases (Chapter 7); desorption with chemical reaction; simultaneous absorption–desorption with reaction (Chapter 8); complex reactions (Chapter 9); use of models in simulation and design of reactors (Chapter 10); solid–liquid reactions (Chapter 11); reactions in fluid–fluid–solid systems (Chapter 12) and solid-catalyzed fluid–fluid reactions (Chapter 13). An extensive chapter (Chapter 14) has been included to give pertinent details of a variety of contactors that are used for the reaction systems considered. An attempt has been made to guide readers in selecting a contactor for a specified duty.

Although practically all industrially important heterogeneous systems are covered in the two volumes, three systems, namely, gas–solid (catalytic), gas–liquid and liquid–liquid, have received greater attention not only because they are truly ubiquitous but also because of the authors' greater personal involvement with these systems than with others.

The contents of the two volumes have been used for undergraduate and graduate courses in many countries. They have also been used for short intensive courses presented both in India and abroad. In addition, a wide cross section of chemical engineers and technologists have made valuable suggestions that have been duly incorporated.

These volumes are addressed not only to students of chemical engineering, chemical technology, and applied chemistry, but also to researchers, designers, and practicing engineers. We believe that all such readers of these books will find some directly useful material. We also believe that our coverage of the English-language literature up to 1980 is reasonably complete. We have made every effort to include literature from all over the world, but our lack of knowledge of Russian and Japanese prevented a fuller coverage of papers in these languages. We have covered some references that appeared in 1981 as well.

In some parts of these volumes, readers may discern an almost encyclopedic approach. While conceding such a disposition in selected areas, we would like to emphasize our main approach: we have cited in most parts of these books only those references which are necessary in building up a comprehensive structure for each system, but in doing so we have not denied the reader the advantage of references that might not be directly relevant but that can be usefully consulted if needed. The approach is not that of a standard textbook but rather that of an advanced treatise.

In a comprehensive effort of this kind there is a temptation to adopt a unified approach to all systems. We quickly discovered the severe limitations of such an effort and decided to adopt prevalent approaches to different systems. For example, in Volume 1 we use the concept of effectiveness factor, which denotes the effect of diffusion on reaction, while in Volume 2 we continue with the practice of using the enhancement factor, which denotes the effect of reaction on diffusion. It would perhaps have been possible to adopt a common approach, for example, one based on effectiveness factor, for all systems; but doing so would have made the books less useful and appealing to readers than we believe it is in the present form. In pursuit of this approach we have also adopted different systems of nomenclature for Volumes 1 and 2 consistent with the more commonly used notation, and these are clearly defined at the beginning of each volume; uncommon notation usually acts as an irritant and makes the reader wary. The choice of units presented another vexing problem, and after considerable thought we decided to adopt widely used units in preference to the SI units.

We have both drawn heavily from our students and associates in writing these volumes. Their attachment to this venture has been a source of great strength to us. It would not be possible for us to place on record our gratitude to all of them individually, but each of us would like to particularly thank a few co-workers who have toiled to help us complete this voluminous and ambitious document. Most of them have witnessed with mute sympathy the protracted evolution of this venture and share our relief at its completion.

LKD would like to thank B. D. Kulkarni for his invaluable assistance, always rendered cheerfully; without his continued help the author doubts if Volume 1 could ever have been completed. Dr. Kulkarni has assisted in many ways, such as literature search, careful editing, and stimulating discussions on various aspects of Volume 1. The author is also grateful to many of his other students and colleagues who have rendered willing assistance: R. V. Choudhary, V. R. Choudhary, R. K. Irani, V. K. Jayaraman, N. G. Karanth, S. D. Prasad, N. S. Raghavan, R. A. Rajadhyaksha, P. A. Ramachandran, V. Ravi Kumar, A. Sadana, and S. S. Tamhankar. He would like in particular to record the assistance so cheerfully extended by Ravi Kumar and Jayaraman. He is thankful to Pratibha Khare for typing the manuscript from sheets of paper often covered with illegible writing and transforming them into readable material.

MMS would like to express his most sincere gratitude to a number of his students and colleagues: M. C. Chhabria, V. G. Gaikar, G. C. Jagirdar, B. Janakiraman, J. B. Joshi, V. A. Juvekar, V. K. Krishnakumar, V. V. Mahajani, R. A. Mashelkar, V. G. Pangarkar, P. A. Ramachandran, S. Shrivastava, T. V. Vasudevan, and V. V. Wadekar. They have rendered invaluable assistance voluntarily.

We would like to express our gratitude to our wives Rajalakshmi and Sudha for having put up with our bursts of writing over a painfully long period of time and for mercifully refraining from expressing what they must undoubtedly have felt—that these volumes were never going to be completed! The satisfaction of not letting them down puts a particularly pleasing conclusion to an arduous undertaking.

Both of us profusely thank Professor Octave Levenspiel and Professor Peter Danckwerts for their sustained interest, constructive comments, and encouragement. Professor Danckwerts' advice, "Let the good not be the enemy of the best," made a deep impression on us, and it is in this spirit that we present these volumes to our readers.

L. K. Doraiswamy

Poona, India

M. M. Sharma

Bombay, India

January 1983

To my wife

Rajalakshmi

In whom simplicity, pure and elemental,
and courage, beautifully concealed,
combined to form the quintessence of life . . . .

Whose unspoken inspiration
sustained me through the
protracted evolution of the book—
the completion of which
I am not destined to share with her.

L.K.D.

Contents

Notation, xix

1. INTRODUCTION 1

2. THEORY OF MASS TRANSFER ACCOMPANIED BY IRREVERSIBLE AND REVERSIBLE REACTIONS OF GENERAL ORDER; METHODS OF DISCERNING CONTROLLING MECHANISM 17

2.1. Regime 1: Very Slow Reactions, 17
2.2. Regime 2: Slow Reactions, 17
2.3. Regime between Very Slow and Slow Reactions (Regime between 1 and 2), 18
2.3.1. Reactions That Are First Order with Respect to Solute A, 19
2.3.2. Reactions That Are Zero Order with Respect to Solute A, 19
2.3.3. Reactions That Are Second Order with Respect to Solute A, 19
2.3.4. General Case, 19
2.4. Fast Reactions (Regime 3) and the Regime between 2 and 3, 20
2.5. Regime Overlapping 1, 2, and 3, 24
2.6. Regime 4: Instantaneous (Very Fast) Reactions, 26
2.7. Transition from Fast to Instantaneous (Very Fast) Reactions: Regime Overlapping 3 and 4, 28
2.8. Mass Transfer Accompanied by Reaction When the Reactant B Is Volatile: Regime between 3 and 4, 31
2.9. Gas Absorption Accompanied by Instantaneous Reaction with a Part of the Resistance on the Gas Side, 33
2.10. Theory of Mass Transfer Accompanied by Reversible Chemical Reaction, 34
2.10.1. Absorption Accompanied by a Fast Reaction, 34
2.10.2. Reversible Instantaneous Reactions, 37
2.11. Methods of Discerning the Controlling Mechanism for Irreversible Reactions, 38
2.11.1. Gas–Liquid Systems, 38
2.11.2. Liquid–Liquid Systems, 42

3. DISCUSSION AND EXAMPLES OF SYSTEMS FALLING IN DIFFERENT REGIMES 46

3.1. Regime 1: Very Slow Reactions, 46

(A) Gas–Liquid Systems, 46

3.1.1. Air Oxidation of a Variety of Aliphatic and Alkyl Aromatic Compounds, 46
3.1.2. Air Oxidation of *p*-Nitrotoluene Sulfonic Acid, 47
3.1.3. Substitution Chlorination of a Variety of Organic Compounds, 47

3.1.4. Reaction between Isobutylene and Acetic Acid, 47
3.1.5. Wacker Processes, 48
3.1.6. Hydrochlorination of Olefins, 48
3.1.7. Absorption of Phosphine in an Aqueous Solution of Formaldehyde and Hydrochloric Acid, 48
3.1.8. Acetic Acid from the Carbonylation of Methanol, 49
3.1.9. Oxidation of Trialkyl Phosphine, 49
3.1.10. Dimerization of Olefins, 50

(B) Liquid–Liquid Systems, 50

3.1.11. Alkaline Hydrolysis of a Variety of Organic Compounds, 50
3.1.12. Nitration of Chlorobenzene, 50
3.1.13. Alkylation of Benzene with Straight-Chain Olefins, 51
3.1.14. Reduction of Aromatic Nitro Compounds to Corresponding Aromatic Amines with Aqueous Na_2S or Na_2S_x, 51

(C) Special Cases, 52

3.1.15. Extractive Reactions, 52
3.1.16. Phase Transfer Catalysis, 52
3.1.17. Micellar Catalysis and Interfacial Reactions, 53
3.1.18. Use of Emulsifying Agent for Increasing the Rate of Two-Phase Reactions: Hydrolysis of α,α,α-Trichlorotoluene (TCT) (Benzotrichloride) to Benzoic Acid, 54
3.1.19. Measurement of Holdup, 54

3.2. Regime 2: Slow Reactions, 55

(A) Gas–Liquid Systems, 55

3.2.1. Absorption of CO_2 in Carbonate Solutions, 55
3.2.2. Absorption of O_2 in Aqueous Acid Solutions of CuCl at Concentrations Less than 1×10^{-4} mol/cm^3, 55
3.2.3. Oxidation of Organic Compounds, 55
3.2.4. Preparation of the C-13 Isotope, 56

(B) Liquid–Liquid Systems, 56

3.2.5. Pyrometallurgical Operations: Open Hearth Steel Furnace, 56
3.2.6. Reaction of Dinitrochlorobenzene, 57
3.2.7. Removal of Mercaptans from Petroleum Fractions, 57
3.2.8. Alkaline Hydrolysis of Esters, 57
3.2.9. Nitration of Aromatic Compounds, 57
3.2.10. Nitration of Higher Olefins, 57
3.2.11. Liquid–Liquid Reactions in Phosphorous Chemistry, 58
3.2.12. Special Case: Measurement of the Solubility of A in the B Phase, 59

3.3. Regime between 1 and 2, 59

(A) Gas–Liquid Systems, 59

3.3.1. Pseudo-First-Order Reactions: Simultaneous Measurement of $k_L a$ and k_1 without Knowing [A*], 59
3.3.2. Absorption of CO_2 in Carbonate Buffer Solutions in Packed Columns, 60
3.3.3. Oxidation of Black Liquor in the Paper and Pulp Industry, 61

3.3.4. Wet Air Oxidation of Soluble Compounds in Wastewater, 61

(B) *Liquid–Liquid Systems*, 62

3.3.5. Alkaline Hydrolysis of Acetate Esters, 62
3.3.6. Sulfonation of Benzene, Toluene, and *p*-Xylene, 62

3.4. Regime 3: Fast Reactions, 62

(A) *Gas–Liquid Systems*, 63

3.4.1. Absorption of CO_2 and COS in Aqueous Solutions of Amines and Alkalies, 63
3.4.2. Absorption of Oxygen in Aqueous Acidic and Neutral Solutions of Cuprous Chloride, and in Cuprous and Cobaltous Amine Complexes in Aqueous and Polar Solutions, 67
3.4.3. Absorption of Oxygen in Aqueous Alkaline Solutions of Sodium Dithionite (Hydrosulfite), 68
3.4.4. Absorption of Oxygen in Aqueous Sodium Sulfite, 68
3.4.5. Absorption of $NO/NO_2/N_2O_4$ in Water and Aqueous Solutions Containing Reactive Species; Reaction between Dissolved NO and O_2, 69
3.4.6. Absorption of Oxygen and Ozone in Aldehydes, 74
3.4.7. Absorption of Isobutylene, 2-Butene, and 2-Methyl-2-Butene in Aqueous Solutions of Sulfuric Acid; Absorption of Isobutylene in Aqueous Solutions Containing Thallium(III) Ions, 75
3.4.8. Absorption of Lean Phosphine in Aqueous Solutions of Sodium Hypochlorite and Concentrated Sulfuric Acid, 77
3.4.9. Absorption of Ozone in Aqueous and Nonaqueous Solutions, with or without Dissolved Organic Chemicals; Oxidation of Cyanide Ions in Aqueous Alkaline Solutions and Organic Media Containing Olefinic Substances; Wastewater Treatment, 77
3.4.10. Oxidation of Organometallic Compounds, 79
3.4.11. Hydrogenation of Unsaturated Compounds with Homogeneous Catalysts, 79
3.4.12. Absorption of Cl_2 in Aqueous Solutions Containing Phenolic Substances and Aromatic Nitro and Sulfonic Compounds; Absorption of Cl_2 in Aqueous and Nonaqueous Solutions of Ketones, 80

(B) *Liquid–Liquid Systems*, 81

3.4.13. Alkaline Hydrolysis of Formate and Halosubstituted Acetic Acid Esters, 81
3.4.14. Manufacture of Cyclohexanone Oxime, 81
3.4.15. Manufacture of Dithiocarbamates, 81
3.4.16. Alkylation of Isobutane with Butenes and of Toluene and Xylenes with Acetaldehyde (or Acetylene), 82
3.4.17. Nitration of Toluene, 83

3.4.18. Extraction of Metals, 83
3.5. Regime between 2 and 3, 83
3.5.1. Pseudo-First-Order Reactions: Measurement of k_1 without Knowing [A*] and D_A, 83
3.5.2. Nitration of Toluene and Other Aromatic Substances, 85
3.6. Regime Overlapping 1, 2, and 3, 85
3.7. Regime 4: Instantaneous Reactions, 86
(A) Gas–Liquid Systems, 87
3.7.1. Absorption of CO_2 in Aqueous Solutions of MEA, 87
3.7.2. Absorption of H_2S and Mercaptans in Aqueous Solutions of Alkanolamines and Caustic Soda, 88
3.7.3. Absorption of Carbon Monoxide in Aqueous Cuprous Ammonium Chloride Solutions, 88
3.7.4. Absorption of Lower Olefins in Aqueous Solutions of Cuprous Ammonium Compounds, 88
3.7.5. Absorption of Pure Chlorine in Aqueous Solutions of Sodium Carbonate or Sodium Hydroxide, 88
3.7.6. Conversion of Dithiocarbamates to Thiuram Disulfides, 89
3.7.7. Sulfonation of Aromatic Compounds with Lean SO_3, 89
3.7.8. Recovery of Bromine from Lean Aqueous Solutions of Bromides, 89
3.7.9. Reactions of Importance in Pyrometallurgy, 90
3.7.10. Special Case: Role of Diffusion in the Absorption of Gases in Blood in the Human Body, 90
(B) Liquid–Liquid Systems, 91
3.7.11. Extraction of Free Fatty Acids from Naturally Occurring Glycerides, 91
3.7.12. Removal of HCl from Chlorinated Organic Compounds, 91
3.7.13. Recovery of Aliphatic Acids and HF and HCl from Aqueous Solutions, 91
3.7.14. Nitration of Phenol, 92
3.7.15. Solvent Extraction in Mineral Processing, 92
3.7.16. Interfacial Polycondensation and Esterification, 95
3.7.17. Manufacture of Organophosphate Pesticides, 96
3.8. Regime between 3 and 4, 97
(A) Gas–Liquid Systems, 97
3.8.1. Absorption of CO_2 in Aqueous Solutions of Caustic Alkalies and Amines, 97
3.8.2. Absorption of O_2 in Aqueous Solutions of Sodium Dithionite, 98
3.8.3. Absorption of O_2 in Aqueous Sodium Sulfite Solutions, 98
3.8.4. Absorption of Oxygen in Alkaline Solutions Containing the Sodium Salt of 1,4-Napthaquinone-2-Sulfonic Acid (NQSA), 98
(B) Liquid–Liquid Systems, 99
3.8.5. Extraction of Chlorosubstituted Acetic Acid Esters into Aqueous NaOH Solutions, 99
3.8.6. Extraction of Copper from Aqueous Solutions, 99

3.9. Chemical Reactions in Molten Salts, 99
3.9.1. Processing of Spent Fuel from Nuclear Reactors, 100
3.9.2. Oxidation of HCl Gas (Deacon's Process), 100
3.9.3. Oxidation of SO_2 over Melts, 101
3.9.4. Phenol from Toluene by the Dow Process, 102
3.9.5. Recovery of Sulfur Dioxide and Sulfur Trioxide from Emissions, 103
3.9.6. Chlorination in Melts, 103
3.9.7. Catalytic Reactions of Olefins, 103
3.9.8. Nitration of Propane, 104
3.9.9. Oxidative Dehydrogenation and Coupling Reactions, 104
3.9.10. Absorption of Butadiene in Molten Maleic Anhydride, 104
3.10. Examples of Reversible Reactions, 105
3.10.1. Absorption of CO_2 and H_2S in Aqueous Solutions of Amines and Alkalies, 105
3.10.2. Absorption of Cl_2 in Water, 105
3.10.3. Manufacture of Isotopes, 106
3.10.4. Absorption of Nitric Oxide in Aqueous Solutions of Ferrous Sulfate, 106
3.11. Effect of Temperature on Mass Transfer Accompanied by Chemical Reaction, 106
3.11.1. Regime 1: Very Slow Reactions, 106
3.11.2. Regime 2: Slow Reactions, 107
3.11.3. Regime 3: Fast Reactions, 108
3.11.4. Regime 4: Instantaneous Reactions, 109
3.12. Temperature at the Fluid–Fluid Interface, 109
3.12.1. Pseudo-*m*th-Order Reactions (Regime 3), 109
3.12.2. Instantaneous Reactions (Regime 4), 110
3.13. Effect of Interfacial Turbulence, 111
3.14. Stability of Two Phase Reactors, 112

4. MASS TRANSFER ACCOMPANIED BY CONSECUTIVE AND TWO-STEP REACTIONS 120

4.1. Consecutive Reactions, 120
4.1.1. Both Reactions in the Slow or Very Slow Reaction Regime (Regime between 1 and 2), 121
4.1.2. First-Step Reaction Is Fast Pseudo-First-Order (Regime 3) or between Regimes 2 and 3; Second-Step Is in the Slow Reaction Regime (Regime 2), 122
4.1.3. Both Reactions Fast Pseudo-First-Order (Regime 3), 124
4.1.4. Fast Reactions Accompanied by Depletion of Reactant B and Intermediate C in the Film (Regime between 3 and 4 for Both Steps), 125
4.1.5. First-Step Reaction Instantaneous (Regime 4), 128
4.1.6. Effect of Temperature on Selectivity, 133
4.1.7. Examples, 134
4.1.8. Selectivity Disguised by Mixing in Homogeneous Systems, 136
4.2. Mass Transfer Accompanied by a Two-Step Chemical Reaction, 136

4.2.1. Fast to Instantaneous Reactions (Regime between 3 and 4 and Regime 4), 137
4.2.2. Depletion of Reactant B in the Film (Regime between 3 and 4), 138
4.2.3. Instantaneous Reaction (Regime 4), 140

5. ABSORPTION OF A GAS INTO A SOLUTION CONTAINING TWO REACTANTS 142

5.1. Very Slow Reactions, 142
5.2. Slow Reactions, 143
5.3. Regime between 2 and 3 and Fast Pseudo-First-Order Reactions (Regime 3), 143
5.4. Instantaneous Reactions, 147
5.5. One Reaction Instantaneous and the Other between Regimes 2 and 3, 149
5.6. Both Reactions in the Depletion Regime (Regime between 3 and 4), 152
5.7. Kinetics of Reactions Involving One Gas and Two Reactants, 155
5.8. Examples, 155
5.8.1. Manufacture of Ethylene and Propylene Chlorohydrin, 155
5.8.2. Absorption of CO_2 in Aqueous Solutions Containing Two Amines, 156
5.8.3. Absorption of NO_2/N_2O_4 in Aqueous Alkaline Solutions of Sodium Sulfite, 156
5.8.4. Chlorination of Aqueous Buffered Solutions of Phenolic Substances, 157
5.8.5. Interfacial Copolycondensation, 157

6. SIMULTANEOUS ABSORPTION AND REACTION OF TWO GASES 158

6.1. Absorption of Two Gases in a Nonreacting Medium, 158
6.2. Absorption of Two Gases in a Reacting Liquid, 158
6.2.1. Mechanism of Absorption, 159
6.2.2. Rate of Absorption for Various Mechanisms, 161
6.2.3. Absorption of Two Gases, One of Which Is Absorbed under Gas-Film-Controlled Conditions, 167
6.2.4. Absorption of Two Gases Accompanied by Reaction in the Bulk Liquid, 168
6.3. Some Examples of the Absorption and Reaction of Two Gases, 168
6.3.1. Simultaneous Absorption of Hydrogen Sulfide and Carbon Dioxide, 168
6.3.2. Absorption of C_4 Fractions in Sulfuric Acid, 169
6.3.3. Absorption of a Mixture of Mercaptans and Carbon Dioxide in Alkaline Solutions, 170
6.3.4. Absorption of a Mixture of Hydrogen Cyanide and Carbon Dioxide in Alkaline Solutions, 170
6.3.5. Simultaneous Absorption of NO_2 and NO and NO/NO_2 and SO_2 in Aqueous Alkaline Solutions, 170
6.3.6. Simultaneous Nitration of Benzene and Toluene, 170
6.4. Absorption of Two Gases Followed by Complex Chemical Reactions, 171
6.4.1. Reaction Product of the First Gas Acting as a Reactant for the Second Gas, 171
6.4.2. Absorption of Two Gases, A_1 and A_2, Where the Reaction of A_1 Results in the Formation of A_2, 172

6.4.3. Absorption of Two Gases Accompanied by Reversible Chemical Reactions, 173
6.5. Absorption of Two Gases That React with Each Other, 174
6.5.1. Gases A_1 and A_2 Present in a Mixture, 174
6.5.2. Gases Introduced Separately, 175
6.5.3. Simultaneous Absorption of NH_3 and CO_2, 176
6.5.4. Chlorination of Acetylene, 177
6.5.5. Manufacture of Trichloroethane, 177
6.5.6. Simultaneous Absorption of SO_2 and Cl_2 in Water, 177
6.5.7. Reaction between H_2S and Ethylene Oxide to Give Thiodiethylene Glycol (TDEG) in the Product as a Solvent, 178
6.5.8. Hydroformylation of Isobutylene with CO and H_2, 178
6.6. Simultaneous Extraction of Two Solutes: Dissociation Extraction, 178
6.6.1. Separation of Water-Soluble Mixtures of Piperidine and *N*-Methyl Piperidine, 180
6.6.2. Separation of Cresols and Mixtures of 2,6-Xylenol with Cresols, 181
6.6.3. Separation of Chlorophenols, Chlorocresols, and Chloroxylenols, 181
6.6.4. Separation of *N*-Alkylanilines and *N*-Alkyl Toluidines, 182
6.6.5. Separation of Substituted Anilines: *m*-Chloroaniline and *o*-Anisidine, 182
6.6.6. Separation and Recovery of Low Molecular Weight Carboxylic Acids from Aqueous Streams, 182

7. REACTION IN BOTH (LIQUID) PHASES 185

7.1. Reactions Occur in the Bulk A and B Phases, 186
7.2. Reaction Occurs Only in the B Phase, 188
7.3. Reaction Occurs in Both Phases in the Films Adjacent to the Interface, 188
7.4. Reaction between A and B Is Instantaneous in Both Phases, 190
7.5. Reaction in Both Phases in the Depletion Regime, 192
7.6. Examples, 192
7.6.1. Manufacture of Cyclohexanone Oxime from Cyclohexanone and Aqueous Hydroxylamine Sulfate, 192
7.6.2. Interfacial Polycondensation Reactions, 193

8. DESORPTION WITH CHEMICAL REACTION; SIMULTANEOUS ABSORPTION–DESORPTION WITH REACTION 194

8.1. Desorption with Reaction, 194
8.2. Physical Desorption, 195
8.3. Desorption Preceded by a Chemical Reaction in Nonpolymeric Systems, 195
8.3.1. Slow Reaction Regime, 196
8.3.2. Fast Reaction Regime, 196
8.3.3. Instantaneously Reversible "Equilibrium" Reaction, 197
8.4. Desorption Preceded by a Chemical Reaction in Polymeric Systems, 198
8.5. Simultaneous Absorption–Desorption with Reaction, 199
8.5.1. Slow Reaction Regime, 200
8.5.2. Fast Reaction Regime, 202

8.5.3. Liquid-Phase-Controlled Desorption of A′, 204
8.5.4. Instantaneous Reaction Regime, 204
8.6. Supersaturation during Simultaneous Absorption–Desorption with Reaction, 205
8.6.1. Physical Absorption–Desorption, 205
8.6.2. Supersaturation during Simultaneous Absorption–Desorption with Reaction, 206
8.7. Examples of Industrial Importance, 207
8.7.1. Very Slow Reaction, 207
8.7.2. Slow Reaction, 208
8.7.3. Fast Reaction, 208
8.7.4. Simultaneous Absorption–Desorption with Reaction, 209

9. COMPLEX REACTIONS 213

9.1. Gas Absorption with Autocatalytic Reaction, 213
9.1.1. Autocatalytic Effect of a Volatile Intermediate: Chlorination of Cyclohexanone: Autocatalytic Effect of Volatile HCl, 216
9.1.2. Gas Absorption with a Radical-Multiplying Chain-Type Reaction, 216
9.2. Gas Absorption with Photochemical Reaction, 216
9.2.1. Photochemical Activation of Liquid-Phase Reactant B, 217
9.2.2. Photochemical Activation of Dissolved Gas A, 218
9.3. Glossary of Reaction Schemes Considered, 219
9.4. Glossary of Complex Reactions: Literature Review, 219

10. USE OF MODELS IN THE SIMULATION AND DESIGN OF FLUID–FLUID REACTORS 225

10.1. Gas–Liquid Systems, 225
10.1.1. Modeling by the Point Method, 225
10.1.2. Modeling by the Integral Method, 228
10.2. Liquid–Liquid Systems, 230
10.3. Use of Small-Scale Apparatus, 230

11. SOLID–LIQUID REACTIONS 233

11.1. Mass Transfer in Solid–Liquid Systems, 233
11.1.1. Methods of Measuring the Solid–Liquid Mass Transfer Coefficient, k_{SL}, 234
11.1.2. Mass Transfer in Stagnant Media, 236
11.1.3. Film Flow (Trickle-Bed) Reactors, 236
11.1.4. Pulsing Flow Reactors, 237
11.1.5. Packed Bubble Column Reactors, 237
11.1.6. Liquid Fluidized-Bed and Spouted-Bed Reactors, 237
11.1.7. Bubble Column Reactors, 238
11.1.8. Mechanically Agitated Reactors, 240
11.1.9. Horizontal Pipeline Reactors, 248
11.1.10. Non-Newtonian Systems, 248
11.2. Solid–Liquid Reactions: Solids Sparingly Soluble, 248
11.2.1. Solid Dissolution Accompanied by Reaction: Only Part of the Reaction Occurs Very Near the Interface, 249
11.2.2. Solid Dissolution Accompanied by

Instantaneous Reaction, 249
11.2.3. Examples, 249
11.3. Solid–Liquid Reactions: Solids Insoluble in the Medium, 254
11.4. Systems Involving Ion-Exchange Resins, 254

12. MASS TRANSFER WITH REACTION IN FLUID–FLUID–SOLID SYSTEMS 258

12.1. Solids Slightly Soluble, 258
12.1.1. Solid Dissolution in the Liquid Film Next to the Gas–Liquid Interface Is Negligible, 258
12.1.2. Solid Dissolution in the Liquid Film Is Significant, 260
12.1.3. Simultaneous Absorption of Two Gases into a Slurry Containing Soluble Fine Particles (One or Two Solid Reactants), 265
12.1.4. Examples, 265
12.2. Solid Particles Insoluble in the Medium, 266
12.2.1. Rate of Reaction for Spherical Particles of Constant Size, 267
12.2.2. Rate of Reaction for Particles with Changing Size, 268
12.2.3. Examples: Solid–Liquid Systems, 269
12.2.4. Examples: Gas–Liquid–Solid Systems, 272

13. MASS TRANSFER ACCOMPANIED BY CHEMICAL REACTION IN FLUID–FLUID SYSTEMS IN THE PRESENCE OF SOLID PARTICLES AS CATALYST 277

13.1. Slurry Reactors, 279
13.1.1. General Considerations, 279
13.1.2. Procedure for Discerning the Controlling Mechanism, 280
13.1.3. Effect of Temperature, 283
13.1.4. Example for Discerning the Controlling Mechanism, 283
13.1.5. Slurry Reactors Involving Reaction of Two Gases on a Suspended Catalyst, 284
13.1.6. Catalyst Particles Smaller than Liquid (Gas–Liquid) Diffusion Film Thickness, 286
13.1.7. Slurry Reactors with Solid Particles as Reactants and Containing Two Immiscible Liquids, 287
13.1.8. Examples of Slurry Reactors, 288
13.2. Fixed-Bed Reactors, 301
13.2.1. Flow Regimes and Mass Transfer Characteristics, 301
13.2.2. Packed-Bubble-Column Reactors, 306
13.2.3. Use of Inert Particles in Trickle-Bed Reactors and Packed-Bubble-Column Reactors, 307
13.2.4. Backmixing in Trickle-Bed Reactors, 307
13.2.5. Effect of Temperature, 307
13.2.6. Procedure for Discerning the Controlling Mechanism, 307
13.2.7. Examples of Fixed-Bed Reactors, 309

14. TYPES OF CONTACTORS AND THEIR RELATIVE MERITS 317

14.1. Gas–Liquid Contactors, 317
14.1.1. Contactors in Which the Liquid Flows as a Thin Film, 318

14.1.2. Contactors with Dispersion of Gas into Liquids, 327
14.1.3. Contactors Where Liquid Is Dispersed in the Continuous Gas Phase, 336
14.1.4. Foaming Problems, 337
14.1.5. Contactors for Non-Newtonian Fluids, 338
14.2. Liquid–Liquid Contactors, 339
14.2.1. Gravity-Operated Extractors, 341
14.2.2. Pipeline Contactors, 348
14.2.3. Centrifugal Extractors, 348
14.3. Gas–Liquid–Solid Contactors (Solids as Reactants), 349
14.4. Gas–Liquid–Solid Contactors (Solids as Catalysts), 350

AUTHOR INDEX 359

SUBJECT INDEX 367

Notation

A = gaseous or liquid-phase species that is being transferred from one phase to another; wetted area per unit height of the model contactor, cm (Eqs. 10.2, 10.3); cross-sectional area of packed tower, cm^2 (Figure 3.16)

A_1, A_2 = gases being absorbed in the case of simultaneous absorption of two gases

A' = species being desorbed

$\overline{A}$ = activated species in photochemical reaction

$[A]$, $[A_1]$, $[A_2]$ = local concentration of A, A_1, and A_2, respectively, at any point in the B phase, mol/cm^3

$[A_{Ai}]$ = interfacial concentration of A in the A-rich phase, mol/cm^3

$[A_{Ao}]$ = bulk concentration of A in the A-rich phase, mol/cm^3

$[A_{Bi}]$ = interfacial concentration of A in the B-rich phase, mol/cm^3

$[A_{Bo}]$ = bulk concentration of A in the B-rich phase, mol/cm^3

$[A_o]$, $[A_{1,o}]$, $[A_{2,o}]$ = bulk concentration of A, A_1, and A_2, respectively, in the bulk B phase, mol/cm^3

$[A_p]$ = concentration of A in pressure units defined as $[A]/H_A$, atm

$[A_{po}]$ = bulk concentration of A defined as $[A_o]/H_A$, atm

$[A_{r_c}]$ = concentration of A at a radial position r_c from the center of a spherical solid particle, mol/cm^3

$[A_s]$, $[A_{1,s}]$, $[A_{2,s}]$ = concentration of A, A_1, and A_2, respectively, at the solid–liquid interface, mol/cm^3 (clear liquid volume)

$[A^*]$, $[A_1^*]$, $[A_2^*]$ = concentration of A, A_1, and A_2, respectively, at the gas–liquid or liquid–liquid interface, mol/cm^3

$[A_p^*]$ = interfacial concentration of A defined as $[A^*]/H_A$, atm

$[A_1^-]$, $[A_2^-]$ = concentration of singly charged anions of acids HA_1 and HA_2, respectively, g ion/liter

$[A_o]^+$ = concentration of A in bulk solution, g/cm^3 (clear liquid volume)

$[A_s]^+$ = concentration of A at solid–liquid interface, g/cm^3 (clear liquid volume)

$[A']$ = local concentration of desorbing species A′ in the liquid, mol/cm^3

$[A'_G]$ = $p_{A'}H_{A'}$, mol/cm^3

$[A'_o]$ = bulk concentration of desorbing species A′ in the liquid, mol/cm^3

$[A'_p]$ = concentration of A′ defined as $[A']/H_{A'}$, atm

$[A'_{po}]$ = bulk concentration of A′ defined as $[A'_o]/H_{A'}$, atm

$[A'^*]$ = interfacial concentration of desorbing species A′, mol/cm^3

$[A'_\lambda]$ = concentration of species A′ in the liquid at $x = \lambda$, mol/cm^3

$\Delta[A]$ = dimensionless concentration driving force (Eq. 11.1)

a = gas–liquid or liquid–liquid interfacial area per unit volume of contactor or dispersion, cm^2/cm^3

a_p = solid–liquid interfacial area, cm^2/cm^3 (clear liquid volume)

a'' = gas–liquid interfacial area, cm^2/cm^3 (clear liquid volume)

B = dissolved reactive species present in the B phase

B_1, B_2 = dissolved reactive species in the case of absorption of one gas in two reactants

$\bar{B}$ = activated species in photochemical reaction

[B] = local concentration of B at any point in the B phase, mol/cm^3

$[B]_T$ = concentration of amine at the top of the packing, mol/cm^3 (Figure 3.16)

$[B_{Ai}]$ = interfacial concentration of B in the A-rich phase, mol/cm^3

$[B_{Ao}]$ = bulk concentration of B in the A-rich phase, mol/cm^3

$[B_{Bi}]$ = interfacial concentration of B in the B-rich phase, mol/cm^3

$[B_{Bo}]$ = bulk concentration of B in the B-rich phase, mol/cm^3

$[B_G]$ = $H_B p_B$, mol/cm^3

$[B_i]$, $[B_{1,i}]$, $[B_{2,i}]$ = concentration of species B, B_1, and B_2, respectively, at the gas–liquid interface, mol/cm^3

$[B_o]$, $[B_{1,o}]$, $[B_{2,o}]$ = concentration of species B, B_1, and B_2, respectively, in the bulk B phase, mol/cm^3

$[B_o]_{avg}$ = arithmetic time-average concentration of the reactive species B in the B phase, mol/cm^3

$[B_o]_f$ = final concentration of B in the B phase; outlet concentration, mol/cm^3

$[B_o]_i$ = initial concentration of B in the B phase; inlet concentration, mol/cm^3

$[B_s]$ = concentration of B at the solid–liquid interface, mol/cm^3

$[C_i]$, $[C_{1,i}]$ = concentration of species C and C_1, respectively, at the gas–liquid interface, mol/cm^3

$[C_o]$, $[C_{1,o}]$ = concentration of species C and C_1 in the bulk B phase, mol/cm^3

$[C_\lambda]$ = concentration of C in the film at $x = \lambda$, mol/cm^3

ΔC = quantity defined by Eq. 2.170, mol/cm^3

$[\bar{c}]$ = quantity defined by Eq. 8.58c, mol/cm^3

D = diffusion coefficient of the dissolved species as indicated by subscript, cm^2/sec

D_{AA} = diffusion coefficient of A in the A-rich phase, cm^2/sec

D_{AB} = diffusion coefficient of A in the B-rich phase, cm^2/sec

D_{BA} = diffusion coefficient of B in the A-rich phase, cm^2/sec

D_{BB} = diffusion coefficient of B in the B-rich phase, cm^2/sec

D_c = axial dispersion coefficient, cm^2/sec

D_i = diameter of impeller, cm

D_s = diffusion coefficient of species A for diffusion through the solid ash layer, cm^2/sec

$[D_o]$ = concentration of species D in the bulk B phase, mol/cm^3

d_B = diameter of gas bubble, cm

d_p = diameter of solid particle, cm

$[E_{1,i}]$ = concentration of species E_1 at the gas–liquid interface, mol/cm^3

$[E_o]$, $[E_{1,o}]$ = concentration of species E and E_1, respectively, in the bulk liquid, mol/cm^3

ΔE = activation energy, cal/mol

erf(x) = $\dfrac{2}{\sqrt{\pi}}\displaystyle\int_0^x e^{-t^2}\,dt$

Fr = Froude number, dimensionless

f = fraction of particle surface covered by liquid

$f(\pi)$ = parameter defined by Eq. 8.57

G = gas flow rate, cm^3/sec

Ga = Galileo number, dimensionless

G' = mass velocity of gas, g/cm^2 sec

g = acceleration due to gravity, cm/sec^2

H = solubility coefficient of species as indicated by the subscript, mol/cm^3 atm

$[HA_1]_a$, $[HA_2]_a$ = concentration of the acids HA_1 and HA_2, respectively, in the aqueous phase, mol/liter

$[HA_1]_s$, $[HA_2]_s$ = concentration of acids HA_1 and HA_2, respectively, in the organic phase, mol/liter

ΔH = heat of the reaction, cal/mol

ΔH_A = heat generated in gas absorption, cal/mol

ΔH_s = heat of solution, cal/mol

h = Planck's constant, erg sec

h_c = clearance of impeller from bottom of reactor, cm
h_t = total height of reactor; height of packing, cm (Figure 3.16)
I = ionic strength of solution, g ion/liter; intensity of light at any point in the film, Ein/cm^2 sec
I_a = rate of absorption of light, Ein/cm^3 sec
I_o = intensity of light at $x = \delta$, Ein/cm^2 sec
K = equilibrium constant for reaction, dimensionless
K_1, K_2 = parameters defined by Eq. 8.7a, dimensionless
K_{A_1}, K_{A_2} = dissociation constants of acids HA_1 and HA_2, respectively, g ion/liter
K_e = equilibrium constant as defined by Eq. 6.48, dimensionless
K_G = true overall gas-side mass-transfer coefficient, mol/cm^2 sec atm
k = first-order rate constant, sec^{-1}
k_o = zero-order rate constant, mol/cm^3 sec
k_1 = pseudo-first-order rate constant defined as $k_n[B_o]^n$, sec^{-1}
k_2 = overall second-order rate constant, cm^3/mol sec
k_3 = overall third-order rate constant, (cm^3/mol)^2 sec^{-1}
k_n = overall nth order rate constant (cm^3/mol)$^{n-1}$ sec^{-1}
k_A, $k_{2,A}$, $k_{A'}$ = overall second-order rate constants, cm^3/mol sec
k_{A_1}, k_{A_2} = rate constant for the reaction of species A_1 and A_2, respectively, with species B, (cm^3/mol)$^{m+n-1}$ sec^{-1}
$k_{A_1A_2}$ = rate constant for the reaction of A_1 and A_2 in the B phase, (cm^3/mol)$^{m+n-1}$ sec^{-1}
k_{A-B_1}, k_{A-B_2} = rate constant for the reaction of gas A with species B_1 and B_2, respectively, (cm^3/mol)$^{m+n-1}$ sec^{-1}
k_G = true gas-side mass-transfer coefficient for the species as indicated by the subscript, mol/cm^2 sec atm
k_L = true liquid-side mass-transfer coefficient in the absence of chemical reaction, cm/sec
$k_{L(A_1)}$, $k_{L(A_2)}$ = true liquid-side mass-transfer coefficient in the absence of chemical reaction for species A_1 and A_2, respectively, cm/sec
$k_{LA,A}$ = true liquid-side mass-transfer coefficient for species A in the A-rich phase, cm/sec
$k_{LB,A}$ = true liquid-side mass-transfer coefficient for species B in the A-rich phase, cm/sec
$k_{LB,B}$ = true liquid-side mass-transfer coefficient for species B in the B-rich phase, cm/sec
k_{LR} = liquid-side mass-transfer coefficient in the presence of reaction, cm/sec
k_{mn} = rate constant for a reaction that is mth order in species A and nth order in species B, (cm^3/mol)$^{m+n-1}$ sec^{-1}
$k_{mn,A}$ = rate constant for the $(m+n)$th-order reaction in the A-rich phase, (cm^3/mol)$^{m+n-1}$ sec^{-1}
$k_{mn,B}$ = rate constant for the $(m+n)$th-order reaction in the B-rich phase, (cm^3/mol)$^{m+n-1}$ sec^{-1}
k_R = surface reaction rate constant, cm/sec
k_{SL} = true solid–liquid mass-transfer coefficient, cm/sec
$k_{SL(A_1)}$, $k_{SL(A_2)}$ = true solid–liquid mass-transfer coefficient for species A_1 and A_2, respectively, cm/sec
k_2^* = second-order rate constant, cm^3/mol sec
$\bar{k}$ = parameter defined by Eq. 9.41, mol/cm^3 sec
$\bar{k}_2$ = second-order rate constant for reaction between A and $\bar{B}$, cm^3/mol sec
$\bar{k}_A$, $\bar{k}_B$ = first-order rate constant for activation of species A and B, respectively, mol/Ein
k' = $k_2'[B_i] + k_2''[C_i]$ (Eq. 4.30)
= $k_{A-B_1}[B_{1,o}] + k_{A-B_2}[B_{2,o}]$ (Eq. 5.2)
k_1' = first-order rate constant for backward reaction;
= $k_{A-B_1}[B_{1,o}]$, sec^{-1} (Eq. 5.27)
k_2', k_2'' = second-order rate constants, cm^3/mol sec
k_L' = $k_L \dfrac{\delta}{\lambda}$

k'_R = defined by Eq. 13.8, mol/cm² sec

L = liquid flow rate, cm³/sec

L_e = scale of primary eddies, cm

L' = mass velocity of liquid, g/cm² sec

l = fractional liquid volume holdup of B phase

$\bar{k}_1$ = $k_2[B] + \bar{k}_A I_o \alpha_\lambda$, sec^{-1} (Eq. 9.55)

$\sqrt{M}$ = $\dfrac{\sqrt{\dfrac{2}{m+1} D_A k_{mn} [A^*]^{m-1} [B_o]^n}}{k_L}$ for an $(m+n)$th-order reaction, dimensionless

$\sqrt{M_{A_1}}$ = $\dfrac{\sqrt{\dfrac{2}{m+1} D_{A_1} k_{mn} [A_1^*]^{m-1} [B_o]^n}}{k_L}$ for an $(m+n)$th-order reaction between A_1 and B, dimensionless

$\sqrt{M_{A_2}}$ = $\dfrac{\sqrt{\dfrac{2}{m+1} D_{A_2} k_{mn} [A_2^*]^{m-1} [B_o]^n}}{k_L}$ for an $(m+n)$th-order reaction A_2 and B, dimensionless

$\sqrt{M_{A,B}}$ = parameter defined by Eq. 7.12b

$\sqrt{M_{A,i}}$ = $\dfrac{\sqrt{\dfrac{2}{m+1} D_A k_{mn} [A^*]^{m-1} [B_i]^n}}{k_L}$ for an $(m+n)$th-order reaction between A and B, dimensionless

$\sqrt{M_{A,o}}$ = $\dfrac{\sqrt{\dfrac{2}{m+1} D_A k_{mn} [A^*]^{m-1} [B_o]^n}}{k_L}$ for an $(m+n)$th-order reaction between A and B

M_B = molecular weight of species B

$\sqrt{M_{B,A}}$ = parameter defined by Eq. 7.12a

$\sqrt{M_{1,i}}$ = parameter defined by Eq. 4.36a

$\sqrt{M_{2,i}}$ = parameter defined by Eq. 4.36b

$\sqrt{M_{1,o}}$ = parameter defined by Eq. 4.39b

$\sqrt{M_{2,o}}$ = parameter defined by Eq. 4.40b

$M_{\dot{R}}$ = parameter defined by Eq. 9.10

$\sqrt{M'}$ = parameter defined by Eq. 8.7a

$\sqrt{M_{2,\lambda}}$ = parameter defined by Eq. 4.62

m = order of reaction with respect to the species A

m_A = distribution coefficient of A between A-rich and B-rich phases

m_B = distribution coefficient of B between A-rich and B-rich phases

m_c = collocation parameter (Eq. 9.6)

N = molarity of the extracting reagent, mol/liter; impeller speed, rev/sec

N_o = critical speed of impeller, rev/sec

N_m = minimum impeller speed required for complete suspension of solids, rev/sec

N_p = power number, dimensionless

n = order of reaction with respect to species B

n_p = number of particles per unit clear liquid volume, cm^{-3}

P = power input, ergs/sec; k_2^*/k_2 (Eq. 4.81)

Pe_L = Peclet number of liquid phase, dimensionless

p_A, p_{A_1} = partial pressure of A, A_1, respectively, in the bulk gas, atm

$p_{A,i}$ = partial pressure of A at the interface, atm

p_B = partial pressure of B in the bulk gas, atm

$p_{A'}$ = partial pressure of A′ in the bulk gas, atm

Q = amount of gas absorbed in time t per unit interfacial area, mol/cm²

q = $\dfrac{[B_o]}{Z[A^*]} \dfrac{D_B}{D_A}$ (film theory)

= $\dfrac{[B_o]}{Z[A^*]} \sqrt{\dfrac{D_B}{D_A}}$ (penetration theory)

q_{A_1} = $\dfrac{[B_o]}{Z_{A_1}[A_1^*]} \sqrt{\dfrac{D_B}{D_{A_1}}}$

q_{A_2} = $\dfrac{[B_o]}{Z_{A_2}[A_2^*]} \sqrt{\dfrac{D_B}{D_{A_2}}}$

$q_{A_1A_2}$ = $\dfrac{[B_o]}{Z_{A_1}[A_1^*](D_{A_1}/D_B) + Z_{A_2}[A_2^*](D_{A_2}/D_B)}$

q_{B_1} = $\dfrac{[B_{1,o}]}{Z_1[A^*]} \sqrt{\dfrac{D_{B_1}}{D_A}}$

q_{B_2} = $\dfrac{[B_{2,o}]}{Z_2[A^*]}\sqrt{\dfrac{D_{B_2}}{D_A}}$

$q_{\dot{R}}$ = $\dfrac{[\dot{R}_o]}{[A^*]}\sqrt{\dfrac{D_{\dot{R}}}{D_A}}$

q', q'' = parameters defined by Eqs. 7.21 and 7.22, respectively

Re = Reynolds number, dimensionless

Re_G, Re_L = Reynolds number for gas phase and liquid phase, respectively, dimensionless

R_A, R_{A_1}, R_{A_2} = specific rate of absorption or extraction or dissolution of species A, A_1, and A_2, respectively, mol/cm^2 sec

$R_{A'}$ = specific rate of desorption of species A′, mol/cm^2 sec

$R_{A,A}$, $R_{A,B}$ = specific rate of reaction of A in A-rich phase and B-rich phase, respectively, mol/cm^2 sec

$R_A(t)$ = specific rate of absorption of species A at time t, mol/cm^2 sec

R_B, R_C = specific rate of reaction of species B and C, respectively, mol/cm^2 sec

R'_A, R'_{A_1}, R'_{A_2} = volumetric rate of absorption of species A, A_1, and A_2, respectively, mol/cm^3 sec

R_{A-B_1}, R_{A-B_2} = specific rate of reaction of A with species B_1 and B_2, respectively, mol/cm^2 sec

$R'_A(t)$ = volumetric rate of absorption of species A at time t, mol/cm^3 sec

R''_A = rate of absorption of A, mol/sec

R^+_A = rate of dissolution of A, g/cm^2 sec

$\dot{R}$ = free radical for autocatalytic reaction

$[\dot{R}_o]$ = concentration of $\dot{R}$ in the bulk liquid phase, mol/cm^3

r = radius of particle, cm

r_A = local rate of reaction of A in the liquid phase, mol/cm^3 sec

$r_{A'}$ = $\dfrac{D_{A'}H_{A'}}{D_A H_A}$

r_B = $\dfrac{D_B}{D_A}$

r_C = $\dfrac{D_C}{D_A}$

r_c = radius of unreacted core, cm

S = selectivity index

S_1 = part of surface area on which cathodic reaction occurs, cm^2

S_2 = part of surface area on which anodic reaction occurs, cm^2

Sc = Schmidt number, dimensionless

S_e = total surface area, $S_1 + S_2$, cm^2

S_i = initial surface area per unit mass of solid, cm^2/g

Sh = Sherwood number, dimensionless

s = surface renewal rate, sec^{-1}

T = $[HA_1]_s + [HA_2]_s$, mol/liter; internal diameter of contactor, cm

T' = absolute temperature, °K

$\Delta T'$ = temperature rise at interface, °K

t = time, sec

t_E = exposure time, sec

t_d = time required for complete dissolution of solids, sec

u = $\dfrac{wV}{\rho_p d_p^3}$, the solid quantity group (Table 11.2)

u_R = resultant relative velocity between particle and liquid, cm/sec (Table 11.2)

$\bar{u}^2_{d_p}$ = mean square fluctuating velocity over the distance d_p, cm^2/sec^2

u_t = terminal settling velocity of a solid particle in a still fluid, cm/sec

V = volume of clear liquid, cm^3; volume of B phase, cm^3

V_G = superficial gas velocity, cm/sec

V_L = superficial liquid velocity, cm/sec

We = Weber number, dimensionless

w = solid loading, g/cm^3 (clear liquid volume)

X = weight percentage of solids

X_{A_1}, X_{A_2} = distribution coefficient for the undissociated acids between aqueous and organic phases (Eq. 6.45)

X_B = fractional conversion of B

X'_{A_1}, X'_{A_2} = overall distribution coefficient for the dissociated acids between aqueous and organic phases

x = distance into B phase from the interface, cm

Z = stoichiometric coefficient

$\bar{Z}$ = $\alpha_\lambda[B]$, cm^{-1} (Eq. 9.41)

GREEK SYMBOLS

α = parameter defined by Eq. 2.94; parameter defined by Eq. 2.149, cm^{-1}; thermal diffusivity, cm^2/sec (Eq. 3.15); parameter defined by Eq. 9.44, cm^{-2}; parameter defined by Eq. 13.35, cm/g

$\alpha_{A_1A_2}$ = separation factor of acids HA_1 and HA_2

α_λ = molal absorptivity, cm^2/mol (Eq. 9.39)

β = parameter defined by Eq. 9.44, mol/cm^3

γ = parameter defined by Eq. 2.26

δ = thickness of diffusion film (liquid) in the film theory of mass transfer, cm

δ' = ratio of concentration of acids HA_1 and HA_2 in organic phase

δ_A = thickness of diffusion film in the A-rich phase, cm

δ_B = thickness of diffusion film in the B-rich phase, cm

δ_g = thickness of diffusion film in the gas phase, cm

ϵ = void fraction of packed bed

ϵ_G = fractional gas holdup

ϵ_p = power input per unit mass of liquid, ergs/g sec

η = $\left(\frac{[B_i]}{[B_o]}\right)^{1/2}$

λ = reaction plane location measured from the interface, cm;
= $(\rho_G\rho_L/\rho_{air}\rho_w)^{0.5}$ (Figures 13.7 and 13.10)

$\lambda(t)$ = position of reaction plane at time t

μ = stripping factor, $k_{G_C}/H_C k_L$

μ_G = viscosity of gas, g/cm sec

μ_L = viscosity of liquid or solution, g/cm sec

μ_w = viscosity of water, g/cm sec

μ_λ = attenuation coefficient, cm^{-1}

ν = kinematic viscosity, cm^2/sec; frequency of light, sec^{-1}

ξ = $\bar{k}/D_A$, mol/cm^5 (Eq. 9.44)

π = $\frac{x}{2\sqrt{D_A t_E}}$ (Eq. 8.58a), dimensionless

ρ_G = density of gas, g/cm^3

ρ_L = density of liquid or solution, g/cm^3

ρ_p = density of solid particle, g/cm^3

ρ_w = density of water, g/cm^3

$\Delta\rho$ = $\rho_p - \rho_L$, g/cm^3

σ = specific heat of liquid, cal/g °C (Eq. 3.15)

σ_L = surface tension of liquid, dyne/cm

σ_w = surface tension of water, dyne/cm

ϕ = enhancement factor, dimensionless

ϕ_A, ϕ_{A_1}, ϕ_{A_2} = enhancement factor for species A, A_1, and A_2, respectively

ϕ_{AB} = enhancement factor for extraction of A in B-phase

ϕ_D = $\sqrt{k_{SL}a_p/D_B}$, cm^{-1} (Eq. 12.29)

ϕ_a = asymptotic value of enhancement factor

$\phi_{a,1}$ = asymptotic value of enhancement factor (Eq. 4.39a)

$\phi_{a,2}$ = asymptotic value of enhancement factor (Eq. 4.40a)

$\phi_{a,A-B_2}$ = asymptotic value of enhancement factor (Eq. 5.36a)

ϕ_d = enhancement factor for desorption of A'

ϕ_s = enhancement factor for solid dissolution (Eq. 12.42)

ϕ_{sa} = asymptotic value of enhancement factor ϕ_s (Eq. 12.43)

ψ = $\frac{d[A]}{dx}$ (Eq. 2.38);
= $\frac{\sigma_w}{\sigma_L}\,[(\mu_L/\mu_w)(\rho_w/\rho_L)^2]^{0.33}$ (Figures 13.7 and 13.10)

ω_i = mass fraction of anhydrous solute A at interface, g/g of solution

ω_o = mass fraction of anhydrous solute A in bulk, g/g of solution

ω_t = mass fraction of anhydrous solute in solids, g of solute/g of solid

HETEROGENEOUS REACTIONS:
ANALYSIS, EXAMPLES, AND REACTOR DESIGN

Volume 2

CHAPTER ONE

Introduction

Mass transfer accompanied by chemical reaction in gas–liquid and liquid–liquid systems is of great industrial, physiological, and biological importance. Tables 1.1 and 1.2 list some examples of industrially important gas–liquid and liquid–liquid reactions, along with the types of contactor that are likely to be used in practice. Most of the examples reported in Table 1.1 supplement those cited by Danckwerts (1970). The human body itself, with its absorption of oxygen by the blood, desorption of CO_2 into the lungs, and the like offers an interesting and complex example of the problems involved in mass transfer with chemical reaction.

Tables 1.3 and 1.4 present examples of industrially important solid–liquid reactions where the solid particles are slightly soluble and insoluble in the medium, respectively. Tables 1.5 and 1.6 give examples of industrially important gas–liquid–solid reacting systems where the solid particles are reactants and may be slightly soluble (Table 1.5) or insoluble (Table 1.6). Table 1.7 gives examples of industrially important gas–liquid–solid reactive systems where the solid particles act as a catalyst.

The problems of mass transfer accompanied by chemical reaction have been known for a long time. However, a systematic approach to dealing with them has been made only in the course of the last 25 years. An attempt is made in the subsequent chapters of this book to present a comprehensive picture of practically the entire gamut of problems that are encountered in the field of mass transfer with chemical reaction in fluid–fluid and fluid–fluid–solid systems. The central theme throughout will be the interaction between diffusional and kinetic factors.

TABLE 1.1. Gas–Liquid Reactions

System	Type of Equipment Normally Used	Reference(s)
Absorption of CO_2, H_2S, CH_3SH, and COS in aqueous solutions of alkalies and amines in the fertilizer and other industries	Packed and plate columns	Danckwerts and Sharma (1966); Ramachandran and Sharma (1971)
Absorption of CO_2 in ammoniated brine for the manufacture of soda ash; Solvay-type processes	Sectionalized bubble column	Pal and Sharma (1983)
Production of C-13 isotope by the carbamate process	Packed column	Schwind (1969)
Absorption of NH_3 in aqueous acid solutions with or without suspended solids for the manufacture of nitrogenous fertilizers	Mechanically agitated contactor; spray column	Sauchel (1960)
Absorption of phosphine from the off-gases of electrothermal phosphorus plants in aqueous solutions of sodium hypochlorite; absorption of phosphine in acetylene gas (obtained from calcium carbide) in aqueous solutions of sulfuric acid or sodium hypochlorite	Packed column	Lawless and Searle (1962); Slizovskaya et al. (1969); Chandrasekaran and Sharma (1977)
Absorption of phosphine in aqueous solutions of formaldehyde and hydrochloric acid	Mechanically agitated contactor	Chaudhari and Doraiswamy (1974)

TABLE 1.1. (*Continued*)

System	Type of Equipment Normally Used	Reference(s)
Liquid-phase air oxidation of a variety of organic compounds, for example, paraffinic hydrocarbons, xylenes; air oxidation of *p*-nitrotoluene sulfonic acid	Agitated contactor; bubble column	Chandalia et al. (1963); Chandalia (1970); Prengle and Barona (1970) Carleton et al. (1969)
Air oxidation of black liquor containing Na_2S in the pulp and paper industry; air oxidation of aqueous solutions of $(NH_4)_2S$	Bubble column	Collins (1962); Murray (1968, 1971); Chandrasekaran and Sharma (1974); Pal et al. (1982) Rosenwald et al. (1975)
	Pipeline reactor	Cooper and Rossano (1973)
Oxidation of *n*-butyl mercaptan to di-*n*-butyl sulfide in the presence of cobalt pyrophosphate as a catalyst; oxidation of propyl mercaptan to sulfonic acid; oxidation of thiophenol	Agitated contactor; tubular coil	Wallace et al. (1964); Sittig (1969); Brooks and Smith (1973)
Air oxidation of *n*-butyraldehyde and 2- ethylhexaldehyde	Agitated contactor; bubble and packed bubble columns	Ladhabhoy and Sharma (1969, 1970)
Conversion of HCl to Cl_2 by Kel-Chlor process; oxidation of solutions of HCN in polar solvents to $(CN)_2$, oxamide, or cyanoformamide	Mechanically agitated contactor; bubble column	Oblad (1969); Rosenzweig (1976); Riemenschneider (1976)
Wacker process for the conversion of lower olefins to the corresponding carbonyl compounds: ethylene to vinyl acetate, ethylene to acetaldehdye, propylene to acetone, etc.	Bubble column; agitated contactor	Chandalia (1967, 1968a, b); Hatch (1970)
Air oxidation of 2-ethylhydroanthraquinone for the production of H_2O_2; oxidation of aqueous alkaline solution of 2,4,6-trimethylphenol	Packed bubble column; bubble column	Kirk and Othmer (1966a); Rosenzweig (1976)
Oxo reaction for the manufacture of butyraldehyde, butanol, and 2-ethylhexanol; hydration of propylene (propylene partly as liquid); hydrogenation of organic compounds with homogeneous catalysts	Bubble column; packed bubble column; mechanically agitated contactor	Goldstein and Waddams (1967); Olivier and Booth (1970); Rylander (1973); James (1973)
Oxidation of PCl_3 with oxygen	Bubble column; pipeline contactor	Kirk and Othmer (1968)
Oxidation of $Al(C_2H_5)_3$ and aluminum trialkyls; oxidation of trialkyl boranes	Bubble column; mechanically agitated contactor	Sittig (1969); Bossier et al. (1973); Brown (1975)
Ozonolysis of unsaturated fatty acids and esters (say, ozonolysis of oleic acid for the production of pelargonic, azelaic, and other by-product acids; ozonolysis of methyl soyate); ozonolysis of cyclododecatriene; purification of water for potable purposes and treatment of effluents with air containing ozone (in the absence or presence of uv light)	Mechanically agitated contactor; bubble column	Throckmorton et al. (1968); Lowndes (1971); Throckmorton and Pryde (1972); Carlson et al. (1977); *Hydrocarbon Process. Petrol. Refiner* (1979); Prengle et al. (1975)
Absorption of CO in ammoniacal CuCl solution; absorption of CO in organic media containing cuprous aluminum complexes; absorption of CO (along with isobutylene) in aqueous solutions of sulfuric acid to give pivalic acid	Packed and plate columns	van Krevelen and Baans (1950); Haase and Waker (1974); *Hydrocarbon Process. Petrol. Refiner* (1979)
Absorption of CO in CH_3OH for the manufacture of acetic acid or methyl formate; absorption of CO in dimethyl amine to give dimethyl formamide	Bubble column	von Kutepow et al. (1965); Hjortkjaer and Jensen (1976); *Hydrocarbon Process. Petrol. Refiner* (1979)

TABLE 1.1. ***(Continued)***

System	Type of Equipment Normally Used	Reference(s)
Absorption of CO in NaOH to manufacture sodium formate	Agitated contactor	Sirotkin (1953)
Liquid-phase chlorination of a variety of organic compounds, namely, benzene, ethylene dichloride, paraffinic hydrocarbons; side-chain chlorination of toluene; chlorination of molten polyethylene	Agitated contactor; bubble and packed columns; coil reactor	Hawkins (1965); Miller (1966); Ratcliffe (1966); Chua and Ratcliffe (1970); Barona and Prengle (1973); Sittig (1969)
Chlorination of CS_2 for the manufacture of CCl_4; chlorination of dimethyl methyl phosphonate in PCl_3 to give methyl phosphonic dichloride	Packed column; Mechanically agitated contactor	Kirk and Othmer (1964a); Whitt (1967)
Absorption of H_2S in propylene tetramer (or triisolutylene) in the presence of BF_3 for the manufacture of dodecylmercaptan	Packed column	Frantz and Glass (1963)
Chlorination of an aqueous solution of HCN for the manufacture of CNCl; chlorination of acetophenone in the presence of aqueous HCl; chlorination–oxidation of furfural with chlorine in the presence of water to mucochloric acid; chlorination in the aqueous phase of dissolved phenolic substances and aromatic sulfonic acids	Packed column; mechanically agitated contactor; bubble column	Sittig (1969); Whitt (1967); Burmakin et al. (1973); Yadav and Sharma (1981a)
Liquid-phase oxychlorination of ethylene for the production of vinyl chloride	Bubble column	Friend et al. (1968)
Conversion of ethylene or propylene to the corresponding chlorohydrin	Packed column; bubble column	Domask and Kobe (1954); Saeki et al. (1972)
Absorption of C_2H_4 in ethylene dibromide containing dissolved Br_2 to make ethylene dibromide or absorption of C_2H_2 in tetrabromoethane containing dissolved Br_2 to make tetrabromoethane	Mechanically agitated contactor; packed column	Miller (1969)
Addition of C_2H_4 to $Al(C_2H_5)_3$	Bubble column	Albright and Smith (1968)
Alkylation of acetic acid with isobutylene to make *tert*-butyl acetate	Agitated contactor	Gehlawat and Sharma (1971)
Reaction between ketene and acetic acid to make acetic anhydride	Plate column	Jeffreys (1961)
Reaction between acetone and HCN to produce cyanohydrin	Bubble cap plate column	Sittig (1969)
Photonitrosation of cyclohexane with NOCl to manufacture cyclohexanone oxime	Bubble column	Hulme and Turner (1967)
Reaction between NH_3 and caprolactone for the manufacture of caprolactam; reaction between NH_3 and phthalic anhydride to give phthalimide	Coil reactor; sectionalized bubble column; plate column	Sittig (1969); Bartholome et al. (1976)
Hydration of propylene with sulfuric acid for the production of isopropanol	Bubble column; packed column	Horie et al. (1970)
Sulfonation and sulfation with SO_3 gas (e.g., reaction between fatty alcohols and SO_3); sulfonation of castor oil with SO_3; sulfonation of α-olefins with SO_3 gas	Agitated contactor; thin-film contactor	Groggins (1958); Mützenberg and Giger (1968); Kremers (1971); Johnson and Crynes (1974); Miyauchi et al. (1971)
Polycondensation reactions for the production of polyamides and polyesters (desorption of water and ethylene glycol)	Mechanically agitated contactor	Hoftyzer and van Krevelen (1968); Secor (1969); Hoftyzer (1975)
Copolymerization of ethylene and propylene in a non-Newtonian solution of the copolymer in a solvent, for the production of rubber	Agitated contactor	Jordon (1968)

TABLE 1.1. (*Continued*)

System	Type of Equipment Normally Used	Reference(s)
Reaction between C_2H_2 and liquid HF for the manufacture of CH_3CHF_2 required for the production of vinyl fluoride	Bubble column	Kirk and Othmer (1966b)
Liquid-phase oxidation of benzoic acid and substituted benzoic acids (molten) to make phenols	Mechanically agitated contactor	Szonyi (1968); van Direndonck et al. (1974, 1975); Ghorpade et al. (1981)
Conversion of HCl to Cl_2 in molten salts containing CuCl (modified Deacon's process)	Agitated contactor	Ruthven and Kenney (1968)
Oxidation of SO_2 in melts and absorption of SO_2 in eutectic mixture of Li, Na, and K carbonates	Agitated contactor	Glueck and Kenney (1968); Holroyd and Kenney (1971a, b); Oldenkamp and Margolin (1969)
Chlorination of $C_2H_4Cl_2$ in salt bath of Na, Ca, and Al chlorides; manufacture of vinyl chloride from ethylene (or ethane), Cl_2 (or HCl), and air (or O_2) by using melts of $CuCl/CuCl_2/KCl$	Bubble column; agitated contactor	Asinger (1968); Riegel et al. (1973)
Simultaneous absorption of NH_3 and CO_2 in water	Agitated contactor; packed column	Hatch and Pigford (1962); Ramachandran and Sharma (1971); Pangarkar and Sharma (1974)
Simultaneous absorption of SO_3 and HCl in chlorosulfonic acid; absorption of N_2O_4 and O_2 in aqueous KCl to give KNO_3 and Cl_2	Packed column or agitated contactor	Kirk and Othmer (1964b); Weinrotter (1971)
Simultaneous absorption of ethylene and chlorine in dichloroethane	Agitated contactor; bubble column	Balasubramanian et al. (1966); Chua and Ratcliffe (1971)
Simultaneous absorption of vinyl chloride and chlorine in trichloroethane	Bubble column	McIver and Ratcliffe (1974)
Simultaneous absorption of NO_2 and dimethyl sulfide in dimethyl sulfoxide	Agitated contactor	Sittig (1969)
Absorption of SO_2 and H_2S in molten sulfur	Agitated contactor	*Chem. Eng. News* (1970)
Absorption of O_2, CO, CO_2 in blood	—	Ramachandran (1969)
Sulfoxidation of hydrocarbons (photochemical)	Bubble column	Hardwick (1962)
Simultaneous absorption of sulfur dioxide and oxygen in $MnSO_4$ solutions; simultaneous absorption of SO_2 and O_2 in the presence of ozone in aqueous solutions of sulfuric acid	Agitated contactor; bubble column	Coughanowr and Krause (1965); Gunn and Saleem (1970); Maslan (1973)
Removal of mercury from hydrogen gas by absorption in aqueous solutions of sodium hypochlorite	Packed column	*Chem. Eng. News* (1972); Nene (1979)

TABLE 1.2. Liquid–Liquid Reactions

System	Type of Equipment Normally Used	Reference(s)
Extraction of malodorous sulfur compounds from petroleum fractions	Agitated contactor	Groothius (1961)
Hydrolysis and/or saponification of a variety of esters	Agitated contactor; spray column	Jeffreys et al. (1961); Sharma and Nanda (1968); Donders et al. (1968)
Removal of free fatty acid from fats	Agitated contactor	Gunstone (1958)
Removal of free acid and esters from the products of the oxidation of cyclohexane	Agitated contactor	Miller (1969); Hancock (1975)
Hydrolysis of organic chloro compounds (C_5 chlorides, nitrochlorobenzenes, polychlorobenzenes, etc.)	Agitated contactor	Groggins (1958)
Removal of dissolved HCl from a variety of chlorinated compounds (obtained by substitution chlorination) by treatment with aqueous NaOH	Agitated contactor	Miller (1968)
Removal of COS from liquefied C_3 fractions by treatment with aqueous NaOH and alkanolamine solutions	Packed column	Goldstein and Waddams (1967); Sharma (1965)
Manufacture of dithiocarbamates by reaction between aqueous solutions of amines and CS_2	Agitated contactor; spray column	Kothari and Sharma (1966)
Nitration of aromatic compounds (benzene, chlorobenzene, toluene, etc.)	Agitated contactor; pipeline or coil reactor	Albright and Hanson (1969); Cox and Strachan (1972a, b); Hanson et al. (1971); Barona and Prengle (1973); Albright and Hanson (1975); Hanson and Ismail (1976)
Oxidation of a number of organic compounds sparingly soluble in water by $KMnO_4$	Agitated contactor	Groggins (1958)
Alkylation of organic compounds (alkylation of phenols with isobutylene; toluene with isobutylene and butenes; isobutane with butenes and isobutylene;[a] xylenes with acetaldehyde to give dixylylethane, etc.)	Agitated contactor; bubble column; tubular (pipeline) reactor	Gehlawat and Sharma (1970); Shah and Sharma (1969); Tiwari and Sharma (1977); Sprow (1969); Jernigan et al. (1965); Mosby and Albright (1966); Albright (1966); Dixon and Saunders (1954)
Oligomerization of 1-butene in sulfuric acid; dimerization of isobutylene and isoamylene	Agitated contactor	Naworski and Harriott (1969); Sankholkar and Sharma (1973, 1975)
Conversion of propylene, butenes,[a] and amylenes into corresponding alcohols via extraction into sulfuric acid; extraction of isoamylene from loaded H_2SO_4 solutions into *n*-heptane	Agitated contactor; pipeline contactor	Goldstein and Waddams (1967); Sankholkar and Sharma (1973, 1975)
Manufacture of oximes (cyclohexanone oxime by reaction between cyclohexanone and aqueous solution of hydroxylamine sulfate)	Multistage agitated contactor; vibrating plate column extractor	Sharma and Nanda (1968); Rod (1974, 1976)
Pyrometallurgical operations, removal of undesirable impurities from molten metals into slags	Bubble agitated contactor	Szekely (1967); Subramanian and Richardson (1968); Richardson (1975); Whiteway (1979)
Conversion of dichlorobutene to chloroprene	Agitated contactor	Miller (1968); Johnson (1976); Weissermel and Arpe (1978)
Electron exchange reactions in heterogeneous systems	Agitated contactor	Scibona et al. (1966); Mansoori and Madden (1969)
Removal of acetaldehyde from diethyl ether	Agitated contactor	Miller (1969)

TABLE 1.2. (*Continued*)

System	Type of Equipment Normally Used	Reference(s)
Removal of HF from aqueous solutions by solvent extraction with amines (e.g., trioctylamine); recovery and separation of lower aliphatic and substituted aliphatic acids from aqueous solutions with trioctylamine	Agitated contactor	Hardwick and Wace (1965); Jagirdar and Sharma (1980)
Reaction between ethylene dichloride and aqueous ammonia for the production of ethylenediamine	Pipeline and coil reactor	Leszezynski et al. (1967)
Extraction with reaction in the recovery of metals via hydrometallurgical route	Agitated contactor; pulse columns centrifugal extractor	Rosenbaum et al. (1971); Hughes (1975); Bailes et al. (1976); Whewell (1977)
Interfacial polycondensation reactions; manufacture of polycarbonates	Agitated contactor	Morgan (1965); Griskey et al. (1974); Wielgosz et al. (1972)
Reduction of a variety of nitroaromatic compounds with aqueous Na_2S, $NaHSO_3/Na_2SO_3$, and $Na_2S_2O_4$	Agitated contactor	Groggins (1958); Bhave and Sharma (1981)
Emulsion polymerization	Agitated contactor	Ugelstad and Hansen (1976)
Separation of close-boiling organic acids and bases by dissociation extraction	Agitated contactor	Anwar et al. (1971); Wadekar and Sharma (1981a)
Purification of molten phosphorus with concentrated sulfuric acid; reaction of molten phosphorus with solutions of caustic soda for the manufacture of phosphine and phosphites; reaction of liquid sodium or sodium–potassium alloys with liquid white phosphorus in inert mixtures of aromatics to make alkali phosphide		Harnisch (1980)

[a] In these cases the pressure of the system is sufficiently high to keep the reactants in the liquid phase.

TABLE 1.3. Solid–Liquid Reactions with Slightly Soluble Solids

System	Reference(s)
Alkaline hydrolysis of solid esters such as di-β-chloroethyl oxalate, dimethyl fumarate, and nitrobenzoic acid esters	Sharma and Sharma (1969, 1970a, b)
Alkaline hydrolysis of polychlorobenzenes (tetra and hexa) in aqueous solutions of caustic soda (containing methanol)	—
Reaction between terephthalic acid and ethylene oxide (with or without solvent) in the presence of dissolved catalysts	*Hydrocarbon Process. Petrol. Refiner* (1971); Bhatia et al. (1976)
Dissolution of azo dyes containing *o*-hydroxy group in alkaline medium	Hague (1971)
Sulfonation and nitration of naphthalene at lower temperatures	Groggins (1958)
Nitration of acetylated *p*-toluidine and acetylated *p*-anisidine	—
Manufacture of benzyl esters by reaction between benzyl chloride and dry sodium benzoate, sodium acetate, etc.	Rueggeberg et al. (1946); Yadav and Sharma (1981b)
Manufacture of diisocyanate by reaction between phosgene and aromatic diamines (second step of the reaction) or reaction between phosgene and hydrochlorides of amines	Twitchett (1974); Tsigin and Konstantinov (1979)
Manufacture of reactive dyes by reaction between cyanuric chloride and amines	Venkataraman (1972)
Dissolution of sparingly soluble acids (benzoic, salicylic, etc.) in aqueous sodium hydroxide solutions	Marangozis and Johnson (1963)
Separation of isomeric chloro- and nitrobenzoic acids, and *p*-chloro-*m*-xylenol and dichloro-*m*-xylenol by reaction with aqueous sodium hydroxide (with a stoichiometric deficiency) (dissociation extraction)	Laddha and Sharma (1978); Wadekar and Sharma (1981b)
Recovery of paraffins by adductive crystallization with urea	Yang and Manning (1970)
Dissolution of silver halides in thiosulfate, sulfite, glycine, etc. solutions (relevant in photographic processes)	Shiao et al. (1975)
Dyeing with reactive dyes	Preston and Fern (1961); Peters (1975); Rattee and Breuer (1974); Motomura and Morita (1977)

TABLE 1.4. **Solid–Liquid Reactions with Insoluble Solids**

System	Reference(s)
Reaction between S and Na_2SO_3 to $Na_2S_2O_3$; reaction between S and PCl_3 to $PSCl_3$	Levenson (1954)
Reaction between RCl and sodium cyanate to give isocyanates	Twitchett (1974)
Reaction between dialkyl maleate (and other unsaturated acid esters) and sodium bisulfite to give the sodium salt of sulfosuccinic ester	Garrett (1972)
Iron–acid reduction of nitro compound	Groggins (1958)
Acidization of dolomite, feldspar, etc.	Lund et al. (1973, 1975); Fogler et al. (1975)
Cementation reactions in hydrometallurgical operations	Burkin (1966); Habashi (1970)
Hydration of lime	—
Reaction between sulfuric acid (or other acids such as nitric, phosphoric, and hydrochloric) and phosphate rock	—
Generation of acetylene by reaction between water and CaC_2	—
Reaction between H_2SO_4 and NaCl, $NaNO_3$, etc.	—
Reduction of vat dyes with aqueous alkaline solutions of sodium hydrosulfite	Peters (1975)
Demetallation of heavier petroleum fractions with manganese nodules	Fischer et al. (1976)
Sulfonation and chloromethylation of styrene divinylbenzene copolymer for the manufacture of ion-exchange resins	Pepper (1951); Pepper et al. (1953)
Desulfurization of higher petroleum fractions with metallic sodium	Sternberg et al. (1974)
Manufacture of organometallic compounds (e.g., Grignard reagent)	Horak et al. (1975)

TABLE 1.5. **Fluid–Fluid–Solid Reactions with Slightly Soluble Solids**

System	Reference(s)
Absorption of CO_2 in an aqueous suspension of lime and $Ba(OH)_2$	Ramachandran and Sharma (1969); Juvekar and Sharma (1973); Sada et al. (1977a)
Absorption of CO_2 in a suspension of BaS	Gupta and Sharma (1967)
Absorption of lean SO_2 in a slurry of $CaCO_3$ and a slurry of MgO	Uchida et al. (1975); Sada et al. (1977b)
Absorption of lean H_2S, $COCl_2$, Cl_2, etc. in an aqueous suspension of lime	
Absorption of CO in a suspension of lime in the manufacture of $(HCOO)_2Ca$	
Extraction of fatty acids into aqueous suspensions of lime and $Ba(OH)_2$	
Alkylation of naphthalene with ethylene, propylene, butylenes, etc., in the presence of catalysts such as BF_3–phosphoric acid	Friedman and Nelson (1969)

TABLE 1.6. Fluid–Fluid–Solid Systems Where the Solid Particles Are Insoluble in the Medium

System	Reference(s)
Absorption of CO_2 in a suspension of MgO	Smithson and Bakhshi (1973)
Absorption of CO_2 in a suspension of CaS	*Chem. Eng.* (1968)
Absorption of SO_2 in a suspension of $CaCO_3$	Bjerle et al. (1972); Volpicelli and Massimilla (1970)
Chlorination of wood pulp	Karter and Bobalek (1971)
Leaching of copper, nickel, cobalt, etc.	Burkin (1966); Habashi (1970); Reilly and Scott (1976)
Carbonation of β-oxynaphthoic acid in kerosene medium	Phadtare and Doraiswamy (1965, 1966)
Hydrogenation of styrene–butadiene rubber latex and other polymeric substances suspended in solvents	Krause (1975); Falk (1976)
Hydrogenation of sodium particles suspended in mineral oil to give NaH	Kirk and Othmer (1966c)
Chlorination of suspended polyethylene (and PVC) particles in water	Lechev et al. (1973)
Air oxidation of nylon particles suspended in water	Sundstrom et al. (1976)
Manufacture of zinc dithionite by reaction between SO_2 and zinc particles suspended in water	Szabo and Kaldi (1976); Sastri and Epstein (1978)

TABLE 1.7. Fluid–Fluid–Solid (Catalytic) Reactions

System	Catalyst	Type of Reactor[a]	Reference(s)
Hydrogenation of unsaturated fats	Raney nickel	SR	Coenen (1960, 1976); Hashimoto et al. (1971); Albright (1973)
	Copper chromite, Raney Cu–Cr, Raney Ni, Cu, Pd	TBR	Mukherjee et al. (1975)
Hydrogenation of a variety of carbonyl compounds		SR	Freifelder (1971)
Hydrogenation of benzene to cyclohexane	Nickel-based catalyst	SR	Dufau et al. (1964)
Hydrogenation of α-methyl styrene	Pd-based catalyst	SR	Sherwood and Farkas (1966); Pruden and Weber (1970)
		TBR	Satterfield et al. (1969); Germain et al. (1974)
Hydrogenation of aqueous butynediol to butenediol	Ni–Cu–Mn on silica-based catalyst	TBR	BIOS 367 (1945)
Hydrogenation of crotonaldehyde	Pd-based catalyst	TBR	Kenney and Sedriks (1972); Sedriks and Kenney (1973)
Selective hydrogenation of acetylenic and diolefinic compounds from the C_3 and C_4 fractions of naphtha crackers	Noble-metal-based catalyst	TBR	
Hydrogenation of nitro compounds such as nitrobenzene, dinitrobenzene, or dinitrotoluene	Pd- or Pt-based catalyst	SR	Dovell et al. (1970); Acres and Cooper (1972)

TABLE 1.7. (*Continued*)

System	Catalyst	Type of Reactor[a]	Reference(s)
Hydrogenation of nitrobenzene sulfonic acid (potassium salt), nitrophenols, etc. in aqueous solutions	Pd-, Pt-, Ni-, etc. based catalyst	SR	Ferrari and Garbei (1969)
Hydrogenation and hydrocracking of α-cellulose (also powdered coal) to liquid and gaseous fuels	Ni catalyst	SR	Gupta et al. (1976)
Hydrogenation of molten benzoic acid	Pd on charcoal	SR	Acres et al. (1974)
Hydrogenation of furfural and its derivatives	Cu–Cr oxide	Tubular SR	Haidegger et al. (1971); Hodossy (1968)
Hydrogenation of caprolactam to hexamethyleneimine	Co–Re	SR	Rosenzweig (1976)
Hydrogenation of α-nitrocaprolactam in aqueous ammoniacal solutions	Ni-based catalyst	SR	van Direndonck and Nelemans (1972)
Hydrogenation of nitriles	Ni-based catalyst	SR	Freifelder (1971)
Hydrogenation of glucose	Raney nickel	SR	Hofmann and Bill (1959); Brahme and Doraiswamy (1976)
Conversion of acetone and H_2 to methyl isobutylketone	Zirconium phosphate—Pd	TBR	Onoue et al. (1977)
Hydroisomerization of butene-1 to butene-2	Undisclosed	TBR Packed bubble column (upflow)	*Chem. Eng.* (1978); Eleazer et al. (1979)
Hydroformylation and hydrogenation of monoolefins, methyl sorbate, etc.	Noble-metal(Rh) based catalyst	SR	Acres et al. (1974); Pittman et al. (1975)
Hydrogenation of xylose; hydrogenolysis of saccharides	Raney nickel; Ru, Rh, and Pd on carbon	SR	Wisniak et al. (1974a, b); van Ling and Vlugter (1969); Rozhdestvenskava et al. (1970)
Fischer–Tropsch synthesis: conversion of CO + H_2 to CH_4, paraffins, etc.	Ni–MgO	SR	Zaidi et al. (1979)
Conversion of CO + H_2 to methanol		Three-phase fluidized bed reactor	Sherwin and Frank (1976)
Reaction between nitrite and H_2 to give hydroxylamine salts; reaction between NH_4NO_3, H_3PO_4, and H_2 to give hydroxylamine phosphate	Noble metal (Pd) on carbon	SR	Acres et al. (1974); van Goolen (1976)
Reduction of sodium chlorate in aqueous caustic liquor (diaphragm cell) with H_2	Not disclosed	TBR	Mitchell and Modan (1979)
Hydrogenation of iodine dissolved in aqueous HI	Ru or Rh on charcoal	SR	Paulik (1975)
Reduction of uranyl(VI) to uranyl(IV) in aqueous solutions with H_2	Pd-based catalyst	TBR; Packed bubble column reactor	Snider and Perona (1974)
Reduction of UF_5 dissolved in molten $LiF–BeF_2–ThF_2$ melt with H_2	Pt-based catalyst	SR	Kelmers and Bennett (1976)
Deuterium exchange between H_2 water	Pt on carbon	TBR	Enright and Chuang (1978)

TABLE 1.7. ***(Continued)***

System	Catalyst	Type of Reactor[a]	Reference(s)
Air oxidation of ethanol to acetic acid; conversion of primary alcohols to the corresponding sodium salt of the acid	Pd-based catalyst, CdO, ZnO, etc.	TBR; SR	Klassen and Kirk (1955); Hsu and Ruether (1978); Mahajani (1979)
2-Ethylhexanol to 2-ethylhexoic acid	CaO, Cu, etc.	SR	Miller and Bennett (1961)
Oxidation of isobutylene glycol to α-hydroxyisobutyric acid	Pt on carbon	SR	*Chem. Tech.* (1975)
Amination of monoethanolamine to ethylene diamine	Undisclosed	TBR	Kohn (1978)
Isomerization of propylene oxide to allyl alcohol; rearrangement of oxirane compounds	Li_3PO_4 suspended in diphenyl; SiO_2–Al_2O_3	SR	Sittig (1967); Sukhdev(1972)
Oxidation of glucose to K–gluconate	Pt on carbon	SR	de Wilt and van der Baan (1972)
Hydrogenation of 1-bromo-2,4-dichlorobenzene to 1,3-dichlorobenzene	Pd on carbon	SR	Britton and Beman (1965)
Alkylation of benzene with propylene	Phosphoric acid on inert support	TBR	Villadson and Livbjerg (1978)
Reaction between isobutylene and aqueous formaldehyde (a step in the manufacture of synthetic isoprene)		TBR	Weissermel and Arpe (1978)
Reaction between isobutylene and methanol to give methyl *tert*-butyl ether	Ion-exchange resins	Multitubular packed-bed reactor	Weissermel and Arpe (1978)
Epoxidation of ethylene to ethylene oxide	Silver oxide on silica gel suspended in dibutyl phthalate	SR	Shingu (1961)
Epoxidation of propylene with *tert*-butyl hydroperoxide, ethyl benzene hydroperoxide, etc.	Mo sulfide/oxides	SR	Sheng and Zajacek (1968)
Epoxidation of styrene and α-olefins with cumene hydroperoxide		SR	Sheldon (1973); Raval and Sharma (1980)
Slurry polymerization	Organometallic compounds	SR	Schmeal and Street (1971); McGreavy (1972)
Oxidation of SO_2 to H_2SO_4 in water; absorption of H_2S from stack gases in alkaline solutions; oxidation of aqueous sodium sulfide (black liquor)	Active carbon	TBR, SR	Hartman and Coughlin (1972); Seaburn and Engel (1973); Komiyama and Smith (1975); Bhatia et al. (1973) Chandrasekaran and Sharma (1977, 1978); Pal et al. (1982)
Air oxidation of dilute formic acid and acetic acid solutions (treatment of waste streams)	Copper oxide–zinc oxide; ferric oxide	TBR	Goto and Smith (1975); Levec and Smith (1976); Goto et al. (1976)
Hydrodesulfurization and hydrocracking of petroleum fractions	Molybdenum- and tungsten-based catalyst	TBR	van Deemter (1965); Schuit and Gates (1973); Henry and Gilbert (1973)
Conversion of propylene to isopropanol	Tungstic-oxide-based catalyst	TBR	Zabor et al. (1960)
Acrylamide from acrylonitrile	Copper chromite	TBR	*Chem. Eng.* (1973)
Reaction between C_2H_2 and aqueous formaldehyde to give butynediol	Copper–bismuth acetylide on silica	TBR	BIOS 367 (1945)

TABLE 1.7. (*Continued*)

System	Catalyst	Type of Reactor[a]	Reference(s)
Isomerization of α-pinene (2-pinene) to camphene; isomerization of Δ^3-carene to Δ^2-carene	TiO_2, $NiSO_4$ etc.	SR	Ohnishi et al. (1974); Wystrach et al. (1975)
Dehydrogenation of secondary alcohols to ketones	Ni or copper chrome	SR	Weissermel and Arpe (1978)
Dehydrogenation of isoborneol to camphor	Cu–Ni–Mn	SR	Golovin et al. (1970)
Hydrogenation of polymeric substances	Raney Ni; Pd/C	SR	Falk (1976)
Hydrogenation of epoxides of styrene, α-olefins etc., in the presence of water as a second liquid phase	Raney Ni	SR	Newman et al. (1949)
Dimerization of ketene		TBR	Weissermel and Arpe (1978)

[a]SR stands for slurry reactor, TBR for trickle-bed reactor.

REFERENCES

Acres, G. J. K., and Cooper, B. J. (1972), *J. Appl. Chem. Biotechnol.*, **22**, 769.

Acres, G. J. K., Bird, A. J., and Davidson, P. J. (1974), *Chem. Eng. (London)*, No. 283, p. 145.

Albright, L. F. (1966), *Chem. Eng.*, **73**(18), 119.

Albright, L. F. (1973), *J. Am. Oil Chem. Soc.*, **50**, 255.

Albright, L. F., and Hanson, C. (1969), *Loss Prev.*, **3**, 26.

Albright, L. F., and Hanson, C. (1975), *Industrial and Laboratory Nitration* (Am. Chem. Soc. Symp. Ser. No. 22), American Chemical Society, Washington, D.C.

Albright, L. F., and Smith, C. S. (1968), *AIChE J.*, **14**, 325.

Anwar, M. M., Hanson, C., and Pratt, M. W. T. (1971), in Gregory, J. G., Evans, B., and Weston, P. C. (Eds.), *Proceedings of the International Solvent Extraction Conference* (The Hague, 19–23 April), Society of Chemical Industry, London, p. 911.

Asinger, F. (1968), *Paraffin Chemistry and Technology*, Pergamon, London.

Bailes, P. J., Hanson, C., and Hughes, M. A. (1976), *Chem. Eng.*, **83**(18), 86.

Balasubramanian, S. N., Rihani, D. N., and Doraiswamy, L. K. (1966), *Ind. Eng. Chem. Fundam.*, **5**, 184.

Barona, N., and Prengle, H. W., Jr. (1973), *Hydrocarbon Process. Petrol. Refiner*, **52**(12), 73.

Bartholome, E., Hetzel, E., Horn, H. C., Molzahn, M., Rotermund, G. W., and Vogel, L. (1976), *Chem. Ing.-Tech.*, **48**(5), 355.

Bhatia, S. P., de Souza, T. L. C., and Prahacs, S. (1973), *Tappi*, **56**(12), 164.

Bhatia, S., Gopala Rao, M., and Rao, M. S. (1976), *Chem. Eng. Sci.*, **31**, 427.

Bhave, R. R., and Sharma, M. M. (1981), *J. Chem. Tech. Biotechnol.*, **31**, 93.

BIOS Final Rept. No. 367, Manufacture of 1,4-Butynediol at I. G. Ludwigshafen, 1945.

Bjerle, I., Bengtsson, S., and Färnkvisi, K. (1972), *Chem. Eng. Sci.*, **27**, 1853.

Bossier, J. A., Farritor, R. E., Hughmark, G. A., and Kao, J. T. F. (1973), *AIChE J.*, **19**, 1065.

Brahme, P. H., and Doraiswamy, L. K. (1976), *Ind. Eng. Chem. Process Design Dev.*, **15**, 130.

Britton, E. C., and Beman, F. L. (1965), U.S. 3,170,961 (23 February); *Chem. Abstr.* (1965), **62**, 13086a.

Brooks, B. W., and Smith, R. M. (1973), *Chem. Eng. Sci.*, **28**, 2013.

Brown, H. C. (1975), *Organic Syntheses via Boranes*, Wiley, New York.

Burkin, A. R. (1966), *The Chemistry of Hydrometallurgical Processes*, Spon, London.

Burmakin, N. M., Kogan, L. M., and Berman, M.Yu (1973), *J. Appl. Chem. USSR (Engl. Transl.)*, **46**, 995.

Carleton, A. J., Rennie, J., and Valentin, F. H. H. (1969), *Chim. Ind. (Paris)*, **101**(10), 1439.

Carlson, K. D., Sohns, V. E., Perkins, R. B., and Huffman, E. L. (1977), *Ind. Eng. Chem. Prod. Res. Dev.*, **6**, 95.

Chandalia, S. B. (1967), *Indian J. Technol.*, **5**, 218.

Chandalia, S. B. (1968a), *Indian J. Technol.*, **6**, 88.

Chandalia, S. B. (1968b), *Indian J. Technol.*, **6**, 249.

Chandalia, S. B. (1970), *Chem. Process. Eng. (India)*, **4**(4), 19.

Chandalia, S. B., Shah, K. H., and Sharma, M. M. (1963), *Indian J. Technol.*, **1**, 345.

Chandrasekaran, K., and Sharma, M. M. (1974), *Chem. Eng. Sci.*, **29**, 2130.

Chandrasekaran, K., and Sharma, M. M. (1977), *Chem. Eng. Sci.*, **32**, 669.

Chandrasekaran, K., and Sharma, M. M. (1978), *Chem. Eng. Sci.*, **33**, 1294.

Chaudhari, R. V., and Doraiswamy, L. K. (1974), *Chem. Eng. Sci.*, **29**, 129.

Chem. Eng. (1968), **75**(10), 94.

Chem. Eng. (1973), **80**(27), 68.

Chem. Eng. (1978), **85**(1), 17.

Chem. Eng. News (1970), **48**(18), 68.

Chem. Eng. News (1972), **50**(7), 14.

Chemtech. (1975), **5**, 189.

Chua, Y. H., and Ratcliffe, J. S. (1970), *Mech. Chem. Eng. Trans.*, **6**(2), 35.

Chua, Y. H., and Ratcliffe, J. S. (1971), *Mech. Chem. Eng. Trans.*, **7**, 6, 11, 17.

Coenen, J. W. E. (1960), in De Boer, J. H. (Ed.), *The Mechanism of Heterogeneous Catalysis*, Elsevier, Amsterdam, p. 126.

Coenen, J. W. E. (1976), *J. Am. Oil Chem. Soc.*, **53**, 382.

Collins, T. T. (1962), *Paper Trade J.*, **146**(July 23), 39.

Cooper, H. B. H., Jr., and Rossano, A. T., Jr. (1973), *Tappi*, **56**(6), 100.

Coughanowr, D. R., and Krause, F. E. (1965), *Ind. Eng. Chem. Fundam.*, **4**, 61.

Cox, P. R., and Strachan, A. N. (1972a), *Chem. Eng. Sci.*, **27**, 457.

Cox, P. R., and Strachan, A. N., (1972b), *Chem. Eng. J.*, **4**, 253.

Danckwerts, P. V. (1970), *Gas–Liquid Reactions*, McGraw-Hill, New York.

Danckwerts, P. V., and Sharma, M. M. (1966), *Chem. Eng., Inst. Chem. Eng.*, No. 202, CE244.

de Wilt, H. G. J., and van der Baan, H. S. (1972), *Ind. Eng. Chem. Prod. Res. Dev.*, **11**, 374.

Dixon, J. K., and Saunders, K. W. (1954), *Ind. Eng. Chem.*, **46**, 652.

Donders, A. J. M., Wijffels, J. B., and Rietema, K. (1968), *Proc. 4th European Symp. Chem. React. Eng.* (Suppl. to *Chem. Eng. Sci.*), p. 159.

Domask, W. G., and Kobe, K. A. (1954), *Ind. Eng. Chem.*, **46**, 680.

Dovell, F. S., Ferguson, W. E., and Greenfield, H. (1970), *Ind. Eng. Chem. Prod. Res. Dev.*, **9**, 224.

Dufau, F. A., Eschard, F., Haddad, A. C., and Thonon, C. H. (1964), *Chem. Eng. Prog.*, **60**(9), 43.

Eleazer, A. E., Heck, R. M., and Witt, M. P. (1979), *Hydrocarbon Process. Petrol. Refiner*, **58**(5), 112.

Enright, J. T., and Chuang, T. T. (1978), *Can. J. Chem. Eng.*, **56**, 246.

Falk, J. C. (1976), in Rylander, P. N., and Greenfield, H. (Eds.), *Catalysis in Organic Syntheses*, Academic Press, New York.

Ferrari, G., and Garbei, A. (1969), Fr. 1,570,990 (June); *Chem. Abstr.* (1970), **72**, 100282.

Fischer, R. H., Garwood, W. E., and Heinemann, H. (1976), *Ind. Eng. Chem. Process Design Dev.*, **15**, 570.

Fogler, H. S., Lund, K., and McCune, C. C. (1975), *Chem. Eng. Sci.*, **30**, 1325.

Frantz, J. F., and Glass, K. I. (1963), *Chem. Eng. Prog.*, **59**(7), 68.

Freifelder, M. (1971), *Practical Catalytic Hydrogenation—Techniques and Applications*, Wiley-Interscience, New York.

Friend, L., Wender, L., and Yarze, J. C. (1968), *Adv. Chem. Ser.*, **70**, 168.

Friedman, H. M., and Nelson, A. L. (1969), *J. Org. Chem.*, **34**, 3211.

Garrett, H. E. (1972), *Surface Active Chemicals*, Pergamon, Oxford.

Gehlawat, J. K., and Sharma, M. M. (1970), *J. Appl. Chem.*, **20**, 93.

Gehlawat, J. K., and Sharma, M. M. (1971), *J. Appl. Chem. Biotechnol.*, **21**, 141.

Germain, A. H., Lefebvre, A. G., and L'Homme, G. A. (1974), *Adv. Chem. Ser.*, **133**, p. 164.

Ghorpade, A. K., Chipalkatti, S. V., and Sharma, M. M. (1981), *Chem. Eng. Sci.*, **36**, 1227.

Glueck, A. R., and Kenney, C. N. (1968), *Chem. Eng. Sci.*, **23**, 1257.

Goldstein, R. F., and Waddams, A. L. (1967), *The Petroleum Chemicals Industry*, 3rd ed., Spon, London, pp. 237, 321.

Golovin, A. I., Vyrodov, V. A., and Korotov, S. Ya. (1970), *Tr. Leningr. Lesotekhn. Akad.*, No. 135, Pt. 1, p. 51 (in Russian); *Chem. Abstr.* (1971), **74**, 142074d.

Goto, S., and Smith, J. M. (1975), *AIChE J.*, **21**, 706; 714.

Goto, S., Watabe, S., and Matsubara, M. (1976), *Can. J. Chem. Eng.*, **54**, 551.

Griskey, R. G., Hudia, S. R., and Siskovic, N. (1974), *J. Appl. Polymer Sci.*, **18**, 3057.

Groggins, P. H. (Ed.) (1958), *Unit Processes in Organic Synthesis*, 5th ed., McGraw-Hill, New York, pp. 279, 282.

Groothuis, H. (1961), *Chem. Eng. Sci.*, **14**, 176.

Gunn, D. J., and Saleem, A. (1970), *Trans. Inst. Chem. Eng.*, **48**, T46.

Gunstone, F. D. (1958), *An Introduction to the Chemistry of Fats and Fatty Acids*, Chapman & Hall, London.

Gupta, D. V., Kranich, W. L., and Weiss, A. H. (1976), *Ind. Eng. Chem. Process Design Dev.*, **15**, 256.

Gupta, R. K., and Sharma, M. M. (1967), *Indian Chem. Engr. (Trans.)*, **9**(3), 100.

Haase, D. J., and Waker, D. G. (1974), *Chem. Eng. Prog.*, **70**(5), 74.

Habashi, F. (1970), *Principles of Extractive Metallurgy*, Vol. 2, *Hydrometallurgy*, Gordon & Breach, New York.

Hague, D. N. (1971), *Fast Reactions*, Wiley, New York.

Haidegger, E., Hodossy, L., Kriza, D., and Peter I. (1971), *Chem. Process Eng.*, **52**(8), 39.

Hancock, E. G. (1975), *Benzene and Its Industrial Derivatives*, Ernest Benn, London.

Hanson, C., and Ismail, H. A. M. (1976), *J. Appl. Chem. Biotechnol.*, **26**, 111.

Hanson, C., Marsland, J. G., and Wilson, G. (1971), *Chem. Eng. Sci.*, **26**, 1513.

Hardwick, T. J. (1962), *Hydrocarbon Process. Petrol. Refiner.*, **41**(11), 197.

Hardwick, W. H., and Wace, P. F. (1965), *Chem. Process. Eng.*, **46**, 283.

Harnisch, H. (1980), *Pure Appl. Chem.*, **52**, 809.

Hartman, M., and Coughlin, R. W. (1972), *Chem. Eng. Sci.*, **27**, 867.

Hashimoto, K., Teramoto, M., and Nagata, S. (1971), *J. Chem. Eng. Japan*, **4**, 150.

Hatch, L. F. (1970), *Hydrocarbon Process. Petrol. Refiner.*, **49**(3), 101.

Hatch, T. F., and Pigford, R. L. (1962), *Ind. Eng. Chem. Fundam.*, **1**, 209.

Hawkins, P. A. (1965), *Trans. Inst. Chem. Eng.*, **43**, T287.

Henry, H. C., and Gilbert, J. B. (1973), *Ind. Eng. Chem. Process Design Dev.*, **12**, 328.

Hjortkjaer, J., and Jensen, V. W. (1976), *Ind. Eng. Chem. Prod. Res. Dev.*, **15**, 46.

Hodossy, L. (1968), *Brit. Chem. Eng.*, **13**, 1277.

Hofmann, H., and Bill, W. (1959), *Chem. Ing. Tech.*, **31**, 81.

Hoftyzer, P. J. (1975), in Platzer, N. A. J. (Ed.), *Polymerization and Polycondensation Processes* (Appl. Polymer Symp. No. 26), Wiley, New York., p. 349.

Hoftyzer, P. J., and van Krevelen, D. W. (1968), *Proc. 4th European Symp. Chem. React. Eng.* (Suppl. to *Chem. Eng. Sci.*), p. 139.

Holroyd, F. P. B., and Kenney, C. N. (1971a), *Chem. Eng. Sci.*, **26**, 1963.

Holroyd, F. P. B., and Kenney, C. N. (1971b), *Chem. Eng. Sci.*, **26**, 1971.

Horak, M., Palm, V., and Soogenbits, U. (1975), *Reaktsii Sposobu. Organ. Soedin.*, **11**(3), 709; *Chem. Abstr.* (1976), **84**, 73330.

Horie, T., Imaizumi, M., and Fujiwara, Y. (1970), *Hydrocarbon Process. Petrol. Refiner.*, **49**(3), 119.

Hughes, M. A. (1975), *Chem. Ind. (London)*, No. 24, 1042.

Hsu, S. H., and Ruether, J. A. (1978), *Ind. Eng. Chem. Process Design Dev.*, **17**, 524.

Hulme, P., and Turner, P. E. (1967), *Chem. Process. Eng.*, **48**(11), 96.

Hydrocarbon Process. Petrol. Refiner. (1971), **50**(11), 226.

Hydrocarbon Process. Petrol. Refiner. (1979), **58**(11), 203, 153.

Jagirdar, G. C., and Sharma, M. M. (1980), *J. Separ. Process. Technol.*, **1**(2), 40.

James, B. R. (1973), *Homogeneous Hydrogenation*, Wiley, New York.

Jeffreys, G. V. (1961), *The Manufacture of Acetic Anhydride*, Institution of Chemical Engineers, London.

Jeffreys, G. V., Jenson, V. G., and Miles, F. R. (1961), *Trans. Inst. Chem. Eng.*, **39**, 389.

Jernigan, E. C., Gwyn, J. E., and Claridge, E. L. (1965), *Chem. Eng. Prog.*, **61**(11), 94.

Johnson, P. R. (1976), *Rubber Chem. Technol.*, **49**, 650.

Johnson, G. R., and Crynes, B. L. (1974), *Ind. Eng. Chem. Process Des. Dev.*, **13**, 6.

Jordon, D. G. (1968), *Chemical Process Development*, Wiley-Interscience, New York.

Juvekar, V. A., and Sharma, M. M. (1973), *Chem. Eng. Sci.*, **28**, 825.

Karter, E. M., and Bobalek, E. G. (1971), *Tappi*, **54**(11), 1882.

Kelmers, A. D., and Bennett, M. R. (1976), *Inorg. Nucl. Chem. Letters*, **12**, 333.

Kenney, C. N., and Sedriks, W. (1972), *Chem. Eng. Sci.*, **27**, 2029.

Kirk, R. E., and Othmer, D. F. (1964a), *Encyclopedia of Chemical Technology*, 2nd ed., Wiley-Interscience, New York, Vol. 4, p. 372.

Kirk, R. E., and Othmer, D. F. (1964b), *Encyclopedia of Chemical Technology*, 2nd ed., Wiley-Interscience, New York, Vol. 5, p. 359.

Kirk, R. E., and Othmer, D. F. (1966a), *Encyclopedia of Chemical Technology*, 2nd ed., Wiley-Interscience, New York, Vol. 11, p. 397.

Kirk, R. E., and Othmer, D. F. (1966b), *Encyclopedia of Chemical Technology*, 2nd ed., Wiley-Interscience, New York, Vol. 9, p. 742.

Kirk, R. E., and Othmer, D. F. (1966c), *Encyclopedia of Chemical Technology*, 2nd ed., Wiley-Interscience, New York, Vol. 11, p. 202.

Kirk, R. E., and Othmer, D. F. (1968), *Encyclopedia of Chemical Technology*, 2nd ed., Wiley-Interscience, New York, Vol. 15, p. 307.

Klassen, J., and Kirk, R. S. (1955), *AIChE J.*, **1**, 488.

Kohn, P. M. (1978), *Chem. Eng.*, **85**(7), 90.

Komiyama, H., and Smith, J. M. (1975), *AIChE J.*, **21**, 664; 670.

Kothari, P. J., and Sharma, M. M. (1966), *Chem. Eng. Sci.*, **21**, 391.

Krause, R. L. (1975), U.S. 3,898,208 (August); *Chem. Abstr.* (1975), **83**, 180774.

Kremers, F. J. (1971), *J. Am. Oil Chem. Soc.*, **48**(7), 314.

Laddha, S. S., and Sharma, M. M. (1978), *J. Appl. Chem. Biotechnol.*, **28**, 69.

Ladhabhoy, M. E., and Sharma, M. M. (1969), *J. Appl. Chem.*, **19**, 267.

Ladhabhoy, M. E., and Sharma, M. M. (1970), *J. Appl. Chem.*, **20**, 274.

Lawless, J. J., and Searle, H. T. (1962), *J. Chem. Soc.*, 4200.

Lechev, P., Argirov, G., Tenchev, C. H. R., Zankova, N., and Ingilisova, M. (1973), *Plaste Kautschuk*, **20**(9), 684 (in German); *Chem. Abstr.* (1973), **79**, 146970u.

Leszezynski, Z., Kubica, J., Pilc, A., and Bacia, W. (1967), *Przemysl Chem.*, **46**(4), 210; *Chem. Abstr.* (1967), **67**, 32273.

Levec, J., and Smith, J. M. (1976), *AIChE J.*, **22**, 159.

Levenson, G. I. P. (1954), *J. Appl. Chem.*, **4**, 13.

Lowndes, M. R. (1971), *Chem. Ind. (London)*, No. 34, 951.

Lund, K., Fogler, H. S., and McCune, C. C. (1973), *Chem. Eng. Sci.*, **28**, 691.

Lund, K., Fogler, H. S., McCune, C. C., and Ault, J. W. (1975), *Chem. Eng. Sci.*, **30**, 825.

McGreavy, C. (1972), *J. Appl. Chem. Biotechnol.*, **22**, 747.

McIver, R. G., and Ratcliffe, J. S. (1974), *Trans. Inst. Chem. Eng.*, **52**, 276.

Mahajani, V. V. (1979), Heterogeneous Reactions, Ph.D. (Tech.) thesis, University of Bombay.

Mansoori, G. A., and Madden, A. J. (1969), *AIChE J.*, **15**, 245.

Marangozis, J., and Johnson, A. I. (1963), *Can. J. Chem. Eng.*, **41**, 195.

Maslan, F. (1973), *Can. J. Chem. Eng.*, **51**, 252.

Miller, J. (1968), *Aromatic Nucleophilic Substitution*, Elsevier, Amsterdam.

Miller, R. E., and Bennett, G. E. (1961), *Ind. Eng. Chem.*, **53**, 33.

Miller, S. A. (1966), *Chem. Process Eng.*, **47**(6), 268.

Miller, S. A. (1969), *Ethylene and Its Industrial Derivatives*, Ernest Benn, London.

Mitchell, L. C., and Modan, M. M. (1979), *Chem. Eng.*, **86**(5), 88.

Miyauchi, T., Kikuchi, T., Ogoshi, T., Susuki, R., and Kataoka, H. (1971), *J. Chem. Eng. Japan*, **4**, 44.

Morgan, P. W. (1965), *Condensation Polymers: By Interfacial and Solution Methods*, Wiley-Interscience, New York, pp. 22, 66.

Mosby, J. F., and Albright, L. F. (1966), *Ind. Eng. Chem. Prod. Res. Dev.*, **5**, 183.

Motomura, H., and Morita, Z. (1977), *J. Appl. Polymer Sci.*, **21**, 487.

Mukherjee, K. D., Kiewitt, I., and Kiewitt, M. (1975), *J. Am. Oil Chem. Soc.*, **52**, 282.

Murray, F. E. (1968), *Pulp Paper Mag. Can.*, **69**, 3.

Murray, F. E. (1971), *Pulp Paper Mag. Can.*, **72**(3), T91.

Mützenberg, A. B., and Giger, A. (1968), *Trans. Inst. Chem. Eng.*, **46**, T187.

Naworski, J. S., and Harriot, P. (1969), *Ind. Eng. Chem. Fundam.*, **8**, 397.

Nene, S. A. (1979), Studies in Absorption of Mercury, M. Tech. thesis, I.I.T., Bombay.

Newman, M. S., Underwood, G., and Renoll, M. (1949), *J. Am. Chem. Soc.*, **71**, 3362.

Oblad, A. G. (1969), *Ind. Eng. Chem.*, **61**(7), 23.

Ohnishi, R., Tanabe, K., Morikawa, S., and Nishizaki, T. (1974), *Bull. Chem. Soc. Japan*, **47**, 571.

Oldenkamp, R. D., and Margolin, E. D. (1969), *Chem. Eng. Prog.*, **65**(11), 73.

Olivier, K. L., and Booth, F. B. (1970), *Hydrocarbon Process. Petrol. Refiner.*, **49**(4), 112.

Onoue, Y., Mizutani, Y., Akiyama, S., Izumi, Y., and Watanabe, Y. (1977), *Chemtech.*, **7**, 36.

Pal, S. K., and Sharma, M. M. (1983), *Ind. Eng. Chem. Process. Design Dev.*, **22**, 76.

Pal, S. K., Sharma, M. M., and Juvekar, V. A. (1982), *Chem. Eng. Sci.*, **37**, 327.

Pangarkar, V. G., and Sharma, M. M. (1974), *Chem. Eng. Sci.*, **29**, 2297.

Paulik, F. E. (1975), U.S. 3,848,065 (12 November 1974); *Chem. Abstr.* (1975), **82**, 45915m.

Pepper, K. W. (1951), *J. Appl. Chem.*, **1**, 124.

Pepper, K. W., Paisley, H. M., and Young, M. A. (1953), *J. Chem. Soc.*, 4097.

Peters, R. H. (1975), *Textile Chemistry*, Vol. 3, *The Physical Chemistry of Dyeing*, Elsevier, Amsterdam, p. 598.

Phadtare, P. G., and Doraiswamy, L. K. (1965), *Ind. Eng. Chem. Process Design Dev.*, **4**, 274.

Phadtare, P. G., and Doraiswamy, L. K. (1966), *Ind. Eng. Chem. Process Design Dev.*, **5**, 351.

Pittman, C. U., Kim, B. T., and Douglas, W. M. (1975), *J. Org. Chem.*, **40**, 590.

Prengle, H. W., Jr., and Barona, N. (1970), *Hydrocarbon Process. Petrol. Refiner.*, **49**(11), 159.

Prengle, H. W., Mauk, C. E., Legan, R. W., and Hewes, C. G. (1975), *Hydrocarbon Process. Petrol. Refiner.*, **54**(10), 82.

Preston, C., and Fern, A. S. (1961), *Chimia (Aarau)*, **15**, 177.

Pruden, B. B., and Weber, M. E. (1970), *Can. J. Chem. Eng.*, **48**, 162.

Ramachandran, P. A. (1969), *Chem. Process Eng. (India)*, **3**(1), 23.

Ramachandran, P. A., and Sharma, M. M. (1969), *Chem. Eng. Sci.*, **24**, 1681.

Ramachandran, P. A., and Sharma, M. M. (1971), *Trans. Inst. Chem. Eng.*, **49**, 253.

Ratcliffe, J. S. (1966), *Brit. Chem. Eng.*, **11**(12), 1535.

Rattee, I. D., and Breuer, M. M. (1974), *The Physical Chemistry of Dye Adsorption*, Academic Press, London, p. 244.

Raval, R. P., and Sharma, M. M. (1980), Unpublished work.

Reilly, I. G., and Scott, D. S. (1976), *Ind. Eng. Chem. Process Design Dev.*, **15**, 60.

Richardson, F. D. (1975), in Dahl, W., Lange, K. W., and Paramantellos, D. (Eds.), *Kinetics of Metallurgical Processes in Steel Making*, Verlag Stahleisen, M. B. H., Düsseldorf, West Germany, p. 279.

Riegel, H., Schindler, H. D., and Sze, M. C. (1973), *Chem. Eng. Prog.*, **69**(10), 89.

Riemenschneider, W. (1976), *Chemtech*, **6**(10), 658.

Rod, V. (1974), *Chem. Eng. J.*, **7**, 137.

Rod, V. (1976), *Proc. 4th Int./6th European Symp. Chem. React. Eng.*, p. 271.

Rosenbaum, J. B., George, D. R., and May, J. T. (1971), *Metallurgical Application of Solvent Extraction*, 2: *Practice and Trends*, U.S. Department of the Interior, Bureau of Mines Information Circular 8502.

Rosenwald, R. H., Hamblin, R. J. J., Urban, P., and Zimmerman, R. P. (1975), *Ind. Eng. Chem. Prod. Res. Dev.*, **14**, 218.

Rosenzweig, M. D. (1976), *Chem. Eng.*, **83**(10), 69.

Rozhdestvenskava, I. D., Fadeeva, T. N., Titova, N. B., and Shileiko, L. V. (1970), *Kinet. Katal.* (in Russian), **11**(3), 696.

Rueggeberg, W. H. C., Ginsburg, A., and Frantz, R. K. (1946), *Ind. Eng. Chem.*, **38**, 207.

Ruthven, D. M., and Kenney, C. N. (1968), *Chem. Eng. Sci.*, **23**, 981.

Rylander, P. N. (1973), *Organic Syntheses with Noble Metal Catalysts*, Academic Press, New York, p. 62.

Sada, E., Kumazawa, H., and Butt, M. A. (1977a), *Chem. Eng. Sci.*, **32**, 1499.

Sada, E., Kumazawa, H., Butt, M. A., and Sumi, T. (1977b), *Chem. Eng. Sci.*, **32**, 972.

Saeki, G., Weng, P. K. J., and Johnson, A. I. (1972), *Can. J. Chem. Eng.*, **50**, 730.

Sankholkar, D. S., and Sharma, M. M. (1973), *Chem. Eng. Sci.*, **28**, 49.

Sankholkar, D. S., and Sharma, M. M. (1975), *Chem. Eng. Sci.*, **30**, 729.

Sastri, N. V. S., and Epstein, N. (1978), *Can. J. Chem. Eng.*, **56**, 124.

Satterfield, C. N., Pelossof, A. A., and Sherwood, T. K. (1969), *AIChE J.*, **15**, 226.

Sauchel, V. (1960), *Chemistry and Technology of Fertilizers*, Reinhold, New York, p. 10.

Schmeal, W. R., and Street, J. R. (1971), *AIChE J.*, **17**, 1188.

Schwind, R. A. (1969), *Chem. Process Eng.*, **50**(7), 75.

Schuit, G. C. A., and Gates, B. C. (1973), *AIChE J.*, **19**, 417.

Scibona, G., Danesi, P. R., and Orlandini, F. (1966), *J. Phys. Chem.*, **70**, 3403.

Seaburn, J. T., and Engel, A. J. (1973), *Am. Inst. Chem. Eng. Symp. Ser.*, **69**(134), p. 71.

Secor, R. M. (1969), *AIChE J.*, **15**, 861.

Sedriks, W., and Kenney, C. N. (1973), *Chem. Eng. Sci.*, **28**, 559.

Shah, A. K., and Sharma, M. M. (1969), *Indian Chem. Engr. (Trans.)*, **11**, 122.

Sharma, M. M. (1965), *Trans. Faraday Soc.*, **61**, 681.

Sharma, M. M., and Nanda, A. K. (1968), *Trans. Inst. Chem. Eng.*, **46**, T44.

Sharma, R. C., and Sharma, M. M. (1969), *J. Appl. Chem.*, **19**, 162.

Sharma, R. C., and Sharma, M. M. (1970a), *Bull. Chem. Soc. Japan*, **43**, 642.

Sharma, R. C., and Sharma, M. M. (1970b), *Bull. Chem. Soc. Japan*, **43**, 1282.

Sheldon, R. A. (1973), *Recl. Trav. Chim. Pays-Bas*, **92**(2), 253.

Sheng, M. N., and Zajacek, J. G. (1968), in Mayo, F. R. (Ed.), *Oxidation of Organic Compounds*, Vol. 2, *Gas Phase Oxidations, Homogeneous and Heterogeneous Catalysis, Applied Oxidations and Synthetic Processes* (Adv. Chem. Ser. No. 76), American Chemical Society, Washington, D.C., p. 418.

Sherwin, M. B., and Frank, M. E. (1976), *Hydrocarbon Process. Petrol. Refiner.*, **55**(11), 122.

Sherwood, T. K., and Farkas, E. J. (1966), *Chem. Eng. Sci.*, **21**, 573.

Shiao, D. D. F., Fortmiller, L. J., and Herz, A. H. (1975), *J. Phys. Chem.*, **79**, 816.

Shingu, H. (1961), U.S. 2,985,668 (23 May).

Sirotkin, G. D. (1953), *Zh. Prikl. Khim.*, **26**, 340.

Sittig, M. (1967), *Organic Chemical Process Encyclopaedia*, Noyes Development Corp., Park Ridge, New Jersey.

Sittig, M. (1969), *Organic Chemical Process Encyclopaedia*, 2nd ed., Noyes Development Corp., Park Ridge, New Jersey.

Slizovskaya, L. V., Leites, I. L., and Strizhevskii, I. I. (1969), *Khim. Prom.*, **45**(7), 524; *Chem. Abstr.* (1969), **71**, 90708.

Smithson, G. L., and Bakhshi, N. N. (1973), *Ind. Eng. Chem. Process Design Dev.*, **12**, 99.

Snider, J. W., and Perona, J. J. (1974), *AIChE J.*, **20**, 1172.

Sprow, F. B. (1969), *Ind. Eng. Chem. Process Design Dev.*, **8**, 254.

Sternberg, H. W., Delle Donne, C. L., Markby, R. E., and Friedman, S. (1974), *Ind. Eng. Chem. Process Design Dev.*, **13**, 433.

Subramanian, K. N., and Richardson, F. D. (1968), *J. Iron Steel Inst. (London)*, **206**, 576.

Sukhdev (1972), *J. Sci. Ind. Res. (India)*, **31**, 60.

Sundstrom, D. W., Luciano, A. J., and Klei, H. E. (1976), *J. Appl. Polymer Sci.*, **20**, 207.

Szabo, M., and Kaldi, P. (1976), *Hungarian J. Ind. Chem.* (in English), **4**, 39.

Szekely, J. (1967), *Chem. Eng. (London)*, No. 206, CE41.

Szonyi, G. (1968), *Adv. Chem. Ser.*, **70**, 53.

Throckmorton, P. E., Hansen, L. I., Christenson, R. C., and Pryde, E. H. (1968), *J. Am. Oil Chem. Soc.*, **45**, 59.

Throckmorton, P. E., and Pryde, E. H. (1972), *J. Am. Oil Chem. Soc.*, **49**, 643.

Tiwari, R. K., and Sharma, M. M. (1977), *Chem. Eng. Sci.*, **32**, 1253.

Tsigin, B. M., and Konstantinov, I. I. (1979), *J. Appl. Chem. USSR (Engl. Transl.)*, **52**, 2181.

Twitchett, H. J. (1974), *Chem. Soc. Rev.*, **3**(2), 209.

Uchida, S., Koide, K., and Shindo, M. (1975), *Chem. Eng. Sci.*, **30**, 644.

Ugelstad, J., and Hansen, F. K. (1976), *Rubber Chem. Technol.*, **49**, 536.

van Deemter, J. J. (1965), *Chem. Eng. Sci.*, **20** (Special Suppl.), 215.

van Direndonck, L., De Jong, P., von Den Hoff, J., Vonker, H., and Vermijs, R. (1974), *Adv. Chem. Ser.*, **133**, 432.

van Direndonck, L., De Jong, P., Vermijs, R., and von Den Hoff, J. (1975), Optimization of the Benzoic Acid Oxidation Step in the Toluene Route towards Phenol, Paper presented at 5th Int. Chisa Cong., Prague, August 1975.

van Direndonck, L., and Nelemans, J. (1972), *Proc. 5th European / 2nd Int. Symp. Chem. React. Eng.*, p. B6.

van Goolen, J. T. J. (1976), *Proc. 4th Int./ 6th European Symp. Chem. React. Eng.*, 4–399.

van Krevelen, D. W., and Baans, C. M. E. (1950), *J. Phys. Chem.*, **54**, 370.

van Ling, G., and Vlugter, J. C. (1969), *J. Appl. Chem. (London)*, **19**, 43.

Venkataraman, K. (Ed.) (1972), *The Chemistry of Synthetic Dyes*, Vol. 6, *Reactive Dyes*, Academic Press, New York.

Villadson, J., and Livbjerg, H. (1978), *Catal. Rev. Sci. Eng.*, **17**(2), 203.

Volpicelli, G., and Massimilla, L. (1970), *Chem. Eng. Sci.*, **25**, 1361.

von Kutepow, N., Himmele, W., and Hohenschutz, H. (1965), *Chem. Ing.-Tech.*, **37**, 383.

Wadekar, V. V., and Sharma, M. M. (1981a), *J. Separ. Process Technol.*, **2**(1), 1.

Wadekar, V. V., and Sharma, M. M. (1981b), *J. Chem. Tech. Biotechnol.*, **31**, 279.

Wallace, T. J., Schriesheim, A., Hurwitz, H., and Glasser, M. B. (1964), *Ind. Eng. Chem. Process Design Dev.*, **3**, 237.

Weinrotter, F. (1971), *Chem. Ing.-Tech.*, **43**, 883.

Weissermel, K., and Arpe, H. J. (1978), *Industrial Organic Chemistry* (translated by A. Mullen), Verlag Chemie, Weinheim, New York.

Whewell, R. J. (1977), *Chem. Ind. (London)*, No. 18, 755.

Whiteway, S. G. (1979), *Can. J. Chem. Eng.*, **57**, 78.

Whitt, F. R. (1967), *Brit. Chem. Eng.*, **12**, 554.

Wielgosz, Z., Dobkowski, Z., and Krajewski, B. (1972), *European Polymer J.*, **8**(9), 1113.

Wisniak, J., Hershkowitz, M., Leibowitz, R., and Stein, S. (1974a), *Ind. Eng. Chem. Prod. Res. Dev.*, **13**, 75.

Wisniak, J., Hershkowitz, M., and Stein, S. (1974b), *Ind. Eng. Chem. Prod. Res. Dev.*, **13**, 232.

Wystrach, V. P., Barnum, H., and Garber, M., (1957), *J. Am. Chem. Soc.*, **79**, 5786.

Yadav, G. D., and Sharma, M. M. (1981a), *Chem. Eng. Sci.*, **36**, 599.

Yadav, G. D., and Sharma, M. M. (1981b), *Ind. Eng. Chem. Process Design Dev.*, **20**, 385.

Yang, W. C., and Manning, F. S. (1970), *Chem. Eng. Sci.*, **25**, 1423, 1431.

Zabor, R. C., Odioso, R. C., Schmid, B. K., and Kaiser, J. R. (1960), *Actes 2me Cong. Int. Catalyse (Paris)*, p. 2601.

Zaidi, A., Louisi, Y., Ralek, M., and Deckwer, W. D. (1979), *Ger. Chem. Eng.*, **2**, 94.

CHAPTER TWO

Theory of Mass Transfer Accompanied by Irreversible and Reversible Reactions of General Order; Methods of Discerning Controlling Mechanism

In this chapter we shall consider theoretical aspects of two-phase (gas–liquid and liquid–liquid) reactions where the reaction occurs in the liquid phase, designated as the B phase. The solute A (gas or liquid) is slightly soluble in the B phase and the reaction occurs exclusively in the B phase. The resistance to mass transfer is confined to the B phase. (In the case of liquid–liquid reactions there is a possibility of reaction occurring in both phases, and Chapter 7 treats such cases.) The reactive species B and the B phase are considered to be nonvolatile (Section 2.8 deals with volatile reactive species B). We shall first deal with irreversible reactions, and in Section 2.10 we shall consider reversible reactions.

The irreversible reaction between the solute A and the reactant B may be represented by

$$A(l) + ZB(l) \rightarrow \text{products} \tag{2.1}$$

Our main objective is to ascertain the effect of chemical reaction on the specific rate of mass transfer. Depending on the relative rates of diffusion and reaction, for convenience the systems may be classified into four regimes:

regime 1, very slow reactions;
regime 2, slow reactions;
regime 3, fast reactions;
regime 4, instantaneous reactions.

We shall use film theory, and as and when important and relevant surface renewal theory will also be considered.

2.1. REGIME 1: VERY SLOW REACTIONS

In regime 1, the rate of reaction between the dissolved A and B is very much slower than the rate of transfer of A into the B phase. Consequently, the B phase, in which the reaction occurs, will be saturated with the solute A at any moment and the rate of formation of the products will be determined by the kinetics of the homogeneous chemical reaction. The diffusional factors are unimportant in this regime.

Reaction 2.1 is irreversible and the order of the chemical reaction with respect to A is m and that with respect to B is n.

The transfer rate of A, $R_A a$, in moles per cubic centimeter per second (mol/cm^3 sec) is given by

$$R_A a = l k_{mn} [A^*]^m [B_o]^n \tag{2.2}$$

The condition for the validity of this mechanism can be expressed as

$$k_L a [A^*] \gg l k_{mn} [A^*]^m [B_o]^n \tag{2.3}$$

The left-hand side of expression 2.3 gives the volumetric rate of mass transfer and the right-hand side gives the rate of homogeneous chemical reaction.

2.2. REGIME 2: SLOW REACTIONS

In regime 2, the rate of reaction between A and B is faster than the rate at which A is transferred to the B phase. The reaction then occurs uniformly throughout

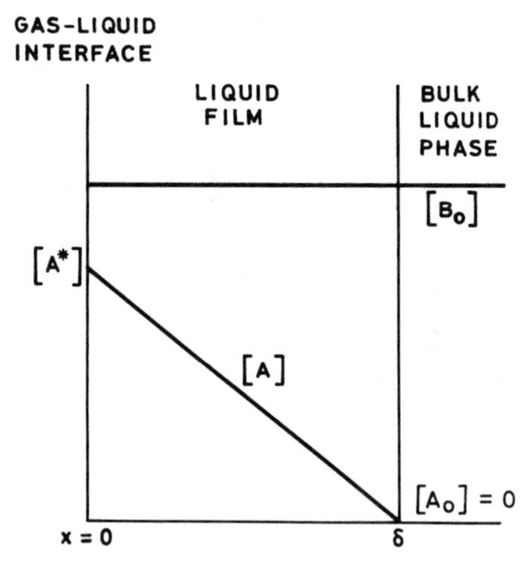

Figure 2.1. Concentration profiles of A and B in the slow reaction regime (regime 2).

the phase containing B, but the rate is controlled by the transfer of A into the phase containing B. The concentration of dissolved A in the bulk B phase is zero. The concentration profiles will be as shown in Figure 2.1.

For unsteady-state mass transfer, the following differential equation describes the transport of A:

$$\frac{\partial[\mathrm{A}]}{\partial t} = D_{\mathrm{A}} \frac{\partial^2[\mathrm{A}]}{\partial x^2} \tag{2.4}$$

According to Higbie's theory, the specific rate of mass transfer, R_{A}, in mol/cm² sec will be given by the following equation:

$$R_{\mathrm{A}} = 2\left(\frac{D_{\mathrm{A}}}{\pi t_{\mathrm{E}}}\right)^{1/2}([\mathrm{A}^*] - [\mathrm{A}_{\mathrm{o}}]) \tag{2.5}$$

$$= k_{\mathrm{L}}([\mathrm{A}^*] - [\mathrm{A}_{\mathrm{o}}]) \tag{2.6}$$

where

$$k_{\mathrm{L}} = 2\left(\frac{D_{\mathrm{A}}}{\pi t_{\mathrm{E}}}\right)^{1/2}$$

Under certain conditions (see Eq. 2.9), it is likely that the value of $[\mathrm{A}_{\mathrm{o}}]$ may become 0 or negligible, that is, the concentration of A in the bulk B phase is zero. Equation 2.6 then reduces to

$$R_{\mathrm{A}} = k_{\mathrm{L}}[\mathrm{A}^*] \tag{2.7}$$

The rate of mass transfer per unit volume of the reactor, $R_{\mathrm{A}}a$ (in mol/cm³ sec), will be given by the following equation:

$$R_{\mathrm{A}}a = k_{\mathrm{L}}a[\mathrm{A}^*] \tag{2.8}$$

In general, for an irreversible reaction that is mth order with respect to A and nth order with respect to B, the condition to be satisfied if $[\mathrm{A}_{\mathrm{o}}]$ is to be zero will be given by the following expression:

$$k_{\mathrm{L}}a[\mathrm{A}^*] \ll lk_{mn}[\mathrm{A}^*]^m[\mathrm{B}_{\mathrm{o}}]^n \tag{2.9}$$

Also, the amount of the dissolved solute that reacts in the diffusion film adjacent to the phase boundary compared to that which reaches the bulk B phase in the unreacted state should be negligible. Thus, practically no reaction occurs in the film. The condition to be satisfied is given by the following expression:

$$\frac{\left(\frac{2}{m+1} D_{\mathrm{A}} k_{mn}[\mathrm{A}^*]^{m-1}[\mathrm{B}_{\mathrm{o}}]^n\right)^{1/2}}{k_{\mathrm{L}}} \ll 1 \tag{2.10}$$

The rationale for condition (2.10) will be brought out in Sections 2.4 and 2.5.

2.3. REGIME BETWEEN VERY SLOW AND SLOW REACTIONS (REGIME BETWEEN 1 AND 2)

For some systems, the condition given by expression 2.10 may be satisfied whereas the condition given by expression 2.9 may not be. Under these conditions, the concentration of dissolved A in the bulk liquid phase is a finite quantity, $[\mathrm{A}_{\mathrm{o}}]$, that is less than $[\mathrm{A}^*]$ (Figure 2.2). The following equations hold for this

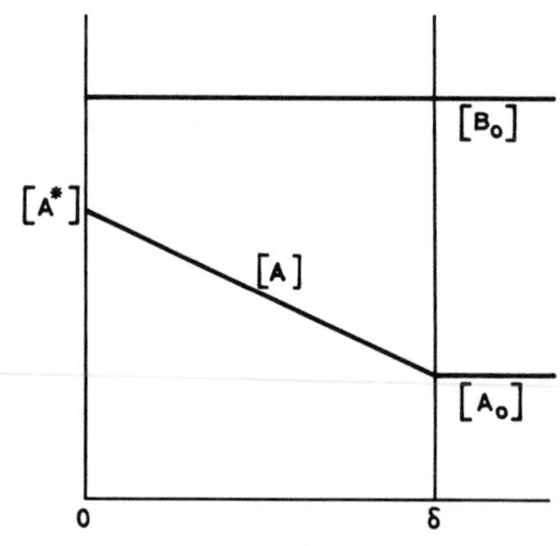

Figure 2.2. Concentration profiles for the reaction between the very slow and slow reaction regimes (regime between 1 and 2).

case:

$$R_A a = l k_{mn}[A_o]^m[B_o]^n \qquad (2.11)$$

$$= k_L a([A^*] - [A_o]) \qquad (2.12)$$

Simultaneous solution of these equations gives the values of $R_A a$ and $[A_o]$. We shall consider some special cases.

2.3.1. Reactions That Are First Order with Respect to the Solute A

For reactions that are first order with respect to A ($m = 1$), Eqs. 2.11 and 2.12 are linear with respect to A and can be solved to give

$$\frac{[A^*]}{R_A a} = \frac{1}{k_L a} + \frac{1}{l k_{1n}[B_o]^n}. \qquad (2.13)$$

We define $k_{LR}a$ by the following equation:

$$R_A a = k_{LR} a [A^*] \qquad (2.14)$$

From Eqs. 2.13 and 2.14, we obtain

$$\frac{1}{k_{LR} a} = \frac{1}{k_L a} + \frac{1}{l k_{1n}[B_o]^n} \qquad (2.15)$$

For the case of n equal to 1, Eq. 2.15 becomes

$$\frac{1}{k_{LR} a} = \frac{1}{k_L a} + \frac{1}{l k_2[B_o]} \qquad (2.16)$$

For this case (i.e., $m = n = 1$), if $k_2[B_o]$ is varied, keeping $k_L a$ constant, then a plot of $1/k_{LR}a$ against $1/k_2[B_o]$ will be a straight line having a slope of $1/l$ and intercept of $1/k_L a$.

2.3.2. Reactions That Are Zero Order with Respect to the Solute A

For reactions that are zero order with respect to A ($m = 0$), Eq. 2.11 becomes

$$R_A a = l k_n[B_o]^n \qquad (2.17)$$

Here the rate of reaction is independent of $[A^*]$. Equation 2.17 is valid as long as there is some free dissolved A in the bulk liquid. From Eq. 2.12 it is seen that the concentration of dissolved A in the bulk is given by

$$[A_o] = [A^*] - \frac{R_A a}{k_L a} \qquad (2.18)$$

$$= [A^*] - \frac{l k_n[B_o]^n}{k_L a} \qquad (2.19)$$

Thus, Eq. 2.17 is valid as long as $[A_o]$ has a finite value; it ceases to be valid if the following condition is satisfied:

$$l k_n[B_o]^n > k_L a[A^*] \qquad (2.20)$$

2.3.3. Reactions That Are Second Order with Respect to the Solute A

For reactions that are second order with respect to A ($m = 2$) we have

$$\frac{l k_{2n}[B_o]^n[A_o]^2}{k_L a} = [A^*] - [A_o] \qquad (2.21)$$

Denoting $(l k_{2n}[B_o]^n[A^*])/k_L a$ by p, we get

$$p\frac{[A_o]^2}{[A^*]^2} + \frac{[A_o]}{[A^*]} - 1 = 0 \qquad (2.22)$$

$$\frac{[A_o]}{[A^*]} = \frac{-1 + \sqrt{1 + 4p}}{2p} \qquad (2.23)$$

The rate of reaction is given by

$$R_A a = k_L a([A^*] - [A_o]) \qquad (2.24)$$

where the value of $[A_o]$ is obtained from Eq. 2.23.
Equation 2.24 can also be written as follows:

$$R_A a = k_L a[A^*]\left(1 + \frac{1}{2p} - \frac{\sqrt{1 + 4p}}{2p}\right) \qquad (2.25)$$

2.3.4. General Case

For the general case we can define a factor, γ, such that

$$\gamma = \frac{R_A a}{k_L a[A^*]} \qquad (2.26)$$

This factor represents the ratio of the actual rate of reaction to that for a system conforming to regime 2. For a general-order reaction, γ would be a function of the quantity $(lk_{mn}[B_o]^n[A^*]^{m-1})/k_L a$, which is designated as p.

From the discussion of Sections 2.3.1–2.3.3 we can show that

$$\gamma = \frac{p}{1+p} \qquad \text{for} \quad m = 1 \tag{2.27}$$

$$\gamma = 1 + \frac{1}{2p} - \frac{\sqrt{1+4p}}{2p} \qquad \text{for} \quad m = 2 \tag{2.28}$$

For $m = 0$

$$\gamma = 1 \qquad \text{if} \quad p > 1 \tag{2.29a}$$

$$\gamma = p \qquad \text{if} \quad p \leqslant 1 \tag{2.29b}$$

2.4. FAST REACTIONS (REGIME 3) AND THE REGIME BETWEEN 2 AND 3

In the following discussion, the physical picture of the problem will be based on the film theory; the treatment of the problem based on the penetration theory will be given subsequently.

Film Theory

Under certain conditions the reaction of the solute A with the reactant B occurs while the solute is diffusing in the film; that is, diffusion and chemical reaction occur simultaneously and therefore are parallel steps. We will first consider the case where the reaction of the gas A takes place completely in the film itself. This will be referred to hereafter as regime 3.

Regime 3:* A *Reacts Entirely in the Film. The condition under which the reaction of solute A occurs entirely in the film is given by the following expression:

$$\sqrt{M} = \frac{\sqrt{\frac{2}{m+1} D_A k_{mn} [A^*]^{m-1} [B_o]^n}}{k_L} \gg 1 \tag{2.30}$$

In fact, it can be shown that the left-hand side of the expression represents the ratio of the amount of A reacting in the film to that reacting in the bulk.

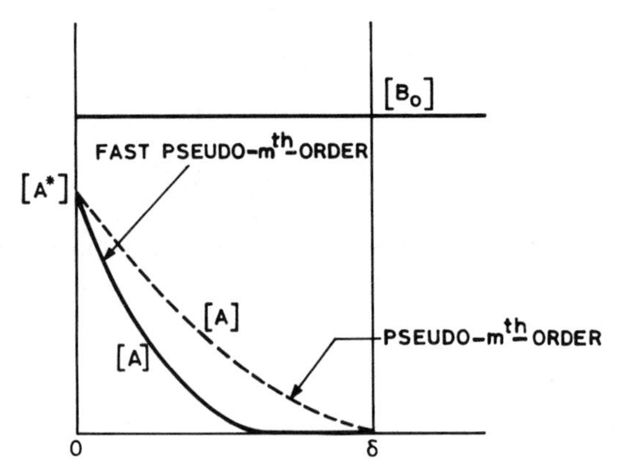

Figure 2.3. Concentration profiles of A and B in the pseudo-mth-order reaction regime (regime between 2 and 3) and fast pseudo-mth-order reaction regime (regime 3).

Further, under certain conditions the interfacial concentration of species B is practically the same as that in the bulk liquid phase; that is, there is no depletion of the species B in the film. Figure 2.3 shows the typical concentration profiles. The condition under which no depletion would occur is given by the following expression:

$$\frac{\sqrt{\frac{2}{m+1} D_A k_{mn} [A^*]^{m-1} [B_o]^n}}{k_L} \ll \frac{[B_o]}{Z[A^*]}\sqrt{\frac{D_B}{D_A}} \tag{2.31}$$

The rationale for the condition given by expression 2.31 will be brought out in Section 2.7. The diffusivity ratio on the right-hand side of expression 2.31 has been taken as the square root of the ratio, since the experimental data are better correlated through the use of $\sqrt{D_B/D_A}$ than of D_B/D_A (see Section 2.7).

The differential equation for the simultaneous diffusion and reaction of the solute A in the film can now be written as

$$D_A \frac{d^2[A]}{dx^2} = k_{mn}[B_o]^n[A]^m \tag{2.32}$$

$$= k_m[A]^m \tag{2.33}$$

where

$$k_m = k_{mn}[B_o]^n \tag{2.34}$$

Equation 2.33 is valid because the concentration of the species B remains constant throughout the film. The boundary conditions are as follows:

$$x = 0, \qquad [A] = [A^*], \qquad \frac{d[B]}{dx} = 0 \quad (2.35)$$

$$x = \delta, \qquad [A] = 0 \quad (2.36)$$

The specific rate of transfer of A is given by the flux at the interface:

$$R_A = -D_A\left(\frac{d[A]}{dx}\right)_{x=0} \quad (2.37)$$

Equation 2.33 can be written in a form that can be integrated by this substitution:

$$\psi = \frac{d[A]}{dx} \quad (2.38)$$

Equation 2.33 now reduces to

$$\psi\frac{d\psi}{d[A]} = \frac{k_m}{D_A}[A]^m \quad (2.39)$$

Integration of Eq. 2.39 gives

$$\frac{\psi^2}{2} = \frac{k_m[A]^{m+1}}{D_A(m+1)} + C \quad (2.40)$$

where C is an integration constant.

Since the reaction of A occurs entirely in the film, we have the following boundary conditions:

$$x = 0, \qquad [A] = [A^*], \qquad \frac{d[B]}{dx} = 0 \quad (2.35)$$

$$x = \delta, \qquad [A] = 0, \quad \psi = \frac{d[A]}{dx} = 0 \quad (2.41)$$

The boundary condition given by Eq. 2.41 stipulates that no unreacted A leaves the film at δ. With these conditions, the value of the integration constant in Eq. 2.40 becomes 0. Also, the specific rate of transfer of A is given by the flux of A at the interface ($x = 0$). Hence we have

$$R_A = -D_A\left(\frac{d[A]}{dx}\right)_{x=0} = -D_A(\psi)_{x=0}$$

$$R_A = D_A\sqrt{\frac{2k_m[A^*]^{m+1}}{(m+1)D_A}} \quad (2.42)$$

(taking the negative value of the square root of the right-hand side of Eq. 2.40 at $x = 0$)

$$R_A = [A^*]\sqrt{\frac{2}{m+1}D_A k_m[A^*]^{m-1}} \quad (2.43)$$

$$R_A = [A^*]\sqrt{\frac{2}{m+1}D_A k_{mn}[A^*]^{m-1}[B_o]^n} \quad (2.44)$$

Table 2.1 gives the equations for R_A for various values of m and n along with the relevant conditions.

Regime Between 2 and 3: Part of the Reaction Occurs in the Film and the Rest in the Bulk B Phase. If we now assume that a part of the reaction occurs in the film and the rest occurs in the bulk, where the concentration of A is zero, the value of $d[A]/dx$ or ψ at x equal to δ will be finite. Let this value be denoted by ψ_δ. The value of the concentration of A at x equal to δ is 0 (provided that the condition given by expression 2.9 is valid). Using these conditions in Eq. 2.40 we obtain

$$C = \frac{\psi_\delta^2}{2} \quad (2.45)$$

The specific rate of transfer of A is given by

$$R_A = -D_A\left(\frac{d[A]}{dx}\right)_{x=0} = -D_A(\psi)_{x=0} \quad (2.46)$$

$$= \sqrt{\frac{2}{m+1}D_A k_{mn}[A^*]^{m+1} + \psi_\delta^2} \quad (2.47)$$

The value of ψ_δ can be evaluated in the following way.

Substitute the value of C from Eq. 2.45 in Equation 2.40. The value of ψ is then given by

$$\psi = \frac{d[A]}{dx} = -\sqrt{\frac{2k_m[A]^{m+1}}{D_A(m+1)} + \psi_\delta^2} \quad (2.48)$$

Here we consider the negative sign while taking the square root because the value of $d[A]/dx$ is intrinsically negative.

Integration of Eq. 2.48 will allow the evaluation of

TABLE 2.1. Mass Transfer Accompanied by a Fast Pseudo-*m*th-Order Reaction (Regime 3)

Order with Respect to		Equation for Specific Rate of Mass Transfer (mol/cm² sec)	Conditions to Be Satisfied
Solute (m)	Reactant (n)		
0	0	$R_A = \sqrt{2D_A[A^*]k_0}$	$\dfrac{\sqrt{2D_A k_0/[A^*]}}{k_L} \ll \dfrac{[B_o]}{Z[A^*]}$
			and $\dfrac{2D_A k_0}{[A^*]} \gg k_L^2$
0	1	$R_A = \sqrt{2[A^*]D_A k_1[B_o]}$	$\dfrac{\sqrt{2D_A k_1[B_o]/[A^*]}}{k_L} \ll \dfrac{[B_o]}{Z[A^*]}$
			and $\dfrac{2D_A k_1[B_o]}{[A^*]} \gg k_L^2$
0	2	$R_A = \sqrt{2[A^*]D_A k_2[B_o]^2}$	$\dfrac{\sqrt{2D_A k_2[B_o]^2/[A^*]}}{k_L} \ll \dfrac{[B_o]}{Z[A^*]}$
			and $\dfrac{2D_A k_2[B_o]^2}{[A^*]} \gg k_L^2$
1	0	$R_A = [A^*]\sqrt{D_A k_1}$	$\dfrac{\sqrt{D_A k_1}}{k_L} \ll \dfrac{[B_o]}{Z[A^*]}$
			and $D_A k_1 \gg k_L^2$
1	1	$R_A = [A^*]\sqrt{D_A k_2[B_o]}$	$\dfrac{\sqrt{D_A k_2[B_o]}}{k_L} \ll \dfrac{[B_o]}{Z[A^*]}$
			and $D_A k_2[B_o] \gg k_L^2$
1	2	$R_A = [A^*]\sqrt{D_A k_3[B_o]^2}$	$\dfrac{\sqrt{D_A k_3[B_o]^2}}{k_L} \ll \dfrac{[B_o]}{Z[A^*]}$
			and $D_A k_3[B_o]^2 \gg k_L^2$
2	0	$R_A = [A^*]\sqrt{\frac{2}{3}D_A k_2[A^*]}$	$\dfrac{\sqrt{\frac{2}{3}D_A k_2[A^*]}}{k_L} \ll \dfrac{[B_o]}{Z[A^*]}$
			and $\frac{2}{3}D_A k_2[A^*] \gg k_L^2$
2	1	$R_A = [A^*]\sqrt{\frac{2}{3}D_A k_3[A^*][B_o]}$	$\dfrac{\sqrt{\frac{2}{3}D_A k_3[A^*][B_o]}}{k_L} \ll \dfrac{[B_o]}{Z[A^*]}$
			and $\frac{2}{3}D_A k_3[A^*][B_o] \gg k_L^2$
2	2	$R_A = [A^*]\sqrt{\frac{2}{3}D_A k_4[A^*][B_o]^2}$	$\dfrac{\sqrt{\frac{2}{3}D_A k_4[A^*][B_o]^2}}{k_L} \ll \dfrac{[B_o]}{Z[A^*]}$
			and $\frac{2}{3}D_A k_4[A^*][B_o]^2 \gg k_L^2$

ψ_δ. Thus,

$$\int_0^\delta dx = \delta = \int_0^{[A^*]} \frac{d[A]}{\sqrt{\frac{2k_m[A]^{m+1}}{D_A(m+1)} + \psi_\delta^2}} \quad (2.49)$$

If the condition given by expression 2.30 is satisfied, the reaction of A is complete in the film itself. This means that no A goes unreacted to the bulk liquid phase and the value of ψ_δ is 0. Hence, the specific rate of transfer of A is given by

$$R_A = [A^*]\sqrt{\frac{2}{m+1} D_A k_m [A^*]^{m-1}}$$

which is the same as Eq. 2.43.

Equation 2.33 is amenable to direct analytical solution for the cases when m is equal to 0 or to 1.

Equation 2.33 reduces to a second-order linear differential equation for the case when m is equal to 1, and can be analytically solved:

$$D_A \frac{d^2[A]}{dx^2} = k_1[A] \quad (2.50)$$

where $k_1 = k_n[B_o]^n$. The concentration profile of A is given by the following equation:

$$[A] = \frac{[A^*]\sinh\left[\sqrt{\frac{k_1}{D_A}}(\delta - x)\right]}{\sinh\left(\sqrt{\frac{k_1}{D_A}}\delta\right)} \quad (2.51)$$

The specific rate of mass transfer of A is then given by

$$R_A = -D_A\left(\frac{d[A]}{dx}\right)_{x=0} = \frac{[A^*]\sqrt{D_A k_1}}{\tanh\left(\frac{\sqrt{D_A k_1}}{k_L}\right)} \quad (2.52)$$

We can also express the data in terms of a dimensionless enhancement factor, ϕ:

$$\phi = \frac{R_A}{k_L[A^*]} = \frac{\sqrt{M}}{\tanh\sqrt{M}} \quad (2.53)$$

where $\sqrt{M}$ is defined in expression 2.30.

For the case of $m = 0$, Eq. 2.33 reduces to the following form:

$$D_A \frac{d^2[A]}{dx^2} = k_0 \quad (2.54)$$

The solution of Eq. 2.54 has been discussed by Hikita and Asai (1964). (Equation 2.54 will hold for regime 3 as long as there is a finite concentration of A and ceases to hold beyond a point in the film where its concentration reaches zero.) The expressions for the enhancement factor are, for $\sqrt{M} < 2$,

$$\phi = \frac{R_A}{k_L[A^*]} = 1 + \frac{M}{4} \quad (2.55)$$

and for $\sqrt{M} > 2$,

$$\phi = \sqrt{M} \quad (2.56)$$

As we saw earlier, the case where m is not equal to 0 or 1, and where part of the reaction occurs in the bulk, leads to complex equations for the specific rate of mass transfer. However, Hikita and Asai have shown that the following equation is a very good approximation for reactions of any general order:

$$\phi = \frac{\sqrt{M}}{\tanh\sqrt{M}} \quad (2.57)$$

where $\sqrt{M}$ is defined in expression 2.30 for a general-order reaction.

In particular, if the value of the hyperbolic tangent term in the denominator of Eq. 2.57 is greater than 3, the enhancement factor is given by

$$\phi = \sqrt{M}$$

which is the same as the equation obtained by the exact solution.

Penetration Theory

In the following discussion, we shall consider the solution to the problem of fast reactions based on the penetration theory.

The following equation holds for the general-order case:

$$D_A \frac{\partial^2[A]}{\partial x^2} = \frac{\partial[A]}{\partial t} + (k_{mn}[B_o]^n)[A]^m \quad (2.58)$$

The boundary conditions for Eq. 2.58 are

$$x = 0, \qquad [A] = [A^*], \qquad t > 0 \qquad (2.59)$$

$$x \to \infty, \qquad [A] = 0, \qquad t > 0 \qquad (2.60)$$

The initial condition is as follows:

$$t = 0, \qquad x = x, \qquad [A] = 0 \qquad (2.61)$$

The specific rate of transfer of A at any time t would be given by the diffusional flux of A at the interface. The average specific rate of transfer of A, based on Higbie's model, is given by the following equation:

$$R_A = \frac{1}{t_E}\int_0^{t_E} R_A(t)\,dt \qquad (2.62)$$

The partial differential equation 2.58 is not amenable to analytical solution for systems where the value of m is other than unity. For the case of $m = 1$, Danckwerts (1951) has shown that the following equation gives the specific rate of mass transfer for A:

$$R_A = [A^*]\left\{\sqrt{\frac{D_A}{k_1}}\left(k_1 + \frac{1}{2t_E}\right)\operatorname{erf}\left(\sqrt{k_1 t_E}\right) + \sqrt{\frac{D_A}{\pi t_E}}\exp(-k_1 t_E)\right\} \qquad (2.63)$$

where k_1 is the pseudo-first-order reaction rate constant, $k_n[B_o]^n$.

Under certain conditions, Eq. 2.63 can be considerably simplified. We shall consider two cases.

1. $k_1 t_E \ll 1$. For this case we have

$$R_A \approx [A^*]2\sqrt{\frac{D_A}{\pi t_E}}\left(1 + \frac{k_1 t_E}{3}\right) \qquad (2.64)$$

2. $k_1 t_E \gg 1$:

$$R_A \approx [A^*]\sqrt{D_A k_1}\left(1 + \frac{1}{2k_1 t_E}\right) \qquad (2.65)$$

Further, Eq. 2.64 shows that if $k_1 t_E$ is far less than unity,

$$R_A = 2\sqrt{\frac{D_A}{\pi t_E}}[A^*] \qquad (2.66)$$

$$= k_L[A^*] \qquad (2.7)$$

and the case degenerates to a slow reaction.

For $k_1 t_E$ greater than 20, Eq. 2.65 becomes

$$R_A = [A^*]\sqrt{D_A k_1} \qquad (2.67)$$

The set of equations 2.63–2.67 were obtained on the basis of the Higbie model. If Danckwerts's surfaces renewal model is employed, the following equation is obtained for a pseudo-first-order reaction:

$$R_A = [A^*]\sqrt{D_A k_1 + k_L^2} \qquad (2.68)$$

where $k_L = \sqrt{D_A s}$. Equation 2.68 reduces to Eq. 2.67 when $D_A k_1$ is very much greater than k_L^2 and to Eq. 2.7 when k_L^2 is very much greater than $D_A k_1$.

2.5. REGIME OVERLAPPING 1, 2, AND 3

It is conceivable that the reaction of the solute A may occur partly in the film and partly in the bulk, and yet there may be a finite concentration of the dissolved solute A in the bulk liquid. Such a case may be considered an example of the regime overlapping 1, 2, and 3. Figure 2.4 shows the typical concentration profiles. We shall consider the problem on the basis

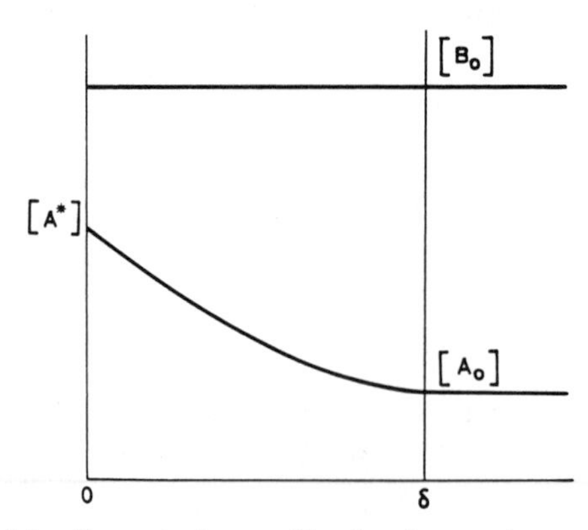

Figure 2.4. Concentration profiles for the reaction overlapping the very slow, slow, and fast reaction regimes (regime overlapping 1, 2, and 3).

of the film theory for the case of m equal to 1. For this case, the differential equation 2.50

$$D_A \frac{d^2[A]}{dx^2} = k_1[A]$$

has to be solved under these boundary conditions:

$$x = 0, \qquad [A] = [A^*] \qquad (2.35)$$

$$x = \delta, \qquad [A] = [A_o] \qquad (2.69)$$

where $[A_o]$ is the concentration of dissolved A in the bulk liquid phase.

The specific rate of mass transfer, R_A, is obtained by evaluating the flux of A at the interface $R_A = -D_A(d[A]/dx)_{x=0}$. This results in the following equation:

$$R_A = \frac{[A^*]\sqrt{D_A k_1}}{\tanh\left(\frac{\sqrt{D_A k_1}}{k_L}\right)} - \frac{[A_o]\sqrt{D_A k_1}}{\sinh\left(\frac{\sqrt{D_A k_1}}{k_L}\right)} \qquad (2.70)$$

It can be shown that Eq. 2.70 reduces to equations relevant to regimes 3, 2, and 1 under appropriate conditions.

When the value of $[A_o]$ is 0, Eq. 2.70 reduces to Eq. 2.52. Further, when $\sqrt{D_A k_1}/k_L$ is greater than 3 Eq. 2.70 reduces to Eq. 2.67.

For regime 2, according to the condition given by expression 2.10,

$$\frac{\sqrt{D_A k_1}}{k_L} \ll 1$$

Therefore, the specific rate of mass transfer is given by

$$R_A = \lim_{\frac{\sqrt{D_A k_1}}{k_L} \to 0} \left[k_L[A^*]\frac{\frac{\sqrt{D_A k_1}}{k_L}}{\tanh\left(\frac{\sqrt{D_A k_1}}{k_L}\right)} - \frac{k_L[A_o]\frac{\sqrt{D_A k_1}}{k_L}}{\sinh\left(\frac{\sqrt{D_A k_1}}{k_L}\right)} \right] \qquad (2.70a)$$

Equation 2.70a reduces to the following equation, which is the same as Eq. 2.6:

$$R_A = k_L([A^*] - [A_o])$$

The value of $[A_o]$ is given by the following equation:

$$[A_o] = \frac{[A^*]k_L}{lk_1/a + k_L}$$

$$= \frac{[A^*]}{lk_1/ak_L + 1} \qquad (2.70b)$$

Substitution of Eq. 2.70b in Eq. 2.6 gives the following equation:

$$R_A = k_L[A^*]\left(1 - \frac{1}{lk_1/k_L a + 1}\right)$$

$$= k_L[A^*]\left(\frac{lk_1/k_L a}{lk_1/k_L a + 1}\right) \qquad (2.70c)$$

For the case of a very slow reaction

$$\frac{lk_1}{k_L a} \ll 1$$

Therefore, the specific rate of mass transfer is given by the following equation, which holds for a pseudo-first-order reaction in regime 1 (for $m = 1$, $n = 0$, Eq. 2.2 reduces to Eq. 2.70d):

$$R_A = \frac{l}{a}k_1[A^*] \qquad (2.70d)$$

Under steady-state conditions, the rate at which the solute leaves the film is equal to the rate at which it reacts in the bulk. Therefore, we have

$$-D_A\left(\frac{d[A]}{dx}\right)_{x=\delta} = \frac{lk_1[A_o]}{a} \qquad (2.71)$$

From the differential equation 2.50 we get

$$-D_A\left(\frac{d[A]}{dx}\right)_{x=\delta} = \frac{[A^*]\sqrt{D_A k_1}}{\sinh\left(\frac{\sqrt{D_A k_1}}{k_L}\right)} - \frac{[A_o]\sqrt{D_A k_1}}{\tanh\left(\frac{\sqrt{D_A k_1}}{k_L}\right)} \qquad (2.72)$$

Equations 2.71 and 2.72 give

$$\frac{[A_o]}{[A^*]} = \frac{\dfrac{\sqrt{D_A k_1}}{\sinh\left(\sqrt{D_A k_1}/k_L\right)}}{\dfrac{lk_1}{a} + \dfrac{\sqrt{D_A k_1}}{\tanh\left(\sqrt{D_A k_1}/k_L\right)}} \tag{2.73}$$

Using the value of $[A_o]$ from Eq. 2.73 in Eq. 2.70, we obtain

$$R_A = \frac{[A^*]\sqrt{D_A k_1}}{\tanh\left(\sqrt{D_A k_1}/k_L\right)} \times \left\{1 - \left[\cosh^2\left(\frac{\sqrt{D_A k_1}}{k_L}\right) \times \left(\frac{lk_1}{a} \cdot \frac{\tanh\left(\sqrt{D_A k_1}/k_L\right)}{\sqrt{D_A k_1}} + 1\right)\right]^{-1}\right\} \tag{2.74}$$

Danckwerts' Surface Renewal Theory

The solution to the problem can also be considered on the basis of Danckwerts' surface renewal theory. The rate of reaction of A for a pseudo-first-order reaction and when there is a finite concentration of A in the bulk is given by

$$R_A a = a([A^*] - [A_o])\sqrt{D_A k_1 + k_L^2} \tag{2.75}$$

Here, $k_1 = k_n[B_o]^n$. The rate of reaction of the solute A in the bulk liquid phase is given by

$$R_A a = lk_1[A_o] \tag{2.76}$$

At steady state, the two rates are equal and hence the unknown concentration term $[A_o]$ can be eliminated. Thus, we obtain

$$R_A a = \left(\frac{1}{a\sqrt{D_A k_1 + k_L^2}} + \frac{1}{lk_1}\right)^{-1} [A^*] \tag{2.77}$$

Now,

$$R_A a = k_{LR} a[A^*], \qquad k_1 = k_n[B_o]^n$$

Therefore, we have

$$\frac{1}{k_{LR} a} = \frac{1}{a\sqrt{D_A k_n[B_o]^n + k_L^2}} + \frac{1}{lk_n[B_o]^n} \tag{2.78}$$

2.6. REGIME 4: INSTANTANEOUS (VERY FAST) REACTIONS

Here, the reaction is potentially so fast that the solute and the reactant cannot coexist. At a certain distance from the interface, a reaction plane is formed at which both the solute and the reactant are instantaneously consumed by the reaction (Figure 2.5). The rate of mass transfer in this case will be governed by the rate at which dissolved A and the reactant B are supplied to the reaction plane from the interface and bulk, respectively. The necessary condition for the validity of this regime is given by the following expression:

$$\frac{\sqrt{\dfrac{2}{m+1} D_A k_{mn}[A^*]^{m-1}[B_o]^n}}{k_L} \gg \frac{[B_o]}{Z[A^*]}\sqrt{\frac{D_B}{D_A}} \tag{2.79}$$

The rationale for the condition given by expression 2.79 will be brought out in Section 2.7. The

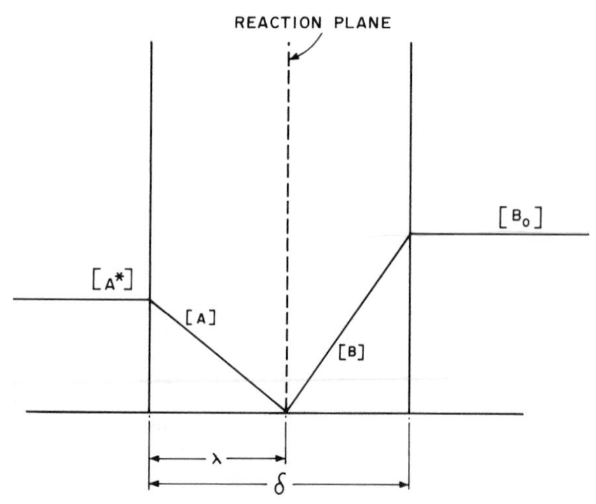

Figure 2.5. Concentration profiles for an instantaneous reaction (regime 4).

diffusivity ratio on the right-hand side of expression 2.79 has been taken as the square root of the ratio, since the experimental data are better correlated through the use of $\sqrt{D_B/D_A}$ than of D_B/D_A (see Section 2.7).

Film Theory

The film theory solution of this regime is relatively simple (Astarita, 1967). At steady state, the rate of diffusion of the dissolved solute A through the region between the interface and the reaction plane (i.e., $0 < x < \lambda$) will be equal to the rate of diffusion of the reactive species B through the region between the reaction plane and the bulk liquid-phase boundary (i.e., $\lambda < x < \delta$). (See Figure 2.5.)

Therefore, we have

$$R_A = \frac{D_A[A^*]}{\lambda} = \frac{D_B[B_o]}{Z(\delta - \lambda)} \tag{2.80}$$

or

$$\frac{\delta - \lambda}{\lambda} = \frac{D_B[B_o]}{ZD_A[A^*]}$$

or

$$\frac{\delta}{\lambda} = \frac{ZD_A[A^*] + D_B[B_o]}{ZD_A[A^*]} \tag{2.81}$$

Eliminating λ from Eqs. 2.80 and 2.81 we get

$$R_A = \frac{D_A[A^*]}{\delta}\left[\frac{ZD_A[A^*] + D_B[B_o]}{ZD_A[A^*]}\right] \tag{2.82}$$

Since $D_A/\delta = k_L$, we have

$$R_A = k_L[A^*]\left[1 + \frac{[B_o]}{Z[A^*]}\frac{D_B}{D_A}\right] \tag{2.83}$$

If

$$\frac{[B_o]}{Z[A^*]}\frac{D_B}{D_A} \gg 1 \tag{2.84}$$

Then,

$$R_A = k_L\frac{[B_o]}{Z}\frac{D_B}{D_A} \tag{2.85}$$

Equation 2.83 can also be expressed in terms of an asymptotic enhancement factor for mass transfer:

$$\phi_a = \frac{R_A}{k_L[A^*]} = 1 + \frac{[B_o]}{Z[A^*]}\frac{D_B}{D_A} \tag{2.86}$$

When the condition given by expression 2.84 is satisfied, Equation 2.86 reduces to the following equation:

$$\phi_a = \frac{[B_o]}{Z[A^*]}\frac{D_B}{D_A} \tag{2.87}$$

Penetration Theory

In the penetration theory treatment, because of the transient nature of the diffusion process, the position of the reaction plane shifts with time. The reaction plane progressively moves away from the interface as more and more of B is consumed by the reaction (see Figure 2.6; Danckwerts, 1950; 1951).

The differential equations to be solved are

$$0 < x < \lambda(t), \qquad \frac{\partial[A]}{\partial t} = D_A\frac{\partial^2[A]}{\partial x^2} \tag{2.88}$$

$$\lambda(t) < x, \qquad \frac{\partial[B]}{\partial t} = D_B\frac{\partial^2[B]}{\partial x^2} \tag{2.89}$$

with the following initial and boundary conditions:

$$t = 0, \quad x = x, \qquad [B] = [B_o], \quad [A] = 0 \tag{2.90}$$

$$t > 0, \quad x = 0, \qquad [A] = [A^*] \tag{2.91}$$

$$t > 0, \quad x = \lambda(t), \quad [A] = [B] = 0,$$

$$-ZD_A\frac{\partial[A]}{\partial x} = D_B\frac{\partial[B]}{\partial x} \tag{2.92}$$

We calculate the specific rate of mass transfer at the

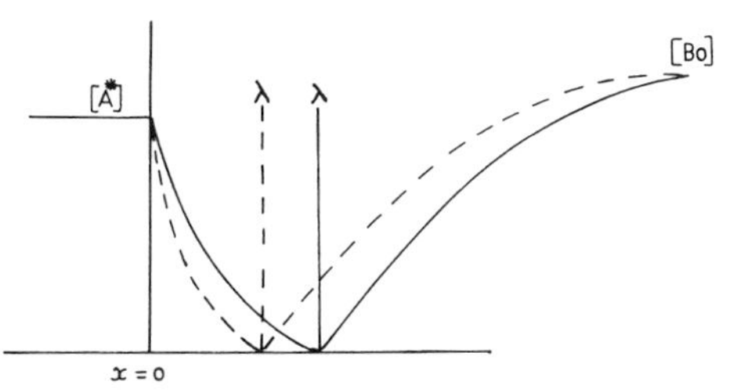

Figure 2.6. Typical concentration profiles for an instantaneous reaction predicted on the basis of the penetration model showing the movement of the reaction plane with time.

interface as

$$R_A(t) = -D_A\left(\frac{\partial[A]}{\partial x}\right)_{x=0}$$

$$= \frac{[A^*]}{\text{erf}\left(\sqrt{\frac{\alpha}{D_A}}\right)}\sqrt{\frac{D_A}{\pi t}} \tag{2.93}$$

where α is given by

$$1 - \text{erf}\sqrt{\frac{\alpha}{D_B}}$$

$$= \frac{[B_o]}{Z[A^*]}\sqrt{\frac{D_B}{D_A}}\,\text{erf}\sqrt{\frac{\alpha}{D_A}}\,\exp\left(\frac{\alpha}{D_A} - \frac{\alpha}{D_B}\right) \tag{2.94}$$

The average specific rate of mass transfer over a time t_E will be given by

$$R_A = \frac{1}{t_E}\int_0^{t_E} R_A(t)\,dt$$

$$= 2\frac{[A^*]}{\text{erf}\left(\sqrt{\alpha/D_A}\right)}\sqrt{\frac{D_A}{\pi t_E}} \tag{2.95}$$

It can be shown that for $[B_o]/Z[A^*]$ greater than 3, Eq. 2.95 reduces to

$$R_A = k_L[A^*]\sqrt{\frac{D_A}{D_B}}\left(1 + \frac{D_B}{D_A}\frac{[B_o]}{Z[A^*]}\right) \tag{2.96}$$

When the condition given by expression 2.84 is satisfied, Eq. 2.96 becomes

$$R_A = k_L\frac{[B_o]}{Z}\sqrt{\frac{D_B}{D_A}} \tag{2.97}$$

Karlsson and Bjerle (1980a) have developed an explicit expression for the enhancement for an irreversible instantaneous reaction on the basis of penetration theory. The original analysis by Danckwerts (1950) gives an implicit relation for ϕ that can be solved by iteration. Karlsson and Bjerle have simplified the analysis by assuming a linear approximation for the error function term. The final relation for ϕ is

$$\phi \simeq \frac{\sqrt{\pi}}{2\sin\{\sin(\sigma)\}}$$

where

$$\sigma = \frac{\sqrt{\pi r_B}}{4}\left\{-1 + \sqrt{1 + \left(\frac{4}{q r_B}\right)\bigg/\exp\left[\frac{\sqrt{\pi}}{2\left(1 + q\sqrt{r_B}\right)}\right]^2}\right\}$$

$$r_B = \frac{D_B}{D_A}, \quad q = \frac{[B_o]}{Z[A^*]}$$

The deviation from the exact implicit expression is no more than 5% for $\phi \geqslant 2$ and r_B between 10^{-2} and 10^3.

It is seen from Eq. 2.97 (or 2.85) that the rate of mass transfer is independent of the concentration of the solute A. In the case of gas absorption, this independence on the concentration of the solute A implies that the specific rate of absorption will be independent of the partial pressure of the gas A.

When Eqs. 2.85 and 2.97 are compared, it is seen that the film theory solution predicts the rate to vary directly as the diffusivity ratio, whereas the penetration theory predicts a square root dependence on the diffusivity ratio. In many systems the difference between Eqs. 2.85 and 2.97 is small for practical purposes. Further, when D_B and D_A are equal, there is no difference between the solutions based on the film and penetration theories.

2.7. TRANSITION FROM FAST TO INSTANTANEOUS (VERY FAST) REACTIONS: REGIME OVERLAPPING 3 AND 4

For systems that do not satisfy expression 2.31 and for which the values of the terms on either side of the expression are comparable, the concentration of B in the liquid film will be substantially lower than that in the bulk. In other words, there is a "depletion" of B in the film. The concentration profiles for this case are shown in Figure 2.7.

Film Theory

Hikita and Asai (1964) have solved, on the basis of the film theory, the problem of the diffusion of the

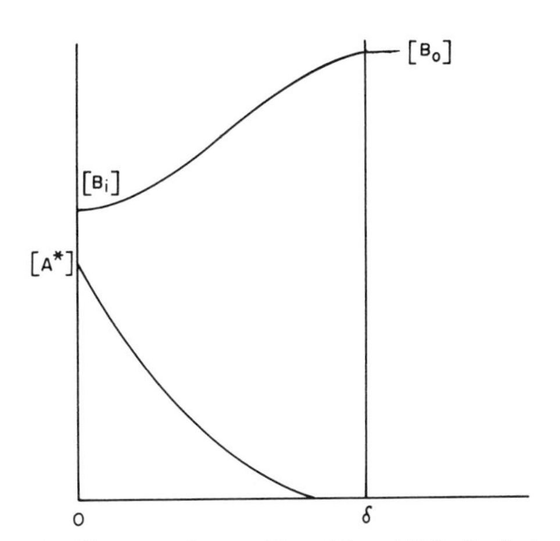

Figure 2.7. Concentration profiles of A and B in the fast general-order (depletion) regime (regime between 3 and 4).

solute A under conditions such that there is depletion of B in the film. The relevant differential equations are as follows:

$$D_A \frac{d^2[A]}{dx^2} = k_{mn}[A]^m[B]^n \tag{2.98}$$

and

$$D_B \frac{d^2[B]}{dx^2} = Zk_{mn}[A]^m[B]^n \tag{2.99}$$

The boundary conditions are

$$x = 0, \quad [A] = [A^*], \quad \frac{d[B]}{dx} = 0, \quad [B] = [B_i] \tag{2.100}$$

$$x = \delta, \quad [A] = 0, \quad [B] = [B_o] \tag{2.101}$$

If the kinetic term in Eq. 2.98 is eliminated by using Eq. 2.99, the following differential equation is obtained:

$$ZD_A \frac{d^2[A]}{dx^2} = D_B \frac{d^2[B]}{dx^2} \tag{2.102}$$

Integration of Eq. 2.102 gives

$$ZD_A \frac{d[A]}{dx} = D_B \frac{d[B]}{dx} - ZR_A \tag{2.103}$$

(The integration constant can be shown to be equal to $-ZR_A$.)

A second integration of Eq. 2.103 gives

$$[B_i] = [B_o] + Z[A^*]\frac{D_A}{D_B} - \frac{ZR_A}{D_B}\delta \tag{2.104}$$

Equation 2.104 gives the interfacial concentration of the species B in terms of R_A. Equation 2.104 thus contains two unknowns. In order to calculate R_A, we must have another equation relating R_A with $[B_i]$, so that the two equations can be simultaneously solved.

We will consider Eq. 2.98 for this purpose. Equation 2.98 is nonlinear and therefore not amenable to analytical solution. We will have to make a simplifying assumption in order to obtain an analytical solution. The boundary condition 2.100 for the flux of B at the interface provides the required basis for a suitable assumption. The boundary condition given by Eq. 2.100 implies a constant reactant concentration, $[B_i]$, in the immediate neighborhood of the interface. By definition, the specific rate of mass transfer is equal to the flux of the solute at the interface. Therefore, for practical purposes we may restrict the solution of Eq. 2.98 to the immediate neighborhood of the interface. Substitution of a constant concentration $[B_i]$ in place of the variable concentration [B] in Eq. 2.98 will therefore be a reasonable assumption. (Equation 2.98 can also be solved analytically by assuming a linear concentration profile for the reactant B. This matter is discussed in Section 2.8.)

With this assumption, Eq. 2.98 becomes

$$D_A \frac{d^2[A]}{dx^2} = (k_{mn}[B_i]^n)[A]^m \tag{2.105}$$

Integrating Eq. 2.105 and following the usual procedure, we get

$$R_A = \frac{k_L[A^*]\sqrt{M}([B_i]/[B_o])^{n/2}}{\tanh\left[\sqrt{M}([B_i]/[B_o])^{n/2}\right]} \tag{2.106}$$

When the term $\sqrt{M}([B_i]/[B_o])^{n/2}$ is greater than 3, the value of the denominator in Eq. 2.106 becomes approximately unity and the specific rate of mass transfer is given by

$$R_A = [A^*]\sqrt{\frac{2}{m+1}D_A k_{mn}[A^*]^{m-1}[B_i]^n} \tag{2.107}$$

Equation 2.106 can be written in an alternate form in terms of the ratio $[B_i]/[B_o]$, denoted by η^2. Thus, η is equal to $\sqrt{[B_i]/[B_o]}$, and noting that

$$\phi = \frac{R_A}{k_L[A^*]} \tag{2.108}$$

we obtain

$$\phi = \frac{\sqrt{M}(\eta)^n}{\tanh(\sqrt{M}\eta^n)} \tag{2.109}$$

The value of η lies between 0 and 1. For reactions that are first order in species A as well as B ($m = 1$, $n = 1$), Eq. 2.104 becomes

$$\eta^2 + \frac{\sqrt{M}}{q}\eta - \left(1 + \frac{1}{q}\right) = 0 \tag{2.110}$$

where

$$q = \frac{[B_o]}{Z[A^*]}\frac{D_B}{D_A} \tag{2.111}$$

We shall now show how the conditions given by expressions 2.31 and 2.79 for the validity of Eqs. 2.44 and 2.83, respectively, are obtained.

The value of η can be obtained from the solution of Eq. 2.110:

$$\eta = \frac{-\dfrac{\sqrt{M}}{q} + \sqrt{\dfrac{M}{q^2} + 4\left(1 + \dfrac{1}{q}\right)}}{2} \tag{2.110a}$$

Now when $\sqrt{M}$ is very much less than q, the value of η tends to unity. Therefore, the interfacial concentration of the reactant is practically the same as the bulk liquid concentration. In other words, there is no depletion of the reactant in the film.

Conversely, when $\sqrt{M}$ is very much greater than q, the value of η as given by Eq. 2.110a tends to 0. The interfacial concentration of the reactant, $[B_i]$, is therefore, zero. The condition for an instantaneous reaction is thus given by expression 2.79, for which Eq. 2.83 is valid.

Equation 2.110 can also be expressed in terms of the asymptotic enhancement factor, namely,

$$\phi_a = 1 + \frac{[B_o]}{Z[A^*]}\frac{D_B}{D_A} \tag{2.112}$$

Substituting this value of ϕ_a in Eq. 2.110 and noting that, provided $\sqrt{M}\eta > 3$,

$$\phi = \sqrt{M}\eta$$

we obtain

$$\eta = \sqrt{\frac{\phi_a - \phi}{\phi_a - 1}} \tag{2.113}$$

Equation 2.113 is obtained for a second-order ($m = 1$, $n = 1$) reaction. Hikita and Asai (1964) have shown that the following equation holds for a general-order reaction:

$$\phi = \sqrt{M}\eta^n = \sqrt{M}\left(\frac{\phi_a - \phi}{\phi_a - 1}\right)^{n/2} \tag{2.114}$$

for an $(m + n)$th-order reaction (when n is equal to 1 Eq. 2.114 reduces to Eq. 2.113).

Penetration Theory

According to the penetration theory, the following differential equations hold:

$$D_A\frac{\partial^2[A]}{\partial x^2} = \frac{\partial[A]}{\partial t} + k_{mn}[A]^m[B]^n \tag{2.115}$$

$$D_B\frac{\partial^2[B]}{\partial x^2} = \frac{\partial[B]}{\partial t} + Zk_{mn}[A]^m[B]^n \tag{2.116}$$

The boundary conditions are

$$t > 0, \quad x = 0, \quad [A] = [A^*], \quad \frac{\partial[B]}{\partial x} = 0 \tag{2.117}$$

$$t > 0, \quad x \to \infty, \quad [A] = 0, \quad [B] = [B_o] \tag{2.118}$$

and the initial condition is

$$t = 0, \quad x = x, \quad [A] = 0, \quad [B] = [B_o] \tag{2.119}$$

It is assumed that the diffusivities of A and B are independent of concentration. The specific rate of mass transfer is given by

$$R_A = \frac{1}{t_E}\int_0^{t_E} - D_A\left(\frac{\partial[A]}{\partial x}\right)_{x=0} dt \tag{2.120}$$

These equations are, however, not amenable to analytical solution, even when D_B is equal to D_A. Brian (1964) has obtained a numerical solution to the foregoing problem. Brian et al. (1961) and Pearson (1963) had earlier reported the results of numerical solution to the problem based on the penetration theory for second-order reactions.

The numerical solutions have been presented in the form of graphs of ϕ against $\sqrt{M}$ with $([B_o]/Z[A^*])\sqrt{D_B/D_A}$ as a parameter. For any given value of q, ϕ increases with an increase in $\sqrt{M}$ until it reaches its asymptotic value. The asymptotic value is reached when the reaction mechanism becomes instantaneous (i.e., regime 4) and no further increase in ϕ occurs with an increase in $\sqrt{M}$. The asymptotic value of ϕ for a given value of q is given by

$$\phi_a = 1 + q, \qquad \text{film theory}$$

and

$$\phi_a = (1 + q)\sqrt{D_A/D_B}, \qquad \text{penetration theory}$$

Effect of the Diffusivity Ratio D_B/D_A on ϕ

The analytical solution based on the film theory and the numerical solution based on the penetration theory agree exactly when the ratio of the diffusivities of B and A is 1. For the case of unequal diffusivities, the solution based on the penetration theory would be expected to be more realistic. The film theory predicts the following value of ϕ_a:

$$\phi_a = 1 + \frac{[B_o]}{Z[A^*]}\frac{D_B}{D_A} \qquad (2.121)$$

The penetration theory predicts the following value for ϕ_a:

$$\phi_a = \sqrt{\frac{D_A}{D_B}} + \frac{[B_o]}{Z[A^*]}\sqrt{\frac{D_B}{D_A}} \qquad (2.122)$$

We shall show that the film theory solution and the penetration theory solution for ϕ agree well, even for the case of unequal diffusivities, if the value of ϕ_a in Eq. 2.114 is calculated from the penetration theory (Eq. 2.122) and not from the film theory (Eq. 2.121). Consider the following examples:

(i) *$m = n = 1$ and $\sqrt{M} = 10$,* $D_B/D_A = 0.1$ *and* $[B_o]/Z[A^*] = 26.5$. The enhancement factor obtained from the numerical solution of Brian et al. (1961) is 7.3.

The asymptotic value of the enhancement factor calculated from the film theory solution is found to be 3.65. The value of ϕ based on this asymptotic value is 3.4.

The asymptotic value of the enhancement factor calculated on the basis of the penetration theory is 11.5. The value of ϕ based on this asymptotic value is 6.8, which is comparable to the value of 7.3 obtained on the basis of the penetration theory.

(ii) $\sqrt{M} = 5$, $D_B/D_A = 10$ *and* $[B_o]/Z[A^*] = 1.76$. The enhancement factor obtained from the numerical solution of Brian et al. is 3.65 for a 1–1 order reaction.

The asymptotic value of the enhancement factor calculated from the film theory solution is found to be 18.6. The value of ϕ based on this asymptotic value is 4.36.

The asymptotic value of the enhancement factor calculated on the basis of the penetration theory is only 5.9. The value of ϕ based on this asymptotic value is 3.5, which is comparable to the value of 3.65 obtained on the basis of the penetration theory.

Thus, the values obtained from the film theory solution agree with those from the penetration theory solution, even for the case of unequal diffusivities, provided that the value of ϕ_a is taken on the basis of the penetration theory.

2.8. MASS TRANSFER ACCOMPANIED BY REACTION WHEN THE REACTANT B IS VOLATILE: REGIME BETWEEN 3 AND 4

In the case when the reactant is volatile and the regime of mass transfer is between regimes 3 and 4, the depletion of the reactant B is caused both by the reaction occurring in the film and by the stripping of the volatile reactant (Figure 2.8). We shall consider the case of a second-order reaction ($m = 1, n = 1$).

The basic differential equation that governs the steady-state diffusion of the solute A accompanied by a second-order reaction is as follows:

$$D_A\frac{d^2[A]}{dx^2} = k_2[A][B] \qquad (2.123)$$

This equation is nonlinear and therefore is not amenable to analytical solution. The approximation made by van Krevelen and Hoftijzer (1948) and Hikita and Asai (1964) is restricted to a nonvolatile reactant for which the zero interfacial flux condition

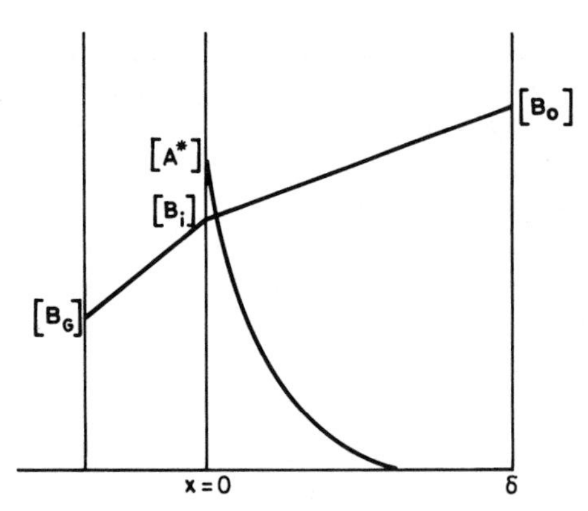

Figure 2.8. Concentration profiles for the depletion reaction regime (regime between 3 and 4) when the reactant is volatile.

is valid. In the case of a volatile reactant, there is a finite flux of the reactant at the interface (see Figure 2.8) and therefore the foregoing assumption is not tenable. Equation 2.123 can probably be solved if the variable [B] term is replaced by a suitable function relating [B] with x. Pangarkar (1974) has made use of the following linear relationship:

$$[\mathrm{B}] = a + bx \tag{2.124}$$

This substitution has an added advantage in that the resulting solution is in a closed form that is easy to evaluate. Thus, when Eq. 2.124 is substituted in Eq. 2.123 we get

$$D_{\mathrm{A}} \frac{d^2[\mathrm{A}]}{dx^2} = k_2(a + bx)[\mathrm{A}] \tag{2.125}$$

The boundary conditions are as follows:

$$x = 0, \quad [\mathrm{A}] = [\mathrm{A}^*], \quad [\mathrm{B}] = [\mathrm{B_i}],$$

$$R_{\mathrm{A}} = -D_{\mathrm{A}}\left(\frac{d[\mathrm{A}]}{dx}\right),$$

$$D_{\mathrm{B}}\left(\frac{d[\mathrm{B}]}{dx}\right) = \frac{k_{\mathrm{G_B}}}{H_{\mathrm{B}}}([\mathrm{B_i}] - [\mathrm{B_G}]) \tag{2.126}$$

$$x = \delta, \quad [\mathrm{A}] = 0, \quad [\mathrm{B}] = [\mathrm{B_o}] \tag{2.127}$$

The constants a and b in Eq. 2.124 are obtained by using the boundary conditions given by Eqs. 2.126 and 2.127. Pangarkar has shown that the specific rate of mass transfer of the gas A is given by the following equation:

$$R_{\mathrm{A}} = -D_{\mathrm{A}}\left(\frac{d[\mathrm{A}]}{dx}\right)_{x=0} = [\mathrm{A}^*]\sqrt{D_{\mathrm{A}} k_2 [\mathrm{B_i}]}$$

$$\times \left[\frac{I_{-1/3}\left(\sqrt{M_o'}\right) I_{-2/3}\left(\sqrt{M_i'}\right) - I_{1/3}\left(\sqrt{M_o'}\right) I_{2/3}\left(\sqrt{M_i'}\right)}{I_{-1/3}\left(\sqrt{M_i'}\right) I_{1/3}\left(\sqrt{M_o'}\right) - I_{-1/3}\left(\sqrt{M_o'}\right) I_{1/3}\left(\sqrt{M_i'}\right)}\right] \tag{2.128}$$

where

$$\sqrt{M_i'} = \frac{2}{3}\frac{\sqrt{D_{\mathrm{A}} k_2 [\mathrm{B_i'}]}}{k_{\mathrm{L}}}, \qquad [\mathrm{B_i'}]^{1/2} = \frac{[\mathrm{B_i}]^{3/2}}{[\mathrm{B_o}] - [\mathrm{B_i}]}$$

$$\sqrt{M_o'} = \frac{2}{3}\frac{\sqrt{D_{\mathrm{A}} k_2 [\mathrm{B_o'}]}}{k_{\mathrm{L}}}, \qquad [\mathrm{B_o'}]^{1/2} = \frac{[\mathrm{B_o}]^{3/2}}{[\mathrm{B_o}] - [\mathrm{B_i}]}$$

Equation 2.128 is obtained for the case of a fast reaction between species A and B and is therefore valid for values of the modified parameter $\sqrt{M_o'}$ greater than 3. It can be shown that when $\sqrt{M_o'}$ is greater than 3, the bracketed term in Eq. 2.128 reduces to unity. The specific rate of absorption is then given by the following equation:

$$R_{\mathrm{A}} = [\mathrm{A}^*]\sqrt{D_{\mathrm{A}} k_2 [\mathrm{B_i}]} \tag{2.129}$$

Noting that $\eta = \sqrt{\dfrac{\mathrm{B_i}}{\mathrm{B_o}}}$ and $\phi = R_{\mathrm{A}}/k_{\mathrm{L}}[\mathrm{A}^*]$ we obtain

$$\phi = \sqrt{M} \cdot \eta \tag{2.129a}$$

Equation 2.129 is the same as Eq. 2.107 (where $m = 1$, $n = 1$), which was obtained for a nonvolatile reactant B. However, Eq. 2.107 was derived on the basis of a zero interfacial flux of the reactant B. It is thus clear from the derivation of Eq. 2.129 that it is not necessary to assume a zero interfacial flux for the reactant B.

Equation 2.129 still contains the unknown term $[\mathrm{B_i}]$. A mass balance similar to that of Eq. 2.102 along with the boundary conditions given by Eqs. 2.126 and 2.127 will be used to calculate $[\mathrm{B_i}]$. The integration procedure employed is similar to that used for the integration of Eq. 2.102. The final result, on simplification, is

$$\frac{[B_i]}{[B_o]} = \eta^2 = \frac{\dfrac{\phi_a - \phi}{\phi_a - 1} + \dfrac{k_{G_B}}{H_B k_L}\dfrac{[B_G]}{[B_o]}}{1 + \dfrac{k_{G_B}}{H_B k_L}} \quad (2.130)$$

where ϕ is related to η by Eq. 2.129a for n equal to unity.

Equation 2.130 reduces to Eq. 2.113 when the reactant is nonvolatile (i.e., $H_B \to \infty$).

The use of Eqs. 2.129a and 2.130 in calculating the enhancement factor is shown next. The data are

$$\frac{k_{G_B}}{H_B k_L} = 1, \qquad \frac{[B_G]}{[B_o]} = 0.1, n = 1$$

$$\sqrt{M} = 16, \qquad \phi_a = 20$$

Equation 2.130 can be written in the quadratic form as follows:

$$\left(1 + \frac{k_{G_B}}{H_B k_L}\right)\eta^2 + \frac{\sqrt{M}}{\phi_a - 1}\eta - \left(\frac{\phi_a}{\phi_a - 1} + \frac{k_{G_B}}{H_B k_L}\frac{[B_G]}{[B_o]}\right) = 0 \quad (2.131)$$

The roots of this equation can be readily obtained. We are interested only in the positive root, since the negative value is absurd. Using the data just given, we obtain

$$\eta = 0.578$$

and from Eq. 2.129a

$$\phi = 9.25$$

The rate of absorption is then obtained from the following equation:

$$R_A = k_L \phi [A^*] \quad (2.132)$$

2.9. GAS ABSORPTION ACCOMPANIED BY INSTANTANEOUS REACTION WITH A PART OF THE RESISTANCE ON THE GAS SIDE

When the absorption of a gas diluted with an inert gas is accompanied by an instantaneous reaction, then in principle a part of the resistance to mass transfer may be found in the gas phase. The following equations will then hold:

$$R_A a = k_{G_A} a (p_A - p_{A,i}) \quad (2.133)$$

$$R_A a = k_L a [A^*]\left(1 + \sqrt{\frac{D_B}{D_A}}\frac{[B_o]}{Z[A^*]}\right) = k_L a H_A p_{A,i}\left(1 + \sqrt{\frac{D_B}{D_A}}\frac{[B_o]}{Z H_A p_{A,i}}\right) \quad (2.134)$$

(For the sake of simplifying the calculations, the first term in the parentheses has been taken as 1 rather than $\sqrt{D_A/D_B}$.)

The overall mass transfer coefficient $K_{G_A}a$ is defined by the following equation:

$$R_A a = K_{G_A} a p_A \quad (2.135)$$

Equation 2.134 on rearrangement gives the value of $p_{A,i}$ explicitly.

$$p_{A,i} = \frac{R_A a - k_L a \dfrac{[B_o]}{Z}\sqrt{\dfrac{D_B}{D_A}}}{k_L a H_A} \quad (2.136)$$

From Eqs. 2.133 and 2.136, we get

$$p_{A,i} = \left[\frac{k_{G_A} a p_A - \dfrac{k_L a [B_o]}{Z}\sqrt{\dfrac{D_B}{D_A}}}{k_{G_A} a + H_A k_L a}\right] \quad (2.136a)$$

From Eqs. 2.133 to 2.136, we get

$$\frac{1}{K_{G_A} a} = \frac{\dfrac{1}{k_{G_A} a} + \dfrac{1}{H_A k_L a}}{1 + \dfrac{[B_o]}{Z H_A p_A}\sqrt{\dfrac{D_B}{D_A}}} \quad (2.137)$$

Equation 2.137 is valid only if $p_{A,i} > 0$, that is, if

$$k_{G_A} p_A > \frac{k_L [B_o]}{Z}\sqrt{\frac{D_B}{D_A}}$$

When

$$k_{G_A} p_A \leqslant \frac{k_L[B_o]}{Z}\sqrt{\frac{D_B}{D_A}}, \qquad p_{A,i} = 0$$

and the operation is totally gas-film-controlled. Equation 2.137 is not valid when $p_{A,i} = 0$, and the rate of absorption for this case is given by $R_A a = k_{G_A} a p_A$. It can also be inferred from Eqs. 2.133 and 2.134 that no gas-side resistance would be present provided that

$$k_{G_A} p_A \gg \frac{k_L[B_o]}{Z} \qquad (2.138)$$

Depletion Reaction with Gas-Side Resistance

A general explicit relation for the enhancement factor for irreversible gas–liquid reactions with gas-side resistance has been developed by Karlsson and Bjerle (1980b) on the basis of penetration theory. The authors have considered a 1–1($m = 1$, $n = 1$)-order reaction but have also extended the treatment to 1–n order reactions. The procedure involves the use of an empirically derived approximation for ϕ,

$$\phi = \frac{\left[(\sqrt{M})^{-3/2} + (\phi_a)^{-3/2}\right]^{-2/3}}{\tanh\left[(\sqrt{M})^{-3/2} + (\phi_a)^{-3/2}\right]^{-2/3}} \qquad (2.138a)$$

where

$$\phi_a = 1 + \frac{D_B[B_o]}{D_A Z H_A p_A}$$

This approximation is accurate to within 5% for $\phi_a \geqslant 2$ but gives much higher deviations if $\phi_a < 2$ and $\sqrt{M} \gg \phi_a$. The approximation can therefore replace the numerical solutions of van Krevelen and Hoftizer (1948). For $\phi > 3$ the tanh term in Eq. 2.138a can be dropped; this cannot be done for the expression of van Krevelen and Hoftizer. The authors have incorporated the effect of the gas-side resistance by eliminating the implicit interfacial concentration of the solute. The general solution has an accuracy of 20% and the maximum deviation occurs at maximum gas-side resistance in the middle of the transition from regime 3 to regime 4. The results can be used to obtain the rate constants of 1–1 order reactions in a simpler manner.

2.10. THEORY OF MASS TRANSFER ACCOMPANIED BY REVERSIBLE CHEMICAL REACTION

In this chapter we have already considered various aspects of mass transfer accompanied by an irreversible reaction of a general order. In many practical situations, the reactions are reversible. Consider, for example, the absorption of carbon dioxide in carbonated amine solutions. When the carbon dioxide loading is greater than 0.3 mol of CO_2 per mole of amine, there is a finite equilibrium partial pressure of CO_2. Likewise, the absorption of CO_2 in carbonate buffer solutions at elevated temperatures, with or without catalysts, is also accompanied by a reversible reaction. The chemical reaction may be fast or instantaneous, depending on the values of

$$\frac{\sqrt{\dfrac{2}{m+1} D_A k_{mn} [A^*]^{m-1} [B_o]^n}}{k_L}$$

and

$$\frac{[B_o]}{Z[A^*]}\sqrt{\frac{D_B}{D_A}}$$

The following treatment is valid for gas–liquid systems. In most cases, the bulk liquid can be assumed to be in equilibrium at the prevailing concentration of the various species. When the liquid-phase reaction is instantaneous it can be assumed that equilibrium exists at all points in the liquid, including the interface, whereas for fast reactions the equilibrium is not reached at every point. The two cases will be considered separately in the following discussion.

2.10.1 Absorption Accompanied by a Fast Reaction

When a reaction follows general-order kinetics, equilibrium is not established at every point in the liquid and the problem is not amenable to an exact analytical solution except for certain special cases. Huang and Kuo (1965) have considered the following simple first-order or pseudo-first-order reactions:

$$A \underset{k_1'}{\overset{k_1}{\rightleftharpoons}} C \qquad (2.139)$$

$$A + B \underset{k_2'}{\overset{k_2}{\rightleftharpoons}} C \qquad (2.140)$$

They have derived analytical solutions for the rate of absorption. Secor and Beutler (1967) have considered a general case,

$$Z_A A + Z_B B \rightleftharpoons Z_C C + Z_E E \qquad (2.141)$$

and have obtained numerical solutions for a reaction of general-order kinetics. Onda et al. (1970) have obtained an analytical solution for a reaction of general-order kinetics based on linearized profiles. We shall consider some specific cases.

(i) *Absorption Accompanied by Reversible Pseudo-First-Order Reaction (Regime 3)*

Consider the reaction scheme 2.139:

$$A \underset{k_1'}{\overset{k_1}{\rightleftharpoons}} C$$

where the equilibrium relation is

$$K = \frac{[C_o]}{[A_o]} = \frac{k_1}{k_1'} \qquad (2.142)$$

The local rate of reaction can be written as

$$r_A = k_1[A] - k_1'[C] \qquad (2.143)$$

The following differential equations, based on the film theory, are valid for the species A and C:

$$D_A \frac{d^2[A]}{dx^2} = k_1[A] - k_1'[C] \qquad (2.144)$$

$$D_C \frac{d^2[C]}{dx^2} = k_1'[C] - k_1[A] \qquad (2.145)$$

The boundary conditions are, at $x = 0$,

$$[A] = [A^*], \qquad \frac{d[C]}{dx} = 0 \qquad (2.146)$$

and at $x = \delta$,

$$[A] = [A_o], \qquad [C] = [C_o] \qquad (2.147)$$

These equations can be solved analytically for the concentration profiles of A and C. Once the concentration profile of A is established, the rate of absorption of A can be calculated (Huang and Kuo, 1965). If we assume chemical equilibrium to prevail in the bulk liquid, we obtain

$$R_A = \frac{k_L\left(1 + K\dfrac{D_C}{D_A}\right)}{\left(1 + K\dfrac{D_C}{D_A}\dfrac{\tanh(\alpha\delta)}{\alpha\delta}\right)}([A^*] - [A_o]) \qquad (2.148)$$

where the quantity α is defined as

$$\alpha = \sqrt{\frac{k_1}{D_A}\left(1 + \frac{1}{K}\frac{D_A}{D_C}\right)} \qquad (2.149)$$

For an irreversible reaction ($K \to \infty$) Eq. 2.148 reduces to the well-established equation for a pseudo-first-order reaction:

$$R_A = \frac{[A^*]\sqrt{D_A k_1}}{\tanh\left(\dfrac{\sqrt{D_A k_1}}{k_L}\right)} \qquad (2.150)$$

(Equation 2.150 is the same as Eq. 2.52.) In practice, reversible reactions that are truly first order in both directions are uncommon. However, we may encounter reactions that are first order in the concentration of the dissolved gas. Also, under certain conditions the concentration of the reactant may be uniform in the liquid phase, so that the forward reaction becomes a pseudo-first-order reaction. Likewise, the concentration of the products may be the same in the film as well as the bulk so that the rate of the reverse reaction becomes the same at all points. Consider the following scheme:

$$A + B \underset{k_2'}{\overset{k_2}{\rightleftharpoons}} C + E \qquad (2.151)$$

The equilibrium constant is defined as

$$K = \frac{k_2}{k_2'} = \frac{[C_o][E_o]}{[A_o][B_o]} \qquad (2.152)$$

The rate of reaction under pseudo-first-order reaction conditions is

$$r_A = k_2[A][B_o] - k_2'[C_o][E_o] \quad (2.153)$$

$$= k_2[B_o]([A] - [A_o]) \quad (2.154)$$

$$(\text{since } k_2'[C_o][E_o] = k_2[A_o][B_o])$$

$$= k_1([A] - [A_o]) \quad (2.155)$$

where $k_1 = k_2[B_o]$. Hence the differential equation for this case becomes

$$D_A \frac{d^2[A]}{dx^2} = k_1([A] - [A_o]) \quad (2.156)$$

The solution of this equation, and noting that

$$R_A = -D_A\left(\frac{d[A]}{dx}\right)_{x=0}$$

gives

$$R_A = ([A^*] - [A_o]) \frac{(D_A k_1)^{1/2}}{\tanh\left[(D_A k_1)^{1/2}/k_L\right]} \quad (2.157)$$

The foregoing problem can also be solved on similar lines on the basis of the Danckwerts' surface renewal theory. This yields the following equation for R_A (Danckwerts, unpublished work, cited in Danckwerts and Sharma, 1966):

$$R_A = ([A^*] - [A_o])\sqrt{D_A k_1 + k_L^2} \quad (2.158)$$

(ii) *Reversible Reaction with Generalized Kinetics (Depletion Regime)*

Secor and Beutler (1967) have considered the problem of mass transfer accompanied by reversible chemical reaction with generalized kinetics. The problem considered is as follows:

$$Z_A A + Z_B B \underset{k'_{m'n'}}{\overset{k_{mn}}{\rightleftharpoons}} Z_C C + Z_E E \quad (2.159)$$

The differential equations for diffusion plus chemical reaction of the various species are

$$Z_A D_A \frac{d^2[A]}{dx^2} = Z_A r_A \quad (2.160)$$

$$Z_A D_B \frac{d^2[B]}{dx^2} = Z_B r_A \quad (2.161)$$

$$Z_A D_C \frac{d^2[C]}{dx^2} = -Z_C r_A \quad (2.162)$$

$$Z_A D_E \frac{d^2[E]}{dx^2} = -Z_E r_A \quad (2.163)$$

where r_A is the local rate of disappearance of the species A and is given by

$$r_A = k_{mn}[A]^m[B]^n - k'_{m'n'}[C]^{m'}[E]^{n'} \quad (2.164)$$

The boundary conditions are, at $x = 0$,

$$[A] = [A^*], \quad [B] = [B_i] \quad (2.165)$$

$$\frac{d[B]}{dx} = \frac{d[C]}{dx} = \frac{d[E]}{dx} = 0 \quad (2.166)$$

and at $x = \delta$,

$$[A] = [A_o], \quad [B] = [B_o] \quad (2.167)$$

$$[C] = [C_o], \quad [E] = [E_o] \quad (2.168)$$

The rate of absorption of the gas A is given by the diffusional flux of A at the interface:

$$R_A = -D_A\left(\frac{d[A]}{dx}\right)_{x=0}$$

The problem can also be formulated on the basis of the penetration theory. Numerical solutions based on the penetration theory have been obtained by Secor and Beutler (1967). The solutions are presented in the form of graphs of ϕ against $k_{mn}[A^*]^{m-1}[B_o]^n t$ for various values of q and $k_{mn}/k'_{m'n'}$. A typical case is reported in Figure 2.9. The graphs are similar to those for the case of irreversible reactions (Brian, 1964). At low values of $k_{mn}[A^*]^{m-1}[B_o]^n t$ for a fixed value of the rate constant, the reaction mechanism is one of pseudo-mth-order reaction; that is, under these conditions the concentration of B at the interface is not significantly different from that in the bulk. As the value of $k_{mn}[A^*]^{m-1}[B_o]^n t$ is increased, there would be significant depletion of B at the interface. For large values of $k_{mn}[A^*]^{m-1}[B_o]^n t$ (when $k_{mn}[A^*]^{m-1}[B_o]^n t \gg q$) the reaction approaches the condition of an equilibrium reaction for this case. The value of the enhancement factor ϕ tends to approach an asymptotic value. The asymptotic value can be obtained independently by the method of Danckwerts (1968) or Olander (1962) for the case of instantaneous reversible reactions discussed next. It is also seen from the results of the numerical solution that the backward reaction tends to decrease the value of the overall mass transfer coefficient with reaction, k_{LR}.

2.10.2. Reversible Instantaneous Reactions

Olander (1960) has considered the following reaction schemes for the case of reversible instantaneous reactions:

$$A \rightleftharpoons C$$
$$A \rightleftharpoons 2C$$
$$A + B \rightleftharpoons C$$
$$A + B \rightleftharpoons C + D$$

Olander has derived equations for the rate of absorption of A for each of these cases separately. Danckwerts (1968) has considered a generalized case represented by

$$A \rightleftharpoons \sum Z_E E \tag{2.169}$$

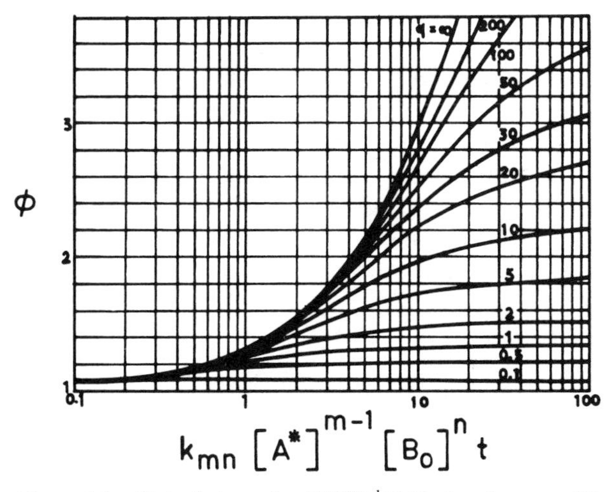

Figure 2.9. Plot of ϕ vs. $k_{mn}[A^*]^{m-1}[B_o]^n t$ for the reversible reaction $A + B \rightleftharpoons C + E$ for $r_B = 1, r_C = 1, r_E = 1, m = 1, n = 1, m' = 1, n' = 1, [A_o]_i = [C_o]_i = [E_o]_i = 0, k_{mn}/k'_{m'n'} = 0.2$ (from Secor and Beutler, 1967).

where E is a reactant or a product formed and Z_E its stoichiometric number (the stoichiometric number is negative for a reactant and positive for a product). The particular cases derived by Olander can be obtained as a special case from the theory proposed by Danckwerts. We shall now consider the application of the Danckwerts model to a reversible instantaneous reaction. According to this model the specific rate of absorption for the case of equal diffusivity of all species is shown to be equal to

$$R_A = k_L \Delta C \tag{2.170}$$

where ΔC is the amount of A which should be absorbed in a unit volume of liquid with given initial composition to bring it to a state where it is completely saturated, with respect to A, that is, $[A] = [A^*]$, and where the other species are in equilibrium with A. The term ΔC may also be looked upon as a driving force for the species A in terms of the total concentration of A (in terms of the concentrations of reacted plus unreacted A).

To illustrate the application of the foregoing theory, consider a reaction scheme represented as

$$A + B \rightleftharpoons C + D \tag{2.171}$$

The scheme would be applicable, for instance, if H_2S were absorbed in an amine solution under conditions such that the amount of H_2S absorbed is more than (say) 0.8 mol per mole of amine:

$$H_2S + RNH_2 \rightleftharpoons RNH_3^+ + HS^-$$

Let the initial concentrations of A, B be $[A_o]$ and $[B_o]$ and assume that the initial concentrations of C and D are equal. Since the solution is at equilibrium, we have

$$[C_o][D_o] = K[A_o][B_o] \tag{2.172}$$

or

$$[C_o] = \sqrt{K[A_o][B_o]} \tag{2.173}$$

since $[C_o] = [D_o]$.

The solution is now exposed to the gas mixture such that the interfacial concentration of the gas is $[A^*]$. When the solution attains equilibrium with the gas, let the concentration of B, C, and D be denoted by $[B^*]$, $[C^*]$, and $[D^*]$, respectively. By stoichiometry we have

$$[C^*] = [D^*]$$

and

$$[C^*] - [C_o] = [B_o] - [B^*] \qquad (2.174)$$

For the equilibrium relation to be valid we have

$$[C^*] = \sqrt{K[A^*][B^*]} \qquad (2.175)$$

Substituting the value of [B*] from Eqs. 2.174 in 2.175 and solving for [C*], we obtain

$$[C^*] = \frac{-K[A^*] + \sqrt{(K[A^*])^2 + 4K[A^*]([B_o] + [C_o])}}{2} \qquad (2.176)$$

The rate of absorption of A is given by

$$R_A = k_L \Delta C$$
$$= k_L([A^*] - [A_o] + [C^*] - [C_o]) \qquad (2.177)$$

Substituting for [C*] and $[C_o]$ from Eqs. 2.176 and 2.173, respectively, we obtain

$$R_A = k_L \Big\{ [A^*] - [A_o] - \tfrac{1}{2}K[A^*] + \tfrac{1}{2}\Big[(K[A^*])^2 + 4K[A^*]\Big([B_o] + \sqrt{K[A_o][B_o]}\Big)\Big]^{1/2} - \sqrt{K[A_o][B_o]} \Big\} \qquad (2.178)$$

This equation has also been derived independently by Olander (1960) by the conventional method of taking the stoichiometric balance of fluxes at various points.

From the foregoing it is clear that the value of the specific rate of absorption can be calculated for a variety of reversible reactions of industrial importance.

2.11. METHODS OF DISCERNING THE CONTROLLING MECHANISM FOR IRREVERSIBLE REACTIONS

In this section we shall outline the procedure that can be followed to discern the controlling mechanism under a specified set of conditions. In other words, we would like to know the regime to which the system belongs. The specific rate of mass transfer, R_A, is a function of hydrodynamic factors in the case of regimes 2 and 4. Thus, in any apparatus where the value of k_L influences the specific rate of mass transfer it would be indicative of regimes 2 and 4. The other differences are with respect to the functional dependence of R_A on the concentration of A and B. A systematic study should be made to find out the effect of the concentration of A and B on R_A.

2.11.1. Gas–Liquid Systems

Various model contactors have been used for measuring the rates of absorption and for discerning the controlling mechanism. They may be grouped under two categories. Both of them have known interfacial area for mass transfer, except the mechanically agitated contactor. In one type the hydrodynamics is well established and these include the wetted wall column, the laminar jet apparatus, the wetted sphere column, and the like. In the other type hydrodynamics is not well defined and these include the stirred cell, the stirred contactor, and the mechanically agitated contactor. The details of all these contactors have been given by Danckwerts (1970) except for the stirred contactor, which is a recent development. The stirred contactor is in effect a stirred vessel with an undisturbed (flat) gas–liquid interface and with provisions for independently stirring the gas and liquid phases (Figure 2.10). The major advantage of this contactor over other contactors is that there is an independent control over the gas-side mass-transfer coefficient, which can be varied over a wide range. The works of Levenspiel and Godfrey (1974), Danckwerts and Alper (1975), Sridharan and Sharma (1976), and Yadav and Sharma (1979) may be consulted for more details on the stirred contactor.

We shall consider the use of four types of contactors for discerning the mechanism of any specified system: jet apparatus; stirred cell; mechanically agitated contactor; and stirred contactor.

(i) *Jet Apparatus*

The jet apparatus can be employed to discern the mechanism for any regime from 2 to 4. We can conveniently vary the concentration of A as well as of B. The concentration of A should be varied by changing the absolute pressure in the jet apparatus. The pressure can easily be varied from about 0.2 atm to about atmospheric pressure. Thus, a fivefold variation in the concentration of A can be realized. It is

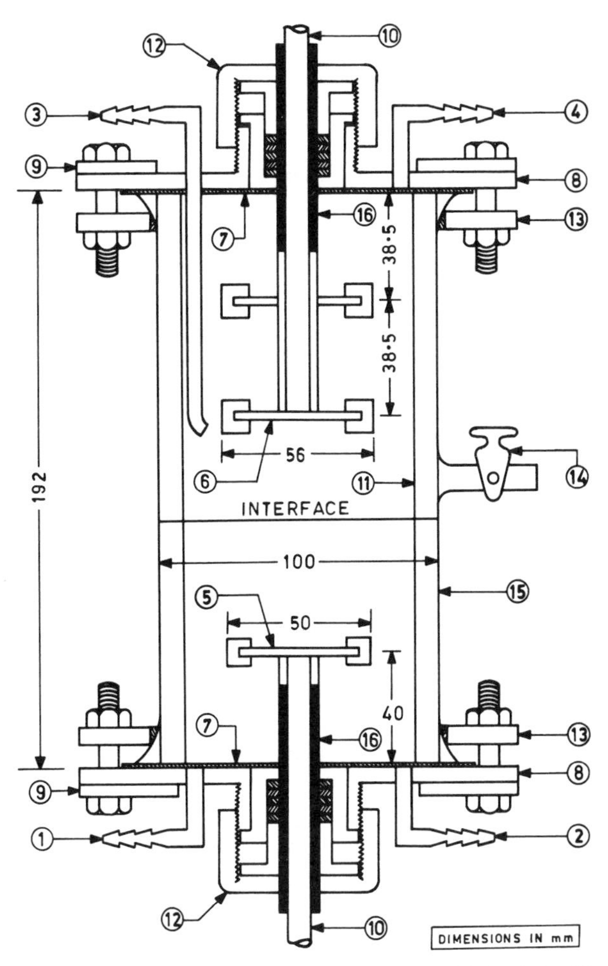

Figure 2.10. Model stirred contactor. (1) Liquid inlet (pp); (2) Liquid outlet (pp); (3) Gas inlet (pp); (4) Gas outlet (pp); (5) Liquid-side stirrer: 4-bladed-disk-turbine impeller (pp) mounted on s.s. shaft lined with Teflon; (6) Gas-side stirrer: 6-bladed-disk-turbine impellers (pp, 2Nos.) mounted on s.s. shaft lined with pp/Teflon. Blades of each impeller in different vertical planes are angled at 15°; (7) Teflon gasket; (8) Cover plate (pp); (9) Support plate (m.s.); (10) Shaft (s.s.); (11) Baffles (pp); (12) Gland and stuffing box: gland and bush (Teflon), packing (Teflon), stuffing box (pp); (13) Flange (m.s.); (14) Plug cock; (15) Main body (Borosil glass vessel); (16) Teflon sleeve on s.s. shaft. (m.s. = mild steel; pp = polypropylene; s.s. = stainless steel.)

not desirable to vary the partial pressure of A by using an inert gas, since doing so would introduce uncertainties about the gas-side resistance. An important advantage offered by the jet apparatus is that the contact time is uniquely determined by the jet length and diameter and the liquid flow rate, and is independent of the viscosity and the density of the liquid. The contact time can be varied over a wide range (from 0.003 to 0.07 sec).

Table 2.2 lists the salient differences that will be observed for the various regimes when experiments are carried out in the jet apparatus. It is thus possible to get a clear idea about the mechanism of absorption. The range of concentration of B should be such that the physicochemical properties of the system are not very much affected. This is particularly important for systems where the viscosity of the liquid changes significantly with an increase in the concentration of B, and for electrolyte solutions. In many cases where electrolytes are involved k_{mn} may be a function of not only the ionic strength but also the nature of the ions. The data should be very carefully analyzed. Consider a case where carbon dioxide is absorbed in aqueous solutions of diethanolamine (DEA). (The reaction is first order in CO_2 as well as DEA.) Here an increase in the concentration of DEA from 2 to 3.8×10^{-3} mol/cm^3 results in an approximate doubling of the value of the viscosity of the solution (Thomas and Furzer, 1962). For this change in viscosity the diffusion coefficient of CO_2 decreases by a factor of 2. Thus, although the specific rate of absorption should be proportional to the square root of the concentration of B, in practice R_A apparently turns out to be "independent" of the concentration of B. The example of the absorption of CO_2 in caustic soda is even more complex, since not only the viscosity of the solution but also the solubility of the CO_2 and k_{OH^-} are affected by the change in OH^- concentration. Danckwerts and Sharma (1966) have given a comprehensive analysis of the data on the absorption of CO_2 in caustic soda solutions. The relative variations in [A*], D_A, and k_{OH^-} are such that the specific rate of absorption of CO_2 in aqueous sodium hydroxide solutions having concentrations of 1×10^{-3} and 3×10^{-3} mol/cm^3 will be practically equal under physically similar conditions. Thus although the specific rate of absorption should have varied as the square root of the concentration of B, it remains practically constant for a threefold variation in the concentration of B.

For any specified values of the concentration of A and B the regime to which the system conforms depends on the value of the contact time and hence on the value of k_L (see the conditions given by expressions 2.30, 2.31, and 2.79). Further, in any given contactor the mechanism of absorption can change as the gas traverses the column, since although the value of k_L is essentially constant throughout the column, the values of the concentration of A and B change. At the top of a column, operated countercurrently, the ratio $[B_o]/Z[A^*]$ has a relatively high value, but at the bottom of the column this value will be low. Consider the absorption of pure CO_2 at atmospheric pressure in an aqueous

TABLE 2.2. Procedure for Discerning Mechanism: Jet Apparatus

Regime	Effect on R_A (in mol/cm² sec) of [A*]	[B$_o$]	Time of Contact
2 (slow reaction)	$\propto$ [A*]	None	$\propto t_E^{-1/2}$
3 (fast reaction)	$\propto [A^*]^{(m+1)/2}$	$\propto [B_o]^{n/2}$ [b]	None
4 (instantaneous reaction)	None[a]	$\propto$ [B$_o$]	$\propto t_E^{-1/2}$

[a]Provided that $[B_o] \gg Z[A^*]$.
[b]It is assumed that the rate constant, k_{mn}, is independent of [B$_o$].

monoethanolamine (MEA) solution in a variety of contactors (see Table 2.3). It is clear from Table 2.3 that the regime of absorption changes with a change in k_L. With respect to case 1 in Table 2.3, if the concentration of A decreases by a factor of (say) 30, then the regime will change from 4 to 3.

(ii) *Stirred Cell*

In stirred cells, too, the value of the concentration of A should be varied by changing the total pressure of the system. In some cases, however, it may be possible to use an inert gas to change the partial pressure of A and hence the concentration of A. For this purpose an additional stirrer may be employed in the gas phase. It is essential for this case that the solubility be relatively small (say $\ll 10 \times 10^{-6}$ mol/cm³). In particular, the solubility of O_2 is relatively small in a variety of solvents. Ladhabhoy and Sharma (1969, 1970) were able to study the effect of the partial pressure of oxygen successfully by using nitrogen as a diluent in their study of the mechanism of absorption of oxygen in *n*-butyraldehyde dissolved in *n*-butyric acid, and in 2-ethylhexaldehyde dissolved in 2-ethylhexanoic acid in a stirred cell. Gehlawat and Sharma (1968) and Sankholkar and Sharma (1973) were also able to study the effect of the concentration of isobutylene, 2-butene, and 2-methyl-2-butene by using N_2 as a diluent in their study of the kinetics of the absorption of olefins in aqueous solutions of sulfuric acid. If it is suspected that gas-side resistance will be important when the solute gas is mixed with an inert gas, we should consider the use of the stirred contactor [see Section (iv)].

The range of concentration of B should be such that the viscosity of the liquid does not change significantly. The speed of agitation should be varied over a wide range under such conditions that no vortex is formed (normal speed range, 20–150 rev/min). The volume of the liquid per unit transfer area can also be conveniently varied here, at least by a factor of 2 without significantly affecting the value of k_L. Table 2.4 lists the salient differences that will be observed for the various regimes. If electrolyte solutions are involved in the system (or even otherwise), a relatively high concentration of an inert

TABLE 2.3. Effect of k_L on the Regime of Absorption[a]

Case	Contactor	Assumed Value of k_L ($\times 10^3$ cm/sec)	$\frac{\sqrt{D_A k_2 [B_o]}}{k_L}$	$\frac{[B_o]}{Z[A^*]}\sqrt{\frac{D_B}{D_A}}$	Regime
1	Spray column	2.5	193	37.8	4
2	Packed column	10	48.2	37.8	Between 3 and 4
3	Plate column	50	9.61	37.8	3

[a]Conditions for the absorption of CO_2 in an aqueous solution of monoethanolamine (MEA): Temperature = 35°C; $k_2 = 1.3 \times 10^7$ cm³/mol sec; [MEA] = [B$_o$] = 1×10^{-3} mol/cm³; [A*] = 1×10^{-5} mol/cm³. The reaction between CO_2 and MEA is first order in A and B, and Z = 2.

TABLE 2.4. Procedure for Discerning Mechanism: Stirred Cell

	Effect on the specific rate of absorption (mol/cm² sec) of			
Regime	[A*]	[B$_o$]	Speed of Stirring (rev/min, for speeds > 30–40 rev/min)	Volume of Liquid (B phase) for Specified Transfer Area
1	$\propto [A^*]^m$	$\propto [B_o]^n$	None	$\propto$ volume
2	$\propto [A^*]$	None	Increases with increase in the speed of stirring	None
3	$\propto [A^*]^{(m+1)/2}$	$\propto [B_o]^{n/2}$	None	None
4	None[a]	$\propto [B_o]$	Increases with increase in the speed of stirring in the same manner as in regime 2	None

[a] Provided that $[B_o] \gg Z[A^*]$.

substance can be taken, so that the physicochemical properties of the system do not change significantly when the concentration of B is varied.

(iii) *Mechanically Agitated Contactor*

It would be desirable to use a small contactor with a capacity in the range of 2–6 liters (e.g., standard Corning resin kettles can be used). The contactor should be fully baffled and the height of the liquid should be slightly less than the diameter of the contactor. The type of stirrer should be a disk turbine having four (or six) straight blades, and its diameter should be approximately 40% of the diameter of the contactor. The speed should be varied in the range of about 400–2800 rev/min. The dependence of the rate of reaction per unit volume of the liquid in the contactor on the concentration of A and B for the various regimes will be the same as listed in Tables 2.2 and 2.4. It should be noted that both phases in the gas–liquid systems are essentially backmixed above the critical speed of stirring. In the case of regime 1, above a certain speed the agitation will have no influence on the rate of absorption per unit volume of the B phase. In all other regimes (i.e., 2, 3, and 4) the rate of absorption per unit volume of the B phase will vary approximately linearly with the speed of stirring. Above the critical agitation speed the gas rate has no influence on the performance of the contactor, and if there is no gas-side resistance, the value of the concentration of A can be varied by simply varying the gas rate of A diluted with an inert gas. For 4- to 6-liter-capacity reactors and for common systems the critical speed of stirring is expected to be in the range of 700–900 rev/min. This type of contactor is particularly useful for studies if the same design is to be used for the large-scale operation. In such cases useful scale-up data can also be obtained concurrently (see Chapter 10). It has been assumed that the change in concentration of B does not change the values of the effective interfacial area and liquid-side mass transfer coefficient. In case the variation in the concentration of B is suspected to affect values of a and $k_L a$, no useful information can be obtained with this contactor as regards the order of the reaction with respect to species B except in the case of regime 1. However, it may be possible to use a higher concentration of an inert substance in the B phase so that a substantial variation in the concentration of B does not cause any significant change in the properties of the B phase.

(iv) *Stirred Contactor*

In many cases it would be desirable to use the stirred contactor as a model apparatus to discern the controlling mechanism. The main advantage of this type of apparatus is that at lower speeds of agitation it can be used as a stirred cell and at higher speeds of agitation it can be used as a mechanically agitated contactor. Further, when it is used as a stirred cell the gas-side mass transfer coefficient can be independently varied over a wide range, and hence it would be very much easier to eliminate the gas-side resistance when we are concerned with finding the order of the reaction with respect to the solute gas by varying its partial pressure by dilution with an inert gas. In many ways this procedure is simpler than that involving the variation of absolute pressure in the laminar jet apparatus.

On the whole, the stirred contactor is probably the most versatile model contactor to employ in the laboratory. The main drawback of this contactor is that k_L values are low and these cannot match the values of k_L encountered in those contactors where a gas is dispersed in a pool of liquid.

2.11.2. Liquid–Liquid Systems

In liquid–liquid systems it would be desirable to use a stirred cell and a small mechanically agitated contactor of the type described in Section 2.11.1(iii). The resistance to mass transfer is located entirely in the B phase. The criteria listed in Table 2.4 for gas–liquid systems in the stirred cell and in Section 2.11.1(iii) for the mechanically agitated contactor will also hold for liquid–liquid systems. In the case of the mechanically agitated contactor at a specified continuous-phase flow rate, the dispersed-phase flow rate and hence the dispersed-phase fraction will also influence the rate of the reaction of A. It would be desirable to keep the flow rates of the two phases constant and then vary the speed of agitation. The actual values of the dispersed-phase holdup should be determined under experimental conditions. In general, at a specified agitation speed the value of the effective interfacial area per unit contactor volume is approximately proportional to the dispersed-phase fraction provided that the latter is less than 0.3.

The effect of k_L on the regime of mass transfer will follow the same pattern as discussed in Section 2.11.1(i). In the case of most liquid–liquid contactors, however, the value of a is very much greater than that in the case of the corresponding type of gas–liquid contactor. In particular, in the case of mechanically agitated contactors the values of a in the liquid–liquid and gas–liquid contactors may lie in the range of 50–500 and 2–10 cm^2/cm^3, respectively. Consider an example of the extraction of n-butyl acetate, saturated with water, into an aqueous solution of sodium hydroxide ($[B_o] = 3 \times 10^{-4}$ mol/cm^3) in a spray column and a mechanically agitated contactor. The typical k_L values in the two contactors may be comparable, but the value of a can easily vary by a factor of 100: spray column, $k_L a = 3 \times 10^{-3}$ sec^{-1}; mechanically agitated contactor, $k_L a = 3 \times 10^{-1}$ sec^{-1}.

The alkaline hydrolysis of butyl acetate follows second-order kinetics; the value of the rate constant is about 100 cm^3/mol sec at 35°C. It is clear from conditions given by expressions 2.9 and 2.3 that in the spray column the system conforms to regime 2 but that in the mechanically agitated contactor the system conforms to regime 1 [spray column, $k_L a = 3 \times 10^{-3} \ll lk_2[B_o] = 2.85 \times 10^{-2}$ ($l = 0.95$); mechanically agitated contactor, $k_L a = 3 \times 10^{-1} \gg lk_2[B_o] = 2.7 \times 10^{-2}$ ($l = 0.9$)].

An additional check for the controlling mechanism can be made by interchanging the two phases. Thus, consider an aromatic–aqueous-phase system. Here a changeover from the aromatic phase as the dispersed phase to the aqueous solutions as the dispersed phase under otherwise uniform conditions will make a large difference in the value of the effective interfacial area and overall mass transfer coefficient. Thus if a system conforms to regime 1, this changeover would not make any difference to the rate of reaction per unit volume of the aqueous phase. Yet another check can be provided by using an emulsifying agent; if we find that there is no effect on the rate of reaction per unit volume of the aqueous phase, it is an indication that diffusional resistance is absent.

Effect of Temperature

In all the cases cited above for gas–liquid and liquid–liquid systems an additional variable can also be tried. The effect of temperature on the rate of absorption can yield useful information. It is necessary to know the solubility and the diffusivity of A in the desired temperature range. The species B is considered to be nonvolatile. In the case of regime 1 the value of ΔE would generally lie in the range of 8–15 kcal/mol. By contrast, in the case of regimes 2 and 4 the value of ΔE would be very small ($\simeq$ 3 kcal/mol), and in the case of regime 3 it would be in the range of 3–6 kcal/mol.

EXAMPLES

1. The absorption of O_2 in aqueous solutions of sodium hydrosulfite was studied in a laboratory stirred cell and a laminar jet apparatus at 30°C.

Composition of the absorbent:

$$[\text{NaOH}] = 2 \times 10^{-4} \text{ mol/cm}^3$$

$$[\text{Na}_2\text{S}_2\text{O}_4] = 8\text{–}16 \times 10^{-5} \text{ mol/cm}^3$$

Solubility of O_2 in water at 30°C

$$= 1.17 \times 10^{-6} \text{ mol/cm}^3$$

Solubility of O_2 in aqueous solutions at 30°C

$$= 1 \times 10^{-6} \text{ mol/cm}^3$$

Stirred Cell

(a) k_L in the absence of chemical reaction:

stirring speed = 40 rev/min, 2×10^{-3} cm/sec

stirring speed = 100 rev/min, 4×10^{-3} cm/sec

(b) The specific rate of absorption, R_A, increased by a factor of 2 when pure O_2 at 1 atm was absorbed in the stirred cell when the speed of agitation was increased from 40 to 100 rev/min. Further, R_A was practically the same for the foregoing speeds of stirring at partial pressures of oxygen, p_{O_2}, of 0.7 and 1 atm. Under these conditions R_A was directly proportional to the concentration of $Na_2S_2O_4$ in the range of concentration of $8\text{–}16 \times 10^{-5}$ mol/cm³.

(c) For p_{O_2} in the range of 0.05–0.15 atm, R_A was independent of the speed of stirring and proportional to the square root of p_{O_2} and directly proportional to the concentration of $Na_2S_2O_4$ in the range of $8\text{–}16 \times 10^{-5}$ mol/cm³.

What is the controlling mechanism in these cases?

Laminar Jet. The specific rate of absorption of pure O_2 at 1 atm was independent of the contact time in the range of 0.007–0.05 sec. Further, R_A varied as the square root of p_{O_2} in the range of 0.2–1 atm. (Pure O_2 was used and the absolute pressure of the system was varied.) Also, R_A varied directly with the concentration of sodium hydrosulfite in the range of $8\text{–}16 \times 10^{-5}$ mol/cm³. What is the controlling mechanism?

Answer

Stirred Cell. *Absorption at p_{O_2} of 1 atm.* Since the specific rate of absorption was found to be a function of the speed of stirring and directly proportional to k_L, the system may conform to either regime 2 or regime 4 (see Table 2.4). Further, since the specific rate of absorption varied directly with the dithionite concentration and was independent of the partial pressure of oxygen in the range of 0.7–1 atm, it is clear that the system conforms to regime 4, and under these conditions R_A is given by Eq. 2.97:

$$R_A = k_L \frac{[B_o]}{Z} \sqrt{\frac{D_B}{D_A}}$$

Absorption at p_{O_2} of 0.05–0.15 atm. At low p_{O_2} it is probable that the condition given by expression 2.31 is satisfied and that the system conforms to regime 3. This is evident from the fact that R_A was found to be independent of the speed of agitation. R_A was found to vary as the square root of p_{O_2} and to be directly proportional to $[B_o]$. From Table 2.4 it is clear that the values of m and n are 0 and 2, respectively, and R_A is given by the following equation:

$$R_A = [A^*]^{1/2}\left(2D_A k_2 [B_o]^2\right)^{1/2}$$

Laminar Jet. In the case of the laminar jet the contact time is relatively low, and hence the condition given by expression 2.31 for the pseudo-mth-order reaction is likely to be satisfied. Consequently, R_A will be independent of the contact time. Thus the system conforms to regime 3. Equation 2.44 and Table 2.2 suggest that the order with respect to O_2 is zero and that with respect to $Na_2S_2O_4$ it is two (i.e., $m = 0$ and $n = 2$).

2. The following data were obtained for the absorption of isobutylene in aqueous solutions of H_2SO_4 in the range of concentrations of 60–70% w/w in a stirred cell and in a laminar jet apparatus.

(a) The specific rate of absorption was found to be independent of the speed of stirring in the stirred cell, and of the jet length and diameter and liquid flow rate in the laminar jet, over a wide range. The two values of specific rates of absorption obtained from the stirred cell and the laminar jet apparatus were practically the same.

(b) In the stirred cell the specific rate of absorption was found to vary directly with the partial pressure of isobutylene. What is the controlling mechanism?

Since the specific rate of absorption is independent of k_L and the contact time, it is clear that the system conforms to either regime 3 or regime 1 (Table 2.4). Since the specific rates of absorption were practically the same in the stirred cell and the laminar jet apparatus, the system definitely conforms to regime 3. The reaction is first order with respect to $i\text{-}C_4H_8$ and hence the following equation should hold:

$$R = [A^*]\sqrt{D_A k_1}$$

3. Some experiments were made in a laboratory 2-liter-capacity glass agitated contactor (fully baffled and provided with a six-bladed turbine impeller) for the alkylation of benzene with C-8 α-olefin in the presence of 98% sulfuric acid. It was found that the rate of alkylation for a specified volume of H_2SO_4 was independent of the speed of stirring in the range of 800–1500 rev/min and also independent of the volume of the organic phase taken of specified composition (the organic phase was dispersed in the acid phase). For a fixed value of the dispersed-phase fraction the rate was found to be directly proportional to the mole fraction of the olefin. What is the controlling mechanism?

In a mechanically agitated contactor the values of $k_L a$ and a increase with an increase in the agitation speed, and hence the system cannot belong to regime 2, 3, or 4. Further, it is known that the alkylation reaction occurs in the acid phase, and the fact that for a fixed volume of the acid phase the rate of alkylation was independent of the volume of the organic phase clearly indicates that diffusional factors were unimportant and that the system belongs to the kinetically controlled regime 1. (It may be noted that the area of contact increases with an increase in the dispersed-phase fraction.)

Since the rate of alkylation was found to be directly proportional to the mole fraction of the olefin, the reaction is first order with respect to the olefin.

4. Some experiments were made for the nitration of benzene with mixed acids ($HNO_3 + H_2SO_4$) in a mechanically agitated contactor (volume of the reactor = 4 liter; fully baffled six-bladed straight turbine impeller). It was observed that the rate of nitration for a specified volume of benzene and acid phases was nearly directly proportional to the speed of agitation in the range of 1000–2000 rev/min. Further, the rate of nitration for a specified volume of the acid phase was found to vary directly as the dispersed-phase fraction in the range of 0.1–0.3. Experiments were also made in the temperature range of 15–40°C, and it was observed that the rate of nitration varied by only about 30%. In the foregoing temperature range the solubility of benzene in the acid phase increases slightly (roughly by about 10%). Under otherwise uniform conditions, the rate of nitration was also found to be independent of active nitrating species over a certain range. What is the controlling mechanism?

Since the rate of nitration varies directly with the speed of stirring and the dispersed-phase fraction, the system can be in either regime 2, 3, or 4 (since a and $k_L a$ vary roughly linearly with the stirring speed and the dispersed-phase fraction). Since the rate is insignificantly affected by temperature, even though the solubility of benzene in the acid phase increases by 10%, the activation energy has a very low value. (It is assumed that over the temperature range studied the value of $k_L a$ and that of a are insignificantly affected.) Further, the rate of nitration is independent of the concentration of the nitrating species and hence regimes 3 and 4 can be ruled out. The system therefore conforms to regime 2.

5. Some experiments were carried out in a wetted-wall column (2 cm in diameter, 5 cm long) to discern the mechanism of absorption of a gas A in aqueous solutions containing reactive species B (chemical reaction: A + B → products). The following data were obtained:

1. The rate of absorption of A was independent of the liquid flow rate in the range of 1–4 cm^3/sec.
2. The rate of absorption of A was independent of the concentration of B in the range from 2×10^{-5} to 1×10^{-4} mol/cm^3.

What is the mechanism of absorption of A in this case? It may be noted that an independent series of experiments indicated that the reaction was first order in A.

Since the rate of absorption is independent of the liquid flow rate (i.e., the contact time and the holdup of the B phase), the system must conform to regime 3. Since the rate of absorption is independent of the concentration of B, the reaction is zero order with respect to B, and the following rate equation should hold, since the reaction is first order in A:

$$R = [A^*]\sqrt{D_A k_1}$$

REFERENCES

Astarita, G. (1967), *Mass Transfer with Chemical Reaction*, Elsevier, Amsterdam.

Brian, P. L. T. (1964), *AIChE J.*, **10**, 5.

Brian, P. L. T., Hurley, J. F., and Hasseltine, E. H. (1961), *AIChE J.*, **7**, 226.

Danckwerts, P. V. (1950), *Trans. Faraday Soc.*, **46**, 300.

Danckwerts, P. V. (1951), *Trans. Faraday Soc.*, **47**, 1014.

Danckwerts, P. V. (1968), *Chem. Eng. Sci.*, **23**, 1045.

Danckwerts, P. V. (1970), *Gas–Liquid Reactions*, McGraw-Hill, New York.

Danckwerts, P. V., and Sharma, M. M. (1966), *Chem. Eng., Inst. Chem. Eng.*, No. 202, CE244.

Danckwerts, P. V., and Alper, E. (1975), *Trans. Inst. Chem. Eng.*, **53**, 34.

Gehlawat, J. K., and Sharma, M. M. (1968), *Chem. Eng. Sci.*, **23**, 1173.

Hikita, H., and Asai, S. (1964), *J. Chem. Eng. Japan*, **2**, 77.

Huang, C. J., and Kuo, C. H. (1965), *AIChE J.*, **11**, 901.

Karlsson, H. T., and Bjerle, I. (1980a), *Trans. Inst. Chem. Eng.*, **58**, 138.

Karlsson, H. T., and Bjerle, I. (1980b), *Chem. Eng. Sci.*, **35**, 1005.

Ladhabhoy, M. E., and Sharma, M. M. (1969), *J. Appl. Chem.*, **19**, 267.

Ladhabhoy, M. E., and Sharma, M. M. (1970), *J. Appl. Chem.*, **20**, 274.

Levenspiel, O., and Godfrey, J. H. (1974), *Chem. Eng. Sci.*, **29**, 1723.

Olander, D. R. (1960), *AIChE J.*, **6**, 233.

Olander, D. R. (1962), *AIChE J.*, **8**, 646.

Onda, K., Sada, E., Kobayashi, T., and Fujine, M. (1970), *Chem. Eng. Sci.*, **25**, 753.

Pangarkar, V. G. (1974), *Chem. Eng. Sci.*, **29**, 877.

Pearson, J. R. A. (1963), *Appl. Sci. Res.*, **A11**, 321.

Sankholkar, D. S., and Sharma, M. M. (1973), *Chem. Eng. Sci.*, **28**, 49.

Secor, R. M., and Beutler, J. A. (1967), *AIChE J.*, **13**, 365.

Sridharan, K., and Sharma, M. M. (1976), *Chem. Eng. Sci.*, **31**, 767.

Thomas, W. J., and Furzer, I. A. (1962), *Chem. Eng. Sci.*, **17**, 115.

van Krevelen, D. W., and Hoftyzer, P. J. (1948), *Chem. Eng. Prog.*, **44**, 529.

Yadav, G. D., and Sharma, M. M. (1979), *Chem. Eng. Sci.*, **34**, 1423.

CHAPTER THREE

Discussion and Examples of Systems Falling in Different Regimes

In this chapter we shall consider various aspects of the gas–liquid and liquid–liquid reactions that fall in the different regimes. A variety of examples will be considered. Further, we shall examine some aspects of the effect of temperature and interfacial turbulence on the specific rate of mass transfer. In addition, we shall consider elementary aspects of the stability of reactors.

3.1 REGIME 1: VERY SLOW REACTIONS

In classical studies in kinetics where, for instance, A is in the gas phase, it must be definitely ensured that the condition given by expression 2.3 is satisfied. In a sparged and agitated gas–liquid contactor, the value of the overall mass transfer coefficient can be increased by increasing the gas rate in the former case and the speed of agitation in the latter. The speed variation should cover a wide range. If the process conforms to this regime, then the speed of agitation will be unimportant. In a typical case, the value of R'_A might follow the pattern shown in Figure 3.1. In the case of liquid–liquid reactions an additional check can be made by interchanging the continuous and the dispersed phases. Thus, for instance, in the case of aromatic hydrocarbon–aqueous systems a change-over from the aqueous solution as the continuous phase to the aromatic substance as the continuous phase will make a substantial difference in the effective interfacial area. If interchanging the continuous phase and the dispersed phase has no effect on the rate of reaction per unit volume of the aqueous phase, we can conclude that diffusional factors are unimportant. It is relatively easy to vary the interfacial area, at any specified speed of agitation, by varying the holdup of the dispersed phase, since up to a dispersed-phase fraction of 0.3 the value of a varies approximately linearly with the dispersed-phase fraction. This strategy can provide an additional check. (See Section 3.1.13.)

It is possible that when studied on a laboratory scale a given reaction may be entirely kinetically controlled but that on the plant scale it could become wholly or partially mass transfer controlled (i.e., at any moment the phase where reaction occurs may show a concentration of A that is less than the saturation concentration and that may even be negligible). This could happen when the $k_L a$ value in an industrial contactor is much less than that in the laboratory apparatus.

The scale-up of units, which may be batch, semi-batch, or continuous, where this mechanism prevails is relatively simple, and data obtained from small-scale experiments, along with the expected residence time distribution of the two phases in the type of equipment envisaged, can be conveniently utilized for the design of larger units.

Since diffusion factors are unimportant, it will be futile to increase the speed of agitation if a mechanically agitated contactor is used. However, high agitation speeds may be required to ensure an adequate supply of or removal of heat.

A large number of industrially important reactions fall in this category. Some typical examples are given next.

(A) Gas–Liquid Systems

3.1.1. Air Oxidation of a Variety of Aliphatic and Alkyl Aromatic Compounds

Nardhani and Chandalia (1969) have studied the liquid-phase air oxidation of ethyl benzene to

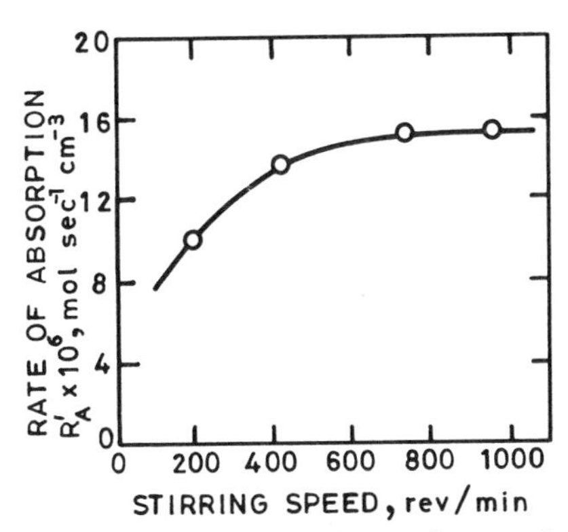

Figure 3.1. Effect of speed of agitation on the rate of absorption of isobutylene in acetic acid in a mechanically agitated contactor.

acetophenone:

$$O_2(g) + C_6H_5CH_2CH_3 \longrightarrow C_6H_5COCH_3 + H_2O$$

It was found that diffusional factors were unimportant and that the rate of oxidation was governed by the slow chemical reaction between O_2 and ethyl benzene.

Chandalia (1970, 1977) has reviewed the literature pertaining to the liquid-phase air oxidation of higher paraffins to fatty acids. It appears that at temperatures below 130°C the system conforms to this regime. In industrial practice this oxidation reaction is usually carried out in the temperature range of 115–125°C.

3.1.2. Air Oxidation of *p*-Nitrotoluene Sulfonic Acid

Carleton et al. (1969) have studied the air oxidation of *p*-nitrotoluene sulfonic acid (PNTSA) to dinitrodibenzyldisulfonic acid (DNDB) in a mechanically agitated batch reactor and a baffled bubble column. This reaction is an important step in the manufacture of diaminostilbenedisulfonic acid (DASDSA), which is an intermediate in the manufacture of optical brightening agents.

$$O_2(g) + \underset{\text{PNTSA}}{CH_3C_6H_3(SO_3H)NO_2} \longrightarrow \underset{\text{DNDB}}{(HO_3S)(NO_2)C_6H_3CH_2{-}CH_2C_6H_3(NO_2)(SO_3H)}$$

$$\longrightarrow (HO_3S)(NO_2)C_6H_3CH{=}CHC_6H_3(NO_2)(SO_3H)$$

$$\downarrow$$

$$\underset{\text{DASDSA}}{(HO_3S)(NH_2)C_6H_3CH{=}CHC_6H_3(NH_2)(SO_3H)}$$

The experimental work of Carleton et al. indicates that in mechanically agitated contactors and bubble columns the diffusional factors are unimportant and the system conforms to regime 1. The oxidation reaction is zero order in oxygen, and hence there is no advantage in using pure oxygen or a large excess of O_2.

3.1.3. Substitution Chlorination of a Variety of Organic Compounds

The chlorination of chlorobenzene to dichlorobenzene and the like has been studied by Bishnoi et al. (1961). These authors found that diffusional factors were unimportant in bubble columns.

3.1.4. Reaction between Isobutylene and Acetic Acid

Gehlawat and Sharma (1970) have studied the reaction between isobutylene and acetic acid in a small 1000-cm^3-capacity mechanically agitated fully baffled reactor.

It was found that above a certain point the agitation speed had no effect on the rate of reaction (Figure 3.1). Thus the rate is controlled by the reaction between dissolved isobutylene and acetic acid in the bulk. At 30°C the value of the second-order rate constant was found to be 1.2 cm^3/mol sec with a catalyst concentration of 10% w/w sulfuric acid.

It can be seen that the necessary condition given by expression 2.3 is satisfied. The reaction is first order in isobutylene and first order in acetic acid ($m = 1$, $n = 1$). Consider the following case: $[B_o] = [AcOH] = 15 \times 10^{-3}$ mol/cm^3, $l = 0.75$. The value of the right-hand side of expression 2.3 works out to be 1.35×10^{-2} sec^{-1}. The value of $k_L a$ would be expected to be in the range of 0.15–0.4 sec^{-1} and hence the necessary condition is satisfied.

3.1.5. Wacker Processes

In these processes, lower olefins can be converted to the corresponding carbonyl compounds by using a $PdCl_2/CuCl_2$ type of catalyst in an aqueous solution. In a typical case, ethylene can be converted to acetaldehyde. The overall reaction can be represented by the following equation:

$$C_2H_4(g) + \tfrac{1}{2}O_2(g) \xrightarrow[\substack{\text{in water} \\ 80\text{–}120°C}]{PdCl_2/CuCl_2} CH_3CHO$$

In related processes ethylene can be converted to vinyl acetate by employing an acetic acid medium; to vinyl alkyl ether (or the corresponding acetal) by using the corresponding alkanol as the medium. All these processes have gained considerable importance in the course of the last decade or so.

Chandalia (1966, 1967, 1968a, b) has shown that in all these processes the system conforms to regime 1. Komiyama and Inoue (1975) have also studied the kinetics of the conversion of ethylene to acetaldehyde in a bubble column reactor where the diffusional factors were eliminated. The reaction was found to be first order in ethylene and the value of the first-order rate constant was found to vary from 0.01 to 0.09 sec^{-1} at 70°C when the Pd concentration was varied from 0.564 to 5.636×10^{-6} mol/cm^3.

3.1.6. Hydrochlorination of Olefins

The hydrochlorination of alpha olefins (C_{12}–C_{18}) has gained importance for the manufacture of biodegradable detergents. Alpha olefins are manufactured by the cracking of wax and oligomerization of ethylene. The reaction between HCl and $RCH{=}CH_2$ proceeds according to the following equation and is catalyzed by, among other catalysts, $FeCl_3$.

$$HCl(g) + RCH{=}CH_2(l) \rightarrow \underset{\displaystyle Cl}{\underset{|}{RCH}}{-}CH_3(l)$$

Scher et al. (1963) studied the reaction between HCl and 1-hexadecene in a laboratory stirred reactor in the temperature range of 25°–55°C using $FeCl_3$ as a catalyst. They showed that diffusional factors are unimportant. The reaction was found to be first order in the olefin and half order in HCl. At 25°C the value of the rate constant was found to be 0.017 $(liter/mol)^{1/2}$ min^{-1}. The saturation concentration of HCl at 25°C in the olefin was approximately 1.2×10^{-4} mol/cm^3 atm. Thus, the rate of homogeneous reaction per unit volume of the dispersion for pure olefin (approximate concentration = 3.5×10^{-3} mol/cm^3) when l is assumed to be about 0.8 works out to be equal to 1.65×10^{-2} mol/liter min or 2.75×10^{-7} mol/cm^3 sec. In order that diffusional factors be negligible, the value of $k_L a$ should be very much greater than the forgoing value of the rate of reaction divided by [A*], which works out to be equal to 2.32×10^{-3} sec^{-1}. The typical values of $k_L a$ in the type of contactor employed by the authors would be expected to be much greater than 3×10^{-2} sec^{-1}.

Bhargava and Sharma (1978) have studied the kinetics of the reaction between HCl and myrcene (in the presence of CuCl as a catalyst) and camphene dissolved in chlorobenzene. The reaction was found to be first order in HCl gas as well as in the olefin. The value of the second-order rate constant for camphene at 27.5°C was found to be 1095 cm^3/mol sec. In the case of HCl–α-pinene and HCl–Δ^3-carene systems the reactions were found to be zero order in HCl and second order in α-pinene and Δ^3-carene and the values of the second-order rate constant at 27.5°C were found to be 16 and 67 cm^3/mol sec, respectively.

The reaction between HCl and olefins appears to show different characteristics with different olefins. In addition to the information just given, Pocker et al. (1969) have reported that the reaction between HCl and olefins, such as 2-methyl-butene-1, 2-methyl-butene-2, and isoprene, is second order in HCl and first order in the olefin. For 2-methyl-butene-1 the value of the overall third-order rate constant at 25°C in a nitromethane medium was found to be 1.9×10^6 $(cm^3/mol)^2$ sec^{-1}. Bhargava and Sharma (1978) have also found the reaction to be second order in HCl and first order in 2-methyl-2-butene, and at 25°C the value of the overall third-order rate constant in chlorobenzene as a solvent was found to be 8.9×10^6 $(cm^3/mol)^2$ sec^{-1}.

Depending on the values of $k_L a$ and $\sqrt{M}$, the foregoing systems may belong to regime 2 or to the regime between 2 and 3.

3.1.7. Absorption of Phosphine in an Aqueous Solution of Formaldehyde and Hydrochloric Acid

Tetrakis(hydroxymethyl)phosphonium chloride (THPC) is an industrially important intermediate for the manufacture of flame-resistant polymers. THPC is prepared by the absorption of phosphine in an aqueous solution of formaldehyde and hydrochloric acid:

$$PH_3 + HCl + 4HCHO \rightarrow (CH_2OH)_4PCl$$

Phosphine is sparingly soluble in water and at a temperature of about 20°C the solubility is around 1×10^{-5} mol/cm³ atm.

Chaudhari and Doraiswamy (1974) have studied this reaction in a laboratory-scale agitated contactor (with an approximate capacity of 1000 cm³) in the temperature range of 4–40°C. The controlling mechanism was found by studying the effect of the agitation speed on the rate of absorption of phosphine. It was observed that the speed of agitation had some effect on the rate of absorption in the range of 700 to 1300 rev/min. However, the agitation speed had no effect on the rate of absorption in the range of 1300–2100 rev/min. It was concluded that at higher speeds of agitation the reaction falls in this regime.

The reaction was found to be first order with respect to phosphine and formaldehyde and approximately half order with respect to hydrochloric acid. The value of the rate constant at 27°C was found to be 1.84×10^3 $(cm^3/mol)^{1.5}$ sec^{-1} and the value of the activation energy was found to be about 14.7 kcal/mol. Consider the following case.

Temperature = 27°C

$$k_{mn} = 1.84 \times 10^3 \,(cm^3/mol)^{1.5}\, sec^{-1}$$

$$[HCHO] = 1 \times 10^{-3}\, mol/cm^3$$

$$[HCl] = 5 \times 10^{-4}\, mol/cm^3$$

$$l = 0.8$$

The value of $lk_{mn}[HCHO][HCl]^{0.5}$ is 3.3×10^{-2} sec^{-1}. At higher agitation speeds the $k_L a$ value would be expected to be about 0.2 sec^{-1}. Thus, the necessary condition given by expression 2.3 is satisfied.

3.1.8. Acetic Acid from the Carbonylation of Methanol

In recent years a modified process for the carbonylation of methanol in the presence of a rhodium complex, promoted with iodine catalyst, has been suggested that works under relatively mild conditions (Roth et al., 1971; Hjortkjaer and Jensen, 1976)

$$CO + CH_3OH \rightarrow CH_3COOH$$

Hjortkjaer and Jensen have studied the kinetics of this reaction. The range of variables was as follows: CO pressure = 1—50 atm; temperature = 150—225°C; [Rh] = 5–27 $\times 10^{-6}$ mol/cm³; and [I] = 0.25–3 $\times 10^{-3}$ mol/cm³. Experiments were carried out in a magnetically stirred batch reactor. The rate was found to be independent of the speed of stirring above a certain level (750 rev/min in their apparatus). This indicates that diffusional factors were unimportant above a speed of stirring of 750 rev/min.

The rate of reaction was found to be independent of CO pressure from 2 to 24 atm. The rate of reaction was also found to be independent of the methanol concentration. Thus the reaction was zero order with respect to CO as well as CH_3OH. The reaction was found to be first order with respect to the concentration of Rh and I. The activation energy was found to be 14.7 kcal/mol, which further confirms that diffusional factors were unimportant. The controlling step was found to be the oxidative addition of CH_3I to the rhodium ligand (RhL_m):

$$RhL_m + CH_3I \rightarrow CH_3Rh(I)L_m$$

It can be shown that the rate of transport of CO is far greater than the highest reaction rate observed in this work.

This example is unique in the category of a very slow reaction where the reaction is zero order in both species A and B.

3.1.9. Oxidation of Trialkyl Phosphine

Air oxidation of tributylphosphine (TBP) in the presence of azobisisobutyronitrile (AIBN) as an initiator gives predominantly tributylphosphine oxide and dibutylphosphonate. (This reaction may have some industrial relevance if high yields of the oxide can be realized.) Floyd and Boozer (1963) have studied the kinetics of this oxidation reaction with *o*-dichlorobenzene as a solvent in the temperature range of 38–60°C by following the oxygen consumption with time. They have also studied the kinetics of the oxidation of tributylphosphite. Since the oxidation of TBP involves free radicals, AIBN was used as a reliable source, since this ensured that there was no induction period. It was ensured that diffusional factors were unimportant. This reaction was found to be first order with respect to AIBN and TBP. At 50.6°C and [AIBN] of 9.08×10^{-6} mol/cm^3 the value of the pseudo-first-order rate constant was found to be 1.38×10^{-4} sec^{-1} in the range of the concentration of TBP of $3.65\text{–}16.4 \times 10^{-5}$ mol/cm^3.

The most peculiar feature of this system was that between a p_{O_2} of 740 and 200 mm the pseudo-first-order rate constant was *inversely proportional to the pressure*. This example has been cited specifically to point out that m can have a value of -1.

3.1.10. Dimerization of Olefins

Olefins can be dimerized with coordination compounds as homogeneous catalysts. Codimerization of a mixture of olefinic compounds can also be carried out. These reactions have gained some industrial importance. Lefebvre and Chauvin (1970) have reviewed this subject. With $NiCl_2$, tetramethylcyclobutadiene, $AlEtCl_2$, or $P(n\text{-Bu})_3$ as catalysts the reactions have been found to be second order with respect to monomers and first order with respect to nickel, but much more complex with respect to aluminum compounds. The activation energy values were found to be in the range of 7–9 kcal/mol. The rate constant for ethylene was about 40 times greater than that for propylene.

The available data indicate that such reactions would probably fall in regime 1 or between regimes 1 and 2.

(B) Liquid–Liquid Systems

3.1.11. Alkaline Hydrolysis of a Variety of Organic Compounds

Benzyl alcohol is manufactured by the alkaline hydrolysis of benzyl chloride:

$$C_6H_5CH_2Cl + OH^-(aq) \rightarrow C_6H_5CH_2OH + Cl^-$$

This reaction is very slow and diffusional factors are unimportant.

Likewise, C_5 alcohols are produced by the alkaline hydrolysis of the C_5 chlorides that are obtained by the chlorination of n-pentane.

$$C_5H_{11}Cl + OH^-(aq) \rightarrow C_5H_{11}OH + Cl^-$$

It appears that in this case too the reaction is very sluggish and diffusional factors are unimportant.

The alkaline hydrolysis of esters has been studied by a number of authors. The reaction is first order in the ester as well as in the hydroxyl ions. In the case of acetate esters, which are only slightly soluble in water, the alkaline hydrolysis is likely to conform to this regime, particularly at temperatures lower than 20°C. In a typical case the value of k_2 will be around 100 cm^3/mol sec. Assuming the value of l to be 0.8 and taking the NaOH concentration as 5×10^{-4} mol/cm^3, we obtain, the value of the right-hand side of expression 2.3, as 4×10^{-2} sec^{-1}. The $k_L a$ value in some liquid–liquid contactors is around 0.5 sec^{-1}; hence the condition given by expression 2.3 is satisfied.

3.1.12. Nitration of Chlorobenzene

The nitration of chlorobenzene is industrially important for the manufacture of nitrochlorobenzenes. Cox and Strachan (1971) have studied the nitration of chlorobenzene in 70.2% sulfuric acid in a homogeneous phase, as well as in a two-phase mechanically agitated contactor. In the homogeneous phase the reaction was followed spectrophotometrically. It was conclusively shown by the authors that practically no reaction occurs in the aromatic phase, and hence the entire reaction occurs in the acid phase. The temperature of the reaction was varied from 20–55°C. The reaction was found to be first order in chlorobenzene and first order in the nitronium ion (and hence in the nitric acid). The values of solubility of chlorobenzene in sulfuric acid were also obtained at various temperatures so that the activation energy for the reaction could be calculated. The value of the activation energy was found to be about 17 kcal/mol. It was shown that under the conditions employed by the authors, mass transfer factors were unimportant. Thus, the reaction was found to be kinetically controlled and the values of the second-order rate constant varied from 10 to 240 cm^3/mol sec. The concentration of HNO_3 used by the authors was inordinately low ($\simeq 3.2 \times 10^{-5}$ mol/cm^3) when compared with that used in industrial practice. It is obvious that the condition given by expression 2.3 is clearly satisfied at very low concentrations of nitric acid. At the higher concentrations of nitric acid employed in industrial practice, however, the system would probably conform to regime 2 (see Section 3.2).

3.1.13. Alkylation of Benzene with Straight-Chain Olefins

The alkylation of benzene with straight-chain olefins is the first step in the manufacture of alkyl benzene sulfonates, which are used as detergents. When concentrated sulfuric acid is employed for alkylation, two phases are involved. The basic reaction can be represented as follows:

$$RCH{=}CH_2 + C_6H_6 \longrightarrow C_6H_5\text{—}CH(CH_3)\text{—}R$$

It is now well established that the alkylation reaction occurs in the acid phase only. Thus, mass transfer of reactants into the acid phase may be important. Komasawa et al. (1972) have made a systematic study of this reaction with hexene, heptene, octene, and decene in a 600-cm^3 stainless steel mechanically agitated contactor. Two flat-blade turbines were provided, and the speed of agitation could be varied up to about 2000 rev/min. Experiments were made batchwise as well as continuously, and the phase ratios were so adjusted as to make either the organic or the acid phase the dispersed phase. The concentration of sulfuric acid was varied from 84 to 97% w/w. In a typical benzene—1–hexene system, at a temperature of 2.5°C, the reaction rate increased approximately twofold when the speed of agitation was increased from about 700 to 1100 rev/min but there was no increase in the reaction rate above a speed of 1500 rev/min (Figure 3.2). This implies that mass transfer resistance was eliminated at speeds of agitation higher than 1500 rev/min. The physical properties of the two phases are markedly different, and hence the dispersion characteristics and the values of the mass transfer coefficient for the two cases, where either the acid phase or the organic phase constituted the dispersed phase, will be substantially different. Experimental data indicated that the rate of reaction was the same in two cases. It was therefore concluded that mass transfer factors were unimportant and the reaction was kinetically controlled.

Tiwari and Sharma (1977) have studied the kinetics of the reaction between benzene and toluene with lower olefins (propylene, and butene-1 and -2) in a continuously operated agitated contactor in the presence of sulfuric acid as the catalyst. To eliminate any resistance in the gas side, the olefin was dissolved in the aromatic phase and then contacted with aqueous

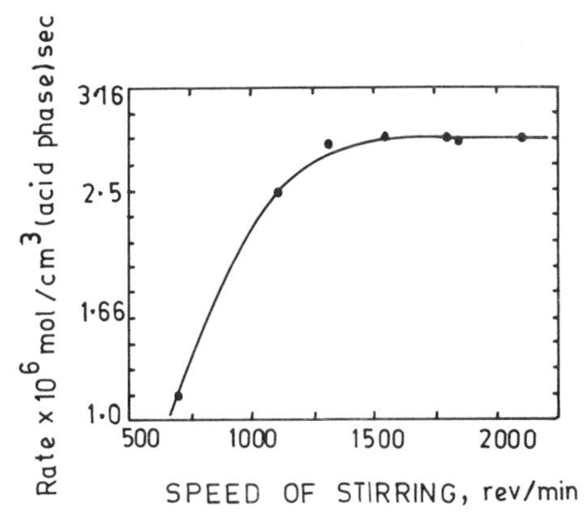

Figure 3.2. Effect of speed of agitation on the rate of alkylation of benzene with straight-chain olefins in the presence of sulfuric acid. (There was no effect of phase inversion on the rate of alkylation in mol/cm^3 (acid phase) sec.)

sulfuric acid (16.3–17.1 × 10^{-3} mol/cm^3). The basic findings of this work are in agreement with those of Komasawa et al. (1972).

Richardson (1977) and Richardson and Rase (1978) have made a similar study for alkylation of benzene with hexene, and their results are in basic agreement with those of Tiwari and Sharma and Komasawa et al.

3.1.14. Reduction of Aromatic Nitro Compounds to Corresponding Aromatic Amines with Aqueous Na_2S or Na_2S_x

Bhave and Sharma (1981) have studied the reduction of a variety of aromatic nitro compounds such as nitrotoluenes, *m*-nitrochlorobenzene, *m*-dinitrobenzene, and *p*-nitroaniline, with aqueous Na_2S/Na_2S_x in a 10-cm-i.d. mechanically agitated contactor. The effect of agitation speed, dispersed-phase holdup, reversal of phases, and the like on the rate of reduction per unit volume of the aqueous phase was studied.

Consider the reduction of *p*-nitroaniline to *p*-phenylenediamine at 60°C. The reaction between dissolved *p*-nitroaniline and aqueous Na_2S_2 can be written as

$$H_2N\text{—}C_6H_4\text{—}NO_2 + Na_2S_2 + H_2O \longrightarrow H_2N\text{—}C_6H_4\text{—}NH_2 + Na_2S_2O_3$$

There was no effect of the speed of agitation beyond 600 rev/min and the dispersed-phase (organic phase) holdup in the range of 0.07–0.26 on the rate of reduction per unit volume of the aqueous phase. Further, there was no effect of the reversal of phases on the rate of reduction per unit volume of the aqueous phase. From the foregoing it is clear that this reaction conforms to the very slow reaction regime and that diffusional factors are unimportant. The reduction was found to be first order in the nitro compounds as well as in the Na_2S or Na_2S_x.

We can check the relevant conditions for the validity of regime 1 from the following data:

$$[A^*] = 2.51 \times 10^{-5}\ \text{mol/cm}^3$$

$$k_2 = 15\ \text{cm}^3/\text{mol sec} \qquad (m = 1, n = 1)$$

$$k_L = 3 \times 10^{-3}\ \text{cm/sec}$$

$$k_L a = 0.4\ \text{sec}^{-1}$$

$$D_A = 1.9 \times 10^{-5}\ \text{cm}^2/\text{sec}$$

$$R_A a = 3.9 \times 10^{-7}\ \text{mol/cm}^3\ \text{sec}$$

$$[B_o]_{avg} = 6.05 \times 10^{-4}\ \text{mol/cm}^3$$

$$\sqrt{M} = \frac{\sqrt{D_A k_2 [B_o]_{avg}}}{k_L}$$

$$= \frac{\sqrt{1.9 \times 10^{-5} \times 15 \times 6.05 \times 10^{-4}}}{3 \times 10^{-3}}$$

$$= 0.138$$

$$\frac{R_A a}{[A^*]} = \frac{3.9 \times 10^{-7}}{2.51 \times 10^{-5}}$$

$$= 1.55 \times 10^{-2}\ \text{sec}^{-1} \qquad (\ll k_L a = 0.4)$$

Thus the necessary conditions for regime 1 are satisfied.

In the case of faster-reacting nitro compounds, at higher temperatures, the controlling regime may change to regime 2 and then to regime 3. Consider the reduction of *m*-nitrochlorobenzene at 90°C in a mechanically agitated contactor. Here the controlling resistance shifts to regime 3 as the rate constant becomes high enough to raise the value of $\sqrt{M}$ to a value higher than 3 and $\sqrt{M}$ is very much less than $[B_o]/(Z[A^*])$. Values of a calculated from measurements of the specific rate of extraction and volumetric rate of extraction in the 9.5-cm-i.d. stirred cell and 10-cm-i.d. mechanically agitated contactor, respectively, agree reasonably well with independent measurements with similar systems.

(C) *Special Cases*

3.1.15. Extractive Reactions

There are a number of reactions of industrial importance that are conducted in a single-phase system where the yield of the desired product is adversely affected because of side reactions. For example, in the manufacture of furfural by the acid hydrolysis of pentosans, the furfural can undergo further reactions and form resins (Hofmann, 1961). In such cases there is a possibility of improving the yields of the desired product by deliberately adding to the system another solvent that is practically insoluble in the phase in which the reaction occurs and that shows a high distribution coefficient for the desired product (e.g., tetralin in the case of furfural). Such reaction systems are referred to as *extractive reactions*, since both reaction and extraction are involved. Piret et al. (1960), Trambouze et al. (1961), and Trambouze (1961) have made an extensive study of this class of reactions. Design procedures for multistage contactors have also been suggested.

Brown et al. (1971) have clearly brought out the advantages of carrying out the oxidation of secondary alcohols (with dichromate) to the corresponding ketones by employing a two-phase system. Of the various solvents studied by these authors, diethylether was found to be the best. High yields of ketones are realized, since ketones are preferentially extracted into the organic phase. Secondary alcohols such as cyclohexanol, 3-methyl-2-butanol, and *l*-menthol have been studied. The overall reaction is

$$3R_2CHOH + Na_2Cr_2O_7 + 4H_2SO_4$$

$$\rightarrow 3R_2CO + Na_2SO_4 + Cr_2(SO_4)_3 + 7H_2O$$

Yields as high as 97% have been realized. The book by Millich and Carraher (1977) deals with different aspects of this type of reaction.

3.1.16. Phase Transfer Catalysis

A number of reactions of industrial importance are conducted in two-phase systems. However, many reactions in the system above are slow and sometimes ineffective. Various attempts have been made to catalyze such reactions by adding trace amounts of substances like quaternary ammonium and phosphonium salts, crown-ethers, and trialkylamines. These substances are called phase transfer catalysts (Dehmlow, 1974; Yadav, 1975; Starks, 1980; Dehmlow and Dehmlow, 1980) and they operate as catalysts and not simply as emulsifying agents for increasing the transfer area in the two-phase systems. There are a number of cases where, in the absence of the catalysts, the desired reaction hardly occurs.

Starks and Owens (1973) have studied some aspects of the conversion of 1-chlorooctane to 1-cyanooctane. The reaction between 1-chlorooctane and aqueous sodium cyanide to give 1-cyanooctane can be accomplished in 1.8 hr in 99% yield if 1.3 mol % tributyl(hexadecyl)phosphonium bromide is present. In this case no 1-cyanooctane is formed without the catalyst even after boiling for two weeks. This new method does not require anhydrous solvents and is therefore likely to be attractive industrially. There is scant information in the literature on the kinetics of these heterogeneous reactions.

The reaction scheme (Q stands for quaternary ammonium or phosphonium) is as follows:

$NaCN + QCl \rightleftharpoons QCN + NaCl$	aqueous phase
- - - - - ⇅ - - - - ⇅ - - - - - -	interface
$RCN + QCl \rightleftharpoons QCN + RCl$	organic phase

In principle, diffusional resistance may be associated with the transfer of the reactant and the catalyst. Anion transfer by the catalyst into the organic phase is considered to be an equilibrium process in which two different ions in the aqueous phase associate with a quaternary cation in the organic phase.

$$(QCl)_{org} + (CN^-)_{aq} \rightleftharpoons (QCN)_{org} + (Cl^-)_{aq}$$

It was found that the rate-determining step of the reaction was in the organic phase of the reaction mixture rather than in the aqueous phase or at the interface or in the micelles (see 3.1.17). The following observations were made by Starks and Owens (1973):

1. The solubility of RCl in the aqueous phase has no effect on the rate of reaction.
2. The reaction was found to be independent of the effective interfacial area; hence diffusional factors are unimportant.
3. The rate of reaction is dependent on the catalyst concentration in the reaction phase and is first order with respect to these species.
4. Poor surfactants like tetra-(dodecyl-)ammonium salts are highly effective catalysts, and simple quaternary salt molecules are themselves capable of undergoing facile displacement.

The phase transfer catalysts are potentially attractive for conducting a variety of industrially important reactions. Dehmlow (1974) and Yadav (1975) have indicated some reactions of industrial importance where these catalysts can possibly be employed.

It appears that phase transfer catalysts can also be applied to gas–liquid reactions, for example, the oxidation of hydrocarbons (Dehmlow and Dehmlow, 1980).

3.1.17. Micellar Catalysis and Interfacial Reactions

In contrast to the foregoing cases, where phase transfer catalysis is operative, Menger et al. (1975) have shown that in some cases surfactants can act as catalysts. For instance, the oxidation of piperonal to piperonylic acid is catalyzed by a cationic surfactant, cetyltrimethylammonium bromide. Fendler and Fendler (1977) have written a monograph on catalysis in micellar and macromolecular systems. *Micelle* is the name given to roughly spherical aggregates formed in water (as well as in nonpolar solvents) by surfactant molecules (molecules having ionic or polar heads and long hydrocarbon tails). Generally, long-chain molecules with asymmetric structure are more likely to form micelles. Although the exact structure of micelles is a matter of considerable controversy, they can be viewed as having their ionic heads near the bulk water and the tails extending inward into the micelle interior (for details refer to Fendler and Fendler, 1977). Micelles can solubilize nonpolar compounds into water.

Menger (1979) has given a concise account of this subject with examples. We will consider some examples to illustrate the unique features of this class of reactions.

Imidazole-Catalyzed Hydrolysis of p-Nitrophenyl Laurate in a Heptane–Water Two-Phase System

Here the ester is insoluble in water and imidazole is insoluble in the heptane phase; therefore the imidazole-catalyzed reaction may well occur at the interface. Experimental data endorse this expectation, as is evident from the following.

1. In the two-phase system without imidazole, no ester could be detected in the water phase even by sensitive spectrophotometric methods. Further, the observed rates of hydrolysis are very fast and cannot be accounted for on the basis of hydrolysis in the bulk aqueous phase.
2. The rate of hydrolysis does not change with the change in the chain length of the ester despite large consequential variation in the interfacial concentration of the ester.
3. An increase in the salt concentration in water would be expected to reduce the rate, but in fact the rate is slightly increased by large amounts of salts.
4. Differences in the behavior of hydrolysis of short-chain esters in a homogeneous system versus that of long-chain esters in two-phase systems have been observed. A plot of the heterogeneous reaction rate against the concentration of ester in the heptane phase shows a pronounced saturation effect, as in the case of an enzyme reaction. Activation energy was relatively low, indicating diffusional resistance. A small amount of laurate anion (2×10^{-8} to 2×10^{-7} mol/cm^3) significantly retarded the rate in the two-phase system, whereas no effect was observed in the homogeneous system. It appears that laurate adsorbs at the interface, where it retards the rate of diffusion of one or both of the reactants to the interface. (This provides a clue for controlling interfacial reactions that would not be possible in a homogeneous system.)

3.1.18. Use of Emulsifying Agent for Increasing the Rate of Two-Phase Reactions: Hydrolysis of α, α, α-Trichlorotoluene (TCT) (Benzotrichloride) to Benzoic Acid

Hydrolysis of TCT in a 20% aqueous solution at 80°C takes about 60 hr to give nearly quantitative yield (Menger, 1979). However, a very low concentration of hexadecyltrimethylammonium bromide of 1×10^{-5} mol/cm^3 reduces the reaction time from 60 to 1.5 hr. This is *not* due to phase transfer catalysis, since *n*-tetrabutylammonium bromide (which is a good phase transfer catalyst) is less active and required 15 hr for completion of the reaction at a concentration of 2×10^{-5} mol/cm^3. It is even more striking to find that 6×10^{-6} mol/cm^3 of a nonionic surface active agent, $C_{12}H_{25}(OCH_2CH_2)_nOH$, allowed the reaction to be completed in 11 hr; here the question of phase transfer catalysis does not arise, since the surface active agent is *nonionic*.

3.1.19. Measurement of Holdup

The rate of reaction of A per unit volume of the contactor is dependent on the fractional holdup of the B phase. If the value of the rate constant is known independently, then Eq. 2.2 can be employed to obtain the value of l (volume of the B phase = volume of dispersion $\times\, l$). Puranik and Sharma (1970b) have used the alkaline hydrolysis of *n*-butyl acetate to obtain the value of l in a laboratory spray extraction column operated in the regime of the dense packing of drops. Consider the extraction of *n*-butyl acetate into an aqueous sodium hydroxide solution under the following conditions.

Dispersed phase—*n*-butyl acetate

Continuous phase—aqueous NaOH

$$[\text{NaOH}] = 1 \times 10^{-4}\ \text{mol/cm}^3$$

$$k_2 = 100\ \text{cm}^3/\text{mol sec}$$

$$l \simeq 0.6$$

The value of $k_L a$ in the case of a spray column operated in the dense-packing regime is much greater than that obtained with the dispersed-packing regime. Here a typical $k_L a$ value would be 4×10^{-2} sec^{-1}. Thus the condition given by expression 2.3 is satisfied ($k_L a = 4 \times 10^{-2} \gg l k_2 [B_o] = 6 \times 10^{-3}$] and the system can be employed for the measurement of the holdup. There is, however, no particular merit of this method for the measurement of holdup in fluid–fluid contactors, and the conventional method can be advantageously employed.

Scale-up

The scale-up of systems belonging to this regime would require a knowledge of the rate constant k_{mn}, the values of m and n, and the residence time distribution of phases A and B.

3.2. REGIME 2: SLOW REACTIONS

(A) Gas–Liquid Systems

3.2.1. Absorption of CO_2 in Carbonate Solutions

The absorption of CO_2 in carbonate solutions is industrially important in the removal of CO_2 from a variety of industrial gases, as well as in the manufacture of sodium bicarbonate (Danckwerts and Sharma, 1966). In most contactors where the gas is dispersed in the liquid, the absorption of CO_2 is controlled by the diffusion of CO_2; the reaction occurs in the bulk (where the concentration of A is zero) and no reaction occurs in the film provided the temperature is less than 50°C. All the conditions necessary for the validity of Eq. 2.8 are satisfied.

Example

For a mechanically agitated vessel $k_L = 0.04$ cm/sec, $a = 2.0$ cm^{-1}, and hence $k_L a = 0.08$ sec^{-1}. For $[CO_3^{2-}]/[HCO_3^-] = 2$,

$$k_2[B_o] = 1.2 \text{ sec}^{-1}$$

$$D_A k_2[B_o] = 1.6 \times 10^{-5} \text{ (cm/sec)}^2$$

$$k_L^2 = 1.6 \times 10^{-3} \text{ (cm/sec)}^2$$

Hence, $k_L^2 \gg D_A k_2[B_o]$. Further, $l = 0.08$, $lk_2[B_o] = 0.96$, and $k_L a = 0.08 \ll lk_2[B_o] = 0.96$.

Actually, this system turns out to be very convenient for obtaining $k_L a$ values in a variety of industrial contactors.

3.2.2. Absorption of O_2 in Aqueous Acid Solutions of CuCl at Concentrations Less than 1×10^{-4} mol / cm^3

Absorption of O_2 in aqueous acid solution of CuCl at concentrations lower than 1×10^{-4} mol/cm^3 is important in Wacker processes. This reaction has been found to be first order in O_2 and second order in CuCl. The kinetic data reported by Jhaveri and Sharma (1967) show clearly that the system will conform to this regime in a variety of contactors.

Example

Consider a mechanically agitated contactor. Let $a = 3$ cm^{-1} and $k_L = 0.03$ cm/sec; then $k_L a = 0.09$ sec^{-1}. At 30°C, $k_3 = 252 \times 10^6$ (cm^3/mol)^2 sec^{-1} (cuprous chloride in aqueous HCl; concentration of HCl = 5 $\times 10^{-3}$ mol/cm^3). Also,

$$[B_o] = 1 \times 10^{-4} \text{ mol/cm}^3$$

$$D_A = 2.8 \times 10^{-5} \text{ cm}^2\text{/sec}$$

$$D_A k_3[B_o]^2 = 7.04 \times 10^{-5} \text{ (cm/sec)}^2$$

$$k_L^2 = 9 \times 10^{-4} \text{ (cm/sec)}^2$$

Hence, $k_L^2 = 9 \times 10^{-4} \gg D_A k_3[B_o]^2 = 7.04 \times 10^{-5}$. Further, $l = 0.8$, $lk_3[B_o]^2 = 2.02$. Thus the necessary conditions are satisfied.

3.2.3. Oxidation of Organic Compounds

Prengle and Barona (1970) have analyzed some published data on the air oxidation of *o*-xylene to *o*-toluic acid in a bubble column and have shown that the reaction conforms to this regime. (These authors have considered many other oxidation reactions as well.)

The oxidation of cumene to cumene hydroperoxide, which is subsequently converted to phenol and acetone, is likely to conform to this regime (Low, 1967). Tiwari (1976) and Kulkarni (1979) have studied the oxidation of cumene, *p*-cymene, and mixtures of diisopropyl benzene isomers, with cumyl hydroperoxide as an initiator, in bubble columns that could be operated under pressures up to 10 atm. Oxidation was carried out under conditions such that the organic phase was emulsified with 4 wt. % aqueous Na_2CO_3 and the fraction of the organic phase could be varied over a wide range. Temperature was varied from 85 to 115°C. There was no effect of the superficial gas (air) velocity on the rate of oxidation over the range of about 4–13 cm/sec. Further, the rate of oxidation (expressed as moles per cubic centimeter of the organic phase per second), under otherwise comparable conditions, was independent of the holdup of the organic phase. These observations clearly indicate that the reaction was kinetically controlled and belonged to regime 1 and that the locale of the reaction is the hydrocarbon phase. Further, the reaction was found to be independent of the partial pressure of O_2 in the range of 0.2–0.63 atm. The value of the activation energy was found to be 20.5 kcal/mol, which further indicates that the diffusional resistance was absent.

Hobbs et al. (1972) have pointed out some interesting aspects of the liquid-phase air oxidation of organic compounds. In a number of oxidation reactions the rate of oxidation is practically independent of the partial pressure of oxygen above a certain minimum value. At low partial pressures, however, the rate of oxidation is directly proportional to the partial pressure of oxygen. The following steps are involved and each of these two steps can be the rate-controlling one:

$$O_2 + R \rightarrow RO_2$$

$$RO_2 + R'H \rightarrow RO_2H + R'$$

Thus, at high partial pressures of oxygen we may have a situation where the chemical rate controls the overall process and the activation energy may be in the range of 20–30 kcal/mol. By contrast, at low partial pressure of oxygen, mass transfer of O_2 may be the controlling factor and the activation energy may be around 3–5 kcal/mol. Hobbs et al. have also given an example of air oxidation of methyl ethyl ketone dissolved in acetic acid in the presence of cobaltous acetate as a catalyst.

Saunby and Kiff (1976) have considered some engineering aspects of liquid-phase oxidation with particular reference to the oxidation of butane to acetic acid and methyl ethyl ketone (MEK). In the case of the oxidation of butane below about 180°C the reaction is chemically rate limited and the reaction shows an overall apparent activation energy of 10–30 kcal/mol. At temperatures higher than 180°C mass transfer becomes controlling and the activation energy drops to 3–5 kcal/mol. It is desirable to operate the reactor under conditions where mass transfer resistance is substantial. If the reaction is kinetically rate limited (i.e., regime 1 holds) then the reactor may be unstable, since a drop in temperature will result in a decrease in the overall rate, which will cause a further drop in temperature until the reaction dies. It may not be desirable to operate under conditions such that mass transfer completely controls (i.e., regime 2 holds), because the absence of O_2 in the bulk liquid, may result in inadequate scavenging of the alkyl radicals and this may give undesirable byproducts.

The type of reactor can greatly influence the product distribution. In the case of the oxidation of butane the ratio of the major products, acetic acid and MEK, can be varied from 10 : 1 to 0.5 : 1 by decreasing the extent of backmixing. Thus acetic acid is the major product in a continuously operated agitated contactor where liquid is backmixed. On the other hand, in a plug flow reactor (e.g., a pipeline reactor) the ratio of acetic acid to MEK is 1 : 1. Some backmixing is desirable in practice in order to maintain an adequate concentration of radicals. One way this can be achieved is by the use of a set of backmixed reactors in series.

3.2.4. Preparation of the C-13 Isotope

Carbon-13 is useful in physical and biological sciences and is particularly attractive for *in vivo* experiments in the biological and medical fields, since it is the only available nonradioactive carbon label. Palko et al. (1971) have suggested a new chemical method of fractionating carbon isotopes that is based on the following heterogeneous exchange reaction:

$$Cu_2(^{12}CO)Cl_2 \cdot 8NH_4Cl(aq) + {}^{13}CO(g)$$

$$= Cu_2(^{13}CO)Cl_2 \cdot 8NH_4Cl(aq) + {}^{12}CO(g)$$

It appears that the average half-life of this reaction is about 5 sec (i.e., the first-order rate constant would be about 0.2 sec^{-1}) at 20°C. The authors have suggested the use of a packed column for this reaction, in which case the reaction would be expected to conform to this regime:

$$D_{CO} \simeq 1 \times 10^{-5}\ \text{cm}^2/\text{sec}, \qquad k_1 \simeq 0.2\ \text{sec}^{-1}$$

$$k_L \simeq 5 \times 10^{-3}\ \text{cm/sec}, \qquad a \simeq 1\ \text{cm}^2/\text{cm}^3$$

$$D_{CO}k_1 \simeq 2 \times 10^{-6}\ \text{cm}^2/\text{sec}^2,$$

$$k_L^2 \simeq 25 \times 10^{-6}\ \text{cm}^2/\text{sec}$$

Hence,

$$k_L^2 = 25 \times 10^{-6} \gg D_{CO}k_1 = 2 \times 10^{-6}$$

$$l \simeq 0.07$$

$$k_L a \simeq 5 \times 10^{-3} < lk_1 \simeq 14 \times 10^{-3}$$

Thus the conditions given by expressions 2.9 and 2.10 for the validity of regime 2 are essentially satisfied.

(B) Liquid–Liquid Systems

3.2.5. Pyrometallurgical Operations: Open Hearth Steel Furnace

The transfer of the undesirable species from the molten metal phase into the slag phase is now known to be diffusion controlled (Subramanian and

Richardson, 1968; Szekely, 1967). Steel making, lead softening, and the like may be cited as examples.

3.2.6. Reaction of Dinitrochlorobenzene

Abramzon and Ostrovskit (1963) studied the following reactions of molten 1-chloro-2,4-dinitrobenzene (DNCB) under conditions such that the transfer of DNCB is the controlling step:

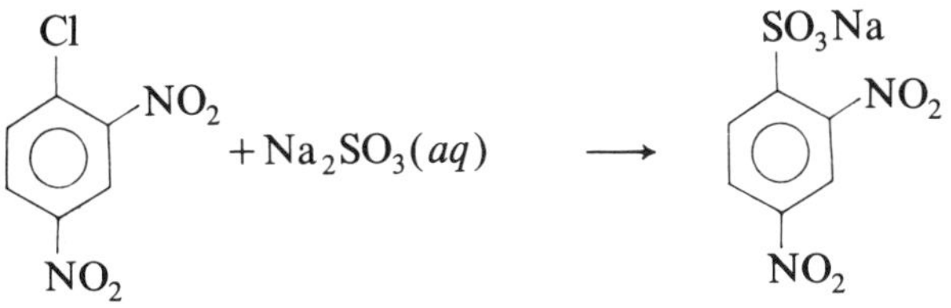

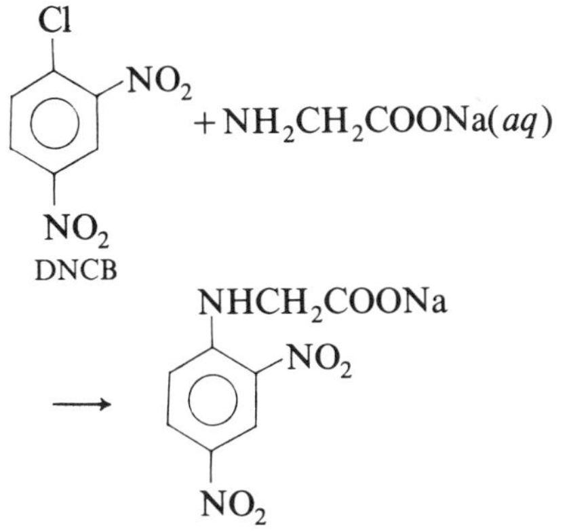

$$\text{1-Cl-2,4-}(NO_2)_2C_6H_3 + Na_2SO_3(aq) \longrightarrow \text{1-}SO_3Na\text{-2,4-}(NO_2)_2C_6H_3$$

$$\underset{\text{DNCB}}{\text{1-Cl-2,4-}(NO_2)_2C_6H_3} + NH_2CH_2COONa(aq) \longrightarrow \text{1-}NHCH_2COONa\text{-2,4-}(NO_2)_2C_6H_3$$

Abramzon and Ostrovskit (1961, 1962) were also able to study these reactions under conditions such that diffusional resistance was eliminated.

3.2.7. Removal of Mercaptans from Petroleum Fractions

Groothuis (1961) has studied the Shell air solutizer process for removing malodorous mercaptans from gasoline by converting them to odorless disulfides by oxidation with O_2:

$$\tfrac{1}{2}O_2 + 2RSH \rightarrow R{-}S{-}S{-}R + H_2O$$

The transfer of O_2 was found to be the controlling factor.

3.2.8. Alkaline Hydrolysis of Esters

Under certain conditions the alkaline hydrolysis of acetic acid esters, which are only slightly soluble in water, conforms to this regime. Indeed this system can be successfully employed to obtain the mass transfer coefficient in the aqueous phase in a variety of liquid–liquid contactors (Sharma and Danckwerts, 1970; Puranik and Sharma, 1970a).

3.2.9. Nitration of Aromatic Compounds

The nitration of aromatic substances like benzene, toluene, phenol, and naphthalene is practiced on a large scale for the manufacture of intermediates for dyestuffs, polymers, pharmaceuticals, and the like. Nitro compounds (e.g., trinitrotoluene) are also used as explosive substances. In most aromatic nitrations two phases—the organic phase and the aqueous acid phase—are involved. In most cases practically all the reaction occurs in the acid phase. The mixed acid (H_2SO_4 + HNO_3) is usually used for nitration. Some chemical aspects of the nitration of aromatic compounds have been studied by Coombes et al. (1968). Albright and Hanson (1969) have analyzed the data available in the literature and have indicated that under industrial conditions the rate of nitration of a number of aromatic substances is essentially controlled by diffusional factors.

Hanson et al. (1971) have studied the macrokinetics of the nitration of toluene. They carried out experiments in a 4.3-cm-diameter continuous-flow stirred-tank reactor (CFSTR) with 15 mol % HNO_3, 30 mol % H_2SO_4, and 55 mol % H_2O under very carefully controlled conditions. The reactor was jacketed and provided with a 3.2-cm-wide paddle agitator, and the agitation speed could be varied up to 8000 rev/min. The temperature was varied over a wide range (2°–48°C). It is clear from the data reported by the authors that the speed of agitation has a profound effect on the reaction rate in the range of 1000–3000 rev/min. Further, the rate of reaction continued to increase slowly, even up to a speed of 8000 rev/min. Thus, it is clear that even at such high stirring speeds diffusional resistance is present. It may be concluded that in industrial practice the nitration of toluene will be essentially diffusion controlled.

Cox and Strachan (1971) also studied the two-phase nitration of toluene using 70.2 wt. % H_2SO_4 containing nitric acid at an initial concentration of 3.2×10^{-5} mol/cm^3 in the temperature range of 15°–35°C. They showed that under certain conditions the nitration reaction will be mass transfer controlled.

3.2.10. Nitration of Higher Olefins

Fatty amines are widely used for a variety of purposes, and it is expected that in coming years their use will increase markedly. Conventionally these are manufactured via the reduction of fatty nitriles, which in turn are obtained via the reaction between NH_3 and fatty acids. A potentially cheap route would be to nitrate long-chain olefins with nitric acid to give nitro compounds, which can then be reduced to the corresponding amine. Gregory et al. (1976) found that refluxing a heterogeneous mixture of 1-dodecene with dilute aqueous nitric acid (30% w/w) containing a small amount of nitrous acid leads to six or seven closely related nitro compounds in greater than 90% yields. The reaction involves a chain reaction mechanism, and hence a small amount of nitrous acid is used as an initiator. The product consisted of three major fractions: a nitrododecane fraction (10–15% of the product), a dinitrodecane fraction (25–30 wt. %), and a nitrododecanol fraction ($\simeq$ 55%, 4 : 1 mixture of 1-nitro-2-dodecanol and 2-nitro-1-dodecanol). Experiments were made in a 1000-cm^3 round-bottomed three-necked flask which was provided with a stirrer and reflux system. There are many interesting features of this system:

1. Similar experiments with N_2O_4 and 1-dodecene at 100°C, followed by hydrolysis with dilute nitric acid, gave nitro products in practically the same proportion as those obtained with 30% nitric acid. This clearly indicates that in both cases the nitrating species is N_2O_4 (dinitro compounds in an acid medium can hydrolyze to give nitro alcohols). Each mole of dodecene consumes 1.3–1.4 mol of nitric acid.
2. The overall rate was found to be zero order in the concentration of 1-dodecene in the olefin phase and first order with respect to the concentration of nitric acid in the acid phase. The rate of nitration of 1-octadecene, under otherwise same conditions, was the same as that of 1-dodecene. Since the solubility of the two olefins in the aqueous phase will be markedly different, it is clear that the reaction occurs in the *olefin phase and not in the aqueous phase*. (This is one of the few cases where the reaction occurs in the A phase and not in the B phase.)
3. Diffusional factors were important, as can be seen from the fact that the addition of 1-dodecane sulfonate (0.1 M) in nitric acid, which acts as an emulsifying agent, increased the rate at least twofold under otherwise uniform conditions. The product distribution was the same in the two cases.
4. That 1,2-dinitrododecane is formed at most to the extent of 35% of the nitro products and that in all about 1.3–1.4 mol of nitric acid per mole of dodecene are used indicates that HNO_2 may be formed via some other reaction. It appears that some dodecene is oxidized to undecanoic acid, which results in 5 mol of HNO_2 per mole of the olefin oxidized.

$$R\text{—}CH\text{=}CH_2 + 5HNO_3 \rightarrow RCOOH + CO_2 + H_2O + 5HNO_2$$

It is very likely that the oxidation of 1-dodecene/nitro products in this manner is the rate-determining step.

Clippinger (1964) has pointed out a number of cases of reactions between α-olefins and reactive species in liquid–liquid and gas–liquid systems where the rate of reaction is independent of the chain length of α-olefin and the reaction occurs in the organic phase.

3.2.11. Liquid–Liquid Reactions in Phosphorus Chemistry

Purification of Phosphorus

Commercial phosphorus contains inorganic and organic impurities that are undesirable for the manufacture of some derivatives. These impurities can be successfully removed by treatment with concentrated sulfuric acid by a series of dehydration, oxidation, and sulfonation reactions (Harnisch, 1980). However, side reactions also occur:

$$2P_4(l) + 20H_2SO_4(l) \rightarrow 2P_4O_{10}(s) + 20H_2O(g) + 20SO_2(g) \quad (\Delta H = 1137.60 \text{ kcal})$$

$$2P_4(l) + 5H_2SO_4(l) \rightarrow 2P_4O_{10}(s) + 5H_2S(g) \quad (\Delta H = -504 \text{ kcal})$$

These reactions are undesirable, particularly the formation of H_2S, which is accompanied by the evolution of heat and may also be subject to an autocatalytic effect.

Reaction of Phosphorus with Caustic Alkalies

Two types of reactions can occur:

Formation of phosphine

$$P_4 + 3NaOH + 3H_2O \rightarrow PH_3 + 3NaH_2PO_2$$

$$P_4 + 4NaOH + 2H_2O \rightarrow 2PH_3 + 2Na_2HPO_3$$

Formation of hydrogen

$$P_4 + 4NaOH + 4H_2O \rightarrow 2H_2 + 4NaH_2PO_2$$

$$P_4 + 8NaOH + 4H_2O \rightarrow 6H_2 + 4Na_2HPO_3$$

It is clear from the stoichiometry of these reactions that with a deficit of NaOH and H_2O, phosphine-forming reactions are promoted, whereas with an excess of NaOH and H_2O, hydrogen-forming reactions are promoted. Further, with high concentrations of NaOH (i.e., a high $NaOH/H_2O$ ratio) phosphite should be formed and with low concentrations of NaOH hypophosphite will be formed. Thus we have an interesting situation in which by manipulating the $(NaOH + H_2O)/P_4$ ratio and the concentration of NaOH we can change the course of the reaction. In addition to this consideration we can possibly increase the rate of reaction by increasing the solubility of P_4 in the aqueous phase where the reaction occurs. Thus long-chain higher alcohols have been reported to achieve this objective. (The output per unit volume of the reactor may be further increased if dispersion characteristics are favorable as compared to the aqueous system.)

Manufacture of Sodium (or Potassium) Phosphide

Liquid sodium or a sodium–potassium alloy reacts with liquid white phosphorus in an inert mixture of aromatics to give the corresponding alkali phosphide. The use of a solvent is highly beneficial for several reasons, including the easy dissipation of the large amounts of heat. (This process has not yet been commercialized.)

The kinetics of the reactions above have not been established and may well belong to any of the regimes from 1 to 4.

3.2.12. Special Case: Measurement of the Solubility of A in the B Phase

If experiments are carried out in a model contactor, where the time of contact is precisely known and the diffusivity of A can be estimated, then the value of the solubility of A in the B phase can be estimated. We thus have a reasonably good means of obtaining the solubility of A in a medium where it reacts, which would be otherwise impossible by the conventional method. Manogue and Pigford (1960) made use of this technique to obtain the solubility of phosgene in water. Phosgene gas was absorbed in jets of water. The necessary condition for the validity of no reaction to occur in the film (expression 2.10) was satisfied. The reaction was found to be first order in phosgene. In a typical case the value of $\sqrt{D_A k_1}/k_L$ was about 0.2. The solubility of phosgene in water at 25°C was found to be 6.9×10^{-5} mol/cm^3 atm.

Scale-up

The scale-up of systems belonging to this regime would require a knowledge of $k_L a$ in the industrial contactor and the residence time distribution of the A phase.

3.3. REGIME BETWEEN 1 AND 2

(A) Gas–Liquid Systems

3.3.1. Pseudo-First-Order Reactions: Simultaneous Measurement of $k_L a$ and k_1 without Knowing [A*]

In principle, it is possible to obtain values of the pseudo-first-order rate constant, k_1, and the value of the liquid-side mass transfer coefficient, $k_L a$, from experiments in a semibatch gas–liquid reactor (i.e., pure gas A is passed continuously through a batch of the B phase). The following equations hold for this case:

$$\frac{d[A_o]}{dt} = k_L a([A^*] - [A_o]) - k_1[A_o] \quad (3.1)$$

$$R'_A(t) = k_L a([A^*] - [A_o]) \quad (3.2)$$

[Here $R'_A(t)$ is the rate of absorption at time t.] Equation 3.2 can be rearranged to give $[A_o]$:

$$[A_o] = [A^*] - \frac{R'_A(t)}{k_L a} \quad (3.3)$$

On integration and simplification of Eq. 3.1, we get

$$t = \frac{1}{k_L a + k_1} \ln \frac{k_L a[A^*]}{k_L a[A^*] - (k_L a + k_1)[A_o]} \tag{3.4}$$

at $t = \infty$, $[A_o] = [A_o]_\infty$. Thus,

$$[A_o]_\infty = \frac{k_L a[A^*]}{k_L a + k_1} \tag{3.5}$$

Now the rate of absorption at infinite time

$$R'_A(\infty) = k_L a([A^*] - [A_o]_\infty) \tag{3.6}$$

From Eqs. 3.5 and 3.6 we get

$$R'_A(\infty) = k_L a[A^*]\left(\frac{k_1}{k_L a + k_1}\right) \tag{3.7}$$

Substitution of $[A_o]$ from Eq. 3.3 into Eq. 3.4 and elimination of the unknown term $[A^*]$ by using Eq. 3.7 yields

$$\ln\left[\frac{R'_A(t)}{R'_A(\infty)} - 1\right] = \ln\frac{k_L a}{k_1} - (k_L a + k_1)t \tag{3.8}$$

Thus a plot of $\ln[R'_A(t)/R'_A(\infty) - 1]$ against t will allow a calculation of $k_L a$ and k_1. Further, Eq. 3.7 along with these values of $k_L a$ and k_1 will permit calculation of $[A^*]$. We therefore have a method of obtaining $k_L a$ and k_1 without knowing the solubility of the solute gas. This method was suggested by Deckwer and Puxbaumer (1975) and adopted for the absorption of butene-1 and butene-2 in dilute aqueous solutions of sulfuric acid. Linek and Sobotka (1973) have considered a similar case with specific reference to obtaining $k_L a$ in aerobic fermenters. Equation 3.4 can be rearranged to give

$$[A_o] = \frac{[A^*]}{1 + k_1/k_L a}\{1 - [\exp - (k_L a + k_1)t]\} \tag{3.4a}$$

If a continuous recording instrument can be used to measure $[A_o]$ as a function of time, then a procedure suggested by Linek and Sobotka can be used for measuring $k_L a$ without knowing $[A^*]$.

3.3.2. Absorption of CO_2 in Carbonate Buffer Solutions in Packed Columns

Packed absorption columns provide very low values of l. In a typical case the value of l is less than 0.1. By contrast, in the case of contactors where the gas is dispersed in the liquid the value of l generally lies in the range of 0.7–0.9. Consider a typical case where for the lower ratio of $[CO_3^{2-}]/[HCO_3^-]$, the value of the first-order rate constant is 0.1 sec^{-1}. Let us assume the $k_L a$ values to be 1×10^{-2} and 3×10^{-2} sec^{-1} in two types of contactors (say a packed column and a bubble column, respectively) where the values of l are 0.1 and 0.9, respectively. In a packed column, the necessary condition (expression 2.9) for the validity of Eq. 2.8 is not satisfied. The values of the terms on the left- and right-hand sides of expression 2.9 are comparable, and hence Eq. 2.16 should be applicable. In the case of a bubble column also, Eq. 2.16 holds.

Mashelkar and Sharma (1970) have correlated the data pertaining to the absorption of CO_2 in carbonate/bicarbonate buffer solutions in a packed bubble column, where the regime falls between 1 and 2. According to Eq. 2.16 a plot of $1/(k_{LR}a)$ against $1/[B_o]$ should be a straight line. Figure 3.3 shows that the experimental data are satisfactorily correlated by Eq. 2.16.

(In the case of packed columns complications may arise because of the existence of relatively stagnant pools of liquid, particularly at lower values of superficial liquid velocity.)

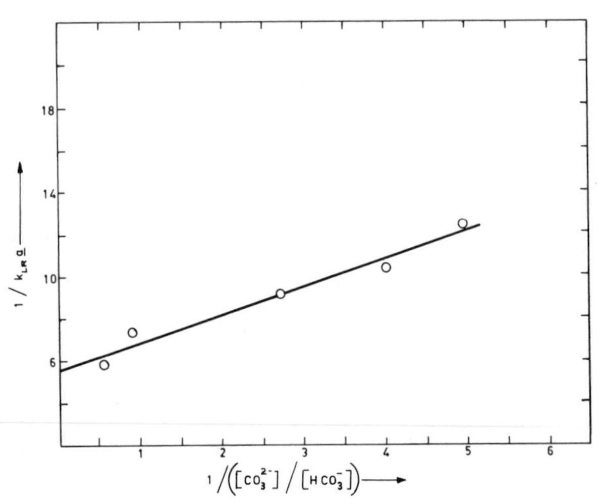

Figure 3.3. Plot of $1/k_{LR}a$ against $1/([CO_3^{2-}]/[HCO_3^-])$ for the absorption of CO_2 in an aqueous Na_2CO_3–$NaHCO_3$ buffer solution.

3.3.3. Oxidation of Black Liquor in the Paper and Pulp Industry

The off-gases from kraft paper mills contain malodorous compounds like H_2S and RSH that must be minimised. The most common process that is employed is based on the oxidation of black liquor with air. The basic reactions in the oxidation process are as follows:

$$7O_2 + 16S^{2-} + 14H_2O \rightarrow 2S_8^{2-} + 28OH^-$$

$$O_2 + 2S_8^{2-} + 2H_2O \rightarrow 2S_8 + 4OH^-$$

$$9O_2 + 2S_8^{2-} + 12OH^- \rightarrow 8S_2O_3^{2-} + 6H_2O$$

The oxidation process "fixes" the sulfide in the spent cooking solution so that the emission of H_2S during the processing of black liquid does not occur. (When the pH of the sodium sulfide solution is low there is a finite partial pressure of H_2S due to the following equilibrium:

$$S^{2-} \rightleftharpoons HS^- \rightleftharpoons H_2S(aq) \rightleftharpoons H_2S(g)$$

The conversion of S^{2-} to $S_2O_3^{2-}$ or sulfur creates a situation where the formation of H_2S does not occur.) The oxidation is usually carried out at temperatures higher than 70°C when no sulfur precipitation occurs and practically all the S^{2-} is converted to $S_2O_3^{2-}$. (The overall reaction is $2O_2 + 2Na_2S + H_2O \rightarrow Na_2S_2O_3 + 2NaOH$.) Methyl mercaptan is converted to dimethyl sulfide. The black liquor oxidation results in reducing the sulfur consumption in kraft paper mills. The oxidation is commonly carried out in air-sparged reactors. Recently pipeline contactors have been suggested.

Murray (1968) and Morgan and Murray (1971) have studied various aspects of this problem. The reaction was found to be first order in O_2 and first order in Na_2S. In sparged contactors for Na_2S concentrations in the range of $1\text{–}3 \times 10^{-5}$ mol/cm³ and at a temperature of about 75°C, the rate of oxidation was found to be partly controlled by diffusional factors and a part of the reaction occurred in the bulk. However, at lower concentrations of Na_2S (say less than 5×10^{-6} mol/cm³) the rate of oxidation was found to be kinetically controlled; that is, the diffusional resistance for the transport of O_2 was negligible.

Chandrasekaran and Sharma (1974, 1978) have studied the kinetics of absorption of O_2 in aqueous solutions of pure sodium sulfide in order to obtain reliable values of the rate constant. They have also found that the reaction is first order in oxygen as well as sulfide. By working at higher agitation speeds in a 13-cm-i.d. mechanically agitated contactor the liquid-side resistance was eliminated. The value of the second-order rate constant at 75°C was found to be 7270 cm³/mol sec. Consider a typical case in an industrial bubble column:

$$[Na_2S] = 4 \times 10^{-5} \text{ mol/cm}^3$$

$$l = 0.75$$

$$k_L a = 0.2 \text{ sec}^{-1}$$

$$lk_2[B_o] = 0.75 \times 7.27 \times 10^3 \times 4 \times 10^{-5}$$

$$= 0.218 \text{ sec}^{-1}$$

Thus the values of $k_L a$ and $lk_2[B_o]$ are comparable, and therefore the system will conform to the regime between 1 and 2 and the bulk aqueous phase will have an oxygen concentration significantly less than the saturation concentration. It is also clear that at very low concentrations of Na_2S the reaction may well become kinetically controlled. For instance, when the concentration of Na_2S is, say, 3×10^{-6} mol/cm³, $k_L a$ will become very much greater than $lk_2[B_o]$ and the absorption will be kinetically controlled.

The oxidation reaction is catalyzed by a number of metal ions, such as Cu, Mn, and Fe, and by activated carbon and the like; even impurities in the Na_2S can affect the rate of oxidation. Some aspects of activated-carbon-catalyzed reactions will be covered in Section 13.1.8 (Example 10).

3.3.4. Wet Air Oxidation of Soluble Compounds in Wastewater

In some cases it may be useful to consider the possibilities of employing the wet air oxidation of effluent liquors at elevated temperatures and pressures. Pruden and Le (1976) have examined this possibility with aqueous solutions containing phenol and nitrilotriacetic acid (NTA) in the temperature range of 200–300°C and at pressures up to about 170 atm. A 1-liter-capacity bubble column reactor was used.

In the case of phenol it was found that the system belonged to the regime overlapping 1 and 2, and plots of $1/R_A$ against $1/[B_o]$ were made. The $k_L a$ value obtained from the intercept appears to be reasonable. (The wet air treatment of effluents in the presence of catalysts in trickle-bed reactors is covered in Section 3.2.7.)

(B) Liquid–Liquid Systems

3.3.5. Alkaline Hydrolysis of Acetate Esters

In the case of the alkaline hydrolysis of acetic acid esters, which are only slightly soluble in water, the data can fall between regimes 1 and 2. Puranik and Sharma (1970b) have correlated the data obtained from a laboratory spray column by Eq. 2.16.

3.3.6. Sulfonation of Benzene, Toluene, and *p*-Xylene

Sohrabi et al. (1977) studied the two-phase sulfonation of benzene, toluene, and *p*-xylene with concentrated sulfuric acid. The aromatic substance was diluted with *o*-dichlorobenzene. Here the reaction occurs in the acid phase and is first order in the dissolved aromatic substance and H_2SO_4. Depending on the concentration of sulfuric acid (range: 15.5–17 *M*) and the speed of agitation, the system may conform to the very slow or slow reaction regime or it may lie between these two regimes. These authors conducted experiments to show this behavior. For instance, in the case of the sulfonation of toluene with sulfuric acid, having a concentration of 16.85×10^{-3} mol/cm³ at 30.2°C, the reaction was essentially mass transfer controlled at a stirring speed of 700 rev/min in a 1-liter agitated contactor. The value of the product of overall liquid-side mass transfer coefficient with the interfacial area based on the unit volume of the acid phase at this speed of stirring was found to be 0.196 sec^{-1}, which is quite reasonable.

Sohrabi et al. also studied the kinetics of the sulfonation reaction in a homogeneous system and the agreement between the rate constants obtained from two-phase experiments (when mass transfer resistance was absent) and homogeneous systems was found to be very good. The rates of sulfonation of toluene and *p*-xylene relative to that of benzene were found to be 64 and 280, respectively.

Hatcher and Hart (1980) have studied sulfonation in a laboratory as well as in a large (6-m³) glass-lined steel mechanically agitated reactor in the temperature range of 140–175°C. Here benzene vapor was passed through the reactor so that water formed as a result of the reaction is stripped. In the case of the large reactor a semibatch mode of operation was adopted. The system was found to conform to the regime between 1 and 2 and plots of $1/k_{LR}a$ vs. $1/[B_o]$ were drawn. The reaction is first order in benzene as well as sulfuric acid; the solubility of benzene at 150°C in sulfuric acid and sulfuric acid and benzenesulfonic acid mixtures was experimentally determined. At 150°C the value of the second-order rate constant from the laboratory reactor was found to be 2.78×10^{-1} cm³/mol sec.

Scale-up

The scale-up of systems belonging to the regime between 1 and 2 would require a knowledge of the kinetics of the reaction, $k_L a$; the fractional holdup of the B phase; and the residence time distribution of both phases.

3.4. REGIME 3: FAST REACTIONS

It is clear from Eq. 2.44 that in regime 3 the specific rate of mass transfer is a unique function of the physicochemical properties of the system and is independent of the hydrodynamic factors. The specific rate of mass transfer, R_A, is proportional to the $[(m+1)/2]$th power of the concentration of A. The reaction is mth order in A and nth order in B. Thus, only in the case of a first-order reaction is R_A proportional to the concentration of A (i.e., the partial pressure of A in the case of gas–liquid systems). If the reaction is zero order in A, then R_A will be proportional to the square root of the concentration of A. On the other hand, if the reaction is second order in A, then R_A will be proportional to the 1.5th power of the concentration of A. In all these cases backmixing in the gas phase will be undesirable.

The specific rate of mass transfer, R_A, is proportional to the $(n/2)$th power of the concentration of B. Thus if a reaction is zero order in B, then R_A is unaffected by the change in the concentration of B. If n has a value like 1 or 2, then an increase in the concentration of B should have a desirable influence on R_A. The capacity of the solvent also increases with an increase in the concentration of B; hence, for a specified amount of gas to be handled, the liquid circulation rate will decrease with an increase in the concentration of B. The effect of the concentration of B on R_A should be very carefully considered. This matter is discussed later in this section.

The value of R_A is proportional to square root of k_{mn}. Thus, when a choice of reactant is available, from the mass transfer point of view it would be desirable to use an absorbent that offers a high value of k_{mn}. Consider the absorption of CO_2 in aqueous solutions of ammonia, monoethanolamine (MEA), diethanolamine (DEA), and diisopropanolamine under conditions such that a fast pseudo-first-order reaction mechanism prevails. As an approximation, it may be assumed that the solution contains 1×10^{-3} mol/cm^3 of the amine and that the viscosities of all the solutions are practically the same (there is actually a small variation in the viscosities of these solutions). The values of the rate constant for these amines at 25°C are approximately 0.45, 7.6, 1.5, and 0.4×10^6 cm^3/mol sec, respectively. Thus the relative specific rates of absorption, with ammonia taken as the basis will be 1 : 4.1 : 1.8 : 0.94, respectively. This is one of the reasons why in practice aqueous MEA (rather than ammonia solutions) is used for the absorption of CO_2. Danckwerts and Sharma (1966) have discussed this matter in detail with respect to the removal of CO_2. They have also discussed the problem of the removal of COS from natural gas streams and liquefied petroleum fractions. The ratio of the rate constants for the reaction of COS with ethylaminoethanol and DEA is about 25. Thus a changeover from DEA to ethylaminoethanol may result in increasing R_A for COS by a factor of about 5 under otherwise similar conditions (Sharma, 1965).

The necessary condition which ensures that the gas-side resistance is absent for situations where the solute gas, A, is diluted with an inert gas is given by the following expression:

$$k_{G_A} \gg H_A k_L \sqrt{M} \tag{3.9}$$

where H_A is the Henry's law constant relating the interfacial partial pressure $p_{A,i}$ of A to [A*]:

$$[A^*] = H_A p_{A,i} \tag{3.10}$$

When the gas-side resistance is significant, the following equation holds for systems where both m and n are equal to 1:

$$\frac{p_A}{R_A a} = \frac{1}{a}\left(\frac{1}{k_{G_A}} + \frac{1}{H_A\sqrt{D_A k_2 [B_o]}}\right) \tag{3.11}$$

Here a plot of $p_A/R_A a$ against $1/\sqrt{[B_o]}$ will be a straight line and the $k_G a$ and a values can be calculated from the intercept and the slope. It is assumed that D_A and k_2 do not vary in the range of concentration of B relevant to the plot.

The theory of mass transfer accompanied by a fast pseudo-mth-order reaction can be employed to study the kinetics of relatively fast reactions. In the conventional methods only relatively slow reactions can be studied. For fast reactions quite sophisticated techniques like the stopped-flow method or relaxation technique have to be used (Caldin, 1964; Hague, 1971). From Eq. 2.44 it is clear that if we know [A*] and D_A, or if these can be estimated, then the value of k_{mn} can be calculated. Table 3.1 gives some examples where this theory has been successfully used. Some reactions have second-order rate constants as high as 10^8 cm^3/mol sec. If the solute is only slightly soluble, but the solubility is known, then extremely fast reactions can be studied. Consider the absorption of O_2 in an aqueous solution where it undergoes a fast pseudo-first-order reaction with a rate constant of 10^6 sec^{-1}. The necessary conditions for the validity of a fast pseudo-first-order mechanism will be easily satisfied when k_L is, say, 4×10^{-2} cm/sec. ($D_A = 2 \times 10^{-5}$ cm^2/sec, $[A^*] = 10^{-6}$ mol/cm^3, $[B_o] = 1 \times 10^{-3}$ mol/cm^3, $D_B = D_A$, $Z = 1$.)

$$\frac{\sqrt{D_A k_1}}{k_L} (\simeq 115) < \frac{[B_o]}{[A^*]} (= 1000).$$

(A) Gas–Liquid Systems

3.4.1. Absorption of CO_2 and COS in Aqueous Solutions of Amines and Alkalies

Absorption of CO_2

In certain circumstances the absorption of CO_2 in aqueous caustic alkaline solutions and aqueous solutions of a variety of amines, which is of great industrial importance, conforms to this regime 3. The reaction is first order in CO_2 and first order in OH^- or amine. Danckwerts and Sharma (1966) have discussed this matter in detail. It appears that in industrial columns for CO_2 absorption, a major part of the height of the column in the case of packed columns and a major number of plates in the case of plate columns satisfy the requirements of this regime. Recently Hikita et al. (1977c, 1980) and Danckwerts (1979) have indicated that in the case of diethanolamine (DEA) the reaction may well be second order in DEA.

Table 3.1. Examples of the Evaluation of the Rate Constant on the Basis of the Theory of Mass Transfer with Chemical Reaction

Solute Gas	Absorbent	Apparatus	Reference(s)
	Gas–Liquid Systems		
CO_2	Carbonate buffers with or without catalyst	Wetted-wall column	Roberts and Danckwerts (1962)
		Jet apparatus	Sharma and Danckwerts (1963)
		Stirred cell	Sharma (1964)
	Aqueous lithium, sodium, potassium hydroxides, and alkanolamines	Jet apparatus	Nijsing et al. (1959); Sharma (1964); Clarke (1964); Sada et al. (1976, 1977a, b)
	Sodium sulfide	Jet apparatus	Sharma and Mashelkar (1968)
	Barium sulfide	Stirred cell	Gupta and Sharma (1967)
	Amines and alkanolamines dissolved in organic solvents such as isopropanol, *n*-butanol, cyclohexanol, aqueous diethylene glycol, toluene, and *o*-xylene	Jet apparatus Stirred contactor	Sharma and Mashelkar (1968); Mehta and Sharma (1971); Juvekar and Sharma (1973); Sridharan and Sharma (1976)
COS	Aqueous sodium hydroxide	Wetted-wall column	Sharma (1965)
	Aqueous alkanolamine	Jet apparatus; stirred cell	Sharma (1965)
$COCl_2$	Water and aqueous sodium hydroxide	Jet apparatus	Manogue and Pigford (1960)
Cl_2	Water	Wetted-wall column	Brian et al. (1962)
	Aqueous solutions of *p*-toluene sulfonic acid and *m*-aminophenol hydrochloride; aqueous solutions of chloro- and nitrophenols	Jet apparatus; stirred contactor	Yadav and Sharma (1981)
	p-Cresol dissolved in .1,1,4-trichlorobenzene	Jet apparatus	Pangarkar and Sharma (1974)
	Substituted phenols in dichlorobenzene and *n*-butylacetate	Stirred contactor	Sheth (1977); Yadav (1980)
HCl	Pinenes, Δ^3-carene, myrcene, camphene, etc., dissolved in chlorobenzene	Stirred cell	Bhargava and Sharma (1978)
O_2	Aqueous sodium sulfite	Jet apparatus	Westerterp et al. (1963)
		Wetted-well column	de Waal and Okeson (1966)
		Wetted-wall column and jet apparatus	Wesselingh and van't Hoog (1970); Sawicki and Barron (1973)
		Stirred cell	Linek (1966)

Table 3.1. (*Continued*)

Solute Gas	Absorbent	Apparatus	Reference(s)
	Gas–Liquid Systems		
O_2	Aqueous sodium dithionite	Jet apparatus; stirred cell	Jhaveri and Sharma (1968)
O_2	Aqueous alkaline solutions containing sodium salt of 1,4-naphthoquinone-2-sulfonic acid as a catalyzer	Jet apparatus	Takeuchi et al. (1980)
O_2	Aqueous neutral and acidic solutions of cuprous chloride; acidic solutions of chromous chloride; ammoniacal cuprous chloride, ammoniacal cuprous carbonate, hydroxide, and sulfide	Stirred cell	Jhaveri and Sharma (1967); Chhabria and Sharma (1974) Kane (1975)
	Solutions of cuprous amine complexes in polar solvents		Sridharan and Sharma (1976)
	Aqueous solutions of cobaltous amine complex	Stirred cell	Bratchley and Green (1976); Jahan (1978)
O_2	Cuprous and cobaltous benzoates in melts of benzoic acid	Stirred cell	Ghorpade et al. (1981)
O_2	*n*-Butyraldehyde dissolved in *n*-butyric acid	Stirred cell	Ladhabhoy and Sharma (1969)
O_2	2-Ethylhexaldehyde dissolved in 2-ethylhexanoic acid	Stirred cell	Ladhabhoy and Sharma (1970)
O_3	*n*-Isobutyraldehyde dissolved in CCl_4	Stirred contactor	Teramoto et al. (1977)
	Aqueous alkaline solutions	Wetted-wall column	Rizzuti et al. (1976)
N_2O_4	Water	Jet apparatus	Kramers et al. (1961)
Isobutylene	Aqueous sulfuric acid	Jet apparatus	Gehlawat and Sharma (1968)
	Aqueous solutions containing thallium (III) ions	Stirred cell	Yano et al. (1974)
2-Butene	Aqueous sulfuric acid	Stirred cell	Sankholkar and Sharma (1973)
PH_3	Aqueous solutions of sodium hypochlorite and sulfuric acid	Stirred cell; stirred contactor	Chandrasekaran and Sharma (1977)
NO	Aqueous solutions of $KMnO_4$ and $NaClO_2$ containing NaOH	Stirred cell	Teramoto et al. (1976a, b)
	Aqueous H_2O_2	Stirred cell	Baveja et al. (1979)
	Aqueous solutions of (alkaline) sodium dithionite, Na_2S	Stirred contactor	Lahiri (1981)

Table 3.1. (*Continued*)

Liquid–Liquid Systems			
Solute	Phase Containing B	Apparatus	Reference(s)
Formate esters	Aqueous solutions of sodium and potassium hydroxide	Stirred cell	Nanda and Sharma (1966); Bidner and de Santiago (1971)
Esters of halosubstituted acetic acid	Aqueous solutions of sodium and potassium hydroxide	Stirred cell	Nanda and Sharma (1967)
A variety of esters	Aqueous solutions of sodium and potassium hydroxide	Stirred cell	Sharma and Sharma (1969, 1970a, 1970b)
Carbon disulfide	Aqueous solutions of amines	Stirred cell	Kothari and Sharma (1966a)
Cyclohexanone	Aqueous solutions of hydroxylammonium sulfate	Stirred cell	Sharma and Nanda (1968)
2-Methyl-2-butene (isoamylene)	Aqueous solutions of sulfuric acid	Stirred cell	Sankholkar and Sharma (1973)
Benzene, toluene, and chlorobenzene	Aqueous solutions of sulfuric acid containing nitric acid	Stirred cell	Cox and Strachan (1972a, b); Chapman and Strachan (1974)
		Laminar jet apparatus	Hanson and Ismail (1976)
Nitroaromatics	Aqueous solutions of Na_2S_x	Stirred cell	Bhave and Sharma (1981)
Copper ions (in aqueous solution)	Benzoyl acetone	Stirred contactor	Kondo et al. (1978)

The absorption of CO_2 in carbonate buffer solutions catalyzed by arsenite ions (Giammarco–Vetrocoke process) also conforms to this regime in packed and plate columns. Actually, the absorption of CO_2 in carbonate buffer solutions catalyzed by arsenite, hypochlorite, and similar ions has proved to be a very convenient system for laboratory studies of aspects of gas absorption with chemical reaction. The major advantage is that the rate constant can be simply varied by changing the concentration of the catalyst and yet the physical properties of the absorbent remain practically the same. Richards et al. (1964), Danckwerts and Gillham (1966), Pohorecki (1968, 1976), Sharma and Mashelkar (1968), McNeil (1970), and others have made use of this system to study the performance of a variety of gas–liquid contactors (see Section 3.5).

Absorption of COS

Sour natural gases invariably contain COS. Further, the C_3 stream from petroleum processing also contains COS whenever sulfur is present in the basic raw material. Sharma (1965) has studied the kinetics of absorption of COS in aqueous caustic alkaline solutions and aqueous solutions of alkanolamines.

The following reactions occur:

Reaction between COS and OH^-

$$COS + 4OH^- \rightarrow CO_3^{2-} + S^{2-} + 2H_2O$$

Reaction between COS and amines

$$\begin{aligned} COS + R_2NH &\rightleftharpoons R_2NCOS^- + H^+ \\ H^+ + R_2NH &\rightleftharpoons R_2NH_2^+ \\ \hline COS + 2R_2NH &\rightleftharpoons R_2NCOS^- + R_2NH_2^+ \end{aligned}$$

The rate of reaction of COS with any amine is slower than that with CO_2 by approximately a factor of 100. Further, at 25°C, the rate constant for the reaction with OH^- (in 1 *M* NaOH) is only 1.2×10^4 cm^3/mol sec compared to an approximate value of 1.3×10^7 cm^3/mol sec for the reaction between CO_2 and OH^- under comparable conditions.

Depending on the reactive species and the type of contactor, the system may conform to regime 3, to the regime between 2 and 3, or to regime 2. (It was pointed out in the introductory part of this section that a changeover from one amine to another fast-reacting amine can substantially increase the specific rate of mass transfer if the system conforms to regime 3.)

The increase in the solubility of COS in ethanol is substantially higher than that in the case of CO_2 and in some cases it may be worthwhile to examine the advantages of employing organic solvents for the removal of COS.

The reaction between COS and amines to give thiocarbamate is also industrially important in the manufacture of pesticides. The reaction between COS and diethylamine is relevant in the manufacture of Saturn herbicide (manufactured by Kamiai Chemicals of Japan). It will be shown later (Section 3.4.15) that the related reaction between CS_2 and amines to give dithiocarbamates is also important for the manufacture of pesticides.

3.4.2. Absorption of Oxygen in Aqueous Acidic and Neutral Solutions of Cuprous Chloride, and in Cuprous and Cobaltous Amine Complexes in Aqueous and Polar Solutions

$$O_2 + 4CuCl + 4HCl \rightarrow 4CuCl_2 + 2H_2O$$

$$\tfrac{3}{2}O_2 + 6CuCl + 3H_2O \rightarrow (3CuOCuCl_2 3H_2O) + 2CuCl_2$$

The oxidation of CuCl by O_2 is of considerable importance in Wacker processes, for the conversion of olefins to the corresponding carbonyl compounds, and in the manufacture of copper oxychloride. It is also important in the liquid-phase oxychlorination of ethylene to ethylene dichloride. Jhaveri and Sharma (1967) have studied the kinetics of this reaction. Under certain conditions, the system above conforms to this regime. The specific rate of absorption was found to be directly proportional to the partial pressure of O_2 and concentration of CuCl (Figures 3.4 and 3.5) and hence the reaction is first order in O_2 and second order in CuCl. It is likely that the active species participating in the reaction is $CuCl_2^-$ and that its concentration is related to the Cu^+ and Cl^- ion concentrations in a complex way. The order of the reaction with respect to $CuCl_2^-$ may be different and may follow a first-order behavior.

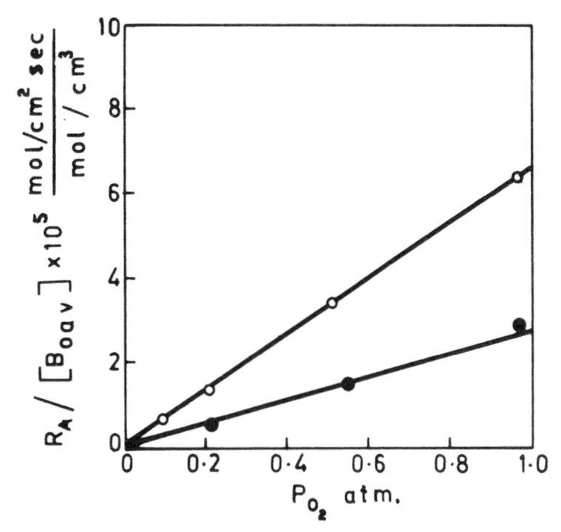

Figure 3.4. Effect of partial pressure of O_2 on the specific rate of absorption of O_2 in an aqueous acidic solution of cuprous chloride (○, 5*M* HCl solution; ●, 3.74*M* NaCl solution).

Chhabria and Sharma (1974) have shown that absorption of O_2 in aqueous solutions of cuprous amine complexes is accompanied by a fast pseudo-first-order reaction (L = amine)

$$O_2 + 4LCu^+ + 4H^+ \rightarrow 4LCu^{+2} + 2H_2O$$

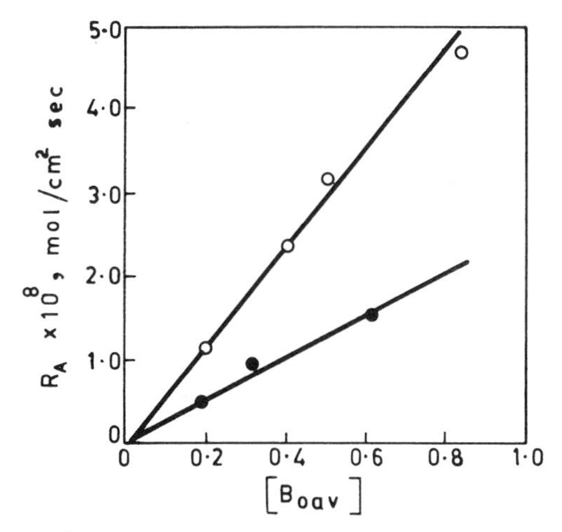

Figure 3.5. Effect of the concentration of CuCl on the specific rate of absorption of O_2 in aqueous acidic solution of cuprous chloride (○, 5*M* HCl solution; ●, 3.74*M* NaCl solution).

The reaction was found to be first order in the cuprous amine complex as well as the free ammonia. The rate constant for the cuprous amine complex is much higher than that for CuCl dissolved in (say) aqueous HCl. Kane (1975) and Jahan (1978) have studied the kinetics of absorption of O_2 in cuprous amine carbonate/hydroxide/sulfide solutions that are relevant in hydrometallurgical processes for the recovery of Cu (which have acquired considerable importance in the recent years).

Sridharan and Sharma (1976) have shown that polar solvents such as isopropyl alcohol, pyridine, or dimethyl formamide can be used for cuprous amine complexes, and here also the reactions are fast and belong to this regime. The oxidation of the cuprous amine complex is also relevant in the manufacture of polyphenyloxide from 2,6-dimethyl phenol. The foregoing systems are useful for the measurement of $k_L a$ and a in contactors.

In the related case of cobaltous amine complexes it has also been reported that the absorption of O_2 is accompanied by a fast pseudo-first-order reaction (Bratchley and Green, 1970). Here the reaction was found to be first order in cobaltous ion concentration. (The related reactions of oxidation of cuprous and cobaltous benzoate in benzoic acid melts are covered in Section 3.9.4.)

3.4.3. Absorption of Oxygen in Aqueous Alkaline Solutions of Sodium Dithionite (Hydrosulfite)

$$O_2 + Na_2S_2O_4 + H_2O \rightarrow NaHSO_4 + NaHSO_3$$

$$NaHSO_4 + NaOH \rightarrow Na_2SO_4 + H_2O$$

$$NaHSO_3 + NaOH \rightarrow Na_2SO_3 + H_2O$$

Sodium dithionite is used extensively as a reducing agent for vat dyes in the dyeing of fabrics. A considerable excess of dithionite over that required theoretically is used in practice. A number of claims have been made for reducing the requirements of sodium dithionite. Jhaveri and Sharma (1968) have studied the kinetics of this reaction and found that in most practical contactors the absorption of O_2 is accompanied by a fast pseudo-mth-order reaction. The specific rate of absorption was found to vary as the square root of the partial pressure of O_2 and hence the order of the reaction in O_2 is zero (Figure 3.6). Below a dithionite concentration of 8×10^{-5} mol/cm³ the reaction was found to be first order with respect to dithionite. However, above a dithionite concentration of 8×10^{-5} mol/cm³ the reaction was found to be second order in dithionite. Recently, Hikita et al. (1978) studied the kinetics of this reaction and found the reaction to be zero order in O_2 and first order in dithionite below a concentration of 1×10^{-4} mol/cm³ and second order in dithionite above this concentration. Singh et al. (1978) also studied the kinetics of this reaction in a homogeneous system and found the reaction to be zero order in O_2. Fukushima et al. (1978) also found that the reaction is zero order in O_2 over dithionite concentrations up to 5×10^{-4} mol/cm³. However, some discrepancies can be seen in the published results. Hikita et al. found that at a dithionite concentration greater than 1×10^{-4} mol/cm³ the reaction is half order in O_2; Fukushima et al. found that throughout the range of dithionite covered (0–5×10^{-4} mol/cm³) the reaction is second order in dithionite. The rate constant of this reaction, unlike that in the case of sulfite oxidation, is not affected by alcohols, glycols, and glycerol (Jhaveri and Sharma, 1968).

The related case of zinc dithionite has been studied by Chhabria (1972), and here also the absorption of O_2 is accompanied by a fast pseudo-zero-order reaction.

3.4.4. Absorption of Oxygen in Aqueous Sodium Sulfite

Interest in the absorption of oxygen in aqueous sodium sulfite arose out of the desirability of using this system to study the performance characteristics of a variety of contactors. This reaction is also of some industrial relevance in pollution abatement for the removal of SO_2 from lean off-gas by absorption in

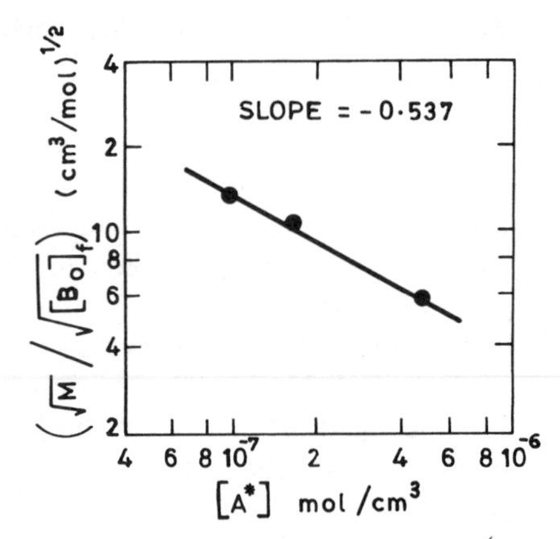

Figure 3.6. Effect of the concentration of O_2 on $\left(\sqrt{M}/\sqrt{[B_o]_f}\right)$ in the absorption of O_2 in aqueous alkaline solutions of sodium dithionite.

aqueous alkaline solutions. This reaction is catalyzed greatly by cobalt ions and can be almost completely inhibited by alcohols and polyols. Apparently the reaction follows the chain reaction mechanism and may show a significant induction period. Table 3.2 lists some of the important findings about the kinetics of this reaction. The reaction has been found to be zero, first, and second order in O_2 under different sets of conditions. It is evident from Table 3.2 that different authors have worked under different set of conditions. Further, the reaction order with respect to O_2 depends on the range of partial pressures of O_2 (and hence the interfacial concentration, [A*]). The impurities in the reactants may also affect the rate but are unlikely to affect the order of the reaction with respect to the various species. The value of R_A, therefore, should always be obtained experimentally, and the functional dependence on the concentration of the various species may be taken as the same as that reported in the literature for the range of interest.

The first-order dependence on O_2 reported by some authors may have been observed because the reaction was not sufficiently fast to occur in the film and may have resulted in a situation where $\sqrt{M}$ was much less than 1 (Sawicki and Barron, 1973). Under such conditions no reaction occurs in the film, the system belongs to regime 2, and Eq. 2.8 holds, which implies that the rate of absorption will be proportional to [A*] and the reaction is then wrongly classified as first order in O_2. When studying the kinetics of absorption, therefore, it is essential that $\sqrt{M}$ be greater than 3.

It is also likely that the controlling steps in the reaction sequence are different for the homogeneous and heterogeneous systems, and this might explain the apparent discrepancy between the reported values of the order with respect to O_2, SO_3^{2-}, and cobalt ion concentration. It appears that in the cobalt-ion-catalyzed reaction the rate of the heterogeneous system is affected by a diffusion-limited catalyst regeneration reaction (Sawicki and Barron, 1973).

3.4.5. Absorption of NO or NO_2 and / or N_2O_4 in Water and Aqueous Solutions Containing Reactive Species; Reaction between Dissolved NO and O_2

The absorption of NO_2 and/or N_2O_4 in water is a key step in the manufacture of nitric acid.

$$3NO_2 + H_2O \rightarrow 2HNO_3 + NO$$
(Actual reactive species is N_2O_4)

Kramers et al. (1961) and Andrew and Hanson (1961) have studied the kinetics of this reaction. The overall kinetics of this reaction, under conditions of industrial importance, is quite complicated. The absorption of pure NO_2 in water, however, is accompanied by a fast pseudo-first-order reaction. Sherwood et al. (1975) have analyzed this case in the light of the foregoing papers as well as of additional data reported in their Table 8.3 (p. 354 of their book). Kameoka and Pigford (1977) have also studied absorption of lean N_2O_4 in water in a string of spheres column. Their findings are basically in agreement with those of Kramers et al. Counce and Perona (1979) have also studied absorption of N_2O_4 in dilute nitric acid in a 7.6-cm-i.d. sieve-plate column containing three plates. These authors also concur with the mechanism suggested by Andrew and Hanson (1961) and the other authors cited above. They have also brought out the detrimental effect of HNO_2 in water on the efficiency of absorption of N_2O_4.

Komiyama and Inoue (1980) have studied absorption of NO_2 and NO—NO_2 mixtures in weak alkaline solutions ($[OH^-] \simeq 1 \times 10^{-5}$ mol/cm^3) in a sparged reactor and a stirred contactor with a plane liquid interface. The NO_x concentration was varied in the range of 5–5000 ppm. The order of the reaction with respect to NO_2 depends on its concentration; above 800 ppm the reaction appears to be second order in NO_2 and below 800 ppm it becomes 3/2 order in NO_2. Further, the absorption rates from NO and NO_2 mixtures show different behavior and are 3/4 order with respect to the product of [NO] and [NO_2]. These authors have proposed a model that considers equilibrium between NO, NO_2, N_2O_3, and N_2O_4 and hydration products of N_2O_3 and N_2O_4. Data on the solubilities of NO_2 and N_2O_4, the rates of hydration of N_2O_3 and N_2O_4, and the relevant equilibrium constants have been reported in the paper. Published experimental data as well as those obtained by these authors agree with the predicted values based on the proposed model. Komiyama and Inoue have reported the pseudo-first-order rate constant for the hydration of N_2O_4 as 554 sec^{-1} at 15°C compared to the value of 250 sec^{-1} at 20°C reported by Kramers et al. (1961). Komiyama and Inoue have brought out reasons for the differences in the rate constant values reported in the literature, which are due at least partly to the differences in the calculation of [A*].

Hoffmann and Emig (1979) have discussed various aspects of the design of absorption columns for the manufacture of nitric acid and a complete worked example is presented.

TABLE 3.2. Kinetics of the Oxidation of Sulfites in the Presence of Catalysts

Method of Study	Temp.	Concentration of Species (mol/cm^3 or $g\ ion/cm^3$)			pH	Order of Reaction with Respect to			Remarks	Reference(s)
		O_2	SO_3^{2-} [a]	Catalyst		O_2	SO_3^{2-}	Catalyst		
Homogeneous (polarographic method)	20	$< 1.11 \times 10^{-6}$	8.1×10^{-6}	$0-5.85 \times 10^{-10}$ ($CoSO_4$)	8–9.2	1	1	—	—	Yagi and Inoue (1962)
Heterogeneous	≃ 20	—	$< 6 \times 10^{-5}$	$CoSO_4$	—	0	—	—	—	Astarita et al. (1964)
			$\simeq 2.5 \times 10^{-4}$	$CoSO_4$	—	1	—	—	—	
			$> 2.5 \times 10^{-4}$ $< 1 \times 10^{-3}$	$CoSO_4$		2	—	—	—	
Heterogeneous (film reactor)	20–33	—	$0.4-0.8 \times 10^{-3}$	3×10^{-8} to 1×10^{-6} ($CoSO_4$)	7.5–8.5	1	0	—	Order with respect to O_2 was assumed	de Waal and Okeson (1966)
Homogeneous (rapid mixing method)	25	$< 3 \times 10^{-6}$	2×10^{-5} to 5×10^{-4}	$0-1 \times 10^{-7}$ (Cu^{2+} ion)	—	0	1.5	—	—	Barron and O'Hern (1966)
Homogeneous (flow thermal method)	20	6×10^{-7} to 2.4×10^{-6}	2×10^{-6} to 2×10^{-5}	$0-3.39 \times 10^{-7}$ (Co^{2+})	8–8.3	1	1	—	For $8 \times 10^{-5} < SO_3^{2-} < 1.6 \times 10^{-4}$ rate is independent of SO_3^{2-} concentration	Srivastava et al. (1968)
Heterogeneous (agitated vessel)	15–35	$< 6 \times 10^{-7}$	$2.5-7.95 \times 10^{-4}$	$0-1 \times 10^{-6}$ ($CoSO_4$)	7.8–9.2	2	0	1	—	Linek and Mayrhoferova (1970)
	15–35	$> 6 \times 10^{-7}$	$2.5-7.95 \times 10^{-4}$		7.8–9.2	1	0	1	—	
Heterogeneous (wetted-wall column and laminar jet)	20–38	5×10^{-8} to 6×10^{-7}	$4-8 \times 10^{-4}$	4×10^{-7} to 2×10^{-6} (Co^{2+})	7.5–8.5	2		1	At lower concentration of O_2 there is some effect of SO_3^{2-} concentration, perhaps due to impurities	Wesselingh and Van't Hoog (1970)
Heterogeneous (stirred cell)	34	1×10^{-7}	8×10^{-4}	4×10^{-7} ($CoSO_4$)	8.2–8.5	2	0	—	—	Danckwerts and Rizvi (1971)
Heterogeneous (packed column)	30	1.15×10^{-7}	3×10^{-4} to 1×10^{-7}	5×10^{-9} to 1×10^{-7}	8.5	2	0	—	Order with respect to O_2 varies gradually from 2 to 1 as p_{O_2} is increased.	Onda et al. (1972)
	30	3×10^{-7}	3×10^{-4} to 1×10^{-7}	5×10^{-9} to 1×10^{-7}	8.5	1.5	0	—		
	30	5.7×10^{-7}	3×10^{-4} to 1×10^{-7}	5×10^{-9} to 1×10^{-7}	8.5	1	0	—		

Homogeneous (rapid mixing method)	25	1.4–4.2 $\times 10^{-7}$	4.5×10^{-6} to 4×10^{-5}	1×10^{-10} to 3×10^{-9} ($CoSO_4$)	9.0–9.7	0	1.5	0.5	—	Chen and Barron (1972)
Heterogeneous (film reactor)	15–60	1–6 $\times 10^{-7}$	4–8 $\times 10^{-4}$	3×10^{-9} to 3×10^{-6} ($CoSO_4$)	7.5–8.5	2	0	1	—	Reith and Beek (1973)
Heterogeneous (wetted-wall column)	25	2.5×10^{-7} to 1.6×10^{-6}	3×10^{-5}	1×10^{-9} to 5×10^{-8} ($CoSO_4$)	10	2	—	0.5	—	Sawicki and Barron (1973)
	25	2.5×10^{-7} to 1.6×10^{-6}	3×10^{-5}	7×10^{-9} to 6×10^{-8} ($[(NH_3)_5CoCl]Cl_2$)	10	2	—	0.5	—	Sawicki and Barron (1973)
	25	2.5×10^{-7} to 1.6×10^{-6}	3×10^{-5}	7×10^{-9} to 6×10^{-8} ($[(NH_3)_5CoCl]SO_4$)	10	2	—	0.5	—	Sawicki and Barron (1973)
Heterogeneous (stirred cell and packed column)	30	$< 6 \times 10^{-7}$	5–10 $\times 10^{-4}$	4×10^{-8} to 1×10^{-6}	9.1–9.3	2	0	—	—	Alper (1973)
		$> 8 \times 10^{-7}$ to $< 6 \times 10^{-6}$	8×10^{-4}		9.1–9.3	1	0	—	—	Alper (1973)
Heterogeneous (stirred cell)	20–50	1–8 $\times 10^{-7}$	4–8 $\times 10^{-4}$	1×10^{-7} to 2×10^{-6} ($CoSO_4$)	7.5–8.5	2	0	1	—	Laurent et al. (1974)
Homogeneous and heterogeneous (stirred cell and laminar jet)	30–60	3×10^{-8} to 1×10^{-6}	3×10^{-8} to 1×10^{-6};	1×10^{-10} to 3×10^{-9} ($CoSO_4$) 2×10^{-11} to 1×10^{-7}	6.0–7.5 7.5–8.5	0	1.5	—	Under heterogeneous conditions the rates of absorption are an order of magnitude lower than that under homogeneous conditions.	Bengtsson and Bjerle (1975)

TABLE 3.2. ***(Continued)***

Method of Study	Temp.	Concentration of Species (mol/cm³ or g ion/cm³): O_2	SO_3^{2-} [a]	Catalyst	pH	Order of Reaction with Respect to: O_2	SO_3^{2-}	Catalyst	Remarks	Reference(s)
Homogeneous	30	3×10^{-7} to 3×10^{-6}	2×10^{-6} to 4×10^{-5} [$(NH_4)_2SO_3$]	2×10^{-10} to 2×10^{-8}	8.5	0	1.5	0.5	—	Mishra and Srivastava (1975)
	30	5×10^{-7} to 3×10^{-6}	2×10^{-6} to 3×10^{-5} [K_2SO_3]	1×10^{-10} to 3×10^{-9} Cobaltous and cupric sulfate	8.5	0	1.5	0.5	—	Mishra and Srivastava (1976)
Heterogeneous (stirred cell)	20	3.75–9 $\times 10^{-7}$	Na_2SO_3 2–4.5 $\times 10^{-4}$; Na_2SO_4 3–4 $\times 10^{-4}$	2.5×10^{-8} to 1.0×10^{-7} ($CoSO_4$)	8.44–8.54	1	0	1	—	Nyvlt and Kastanek (1975)
	≃ 20	$< 3.75 \times 10^{-7}$		2.5×10^{-8} to 1.0×10^{-7} ($CoSO_4$)	8.44–8.54	2	0	1	—	
Heterogeneous (wetted-wall) column)	30	7×10^{-7}	$> 2 \times 10^{-4}$ $< 2 \times 10^{-4}$	1.55×10^{-8} 1.0×10^{-6}	7.5–8.5	Not studied	0 1			Trushanov et al. (1975)
Heterogeneous (stirred cell)	30	2–7 $\times 10^{-7}$	SO_3^{2-} SO_4^{2-} 5.3–8.3 $\times 10^{-4}$	Cobalt 5×10^{-7} to 1×10^{-8}	7.5–8.5	2	0	1	Above the critical concentration of sulfite, the order with respect to SO_3^{2-} is zero.	Satyamurthy (1976); Satyamurthy et al. (1979)
				Ammonium ferrous sulfate 5×10^{-7} to 1×10^{-8}		2	0	0.9		
Heterogeneous (stirred cell)	30	1–8 $\times 10^{-7}$	4.5×10^{-5} to 4.5×10^{-4} [$(NH_4)_2SO_3$]	Cobalt sulfate 1–5 $\times 10^{-6}$	7.9–8.1	1	2	—	—	Neelkantan and Gehlawat (1980)

[a] Sodium sulfite is meant unless specified.

The removal of NO_x from off-gases by absorption in aqueous alkaline solutions of sodium hypochlorite has been suggested (Krueger and Schmitz, 1970). Here NO is rapidly oxidized to NO_2. Baveja (1979) has studied the kinetics of absorption of lean NO in aqueous alkaline solutions of sodium hypochlorite in a stirred cell. It was observed that the reaction falls in regime 3 and that it is first order in NO and zero order in hypochlorite; the first-order rate constant values ranged from 2×10^3 sec^{-1} to 3.17×10^7 sec^{-1} at 20°C, depending on the pH of the solution. Since this reaction is zero order in B it shows interesting behavior as regards the transition from regime 3 to 4, and this matter is discussed in Section 3.8. The practical utility of hypochlorite liquors will at best be restricted to those off-gases where no CO_2 is present, since CO_2 reacts at a fairly fast rate in the aqueous alkaline solutions of hypochlorite. Such off-gases, without any CO_2, are encountered in nitric acid plants, the oxidation of organic compounds based on nitric acid, and the like.

Lahiri (1981) has studied the kinetics of absorption of lean NO in aqueous alkaline solutions of sodium dithionite (sodium hydrosulfite) and sodium sulfide. In the case of dithionite the reaction

$$6NO + Na_2S_2O_4 + 2NaOH \rightarrow Na_2SO_3 \cdot N_2O_2 + Na_2SO_4 + 2N_2O + H_2O$$

or

$$5NO + Na_2S_2O_4 + 2NaOH \rightarrow 2Na_2SO_3 \cdot N_2O_2 + \tfrac{1}{2}N_2 + H_2O$$

or

$$4NO + Na_2S_2O_4 + 2NaOH \rightarrow Na_2SO_3 \cdot N_2O_2 + N_2 + H_2O$$

was found to conform to regime 3 and it was first order in NO and zero order in dithionite. In the case of the reaction of NO with Na_2S,

$$2NO + S^{2-} + H_2O \rightarrow S + N_2O + 2OH^-.$$

$$6NO + S + 2OH^- \rightarrow [(NO)_2SO_3]^{2-} + 2N_2O + H_2O$$

the reaction was also found to conform to regime 3 and it was found to be zero order in NO and zero order in Na_2S. This kinetic behavior is very unusual. In the case of alkaline dithionite solutions the utility of the absorbent will be restricted to gaseous mixtures that do not contain O_2 and CO_2.

Hikita et al. (1978) have studied the kinetics of absorption of NO into an aqueous sodium sulfite solution containing Fe(III)—EDTA(ethylenediamine-tetraacetic acid)—Na and $Fe_2(SO_4)_3$. The concentration of chelate plays an important role. The reaction was found to be first order in NO and zero order in Na_2SO_3.

Teramoto et al. (1976a) have studied the absorption of NO in aqueous solutions of $KMnO_4$ containing NaOH in a stirred cell and have found that the absorption of NO is accompanied by a fast pseudo-first-order reaction:

$$NO + MnO_4^- + 2OH^- \rightarrow NO_2^- + MnO_4^{2-} + H_2O$$

The reaction was found to be first order in NO as well as the oxidizing agent. At 25°C, the values of the second-order rate constant for the NO—$KMnO_4$ and NO—K_2MnO_4 + KOH systems were found to be 3.1×10^9 and 4×10^9 cm^3/mol sec, respectively.

Teramoto et al (1976b) have studied the absorption of NO in aqueous solutions of $NaClO_2$ and NaOH in a stirred cell and have found that absorption of NO is accompanied by a fast pseudo-*m*th-order reaction. At low pH, $NaClO_2$ gives ClO_2, which gets desorbed in the gas phase and oxidizes NO to NO_2. Thus at lower pH values we may get much higher values of R_A as compared to predicted values, which does not account for the gas-phase oxidation of NO.

Sada et al. (1979a) have studied the kinetics of absorption of NO as well as NO_2 in aqueous alkaline solutions of $NaClO_2$ (reaction: $2NO + ClO_2^- \rightarrow 2NO_2 + Cl^-$; $4NO_2 + ClO_2^- + 4OH^- \rightarrow 4NO_3^- + Cl^- + 2H_2O$). In the case of NO the reaction was found to be second order in NO above an NO concentration of 2×10^{-9} mol/cm^3 and first order in NO below a concentration of 5×10^{-10} mol/cm^3. In the case of NO_2 the reaction was found to be second order in NO_2 and first order in ClO_2^- for a concentration greater than 1×10^{-3} mol/cm^3. Sada et al. (1979b) have also studied the absorption of NO in aqueous slurries of $Ca(OH)_2$ and $Mg(OH)_2$ containing $NaClO_2$, since lower pH values give higher values of the rate constant. This matter will be discussed in Section 12.1.

Baveja et al. (1979) have studied the kinetics of absorption of NO in aqueous solutions of hydrogen peroxide where the product of the reaction is nitric acid (reaction: $4NO + 6H_2O_2 \rightarrow 4HNO_3 + 4H_2O$). This process is potentially attractive in a nitric acid plant since the dilute nitric acid solution obtained from the absorber can be recycled. The reaction between NO and H_2O_2 was found to be very fast and conformed to regime 3. The reaction was found to be first order in NO and first order in H_2O_2.

The absorption of a mixture of NO and NO_2 in aqueous solutions of sodium hydroxide or sodium carbonate is practiced for the manufacture of sodium nitrite and sometimes for pollution abatement ($NO + NO_2 + 2NaOH = 2NaNO_2 + H_2O$; $NO + NO_2 + Na_2CO_3 = 2NaNO_2 + CO_2$). However, no systematic studies have been made to discern the controlling mechanism.

Absorption of lean NO_2/N_2O_4 in aqueous alkaline solutions, with or without Na_2SO_3, has been studied by Kameoka and Pigford (1977) and this matter will be covered in Section 5.7, since it involves reaction between one gas and more than one reactant in the liquid phase. Sada et al. (1978) have studied the absorption of NO and SO_2 individually and together in aqueous alkaline solutions of sodium chlorite; aspects of the simultaneous absorption of NO and SO_2 is covered in Section 6.3.5. The simultaneous absorption of NO_2 and SO_2 in aqueous solutions of NaOH and Na_2SO_3 has been studied by Takeuchi and Yamanaka (1978) and this is also covered in Section 6.3.5.

The absorption of NO in aqueous solutions of ferrous sulfate, where a reversible reaction is encountered, is covered in Section 3.10.

The absorption of lean NO in aqueous solutions of nitric acid where the reaction occurs in the gas phase also is considered. Pogrebnaya et al. (1975) have shown that the reaction between NO and O_2, which is very important in the manufacture of nitric acid by absorption of $NO_2 + N_2O_4$, occurs not only in the gas phase but also in the liquid phase. The reaction in the aqueous phase is much faster than in the gas phase. The kinetics of this reaction was studied in a flow reactor and was found to be second order in NO and first order in O_2; the value of the overall third-order rate constant was found to be 8.8×10^6 $(cm^3/mol)^2\ sec^{-1}$ at 25°C. The reaction between dissolved NO and O_2 under conditions of industrial importance would be expected to fall in regime 1.

Reaction Occurring in the Gas Phase: Absorption of Lean NO *in Aqueous* HNO_3

Lefers et al. (1980) have suggested that concentrated nitric acid (60–80%) itself can be used as an absorbent for NO in tail gases. The following reaction occurs:

$$NO + 2HNO_3 \rightarrow 3NO_2 + H_2O$$

This process is likely to be attractive for nitric acid plants, since no liquid effluent disposal problem will then be encountered. Experiments were made in a wetted-wall column. Concentrated nitric acid solutions exhibit considerable nitric acid vapor pressure, and therefore it is likely that the reaction between NO and HNO_3 occurs in the vapor phase. Further, the rate of evaporation of HNO_3 will be increased by the reaction. Lefers et al. have demonstrated that oxidation of NO in fact occurs in the gas phase on a reaction plane parallel to the gas–liquid interface. Danckwerts' solution for an instantaneous irreversible reaction can also be applied to the gas-phase reaction. The enhancement in the rate of evaporation of HNO_3 can also be calculated on the basis of surface renewal theories provided it is assumed that the gas phase is infinitely deep. The product of oxidation, NO_2, is in equilibrium with N_2O_4 and these can diffuse into the bulk gas phase or to the gas–liquid interface; N_2O_4 physically dissolves in concentrated nitric acid. A good agreement between the experimental and predicted values was observed.

3.4.6. Absorption of Oxygen and Ozone in Aldehydes

A number of aliphatic carboxylic acids and their corresponding anhydrides are manufactured by the liquid-phase air oxidation of aldehyde in the presence of manganese or copper plus cobalt salts of the carboxylic acid as the catalyst.

$$O_2 + 2RCHO \rightarrow 2RCOOH \rightarrow [RCO]_2O + H_2O$$

Acetic acid, butyric acid, 2-ethylhexoic acid and their corresponding anhydrides are manufactured in this manner. Ladhabhoy and Sharma (1969, 1970) have studied the mechanism of absorption of O_2 in *n*-butyraldehyde and 2-ethylhexaldehyde dissolved in the corresponding carboxylic acids. These systems were found to conform to this regime when the value of k_L was less than 8×10^{-3} cm/sec. The specific rate of absorption was found to be independent of the speed of stirring in a stirred cell and directly proportional to the partial pressure of O_2 and the concentration of the aldehyde (Figures 3.7–3.9). Thus

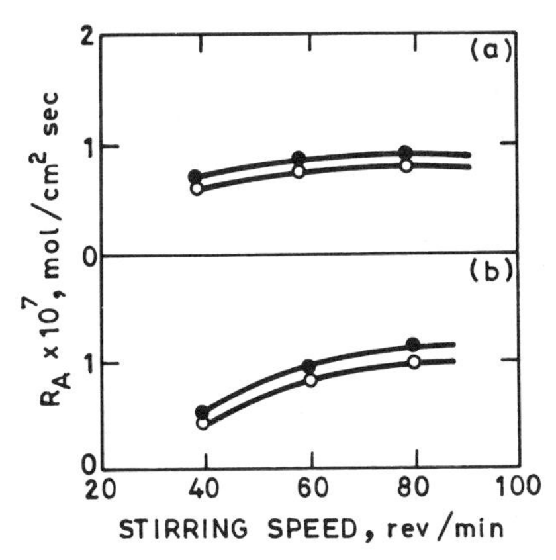

Figure 3.7. Effect of speed of stirring on the specific rate of absorption of O_2 in *n*-butyraldehyde dissolved in *n*-butyric acid in a stirred cell (○, 0.1 wt. % catalyst; ●, 0.2 wt. % catalyst). (*a*) Co^{2+} acetate. (*b*) Co^{2+} + Cu^{2+}(1 : 4) acetates.

the reactions are first order in O_2 and second order in the aldehyde.

Teramoto et al. (1977) have studied the reaction between ozone and aldehydes, such as *n*- and iso-butyraldehydes and benzaldehydes, dissolved in carbon tetrachloride. Ozone diluted with O_2 was absorbed in a 7.5-cm-i.d. stirred contactor. In the stirred contactor the necessary conditions for the validity of regime 3 were satisfied. The reaction was found to be first order in O_3 and aldehyde and the values of the second-order rate constant at 30°C for *n*-butyraldehyde, isobutyraldehyde, and hexaldehyde were found to be 5.2×10^5, 7.2×10^5, 2.9×10^4 $cm^3/mol\ sec$, respectively. It may be noted that in the case of benzaldehyde if a sparged reactor is used then the absorption of O_3 may be accompanied by slow reaction in the bulk liquid phase where its concentration may well be zero.

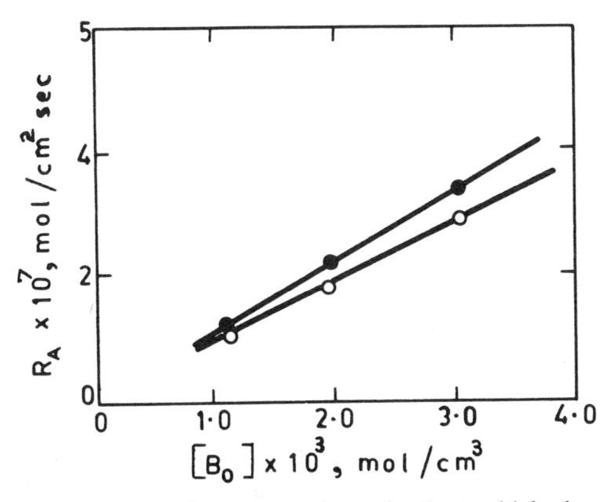

Figure 3.8. Effect of concentration of *n*-butyraldehyde on the specific rate of absorption of O_2 in *n*-butyraldehyde dissolved in *n*-butyric acid in a stirred cell, (○, 0.1 wt. %; ●, 0.2 wt. % of manganese acetate).

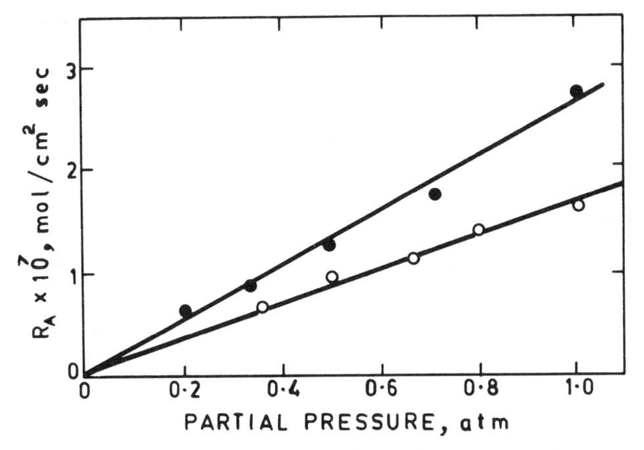

Figure 3.9. Effect of the partial pressure of O_2 on the specific rate of absorption of O_2 in *n*-butyraldehyde dissolved in *n*-butyric acid in a stirred cell (○, 1.16×10^{-3} mol/cm^3 at 29°C; ●, 3.16×10^{-3} mol/cm^3 at 20°C).

3.4.7. Absorption of Isobutylene, 2-Butene, and 2-Methyl-2-Butene in Aqueous Solutions of Sulfuric Acid; Absorption of Isobutylene in Aqueous Solutions Containing Thallium(III) Ions

The recovery of isobutylene from a variety of C_4 streams is accomplished by the selective absorption in 50–65% (by weight) sulfuric acid solutions at 30–40°C (under these conditions butenes are absorbed to an insignificant extent). The mechanism of absorption is as follows (Popovic and Deckwer, 1975):

$$(H_3C)_2C{=}CH_2 + H_3O^+ \rightleftharpoons (H_3C)_2C{=}CH_2\cdot H^+ + H_2O$$

$$(H_3C)_2C{=}CH_2\cdot H^+ \rightleftharpoons C_4H_9^+$$

$$C_4H_9^+ + H_2O \rightleftharpoons C_4H_9OH_2^+$$

$$C_4H_9OH_2^+ + H_2O \rightleftharpoons C_4H_9OH + H_3O^+$$

$$(CH_3)_2C{=}CH_2 \rightarrow \text{diisobutylene and polymers}$$

If the absorption is carried out at a relatively higher temperature (> 70°C), then isobutylene is oligomerized to di- and triisobutylenes.

Gehlawat and Sharma (1968) have studied the kinetics of the absorption of isobutylene in aqueous

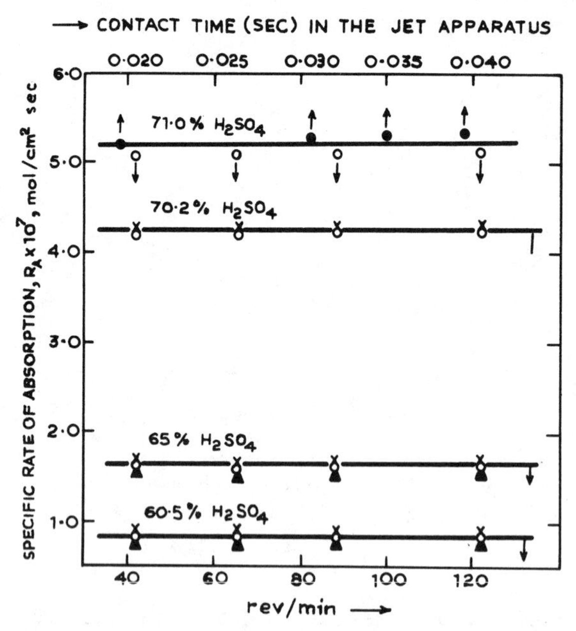

Figure 3.10. Effect of speed of stirring/contact time on the specific rate of absorption of isobutylene in aqueous solutions of sulfuric acid in stirred cell and jet apparatus at 30°C x, stirred cell interfacial area 19.3 cm^2; ○, stirred cell interfacial area 57 cm^2; ▲, stirred cell interfacial area 160 cm^2; ●, jet apparatus interfacial area 1.73 cm^2.

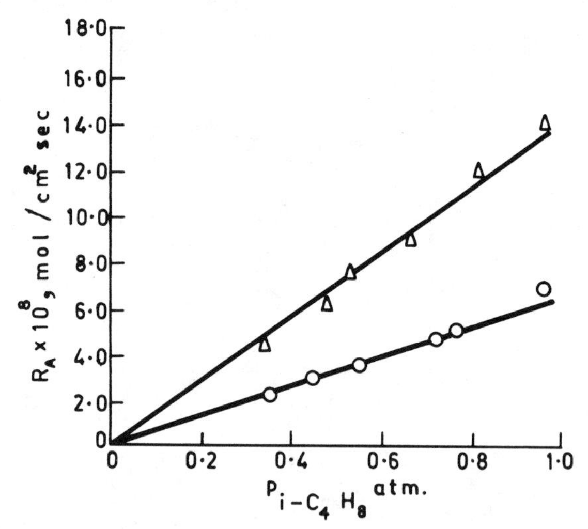

Figure 3.11. Effect of partial pressure of isobutylene on the specific rate of absorption of isobutylene in aqueous solutions of sulfuric acid. △, 65% w/w aqueous H_2SO_4; ○ 60% w/w aqueous H_2SO_4.

solutions of sulfuric acid in a stirred cell and a laminar jet apparatus. Sankholkar and Sharma (1973) have studied the absorption of 2-methyl-2-butene (isoamylene) in aqueous solutions of sulfuric acid (61–75% w/w) in a stirred cell. Sankholkar and Sharma have also studied the absorption of 2-butene in relatively concentrated sulfuric acid solutions (70–80% w/w). In all these cases the specific rate of mass transfer was found to be independent of k_L and directly proportional to the partial pressure of the olefin (Figures 3.10 and 3.11). The system, therefore, conforms to this regime.

Popovic and Deckwer (1975), Deckwer (1977), and Deckwer et al. (1977) have made an extensive study of the absorption of isobutylene in aqueous solutions of sulfuric acid in bubble columns. They have also studied the effect of tertiary butanol (a product of the reaction) on the solubility of isobutylene as well as on the rate constant. Depending on the concentration of sulfuric acid and *tert*-butanol, the absorption may fall in the fast reaction regime (regime 3) or slow reaction regime (regime 2) or between the very slow and slow reaction regimes (between regimes 1 and 2). The presence of *tert*-butanol lowers the value of the rate constant but increases the solubility of isobutylene (Deckwer, 1976). Further, in bubble columns the presence of *tert*-butanol results in increasing the effective interfacial area very substantially (Allenbach et al., 1977).

In order to achieve high selectivity with respect to the absorption of isobutylene from its mixtures with butenes, and to avoid any oligomerization, it is recommended that the absorption be carried out in bubble columns with aqueous sulfuric acid in the range of 40–45% and with a *tert*-butanol concentration in the range of 3.5–4.5 $\times$ 10^{-3} mol/cm^3. Under these conditions the reaction may well fall in the very slow reaction regime (regime 1) or between the very slow and slow reaction regimes (between regimes 1 and 2).

Shaffer et al. (1974) have considered the use of 70% trifluoroacetic acid (TFA) as an absorbent for isobutylene. The equilibrium data for this acid are probably such that isobutylene can be stripped by heating the acid, and therefore dilution of the acid can be avoided. Thus a regenerative process may be possible for the recovery of isobutylene. These authors have studied the mechanism of absorption in a stirred cell and have followed a procedure similar to that followed by Gehlawat and Sharma (1968). The absorption of isobutylene in 70% TFA was found to be accompanied by a fast pseudo-first-order reaction. The commercial exploitation of TFA will depend on the ease of regeneration and losses of the acid. It may be noted that TFA is a very expensive chemical.

Yano et al. (1974) have studied the absorption of isobutylene in aqueous solutions containing thallium(III) ions in a stirred vessel with a flat gas–liquid interface (stirred cell). The following reaction occurs:

$$2i\text{-}C_4H_8 + 3H_2O + Tl^{3+} \rightarrow$$

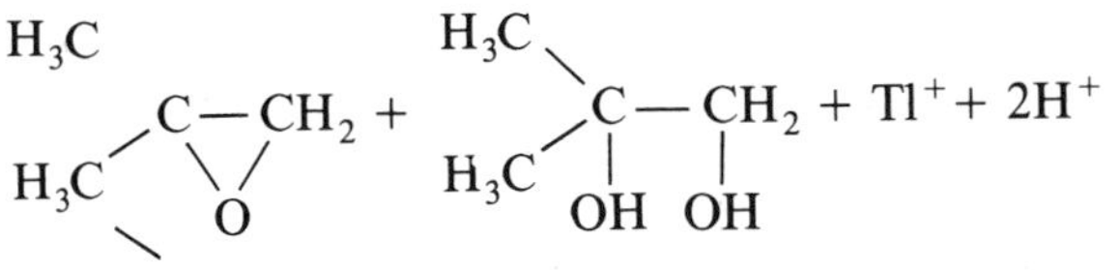

$$(CH_3)_2C\overset{O}{—}CH_2 + (CH_3)_2C(OH)—CH_2(OH) + Tl^{+} + 2H^{+}$$

The reaction was found to be fast and the absorption of isobutylene was accompanied by a fast pseudo-first-order reaction; the reaction was also found to be first order in Tl^{3+} ions. The value of the second-order rate constant was found to be in the range of 1.4–2.8 $\times 10^6$ cm^3/mol sec at 45°C.

3.4.8. Absorption of Lean Phosphine in Aqueous Solutions of Sodium Hypochlorite and Concentrated Sulfuric Acid

In the manufacture of acetylene from calcium carbide the gas invariably contains phosphine, which must be removed before the acetylene is utilized for further use. The amount of phosphine is dependent on the calcium phosphate content of the calcium carbonate (limestone) that is the basic raw material for the manufacture of calcium carbide, and varies from a few parts per million (ppm) to as much as 1000–2000 ppm. Further, in the manufacture of phosphorus by the electrothermal route the off-gases from the furnace contain varying amounts of phosphine. In the manufacture of calcium hypophosphite by reaction between lime and phosphorus, phosphine (which must be suitably disposed of) is generated.

One of the established processes for the removal of phosphine involves absorption in aqueous solutions of sodium hypochlorite. Lawless and Searle (1962) have studied the kinetics of the reaction between phosphine and hypochlorite and found the reaction to be very fast and first order in phosphine as well as in sodium hypochlorite. The value of the second-order rate constant depends on the pH of the solution.

Chandrasekaran and Sharma (1977) have studied the kinetics of absorption of phosphine in aqueous solutions of sodium hypochlorite at different values of pH. They have also found the reaction to be first order in phosphine as well as hypochlorite. Their data cover the range of industrial importance and clearly bring out the desirability of conducting the reaction at a lower pH (9.5–9.8), since the value of the rate constant at a lower pH is substantially higher than at a higher pH. Thus the value of the rate constant at 28°C varies from 2.3×10^5 to 7.7×10^7 cm^3/mol sec when the pH is varied from 12.95 to 9.40, respectively.

Chandrasekaran and Sharma have also studied the kinetics of absorption of phosphine in aqueous solutions of sulfuric acid in the range of 80–92% and here too the absorption of phosphine is accompanied by a fast pseudo-first-order reaction. The value of the pseudo-first-order rate constant at 28°C ranges from 3×10^6 to 48×10^6 sec^{-1} when the sulfuric acid concentration is varied from 80 to 92% w/w.

The solubility of phosphine in water at about 25°C is approximately equal to 10^{-5} mol/cm^3 atm. Thus when the partial pressure of PH_3 is about 0.001 atm and (say) a 1 *M* solution of NaOCl is employed as an absorbent, all the conditions for the fast pseudo-first-order reaction will be satisfied in all industrial contactors and the system will conform to regime 3 at a pH lower than 12.5.

3.4.9. Absorption of Ozone in Aqueous and Nonaqueous Solutions with or without Dissolved Organic Chemicals; Oxidation of Cyanide Ions in Aqueous Alkaline Solutions and Organic Media Containing Olefinic Substances; Wastewater Treatment

The use of ozone in the treatment of wastewater is receiving increasing attention. Ultraviolet radiation has also been suggested for ozone treatment systems (Prengle et al., 1975: see Section 9.2). The absorption of O_3 in aqueous alkaline solutions is known to be accompanied by a fast reaction (Rizzuti et al., 1976). At higher pH values (in the range of 8–13.5), the reaction of O_3 has been found to be first order in O_3 as well as OH^-. Further, the value of the second-order rate constant at a temperature of about 25°C has been found to be as high as 1.5×10^6 cm^3/mol sec at a higher pH ($\simeq$ 12.6). Thus in a variety of gas–liquid contactors the absorption of O_3 will be accompanied by a fast pseudo-first-order reaction. Rizzuti et al. have also indicated that the presence of phenol (which may be an important pollutant) enhances the rate of absorption of O_3 in the pH range of 10–13. Augugliaro and Rizzuti (1978) have studied the kinetics of absorption of O_3 in aqueous solutions of phenol over a pH range of 1.75–12 and a phenol concentration of 7–800 ppm. The rate-determining step appears to be different in acidic and alkaline solutions. Razumovskii et al. (1975) have reported values of second-order rate constants for a variety of phenolic substances in a CCl_4 medium.

Kuo et al. (1977) have studied the kinetics of decomposition of O_3 in aqueous solutions in the pH range of 2.2–11.0 and temperature range of 15–35°C. These authors have studied the kinetics in a homogeneous system with a stopped-flow spectrophotometer. The reaction was found to be three-halves order with respect to the O_3 concentration. The rate of decomposition of O_3 was found to be a strong function of the pH of the solution. It will thus be seen that there is some discrepancy in the literature as regards the order with respect to O_3.

Balyanski et al. (1972) have studied the oxidation of aqueous alkaline solutions of potassium cyanide with O_3—O_2 mixtures in the temperature range of 10–30°C in a 3.2-cm-i.d. sparaged reactor (reaction: $O_3 + CN^- \rightarrow CNO^- + O_2$). The problem is relevant in the treatment of cyanide liquors discharged from electroplating and other industries. It is clear from their work that the gas flow rate had a substantial effect on the rate of oxidation and that diffusional factors were important. It is not clear, however, whether any reaction occurred in the film. The order of the reaction with respect to O_3 has not been established.

Razumovskii et al. (1975) have reported rate constants for the reaction between O_3 and sulfides.

Kuo and Wen (1977) have studied the reaction between O_3 and formic acid, formaldehyde, and methanol in aqueous solutions with a view to exploring the possibilities of using O_3 for the treatment of wastewater containing these compounds. These reactions were studied in a homogeneous system and the pH was varied from 2.7 to 11.0 and the temperature from 15 to 35°C. The rate of reaction with formic acid was the fastest, and the rates of reaction with methanol and formaldehyde were comparable. The reaction with formic acid was found to be first order in ozone.

It was pointed out earlier that O_3 decomposes rapidly in aqueous alkaline solutions. Thus to achieve economies in the use of O_3 it may be desirable to use O_3 for treatment of waste in acidic rather than basic conditions.

Melnyk et al. (1977) have explored the use of O_3 for the removal of color from kraft pulp bleaching wastes. These authors have found, on the basis of experiments in a 7.6-cm-i.d. mechanically agitated contactor with gas dispersed in the liquid, that the enhancement factor varies between 3 and 12. Since the O_3 concentration was very small, [A*] will be very low and conditions for fast pseudo-*m*th-order reaction will be satisfied. It may be noted that O_3 also decomposes in alkaline solutions and may also react with species other than coloring matter.

Reaction between O_3 and 1-(p-Nitrophenyl)-2-Acetylamino-1,3-Propanediol in Acetic Acid Medium

In the manufacture of chloromycetine the oxidation of *sec*-OH in 1-(*p*-nitrophenyl)-2-acetylamino-1,3-propanediol to the corresponding keto compound is encountered. This oxidation can be carried out with Mn and Cr compounds but doing so has serious disadvantages. Ozone can be used to selectively oxidize the *sec*-OH to the keto group. Yields of the order of 70% were realized. It was possible to eliminate diffusional resistance in a bubble column, and the reaction was found to be first order in O_3 and the organic compound. At 20°C the value of the second-order rate constant in acetic acid as a medium was found to be about 5.6×10^2 $cm^3/mol\ sec$.

Reaction between O_3 and Olefinic Compounds

The reaction between ozone and olefinic compounds is of industrial importance. For instance, azelaic acid is manufactured via the ozonolysis of methyl oleate (Throckmorton et al., 1968). These reactions are expected to be fast. An estimate of the rate constant can be made by noting the value of the second-order rate constant (first order in ozone and first order in the olefin) at 25°C for 2-hexene in CCl_4 of 1.7×10^8 $cm^3/mol\ sec$ (Williamson and Cvetanovic, 1968). Since the solubility of O_3 in the medium of interest is very small, it is expected that the reaction between O_3 and methyl oleate may conform to this regime.

A considerable amount of information pertaining to laboratory-scale and pilot-plant-scale work is available in the literature for the manufacture of a variety of products where ozonization is an important step. Throckmorton and Pryde (1972) have reported the results of the ozonization of methyl soyate from a continuously operated 10-cm-i.d. sectionalized bubble column. Here water was used as a second liquid phase to ensure rapid heat removal. Carlson et al. (1977) have reported valuable information on the two-stage reaction of erucic acid, dissolved in acetic acid, to brassylic acid (C_{13} dicarboxylic acid) and pelargonic acid.

Rossi et al. (1979) have given some details of a new process to make nylon-12 where the first step involves the ozonization of cyclododecatriene in an acetic acid/acetic anhydride medium.

3.4.10. Oxidation of Organometallic Compounds

Aluminum Trialkyl

The oxidation of aluminum trialkyl to the corresponding alkoxide is a key step in the manufacture of synthetic fatty alcohols; the alkoxide is hydrolyzed or treated with an acid to give the corresponding fatty alcohol. This process is commercially practiced by a number of companies.

$$3O_2 + 2AlR_3 \rightarrow 2Al(OR)_3$$

Bossier et al. (1973) have studied the kinetics of this reaction in a stirred contactor with a plane gas–liquid interface. The aluminum alkyls were dissolved in different solvents, such as *p*-xylene and tetradecane. The value of $\sqrt{M}$ was found to be very high ($\gg 10$) and was much less than the value of q. Thus the conditions for the validity of the fast pseudo-mth-order reaction mechanism were satisfied. The reaction was found to be first order in O_2 as well as in aluminum trialkyl, and the second-order rate constant for aluminum tridecyl in *p*-xylene at 23°C was found to be 1.4×10^7 cm^3/mol sec. This reaction system has been successfully employed to measure the effective interfacial area with nonpolar organic solvents.

It is not very clear whether this reaction was considered to be a one-step reaction by Bossier et al. It appears that this reaction follows a consecutive reaction mechanism and that each atom of oxygen is added step by step (Grobler et al., 1967).

Organoboron Compounds

The oxidation of trialkyl boranes is of some practical value (Brown, 1975). The kinetics of such reactions has not been systematically studied. It appears, however, that these reactions are relatively fast and that diffusional factors play an important role (Grummitt, 1942). A study of the oxidation of tri-*n*-butyl boron dissolved in *n*-heptane has indicated that even a 100°C rise in the temperature had little effect on the rate of absorption of O_2 (Mirviss, 1961). It is very likely that the absorption of O_2 is accompanied by an instantaneous reaction and that the rate is controlled by diffusion of trialkyl boron to the interface (thus the system belongs to regime 4). Here also a consecutive reaction scheme is encountered and oxygen addition occurs step by step. It is not unlikely that at very low partial pressures of O_2 and high concentrations of trialkyl borons and high values of k_L the system shifts to the fast pseudo-mth-order reaction regime (regime 3).

3.4.11. Hydrogenation of Unsaturated Compounds with Homogeneous Catalysts

In recent years the use of homogeneous catalysts for a variety of hydrogenation reactions has gained considerable importance, since it allows milder conditions, and in some cases gives the desired product distribution (James, 1973; Rylander, 1973; Rylander and Greenfield, 1976). A variety of catalysts, such as Ziegler–Natta type and rhodium and ruthenium (alkyl or aryl) phosphine ligands, have been suggested. Depending on the nature of the substance, the type and concentration of the catalyst, and the type of gas–liquid contactor, the reaction may conform to the very slow reaction (regime 1), or the slow reaction (regime 2), or the fast reaction (regime 3) regimes.

Ganguli and van den Berg (1978) have studied the kinetics of the hydrogenation of soybean and safflower oils, in the presence of dissolved nickel diisopropyl salicylate and aluminum triisobutyl as catalyst, in a wetted-wall column. Their experiments clearly established that the reaction occurred entirely in the film and absorption was accompanied by a fast pseudo-mth-order reaction. The reaction was found to have an order of 1.7 with respect to H_2.

Coffey (1970) has reviewed the subject of the homogeneous hydrogenation of carbon–carbon bonds. With benzene as a solvent and 1.25×10^{-3} mol/cm^3 $RhCl(PPh_3)_3$ as a catalyst, the values of the second-order rate constant for a variety of olefins have been reported to be in the range of 10–10^3 cm^3/mol sec in the temperature range of 15–30°C. For instance, the values of the second-order rate constant for hexene-1 and styrene are 291 and 930 cm^3/mol sec, respectively.

When organometallic catalysts are used, the situation is somewhat different. In the case of transition metal acetylacetonates ($10^{-3}M$) and aluminum alkyls, with paraffin solvent, the reaction has been found to be first order in H_2 as well as catalyst concentration but zero order with respect to the olefin concentration. (See also Section 13.1.8, Example 1).

Hydrogenation of Olefins Catalyzed by Nobel Metal Catalysts

(*a*) $RhCl(Cl)(PPh_3)_3$. Osborn et al. (1966) have made an extensive study of the kinetics of the homogeneous hydrogenation of 1-heptene, cyclohexene, and 1-hexyne with $RhCl(PPh_3)_3$, using a benzene + hexane fraction as a solvent in the temperature range of 15–30°C. Diffusional resistance was eliminated. The kinetics of hydrogenation shows some interesting characteristics. The reaction was found to be first order in the catalyst concentration but the dependence on H_2 and olefin concentration is complex:

$$R'_A = \frac{k^* K_1[A^*][\text{olefin}][\text{catalyst}]}{1 + K_1[A^*] + K_2[\text{olefin}]}$$

(Here k^* is the rate constant and K_1 and K_2 are equilibrium constants.) The value of the activation energy was found to be 22.9 kcal/mol.

It is likely that at higher temperatures and catalyst concentration diffusional factors become important and the system shifts to regime 2.

(*b*) $IrX(CO)(PPh_3)_2$ *and Ruthenium Olefin Complexes.* In a related study Chock and Halpern (1966) have studied the kinetics of addition of H_2 to some iridium(I) complexes dissolved in benzene and dimethyl formamide. The reaction was found to be first order in H_2 and the Ir complex [$IrX(CO)(PPh_3)_2$ where X may be Cl or Br or I]. The value of the second-order rate constant varies over a wide range, depending on the nature of X. Thus with I and benzene as a solvent the value of the second-order rate constant is higher than 10^5 cm^3/mol sec at 30°C (with X as Cl the value is only 930 cm^3/mol sec).

Halpern et al. (1966) have studied the hydrogenation of maleic and fumaric acids in aqueous solutions containing 3 molar HCl and ruthenium(II) chloride. The reaction was found to be first order in H_2 and first order in the Ru II (olefin) complex; the value of the second-order rate constant for fumaric acid at 80°C was found to be 3.6×10^3 ($\pm 0.6 \times 10^3$) cm^3/mol sec.

3.4.12. Absorption of Cl_2 in Aqueous Solutions Containing Phenolic Substances and Aromatic Nitro and Sulfonic Compounds; Absorption of Cl_2 in Aqueous and Nonaqueous Solutions of Ketones

The absorption of Cl_2 in an organic medium has received considerable attention because of its great commercial importance. However, very limited attention has been paid to the kinetics of chlorination in aqueous solutions. This type of chlorination is relevant in the manufacture of certain organic chemicals as well as in pollution abatement. In the latter case, possibilities of simultaneous desulfonation, decarboxylation, and so on of relevant aromatic compounds exist (Datta and Mitter 1919; Larson and Rockwell, 1979).

Yadav and Sharma (1981) have studied the kinetics of absorption of Cl_2 in aqueous solutions containing a variety of substances such as phenol, *o*-chlorophenol, *p*-chlorophenol, *p*-nitrophenol, *m*-aminophenol hydrochloride, *p*-toluenesulfonic acid, and *m*-nitrobenzenesulfonic acid in a 10-cm-i.d. stirred contactor with a provision for independent stirring of the gas and liquid phases as well as in a laminar jet apparatus. It was found that the absorption of lean Cl_2 in aqueous solutions of phenol, resorcinol, hydroquinone, and the like in the stirred contactor, where the gas-phase stirrer was operated up to 2300 rev/min, was essentially gas film controlled. However, slower-reacting phenols and the sulfonic acids showed fast pseudo-first-order kinetic behavior under certain conditions. It was also observed that the rate of reaction was a function of the pH of the solution of phenolic substance.

Consider typical cases of *p*-chlorophenol and *p*-toluenesulfonic acid. In the case of *p*-chlorophenol only the stirred contactor was used and the reaction was found to be first order in both the Cl_2 and *p*-chlorophenol concentrations; the value of the second-order rate constant at 30°C was found to be 1.1×10^8 cm^3/mol sec over a pH between 2 and 3.5. In the case of *p*-toluenesulfonic acid both the stirred contactor and the laminar jet apparatus were used, and excellent agreement was found between the two sets of values when the reaction conformed to regime 3. The reaction was found to be first order in the Cl_2 and first order in the *p*-toluenesulfonic acid concentrations and the value of the second-order rate constant at 30°C was found to be 1.17×10^6 cm^3/mol sec.

These data pertain to the first stage of chlorination and are indicative of the problems encountered in aqueous-phase chlorinations.

Absorption of Cl_2 in Aqueous and Nonaqueous Solutions of Ketones

The chlorination of aqueous solutions of ketones such as acetone shows interesting behavior. Such reactions are relatively fast and under certain conditions conform to regime 3. Bell and Yates (1962) have shown that the reaction between Cl_2 and acetone is relatively fast and under certain conditions zero order in chlorine. Joosten et al. (1980) have shown that the chlorination of cyclohexanone dissolved in CCl_4 is relatively fast. However, this reaction system exhibits autocatalytic behavior and will be covered in Section 9.1.

(B) Liquid–Liquid Systems

3.4.13. Alkaline Hydrolysis of Formate and Halosubstituted Acetic Acid Esters

$$HCOOR' + OH^- \rightarrow HCOO^- + R'OH$$

$$XCH_2COOR' + OH^- \rightarrow XCH_2COO^- + R'OH$$

The alkaline hydrolysis of a variety of esters has been the subject of laboratory studies for almost half a century. These reactions are first order in OH^- and first order in the ester. In some cases these reactions are industrially important. An instance is the alkaline hydrolysis of FCH_2COOR' to sodium fluoroacetate, since the latter substance is a powerful rodenticide. The alkaline hydrolysis of isobornyl formate is an important step in the manufacture of camphor. The extraction of cyclohexyl formate into aqueous solutions of sodium hydroxide is relevant in the manufacture of cyclohexanone by the oxidation of cyclohexane (Hancock, 1975). The alkaline hydrolysis of a variety of formate esters in a number of industrial contactors will conform to this regime. Consider the following case:

$$[A^*] = 5 \times 10^{-5} \text{ mol/cm}^3$$

$$[B_o] = 2 \times 10^{-3} \text{ mol/cm}^3 \qquad (Z = 1)$$

$$k_L = 3 \times 10^{-3} \text{ cm/sec}$$

$$D_A = 8 \times 10^{-6} \text{ cm}^2\text{/sec}$$

$$D_B = 2.12 \times 10^{-5} \text{ cm}^2\text{/sec}$$

$$k_2 = 3 \times 10^4 \text{ cm}^3\text{/mol sec}$$

$$\frac{\sqrt{D_A k_2 [B_o]}}{k_L} = \frac{2.19 \times 10^{-2}}{3 \times 10^{-3}} = 7.3$$

$$< \frac{[B_o]}{Z[A^*]}\sqrt{\frac{D_B}{D_A}} = 65$$

Thus the necessary conditions for the validity of regime 3 are satisfied.

3.4.14. Manufacture of Cyclohexanone Oxime

The conversion of cyclohexanone, which is only slightly soluble in water, to cyclohexanone oxime by treatment with an aqueous solution of hydroxylammonium sulfate is an important step in the manufacture of caprolactam (the monomer for nylon-6):

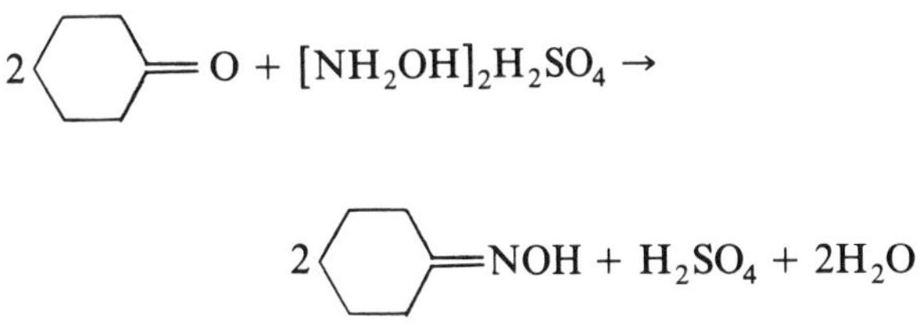

$$2\,(C_6H_{10})\!=\!O + [NH_2OH]_2H_2SO_4 \rightarrow$$

$$2\,(C_6H_{10})\!=\!NOH + H_2SO_4 + 2H_2O$$

Sharma and Nanda (1968) have studied some aspects of this problem. In a spray column, the reaction was found to conform to regime 3.

At high levels of conversion of cyclohexanone (which is required in commercial practice) the reaction can occur in both phases. Some aspects of this problem will be considered in Section 7.6.

In the modified process, hydroxylammonium phosphate is employed. Further, nylon-12 is manufactured by an analogous process based on cyclododecanone.

3.4.15. Manufacture of Dithiocarbamates

Dithiocarbamates and their derivatives are used extensively in the rubber and pesticides industries. The basic reaction is as follows (CS_2 is slightly soluble in water and aqueous amine solutions are used):

$$CS_2 + R_2NH \rightarrow R_2NCSS^- + H^+$$

$$R_2NH + H^+ \xrightarrow{\text{instantaneous}} R_2NH_2^+$$

$$\overline{CS_2 + 2R_2NH \rightarrow R_2NCSS^- + R_2NH_2^+}$$

Kothari and Sharma (1966a) have studied the kinetics of this reaction and found that under certain conditions the system conforms to this regime. The reaction was found to be first order in CS_2 as well as the amine. The specific rate of mass transfer was found to be independent of the stirring speed in a stirred cell (Figure 3.12). Consider the following ex-

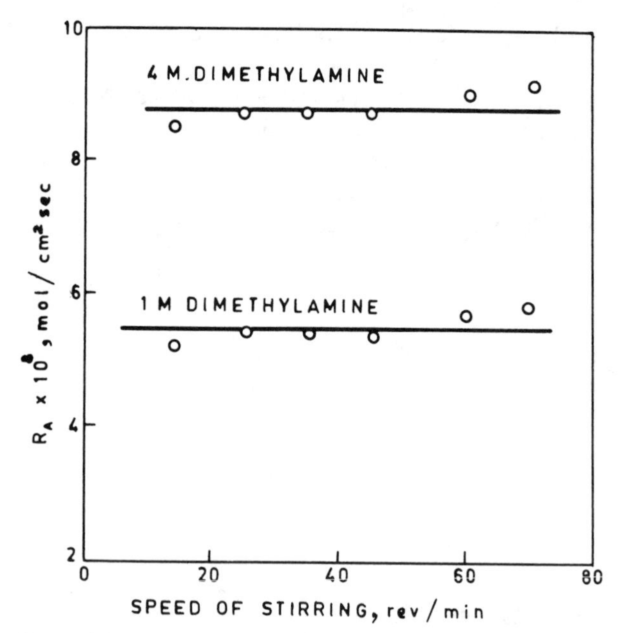

Figure 3.12. Effect of speed of stirring on the specific rate of extraction of CS_2 into an aqueous solution of amines.

periment in a stirred cell:

$$k_L = 2 \times 10^{-3} \text{ cm/sec}$$

$$[A^*] = 2 \times 10^{-5} \text{ mol/cm}^3$$

$$[B_o] = [\text{diethylamine}] = 2 \times 10^{-3} \text{ mol/cm}^3$$

$$D_A = 1 \times 10^{-5} \text{ cm}^2/\text{sec},$$

$$D_B = 1.26 \times 10^{-5} \text{ cm}^2/\text{sec}$$

$$k_2 = 2.8 \times 10^3 \text{ cm}^3/\text{mol sec}, \qquad Z = 2$$

$$\frac{\sqrt{D_A k_2 [B_o]}}{k_L} = \frac{7.47 \times 10^{-3}}{2 \times 10^{-3}} = 3.73$$

$$< \frac{2 \times 10^{-3}}{2 \times 2 \times 10^{-5}} \sqrt{\frac{D_B}{D_A}} = 56$$

Thus the necessary conditions are satisfied.

3.4.16. Alkylation of Isobutane with Butenes and of Toluene and Xylenes with Acetaldehyde (or Acetylene)

Alkylation of Isobutane with Butenes

The production of high-octane motor and aviation fuel involves the alkylation of isobutane with butenes in the presence of concentrated sulfuric acid as the catalyst. The basic reactions are as follows:

$$C_4^= + H^+ \rightarrow C_4^+$$

$$C_4^+ + C_4^= \rightarrow C_8^+$$

$$C_8^+ + C_4 \rightarrow C_8 + C_4^+$$

where

$C_4^=$ = olefin, butene

H^+ = proton, from sulfuric acid

C_4^+ = carbonium ion of isobutane

C_8^+ = carbonium ion of octane

It appears that the system conforms to regime 3 (Sprow, 1969).

A related example of the oligomerization of butene-1 using sulfuric acid as a catalyst also conforms to this regime (Naworski and Harriott, 1969). The transfer of butene-1 is accompanied by a fast pseudo-first-order reaction.

Lee and Harriott (1977) have studied the alkylation of isobutane with butene-1, and the simultaneous oligomerization of butene-1, in the presence of sulfuric acid as a catalyst. The alkylation reaction was found to be first order in isobutane as well as butene-1, and the value of the second-order rate constant at 25°C with 98% H_2SO_4 was found to be 2.25×10^8 cm³/mol sec.

Alkylation of Toluene or Xylenes with Acetaldehyde (or Acetylene)

The alkylation of toluene and different isomers of xylenes with acetaldehyde or acetylene in the presence of sulfuric acid as a catalyst is industrially relevant for the manufacture of diarylethanes (DAE), which are useful as heat transfer fluids and are intermediates in the manufacture of methyl and dimethyl styrenes and polyfunctional aromatic acids.

Dixon and Saunders (1954) have studied the two-phase reaction between xylenes containing dissolved acetaldehyde and sulfuric acid as a catalyst. It is clear from their work that agitation plays an important role and that the interfacial area is important. The kinetics of this type of reaction has not been clearly established, but it appears that these reactions are fast and that for a relatively fast-reacting isomer, such as *m*-xylene, and at higher concentrations of

H_2SO_4 it may conceivably fall in regime 2. (In fact, the reactivity of *m*-xylene in relation to *p*-xylene can be exploited to separate the two isomeric substances; dixylyl ethane obtained from *m*-xylene on cracking will give 1 mol of dimethyl styrene and 1 mol of *m*-xylene.) The intensity of agitation may affect not only the rate but also the yield, since several side reactions can take place.

Vasudevan and Sharma (1983a) have also studied some aspects of the alkylation of toluene and xylenes with paraldehyde or acetaldehyde and have found that the reaction conforms to regime 1 in a mechanically agitated contactor.

Use of Acetylene

When acetylene is used we have a three-phase system, and there could well be a four-phase system if particles of mercuric sulfate are present (Vasudevan and Sharma, 1983b). The exact site of reaction is not known, but it is likely to be at the interface between the acid and the aromatic substance.

3.4.17. Nitration of Toluene

Hanson and Ismail (1976) have made a systematic study of the nitration of toluene in a laminar jet apparatus with nitrating mixtures containing approximately 30 mol % H_2SO_4 (approximately equivalent to 71% w/w H_2SO_4) and 1.7 mol % HNO_3 at 30°C. They have unequivocally established that nitration is accompanied by a fast pseudo-first-order reaction under these conditions, which are quite close to those employed industrially. Similar observations were made with respect to the nitration of benzene.

Some additional aspects of the nitration of aromatic substances will be discussed in Section 3.5.2. Recent work of Albright et al. (1976) indicates that under certain conditions some reaction can occur in the aromatic phase.

3.4.18. Extraction of Metals

Depending on circumstances, the extraction of species like copper ions from acidic solutions may conform to the fast pseudo-*m*th-order reaction regime (regime 3), or to the instantaneous reaction regime (regime 4) or the regime between 3 and 4 (see Section 3.7.15).

Scale-up

The scale-up of a system belonging to regime 3 will require a knowledge of the specific rate of mass transfer and the value of effective interfacial area in the proposed industrial contactor. It would be advantageous to employ units that provide higher interfacial areas under otherwise comparable conditions. It is presumed that no complications arise as a result of undesirable effects of the reaction products on the yield. There are certain situations, particularly in the oxidation of organic compounds, where the level of conversion may be restricted to only 10–15% in order to overcome the problem of falling yields with an increase in the percentage of conversion.

It is necessary to know the residence time distribution of both phases for the design of the large-scale units. [The residence time distribution of the B phase will be unimportant for a reaction that is zero order in B (i.e., $n = 0$).]

3.5. REGIME BETWEEN 2 AND 3:

3.5.1. Pseudo-First-Order Reactions: Measurement of k_1 without Knowing [A*] and D_A

When the condition given by expression 2.30 is not satisfied, a part of the reaction occurs in the film and the rest occurs in the bulk. The hydrodynamic factors will affect the value of R_A, as is evident from Eq. 2.63. For a general-order reaction the film theory solution given by Eq. 2.47 holds, but the value of ψ_δ has to be known. Only in some special cases are analytical solutions possible. The solutions for the case of a pseudo-first-order reaction are particularly interesting.

In any model apparatus, such as a jet apparatus or wetted-wall column, where the hydrodynamics is well understood and where the contact time t_E can be calculated, Eqs. 2.64 and 2.65, which are based on the penetration theory, hold. For $k_1 t_E \ll 1$,

$$R_A\sqrt{t_E} \simeq \frac{2}{\sqrt{\pi}}[A^*]\sqrt{D_A}\left[1 + \frac{k_1 t_E}{3}\right] \qquad (2.64)$$

and for $k_1 t_E \gg 1$,

$$R_A \simeq [A^*]\sqrt{D_A k_1}\left[1 + \frac{1}{2k_1 t_E}\right] \qquad (2.65)$$

Consider the case when $k_1 t_E$ is less than 1. A plot of $R_A\sqrt{t_E}$ against t_E should be a straight line, and from a knowledge of the intercept and the slope we can calculate the value of $[A^*]\sqrt{D_A}$ and k_1. It is not necessary to know the values of [A*] and D_A separately to calculate the value of k_1. However, it is clear from Eq. 2.64 that the maximum contribution

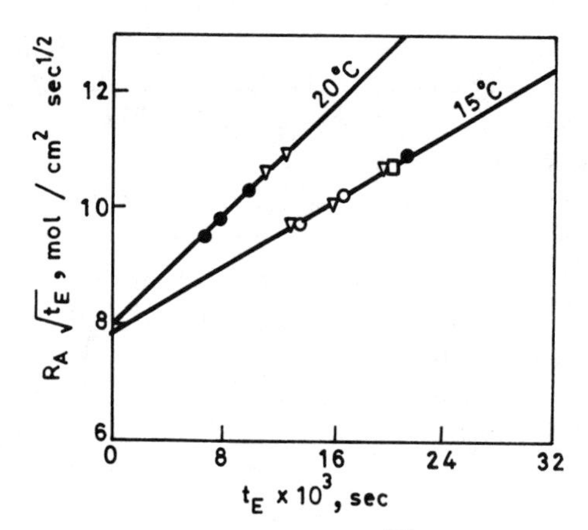

Figure 3.13. A plot of $R_A\sqrt{t_E}$ against t_E.

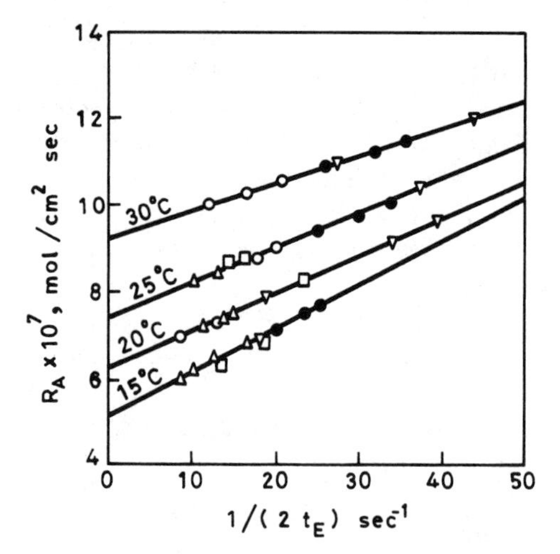

Figure 3.14. A plot of R_A against $1/(2t_E)$.

of the second term is about 30% and hence very accurate values of R_A and t_E are required to obtain k_1. Here data are best suited to obtain the value of $[A^*]\sqrt{D_A}$ from the intercept. Sharma and Danckwerts (1963) absorbed CO_2 in jets of carbonate buffer solutions containing various catalysts. The value of k_1 was varied by increasing the concentration of the catalyst without significantly affecting the physical properties of the liquid. It was found that the data can be satisfactorily correlated by Eq. 2.64 (Figure 3.13). Wild and Potter (1968) have also verified this type of correlation for the absorption of CO_2 in carbonate buffer solutions flowing over a wetted sphere.

For k_1t_E greater than 1 a plot of R_A against $1/(2t_E)$ will give a straight line, and from the values of the slope and the intercept the values of $[A^*]\sqrt{D_A}$ and k_1 can be calculated. It is again not necessary to know the values of $[A^*]$ and D_A separately to calculate the value of k_1. This feature can be an advantage in some specific cases. Consider the case of the absorption of N_2O_4 in water. N_2O_4 undergoes a fast pseudo-first-order reaction in water and there is no way of estimating its solubility with confidence. Kramers et al. (1961) have reported data on the absorption of N_2O_4 in jets of water under conditions such that k_1t_E was greater than 1. From the plots of R_A against $1/(2t_E)$ the value of the rate constant can be calculated. Further, it is reasonable to estimate the value of D_A for N_2O_4 from the equation proposed by Wilke and Chang (1955). This value of D_A in conjunction with the value of the intercept, $[A^*]\sqrt{D_A}$, enables us to calculate the value of $[A^*]$. The solubility of N_2O_4 in water at 30°C was found to be 1.23×10^{-3} mol/cm^3 atm. The value of the first-order rate constant at 30°C was found to be 330 sec^{-1}.

Sharma and Danckwerts (1963) absorbed CO_2 in jets of carbonate buffer solution containing various catalysts. Here the data were satisfactorily correlated by Eq. 2.65 (Figure 3.14). The values of $[A^*]\sqrt{D_A}$ and k_1 obtained from the two types of plots, namely, $R_A\sqrt{t_E}$ against t_E and R_A against $1/(2t_E)$, agreed reasonably well. Further, the values of $[A^*]\sqrt{D_Ak_1}$ obtained independently also agreed with those obtained from the intercepts of the plots of R_A against $1/(2t_E)$ (see Table 3.3). The maximum contibution of the second term in Eq. 2.65 is about 50%, and hence some confidence can be placed in the calculated values of k_1.

In industrial contactors it is not possible to calculate the value of t_E. Under these conditions the equation obtained from Danckwerts' surface renewal theory is very useful for pseudo-first-order reactions.

$$R_A = [A^*]\sqrt{D_Ak_1 + k_L^2} \tag{2.68}$$

A plot of $(R_A/[A^*])^2$ against k_1 will give a straight line with the slope equal to D_A and the intercept equal to k_L^2. When the effective interfacial area is not known, $R_Aa/[A^*]$ is plotted against k_1. The slope of the straight line gives a^2D_A and the intercept $[k_La]^2$. It is thus possible to get values of k_L and a separately from a set of data. These types of plots are referred to as Danckwerts' plots. A number of investigations have been reported in the literature for gas–liquid and liquid–liquid contactors where the applicability of Eq. 2.68 has been tested. We shall consider next a specific case of the nitration of toluene.

TABLE 3.3. Absorption of CO_2 in Sodium Carbonate Buffers Containing Hypochlorite[a]

Temperature (°C)	$[A^*]\sqrt{D_A} \times 10^8$ (mol/cm² sec$^{1/2}$)		k_1 (sec^{-1})		$k_{ClO^-} \times 10^{-6}$ (cm³/mol sec)
	Eq. 2.65	Eq. 2.64	Eq. 2.65	Eq. 2.64	Eq. 2.65
20	7.6	7.6	71.5	68	1.43
25	7.1		108.5		2.17
35	7.1		152		3.04

[a]From Sharma and Danckwerts (1963); $[CO_3^{2-}]/[HCO_3^-] = 1$; $Na_2CO_3 = 5 \times 10^{-4}$ mol/cm³; $[ClO^-] = 5 \times 10^{-5}$ mol/cm³; $I = 2.05$ g ion/liter

3.5.2. Nitration of Toluene and Other Aromatic Substances

At relatively higher concentrations of sulfuric acid and nitric acid the nitration of toluene can become sufficiently fast to occur, either entirely or at least partly, in the film adjacent to the interface. In cases where a part of the reaction occurs in the film, a Danckwerts' plot can be made. Cox and Strachan (1972a,b), Chapman et al. (1974), and Chapman and Strachan (1974) have studied the nitration of toluene under these conditions and some unsuspected results were obtained. Experiments were carried out with pure as well as diluted toluene (the diluent was 2,2,4-trimethyl pentane) in a stirred as well as an agitated contactor. Experimental data show clearly that a Danckwerts' plot can be made for data obtained with pure as well as diluted toluene. (The value of the rate constant was varied by changing the concentration of the nitric acid.) However, an analysis of these plots clearly indicated that the values of the physicochemical properties derived from data pertaining to pure toluene differed markedly from those obtained from diluted toluene. (The results obtained from diluted toluene were close to the expected values.)

The nitration of toluene involves two steps: (i) the formation of nitronium ions; (ii) reaction between dissolved toluene and nitronium ions.

$$HONO_2 + H^+ \rightleftharpoons H_2O + NO_2^+$$

$$NO_2^+ + ArH \rightleftharpoons ArNO_2 + H^+$$

(ArH stands for aromatic hydrocarbon.) It appears that at higher concentrations of toluene the first step controls the kinetics, whereas at lower concentrations the second step controls the overall kinetics. The first-step reaction does not involve toluene and is thus zero order in the toluene concentration. Thus the data pertaining to pure toluene should be analyzed on the basis of extraction accompanied by a zero-order reaction.

Chapman and Strachan (1974) have shown, by conducting experiments in the homogeneous phase, that at high concentrations of toluene the overall reaction is zero order in toluene. A distinct change in the kinetics occurs at lower concentrations of toluene when the reaction becomes first order with respect to toluene. It is clear that when the reaction is zero order in toluene the Danckwerts' plot cannot be made, since it is applicable to only pseudo-first-order or first-order reactions.

The recent book by Albright and Hanson (1975) on industrial and laboratory nitration covers various aspects of the two-phase nitration of benzene, toluene, and chlorobenzene. In particular, it is clearly brought out how, with a change in the concentrations of sulfuric and nitric acids, the controlling mechanism can change and the system can belong to regime 1, 2, or 3.

3.6. REGIME OVERLAPPING 1, 2, AND 3

In the regime overlapping 1, 2, and 3, as pointed out in Section 2.5, mass transfer is accompanied by reaction in such a way that a part of the reaction occurs in the film and yet the reaction is not fast enough to render the concentration of dissolved A in the bulk B phase (i.e., $[A_o]$) zero. Such situations are rather uncommon in practice.

For the sake of illustration we shall consider the following case of a pseudo-first-order reaction:

$$k_L = 1.5 \times 10^{-2} \text{ cm/sec}$$
$$a = 5 \text{ cm}^2/\text{cm}^3$$
$$l = 0.1$$
$$D_A = 1.8 \times 10^{-5} \text{ cm}^2/\text{sec}$$
$$k_1 = 4 \text{ sec}^{-1}$$

Here,

$$k_L a = 0.075, \qquad k_L^2 = 2.25 \times 10^{-4}\ \text{cm}^2/\text{sec}^2$$

$$lk_1 = 0.4$$

$$D_A k_1 = 7.2 \times 10^{-5}$$

In this case k_L^2 is only about 3.1 times the value of $D_A k_1$ and lk_1 is about 5.3 times the value of $k_L a$. Thus a part of the reaction will occur in the film and yet some free A will also exist in the bulk liquid phase.

Equation 2.78 shows that a plot of

$$\left(\frac{1}{k_{LR}a} - \frac{1}{lk_n[B_o]^n}\right)^{-2}$$

against $[B_o]^n$ will be a straight line with the slope equal to $a^2 D_A k_n$ and the intercept equal to $(k_L a)^2$.

3.7. REGIME 4: INSTANTANEOUS REACTIONS

The most notable feature of regime 4 is that (provided the conditions given by expressions 2.79 and 2.84 are satisfied) the specific rate of mass transfer is independent of the concentration of A. In the case of gas–liquid systems, the rate of absorption of A is independent of the partial pressure of A. However, a situation can arise where a shift in the mechanism occurs and the resistance to mass transfer is entirely confined to the gas phase. The necessary condition for gas-film-controlled mass transfer is given by the expression

$$k_{G_A} p_A < \frac{k_L[B_o]}{Z} \tag{3.12}$$

The rate of absorption of A is then given by the following equation:

$$R_A a = k_{G_A} a p_A \tag{3.13}$$

Consider the absorption of 1% Cl_2 in air at atmospheric pressure in an aqueous solution of NaOH ($[B_o] = 1 \times 10^{-3}$ mol/cm^3) in an apparatus where $k_L = 8 \times 10^{-3}$ cm/sec and $k_{G_A} = 5 \times 10^{-5}$ mol/cm^2 sec atm. Here the condition given by expression 3.12 is satisfied:

$$k_{G_A} p_A (= 5 \times 10^{-7}) \ll \frac{k_L[B_o]}{Z} (= 8 \times 10^{-6})$$

$$(Z = 2)$$

However, if (say) 50% Cl_2 is absorbed, then resistance to mass transfer will essentially be confined to the B phase. Similar examples of the absorption of lean mixtures of ammonia in mineral acids, SO_2 in alkaline solutions, and the like can be cited.

Film versus Surface Renewal Theories

There is an important difference between the solutions obtained from the film and surface renewal theories (Eq. 2.85 and 2.97). The solution based on film theory indicates that the specific rate of mass transfer is directly proportional to D_B/D_A. However, the term D_B/D_A appears as a square root in the case of the solution obtained from surface renewal theories. When the difference between D_B and D_A is small, then the difference between the two equations 2.85 and 2.97 is insignificant. However, if the value of D_B is significantly different from D_A, then it is important to know which equation holds in practice. There are many practical situations where the differences between D_B and D_A are large. Consider the absorption of H_2S in a variety of amines. Here the ratio of D_B to D_A can easily vary from about 0.3 to 1.2 (Danckwerts and Sharma, 1966; da Silva and Danckwerts, 1968). In the case of the extraction of fatty acids into aqueous caustic soda solutions, the D_B/D_A ratio can be from 5 to 6. In the human body, where the uptake of O_2 by hemoglobin

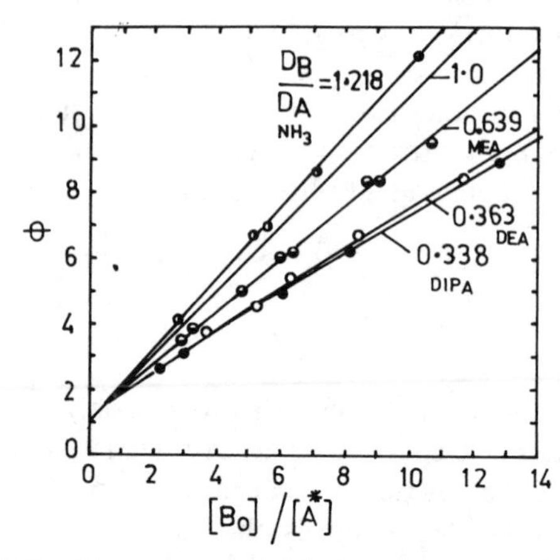

Figure 3.15. Absorption of H_2S in jets of aqueous solutions of amines: instantaneous reaction (da Silva and Danckwerts, 1968).

is vital and where transfer of O_2 is accompanied by a fast reaction, the value of D_B/D_A is about 0.05 (Ramachandran, 1969).

Some preliminary work by Sharma (1964) on the absorption of CO_2 in aqueous solutions of MEA and DEA (under conditions such that regime 4 prevailed) in a small packed column indicated that Eq. 2.97 rather than 2.85 holds. The work of da Silva and Danckwerts (1968) on the absorption of H_2S in aqueous solutions of a variety of amines in a stirred cell and a packed column shows fairly unambiguously that Eq. 2.96 or 2.97 rather than Eq. 2.83 or 2.85 holds (Figures 3.15 and 3.16.)

From Eq. 2.96 it is clear that if experiments are performed in equipment such as a jet apparatus or a wetted column, where the contact time can be accurately calculated and the value of D_A is known, then the value of D_B can be calculated ($k_L = 2\sqrt{D_A/\pi t_E}$). This method provides a novel way of obtaining the diffusion coefficient of species B. This idea was originally suggested by Sharma (1964). Da Silva and Danckwerts (1968) were successful in using this method to obtain the diffusion coefficient of a variety of amines. For this purpose H_2S was absorbed in jets of aqueous solutions of NH_3, MEA, DEA, and diisopropanol amine (DIPA). These diffusion coefficient values agreed closely with those reported in the literature (for DIPA no information on the diffusivity is available in the published literature). Recently Sridharan and Sharma (1976) have reported values of the diffusivity of cuprous amine complexes that were obtained from the absorption of pure CO or C_3H_6 in jets of amine complexes. Here the reaction between CO or C_3H_6 and the amine complex is instantaneous.

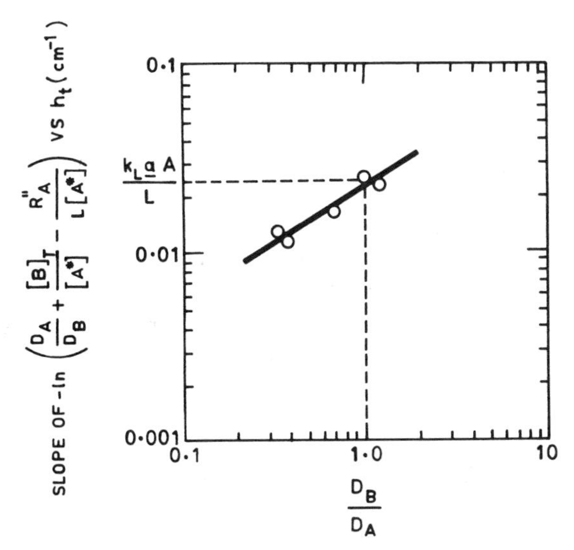

Figure 3.16. Absorption of H_2S in a packed column in aqueous solutions of amine: instantaneous reaction (da Silva and Danckwerts, 1968).

Contribution of Gas-Side Resistance

When a part of the resistance is found in the gas phase, then as shown in Section 2.9, the following equation holds:

$$\frac{1}{K_{G_A}a} = \frac{\dfrac{1}{k_{G_A}a} + \dfrac{1}{H_A k_L a}}{\left[1 + \dfrac{[B_o]}{ZH_A p_A}\sqrt{\dfrac{D_B}{D_A}}\right]} \tag{2.137}$$

Thus if we separately know the values of $k_{G_A}a$ and $k_L a$, the value of $K_{G_A}a$ and hence that of $R_A a$ can be assessed. Further, unlike the case of a fast pseudo-first-order reaction, where a part of the resistance is found in the gas phase, we cannot make simple plots like that of $1/R_A a$ against $1/\sqrt{B_o}$ in order to obtain separate values of $k_{G_A}a$ and a from the intercept and slope, respectively (see Section 3.4). It will be seen from Eq. 2.137 that we can plot $1/K_{G_A}a$ against $[(1 + [B_o]/ZH_A p_A)\sqrt{D_B/D_A}]^{-1}$ and obtain a straight line with a slope of $1/k_{G_A}a + 1/H_A k_L a$. In any practical situation it would be difficult to make such a plot, since $[B_o]$ and p_A would change along the contactor; hence a suitable expression has to be derived. It appears, therefore, that although in the case of instantaneous reaction where a part of the resistance is found in the gas phase, the value of $R_A a$ can be calculated for design purposes, no additional basic information can be derived from a study of the effect of $[B_o]$ on $R_A a$.

(A) Gas–Liquid Systems

3.7.1. Absorption of CO_2 in Aqueous Solutions of MEA

Some aspects of the absorption of CO_2 in solutions of alkanolamines were considered in Section 3.4.1. Under certain conditions, when the partial pressure of CO_2 is relatively high and the MEA concentration is low, the system conforms to this regime. Consider a typical case where the partial pressure of CO_2 is 4 atm and the free MEA concentration is 5×10^{-4} mol/cm^3 (temperature = 35°C and $k_L = 1 \times 10^{-2}$ cm/sec).

The value of the left-hand side in expression 2.79 works out to be about 30, which is much greater than the value of the term on the right-hand side (here $Z = 2$). The system therefore conforms to regime 4.

3.7.2. Absorption of H_2S and Mercaptans in Aqueous Solutions of Alkanolamines and Caustic Soda

The reaction between H_2S (or RSH) and an amine is instantaneous. The mechanism of this system should therefore conform to this regime 4. However, if the partial pressure of H_2S or RSH is relatively low and the concentration of the amine very high, then the resistance to mass transfer may lie entirely on the gas side. The necessary condition for the absorption to be gas film controlled is given by expression 3.12. Thus, if the partial pressure of H_2S is 0.01 atm and the concentration of the free amine is 1×10^{-3} mol/cm^3 (here $Z = 1$) and k_G and k_L are taken as 7×10^{-5} mol/cm^2 sec atm and 1×10^{-2} cm/sec, respectively, then the left-hand side of expression 3.12 works out to be 7×10^{-7}, which is very much less than the term on the right-hand side ($= 10^{-5}$).

The absorption of H_2S and mercaptans (notably methyl mercaptan) from off-gases in aqueous solutions of caustic soda is also relevant in the pulp and paper and pesticide industries. Methyl mercaptan is also expected to react instantaneously with OH^-. Laudry (1967) has studied the absorption of pure methyl mercaptan in jets of aqueous caustic soda solutions and has shown that the system conforms to the instantaneous reaction regime. The corresponding case of the removal of mercaptans from liquid pentane by aqueous caustic soda solutions has been discussed by Carr and Shah (1979).

3.7.3. Absorption of Carbon Monoxide in Aqueous Cuprous Ammonium Chloride Solutions

In many old nitrogenous fertilizer plants the synthesis gas, after removal of CO_2, is subjected to the removal of CO by absorption in solutions of cuprous ammonium chloride. (In modern practice CO is generally removed by methanation.) The reaction between CO and $Cu(NH_3)_2^+$ is known to be instantaneous (Gilliland and Seebold, 1941; van Krevelen and Baans, 1950):

$$CO + Cu(NH_3)_2^+ + NH_3 \rightarrow Cu((NH_3)_3CO)^+$$

Sridharan and Sharma (1976) have also studied the absorption of pure CO in cuprous amine complexes in aqueous as well as polar solvents in a mechanically agitated contactor as well as in a packed column. In fact, they have successfully used this system for the measurement of $k_L a$.

This type of complexing reaction has once again attracted attention. In the aqueous phase there are apparently severe corrosion problems. Haase and Waker (1974) have proposed a modified version of this type of process which makes use of aromatic solvents and cuprous aluminum complexes (commercially this process is called COSORB). It is likely that the reaction between CO and this complex is instantaneous. The complex can be easily decomposed at higher temperatures to give CO. Mild steel (carbon steel) can be used throughout this part of the plant, since the system is noncorrosive. This process can also be used for the manufacture of pure CO in tonnage plants. An advantage of this process is that CO can be selectively recovered in the presence of CO_2, since CO_2 does not react with $CuAlO_4$. In the case of cuprous amine solutions CO_2 also reacts with the amine liquor.

3.7.4. Absorption of Lower Olefins in Aqueous Solutions of Cuprous Ammonium Compounds

Lower olefins (e.g., C_2H_4, C_3H_6) can be recovered from a variety of gaseous mixtures by absorption in aqueous solutions of cuprous ammonium chloride. The reaction between the olefin and the complex is instantaneous (Thomas, 1963):

$$C_2H_4 + Cu(NH_3)_2^+ + 2HCl \rightarrow Cu((NH_4Cl)_2C_2H_4)^+$$

The related example of the absorption of butadiene in aqueous solutions of cupric compounds has been discussed by Morrel et al. (1946). The aqueous solutions of amine complexes are corrosive and alternate processes have been developed by the recovery of butadiene and hence these reactions are no longer of practical relevance. The use of a cuprous aluminum complex dissolved in aromatic solvents for the recovery of ethylene/propylene from lean mixtures has also been considered.

3.7.5. Absorption of Pure Chlorine in Aqueous Solutions of Sodium Carbonate or Sodium Hydroxide

Sodium hypochlorite is manufactured by reacting chlorine with either Na_2CO_3 or NaOH. The reaction between Cl_2 and OH^- is known to be extremely fast (Eigen and Kustin, 1962). Thus, if pure Cl_2 is absorbed in aqueous alkaline solutions, then the system would conform to this regime. (The absorption of lean chlorine in aqueous alkaline solutions can become completely gas film controlled.)

3.7.6. Conversion of Dithiocarbamates to Thiuram Disulfides

The conversion of aqueous solutions of the sodium salt of dimethyl dithiocarbamic acid to the corresponding disulfide is practiced for the manufacture of the corresponding thiuram disulfide, which is required in the rubber industry. A variety of oxidizing agents (e.g., H_2O_2) can be used. It is, however, attractive to use dilute Cl_2 for this reaction in view of its low cost. The following reaction occurs:

$$Cl_2 + 2NaS\text{—}\underset{\underset{S}{\|}}{C}\text{—}N(CH_3)_2(aq) \rightarrow$$

$$(CH_3)_2N\text{—}\underset{\underset{S}{\|}}{C}\text{—}S\text{—}S\text{—}\underset{\underset{S}{\|}}{C}\text{—}N(CH_3)_2$$

$$+2NaCl(aq)$$

Kothari and Sharma (1966b) have studied the kinetics of this reaction and have shown that for dilute chlorine mixtures and higher concentrations of the dithiocarbamate ($> 5 \times 10^{-4}$ mol/cm^3) the process is gas film controlled. The reaction between Cl_2 and the dithiocarbamate is expected to be extremely fast, and the system conforms to this regime. However, since $k_G p_A$ becomes much less than $k_L([B_o]/Z)$, the process becomes gas film controlled.

3.7.7. Sulfonation of Aromatic Compounds with Lean SO_3

Sulfonation of aromatic substances, such as benzene, toluene, xylene, dodecyl benzene (DDB), nitrobenzene, and nitrotoluene, is industrially practiced for the manufacture of a variety of products. Among these the sulfonation of DDB for the manufacture of synthetic detergents is perhaps practiced on the largest scale and has also received considerable attention. There are a number of advantages associated with the use of SO_3: (i) production of dilute sulfuric acid is avoided; (ii) yields are high and products of good quality are obtained; (iii) continuous operation can be easily adopted. The main disadvantage is associated with the high heat of reaction, which may cause a rise in temperature resulting in darker products if adequate heat removal is not ensured. Thin-film reactors can overcome these difficulties.

The available information in the literature (Johnson and Crynes, 1974; Broström, 1975) suggests that the sulfonation of DDB with lean SO_3 is gas film controlled.

$$SO_3(g) + C_6H_5\text{—}C_{12}H_{25} \longrightarrow HO_3S\text{—}C_6H_4\text{—}C_{12}H_{25}$$

(Some by-product is also formed.) This situation arises because the "solubility" of SO_3 in aromatic hydrocarbons is expected to be very high (say, $> 2 \times 10^{-3}$ mol/cm^3 atm) and the rate constant is also expected to be relatively high. Thus the necessary conditions for the instantaneous reaction will be satisfied, and since $k_G p_A$ becomes smaller than $k_L[B_o]$, the process becomes gas film controlled.

Beenackers and van Swaaij (1978) have recently studied the reaction between SO_3 and benzene in different types of contactors, including a stirred cell. Results from the stirred cell indicate that the reaction between dissolved SO_3 and benzene is instantaneous. Thus when lean SO_3 is absorbed in benzene, gas-side resistance may dominate.

The controlling regime may change if the reaction between SO_3 and the aromatic substance is slow. For instance, in the case of *p*-nitrotoluene (PNT) the second-order rate constant at 96.5°C with oleum is as low as 1.83×10^{-2} cm^3/mol sec. (The reaction has been found to be first order in PNT and first order in SO_3 by Cowdrey and Davies, 1949.) In such cases we may have considerable liquid-side resistance and the reaction may or may not occur in the film. The ratio of the rate constant for the reaction of SO_3 with benzene to that with nitrobenzene has been reported to be of the order of 5×10^6 (Cerfontain, 1968). The sulfonation reaction with SO_3 has been reported to be second order with respect to SO_3 (Cerfontain, 1968).

3.7.8. Recovery of Bromine from Lean Aqueous Solutions of Bromides

In the common method of recovery of bromine from bitterns the liquor is chlorinated to liberate bromine, which is stripped with air or steam. In view of the high cost of steam, air is frequently employed to strip out bromine. Thus, lean mixtures of bromine in air have to be subjected for bromine recovery. A number of methods can be considered. The standard method consists of absorption in an aqueous solution of sodium hydroxide or sodium carbonate, and a rich liquor of sodium bromide/bromate is subsequently processed. The absorption of lean bromine in alkaline liquors would be expected to be gas film controlled.

Bromine reacts with dissolved SO_2, and this reaction has also been employed for the recovery of bromine as well as manufacture of HBr.

$$Br_2 + 2H_2O + SO_2 \rightarrow 2HBr + H_2SO_4$$

The kinetics of this reaction has not been studied, but the related case of chlorine has been reported (see Section 6.5.6).

Some novel approaches for the recovery and transport of bromine have been reported. For instance, dissolved bromine can be reacted with acetylene or ethylene to give tetrabromoethane or dibromoethane; the bromo compound can be conveniently transported. In another approach a process has been patented where lean bromine is absorbed in an aqueous solution of some specific quaternary ammonium bromide where a liquid water-immiscible bromine compound is formed that can be stored and readily transported and can be easily dissociated to liberate molecular bromine. A number of quaternary ammonium bromides, such as *N*-ethyl morpholinium bromide or *N*-ethyl pyrrolidinium bromide, have been patented (Shropshire and Eustace, 1978). The kinetics of the reaction between bromine and quaternary ammonium bromide has apparently not been reported.

3.7.9. Reactions of Importance in Pyrometallurgy

Szekely (1967), Szekely and Themelis (1971), and Richardson (1975) have considered this subject in detail. Richardson has pointed out that a number of gas–liquid reactions are controlled by gas-side resistance. For instance, in the deoxidation of copper by 1% H_2 in N_2 in the temperature range of 1400–1600°C, the overall value of the mass transfer coefficient agrees with that calculated on the assumption that the process is gas film controlled. The gas-film-controlled mechanism also holds for the decarburization of iron by O_2 and CO_2. Whiteway (1979) has studied the decarburization of molten iron by hydrogen at 1327°C; this decarburization reaction gives methane. It was found that the process is essentially controlled by the diffusion of methane in the gas phase.

It is likely that in the case of some reactions of practical importance the chemical kinetics in the liquid phase may play an important role.

3.7.10. Special Case: Role of Diffusion in the Absorption of Gases in Blood in the Human Body

Absorption of O_2 in Hemoglobin

Diffusion accompanied by chemical reaction plays an important role in systems of physiological importance (Roughton, 1959; Ramachandran, 1969). The absorption of oxygen from air into the red cells of the blood in the human body is of great importance. The transport of gases into the red cells involves four steps in series:

1. Diffusion through the alveolor epithelium and the walls of the blood capillaries;
2. Passage through the blood plasma, which separates the walls of the blood capillaries from the surface of the red cells;
3. Diffusion through the red cell membrane, which separates the plasma from the hemoglobin mass in the blood;
4. Diffusion accompanied by chemical reaction with hemoglobin in the interior of the red cells.

It is known that steps 3 and 4 are not sufficiently fast and that they have a rate-limiting action on the uptake of gases by the lungs. The rate equations for the various steps can be formulated by assigning suitable transfer coefficients for each step. The transfer coefficient for step 4 will depend on the mechanism or regime under which the reaction takes place. This in turn will depend on the prevailing conditions, such as the partial pressure of oxygen, concentration of free hemoglobin, and other physicochemical parameters (see Chapter 2). Overall equations for the rate of absorption can then be obtained by combining the rate expression for the various steps. The necessary physicochemical data have been summarized by Ramachandran (1969).

The absorption of O_2 may well be accompanied by an instantaneous reaction (regime 4) in view of the relatively high value of the rate constant. Consider the following case:

Partial pressure of O_2 = 0.21 atm

$$D_{O_2} = 7.0 \times 10^{-6}\ \text{cm}^2/\text{sec}$$

$$D_{Hb} = 7.5 \times 10^{-8}\ \text{cm}^2/\text{sec}$$

Henry's constant for O_2 in hemoglobin

$$= 9.4 \times 10^{-7}\ \text{mol/cm}^3\ \text{atm}$$

$$k_L = 1 \times 10^{-2}\ \text{cm/sec}$$

$$[\text{Hb}] = 2 \times 10^{-5}\ \text{mol/cm}^3$$

$$k_2 = 1.8 \times 10^{9}\ \text{cm}^3/\text{mol sec}$$

$$\frac{\sqrt{D_{O_2} k_2 [\text{Hb}]}}{k_L} = 50.2$$

$$\frac{[\text{Hb}]}{[O_2^*]}\sqrt{\frac{D_{Hb}}{D_{O_2}}} = 10.49$$

Thus the necessary condition (expression 2.79) for the validity of the instantaneous reaction regime is satisfied.

If the value of k_L is high and the partial pressure of O_2 is low, the system can shift to regime 3 and the absorption of O_2 will be accompanied by a fast pseudo-first-order reaction.

Absorption / Desorption of CO_2

The carbon dioxide produced in the metabolism taking place in the human body has to be carried from tissues where it is produced and exhaled from the lungs. Both plasma and red cells act as carriers for carbon dioxide. The modes by which carbon dioxide is transported in human body have been summarized by Ramachandran. The enzyme carbonic anhydrase speeds up the hydration reaction of carbon dioxide in blood. This enzyme is one of the most powerful catalysts for the hydration of CO_2 (Sharma and Danckwerts, 1963).

Roughton and Rossi-Bernardi (1966) have suggested that the carbamino reaction of carbon dioxide with glycyl glycine should be a simple and useful model for the carbamino hemoglobin formation in blood.

Absorption of CO

The reaction of CO with hemoglobin is first order in CO as well as hemoglobin and the value of the second-order rate constant at 37°C has been estimated to be 6.7×10^8 cm^3/mol sec. Because Henry's constant for CO in hemoglobin is low ($\sim 7 \times 10^{-6}$ mol/cm^3 atm at 37°C), the absorption of CO at low partial pressures of CO will conform to the fast pseudo-first-order reaction regime (regime 3), since the necessary condition given by expression 2.31 will be satisfied. Thus the rate of uptake of CO by blood can be estimated and a realistic idea about CO poisoning can be obtained.

The reaction between CO and hemoglobin is reversible and CO can be desorbed by the absorption of O_2.

(B) Liquid–Liquid Systems

3.7.11. Extraction of Free Fatty Acids from Naturally Occurring Glycerides

A variety of natural fats, such as groundnut oil and sesame oil, contain some free fatty acids. Some substances, particularly rice bran oil, contain a relatively high amount of free fatty acids. In the processing of oils it is necessary to remove the free fatty acid by treatment with aqueous or alcoholic caustic soda. The reaction between RCOOH and OH^- is instantaneous.

3.7.12. Removal of HCl from Chlorinated Organic Compounds

In the manufacture of a variety of chlorinated organic compounds by substitution chlorination it usually becomes necessary to remove the dissolved HCl in the organic compound. The removal of HCl is sometimes accomplished by extraction into aqueous solutions of NaOH. Thus in the manufacture of chlorinated paraffins by the chlorination of paraffins the product will be nearly saturated with HCl at the conditions of the reactor. The product from the chlorination can then be processed further for the removal of HCl by treatment with aqueous NaOH or Na_2CO_3. (If the substance is relatively nonvolatile, it may be desirable to adopt air stripping to expel the dissolved HCl.)

3.7.13. Recovery of Aliphatic Acids and HF and HCl from Aqueous Solutions

The recovery of lower aliphatic acids from their aqueous solutions is usually accomplished by straight or azeotropic or extractive distillation. Yakushkin (1969) has suggested that it may be desirable to recover them by extraction into trioctylamine. This amine is insoluble in water. The amine salt is also insoluble in water and it breaks down to the corresponding acid and the amine on heating. Here the reaction between the acid and the amine will be instantaneous. Jagirdar and Sharma (1980) have also studied some aspects of the recovery of aliphatic acids from aqueous solutions and have shown that in some cases it may be possible to separate the acids simultaneously. Yagodin et al. (1974) have considered the extraction of $HClO_4$ with tertiary amines.

Similarly, in the manufacture of synthetic fatty acids by liquid-phase air oxidation of paraffins, the recovery of fatty acids may be accomplished by extraction into an aqueous solution of ammonia (and possibly aqueous solutions of amines like trimethylamine). The reaction between fatty acids and ammonia is instantaneous.

The manufacture of anhydrous HF from its aqueous solution by straight distillation is not possible because of the existence of an azeotrope. Hardwick and Wace (1965) have shown that HF can be successfully extracted into trinonylamine. The trinonylamine hydrofluoride is insoluble in the aqueous medium and can be converted to the amine and HF by heating.

Harada et al. (1971) have studied the mechanism of acid extraction by tri-*n*-octylamine–benzene mixed solvent by the Schlieren method. This method is efficient for the recognition of the reaction plane, since the gradient of the refractive index varies steeply near the reaction plane. Kataoka et al. (1971) have also studied the mechanism of extraction of HCl by a liquid anion exchanger Amberlite-II(10 vol %)–benzene solution in a jet apparatus where the organic phase was spread as a thin film on the surface of an aqueous jet. Their results indicate that the transfer of HCl is accompanied by an instantaneous reaction and the neutralized product diffuses into the organic phase as the salt of amine. Kataoka et al. (1975) have studied some aspects of mass transfer in such systems.

3.7.14. Nitration of Phenol

The direct nitration of phenol, resorcinol, and the like with nitric acid (75%) under homogeneous conditions is very rapid and results in the evolution of a large amount of heat and the oxidation and resinification of the substances. The use of a very low strength of nitric acid is economically unattractive. Kaloshin (1971) has suggested that the nitration may be carried out in a heterogeneous system where phenol is dissolved in a solvent such as benzene and is contacted with aqueous nitric acid. Experimental work was carried out in a 9-cm-i.d. stirred reactor with benzene as a solvent and a dispersed-phase fraction of 0.25. The speed of agitation, which was varied from 30 to 150 rev/min, was found to have a substantial effect on the rate of nitration. It was concluded that the process is feasible and is diffusion controlled. On the basis of the available information (see Sections 3.4.17 and 3.5.2) the nitration of phenol would be expected to be very fast and is likely to conform to the instantaneous reaction regime.

3.7.15. Solvent Extraction in Mineral Processing

A number of elements are recovered by solvent extraction with chemical reaction (Rosenbaum et al. 1971; Hughes, 1975; Bailes et al. 1976) and this method has acquired great commercial importance. Table 3.4 lists some important examples. This subject is now receiving increasing attention in view of the urgent need to recover metals from their lean ores via hydrometallurgical processes. Hanson et al. (1974) have considered some aspects of extraction with reaction in such systems.

(*a*) *Extraction of Anions*

Consider the extraction of uranium anions with tertiary amines. The reaction scheme is as follows:

$$2R_3N + H_2SO_4 \rightarrow (R_3NH)_2SO_4 \qquad \text{(i)}$$

$$UO_2(SO_4)_2^{2-}(aq) + (R_3NH)_2SO_4(org) \rightarrow (R_3NH)_2UO_2(SO_4)_2(org) + SO_4^{2-} \qquad \text{(ii)}$$

$$(R_3NH)_2UO_2(SO_4)_2(org) + 2NH_3(aq) \rightarrow 2R_3N(org) + UO_2(SO_4)(aq) + (NH_4)_2SO_4(aq) \qquad \text{(iii)}$$

Reaction (ii) shows the reaction of a uranyl sulfate anion with an amine sulfate molecule to yield amine uranyl sulfate and a sulfate anion. The stripping

TABLE 3.4. Extraction with Reaction in Mineral Processing[a]

Element	Extracted Species	Feed Solution	Organic Solution	Strip Solution
Beryllium	Cation	Acid sulfate	EHPA	$(NH_4)_2CO_3$
Boron	Neutral	Alkaline brine	Phenyl glycol	H_2SO_4
Copper[b]	Cation	Acid sulfate or NH_4OH–$(NH_4)_2CO_3$	LIX-64N	H_2SO_4
Molybdenum	Anion	Acid sulfate	Tertiary amine	NH_4OH
Tungsten	Anion	Acid sulfate	Secondary amine	NH_4OH
Uranium	Anion	Acid sulfate	Tertiary amine	NH_3–$(NH_4)_2SO_4$
Mercury[c]	Cation	Chloride	Xylene containing triisoctylamine	Nonacidic salt solution

[a]Adapted from Rosenbaum et al. (1971).
[b]Also see Bailes et al. (1976).
[c]*Chem. Eng.* (1972).

operation is carried out with aqueous ammonia. These reactions are expected to be instantaneous.

(b) Extraction of Cations

Consider the example of the extraction of beryllium cations with 2-ethyl hexyl phosphoric acid (EHPA). The reaction scheme [$X =$ (2-ethyl hexyl)$_2PO_4^-$] is as follows:

$$Be^{+2}(aq) + 2HX(org) \rightarrow BeX_2(org) + 2H^+(aq) \quad \text{(i)}$$

$$Be^{+2}(aq) + 2H_2X_2(org) \rightarrow BeH_2X_4(org) + 2H^+(aq) \quad \text{(ii)}$$

$$BeH_2X_4(org) + 2(NH_4)_2CO_3(aq) \rightarrow BeCO_3(aq) + H_2CO_3(aq) + 4(NH_4)X(org) \quad \text{(iii)}$$

$$4(NH_4)X(org) + 2H_2SO_4(aq) \rightarrow 2H_2X_2(org) + 2(NH_4)_2SO_4(aq) \quad \text{(iv)}$$

Kerosene is used as a solvent and in this medium the acid exists as a dimer; hence reaction (ii) rather than reaction (i) actually represents the stoichiometry of the process. The stripping operation is carried out with ammonium carbonate. The regeneration of the organophosphate is carried out with sulfuric acid. In practice, if the leach liquor contains a sufficient concentration of sulfuric acid, then the first stage can be used for both regeneration and extraction. The reactions involved in this process are expected to be instantaneous.

(c) Extraction of Neutral Molecules

The extraction of borates with polyols is an interesting example. It is well known that boric acid forms chelates with polyols. The reaction scheme is as follows:

$$NaB(OH)_4(aq) + 2R(OH)_2(org) \rightarrow NaR_2BO_4(aq) + 4H_2O$$

$$NaR_2BO_4 + \tfrac{1}{2}H_2SO_4 + 3H_2O \rightarrow 2R(OH)_2(org) + B(OH)_3(aq) + \tfrac{1}{2}Na_2SO_4(aq)$$

The chelation reaction is expected to be instantaneous.

(d) Extraction of Copper

We shall consider the case of the extraction of copper sulfate from aqueous solutions both because of its great commercial importance and because of the availability of information on the kinetics.

Solvent Extraction of Copper Sulfate from Aqueous Solutions. Two types of reagents have been considered for the extraction of copper from aqueous acidic solutions: (i) hydroxy oximes (one of the well-known commercial brands, marketed by General Mills in the United States, is known by the name of LIX); (ii) alkylated 8-hydroxyquinoline (commercially available as Kelex from the Ashland Chemical Company in the United States). A variety of hydrocarbon solvents are used as diluents, and these play a vital role in the extraction process.

Extraction with Hydroxy Oximes. The most widely used reagent is called LIX64N, which is a mixture of LIX63 (*syn* form of 5,8-diethyl-7-hydroxy-6-dodecanone oxime) and LIX65N (*anti* form) (other hydroxy oximes have also been suggested in the recent literature). Whewell et al. (1975, 1976) have studied the kinetics with LIX64N, dissolved in a low aromatic hydrocarbon solvent ESCAD-100, in an apparatus that involved mass transfer to a single drop. It is clear from their work that diffusional factors were important and that the specific rate of extraction was independent of the drop size (in other words, the rate of mass transfer was directly proportional to the interfacial area). Hughes et al. (1976) have found that the value of the activation energy in this system is approximately three times that encountered in a purely diffusion-controlled process. It has also been indicated that the diffusion of copper-loaded reagent from the interfacial zone may also offer significant resistance.

Finkelstein and Fleming (1976) have studied the kinetics of extraction with LIX64N in a Lewis-type stirred cell with chloroform as a solvent. The interfacial area was varied from 79.7 to 283.5 cm^2 and the aqueous phase volume from 250 to 900 cm^3. At lower speeds of agitation the rate of extraction increased with an increase in the speed of agitation, indicating that diffusional resistance was important. However, beyond a certain speed of agitation there was no effect of further increase in agitation speed on the specific rate of extraction up to the point where the quiescent nature of the interface was maintained and the effective area was basically the same as the cross-sectional area. The specific rate of extraction was independent of the interfacial area and the volume of the aqueous phase. The basic findings of this work are in agreement with those of Whewell et al. (1975, 1976). Thus, the system probably conforms to regime 3 and the extraction of hydroxy oxime is accompanied by a fast pseudo-mth-order reaction in the aqueous phase. The recent work of Whewell et al. (1977) gives good evidence in favor of this mechanism. The more recent work of Hanson et al. (1978) also lends support to the conclusion that the mass transfer of oxime is accompanied by a fast reaction and that the system probably conforms to regime 3 (the solubility of LIX63 in water at 25°C is about 15.5 ppm; the solubility of LIX65N (*anti*) in water is about 1 ppm).

The specific rate of extraction of copper from an aqueous sulfate medium with LIX65N appears to be first order with respect to copper, slightly greater than first order with respect to LIX65N, and close to negative first order in the proton concentration. There is a very substantial effect of the concentration of LIX63 in LIX64N. (The specific rate of extraction is approximately half order in LIX63.) Various other aspects pertaining to the mechanism of these reactions have been studied by different authors. The interfacial tension characteristics of the system also seem to play a significant role in affecting the rate of reaction.

Whewell et al. (1977) have discussed some complications that are encountered in a study of the kinetics of such systems. They have clearly shown how data can be wrongly interpreted with respect to the catalytic (synergetic) effect of some species; how kinetics can be affected by impurities; and so on. They have also shown how a relatively high activation energy of about 10.75 kcal/mol for this extraction process may be misconstrued as that belonging to a kinetically controlled transfer reaction. Thus great caution must be exercised in interpreting experimental results, and experiments should in turn be planned very carefully.

Extraction with Alkylated 8-Hydroxyquinoline. The best-known alkylated hydroxyquinoline is Kelex-100, which has a C_{12} alkyl substituent in the seventh position. Finkelstein and Fleming (1976) have found basically the same controlling mechanism (regime 3) for this reagent as in the case of LIX64N. The specific rate of extraction was found to be first order in copper, approximately second order in the reagent, and negative first order in the concentration of the hydrogen ion. Flett et al. (1975) have made similar observations.

Rod and Rychnovsky (1975) have studied the extraction of copper sulfate with 8-hydroxyquinoline (oxine) in a modified stirred cell. Chloroform and benzene were used as solvents, since these are good solvents for copper oxinate. Here the reaction was found to be instantaneous and the overall rate of the process was found to be controlled by the diffusion of the reaction components to the reaction plane in the aqueous phase. (The copper oxinate formed in the aqueous phase is extracted into the organic phase.) Thus in this case the system conforms to regime 4.

3.7.16. Interfacial Polycondensation and Esterification

The interfacial polycondensation method is based on the reaction between diacid halide (usually chloride), dissolved in an organic solvent that is insoluble in water, such as xylene, carbon tetrachloride, methylene chloride, or hexane, and a diamine or diol dissolved in water. Alkali is added to the aqueous phase to neutralize the liberated hydrogen halide. Thus two phases are involved.

The following reaction occurs between the diacyl chloride (sebacyl chloride) and diamine (hexamethylenediamine) (sebacyl chloride + hexamethylenediamine → nylon-6–10):

$$xH_2N(CH_2)_6NH_2 + xClCO(CH_2)_8COCl \rightarrow$$

$$(-NH(CH_2)_6NHCO(CH_2)_8CO-)_x + 2xHCl$$

$$2xHCl + 2xNaOH \rightarrow 2xNaCl + 2xH_2O$$

These reactions can be conducted at ambient conditions and are highly versatile from the point of view of preparing polymers of all types in bulk form. Morgan (1965) has discussed this subject extensively.

It is not essential that an aqueous phase be used, and in fact nonaqueous two-phase interfacial polycondensation reactions have been studied with ethylene or propylene glycol in place of the aqueous phase. These nonaqueous solvents offer no advantage over the aqueous phase. Water possesses a number of advantages associated with the low miscibility of many commonly employed organic liquids and is a good solvent for many diamines, bisphenoxides, and alkalies, and is also a good solvent for the salt formed from the neutralization of the acid and the alkali.

This type of reaction is rather unusual in that the reaction occurs in the organic phase (A phase) and *not* in the aqueous phase. There is enough evidence in the literature to support this contention (Morgan, 1965). Thus, for instance, if an analogous monofunctional acid chloride (such as benzoyl chloride) dissolved in benzene is reacted with equivalent quantities of aniline and ammonia dissolved in an aqueous phase, then only benzanilide and ammonium chloride are obtained, even though ammonia is a much stronger base than aniline (pK values are 9.26 and 4.58, respectively). It is also known that in a homogeneous phase ammonia reacts several thousand times faster than aniline with benzoyl chloride. The distribution coefficient for aniline in the organic phase is very favorable as compared to that for ammonia. In principle, the polycondensation reaction can occur in the aqueous phase for situations where the diacyl chloride has substantial solubility in the aqueous phase and high hydrolytic stability.

The reactions between diacyl chlorides and diamines are known to be very fast, even in an organic phase. A rough estimate can be made from the available value of the second-order rate constant for the reaction between benzoyl chloride and morpholine in a cyclohexane medium at 25°C of 2.64×10^6 $cm^3/mol\ sec$ (Bender and Jones, 1962). The value of the rate constant for diacyl chloride–diamine reaction would be expected to be quite high and therefore the necessary conditions for the instantaneous reaction regime will be satisfied. Bekhli et al. (1967) have indicated that the second-order rate constant for the reaction between a diacyl chloride, such as terephthaloyl chloride, and amines, such as piperazine, would be in the range of 10^7–10^8 $cm^3/mol\ sec$. In the specific case of decamethylenediamine–isophthaloyl chloride (dissolved in chloroform) the value of the second-order rate constant has been reported to be 2.4×10^7 $cm^3/mol\ sec$ (Sokolov and Nikonov, 1977). Griskey et al. (1974) have also indicated that the system will conform to the instantaneous reaction regime. A situation can possibly arise where the resistance to mass transfer is shifted to the aqueous phase, in a manner analogous to gas–liquid systems, where the reaction can become completely gas-film-controlled. In such a case the rate would be directly proportional to the concentration of the diamine in the aqueous phase. If the polymer film is stable, then the resistance associated with the diffusion through this film may also have to be considered (Sokolov and Nikonov, 1977).

Carraher (1969) has studied the interfacial polycondensation of ethylene glycol with diphenyl dichlorosilane dissolved in a variety of water-immiscible solvents such as cyclohexane or CCl_4. Here ethylene glycol was dispersed in the organic phase. It is clear from this work that the interfacial area of contact directly affects the rate of polycondensation.

The reaction between bischloroformate and aromatic diamines is known to have rate constant values of the order of 10 cm^3/mol sec, and in such cases the reaction may well become kinetically controlled and diffusional factors may be absent (Wittbecker and Katz, 1959). In other cases intermediate values of the rate constant may be found and therefore the system may conform to regime 2 or 3.

The technique of interfacial polycondensation has also been adopted in gas–liquid systems to achieve certain results. For instance, oxalyl chloride diluted with an inert gas can be absorbed in a suitable solvent containing a diamine to give a polyamide (Sokolov, 1977).

Interfacial esterification of sucrose with benzoyl chloride to make sucrose benzoate is industrially practiced and is referred to as the Schotten–Baumann technique. Here an aqueous solution of sucrose is reacted with benzoyl chloride dissolved in toluene at ambient conditions; sodium hydroxide is added to neutralize the HCl formed by the reaction. The extent of esterification is reported to be 7.4 mol of benzoate per mole of sucrose (Lira and Anderson, 1977).

Manufacture of Polycarbonates by Interfacial Polycondensation

Polycarbonate resins have acquired considerable importance as engineering plastics. The most extensively used polycarbonate is based on the reaction between bisphenol-A and phosgene:

$$m\text{HO}-\text{C}_6\text{H}_4-\underset{\text{CH}_3}{\overset{\text{CH}_3}{\underset{|}{\overset{|}{\text{C}}}}}-\text{C}_6\text{H}_4-\text{OH} + m\text{COCl}_2 \longrightarrow$$

$$\left[-\text{O}-\text{C}_6\text{H}_4-\underset{\text{CH}_3}{\overset{\text{CH}_3}{\underset{|}{\overset{|}{\text{C}}}}}-\text{C}_6\text{H}_4-\text{O}-\overset{\text{O}}{\overset{\|}{\text{C}}}-\right]_m + 2m\text{HCl}$$

It is necessary to fix the HCl formed in the reaction to obtain the desired molecular weight. Further, *p-tert*-butylphenol is used as a chain terminator.

The polymerization reaction can be conducted in a solution with methylene chloride as a solvent and pyridine as HCl acceptor. Lime can also be used as an HCl acceptor but this will constitute a separate phase. The technique of interfacial polycondensation (Wielgosz et al., 1972) can be advantageously employed, since an aqueous solution of sodium hydroxide (7–10% by weight) can be used; methylene chloride is usually employed as a solvent. It appears that in recent years this technique has become industrially very important for the manufacture of polycarbonates.

In a typical practice, a series of mechanically agitated reactors are used and great flexibility of operation is possible, since the addition of reactants to different reactors can be manipulated. It appears that triethylamine (1% in methylene chloride) is used as a catalyst. It may not be possible to remove all the heat in the first reactor because of the high rate of reaction and hence the aqueous and organic feed can be chilled to below 0°C (say, −4 to −5°C) and then introduced into the reactor, where the temperature has to be maintained at about 30°C. Various types of reactors for different stages (e.g., oligomer formation followed by polymer formation) have been considered. It is necessary to have very vigorous agitation, since mass transfer plays an important role and phosgene can react with NaOH to give sodium carbonate.

3.7.17. Manufacture of Organophosphate Pesticides

The manufacture of some important organophosphate pesticides involves heterogeneous reactions. In principle, some of these reactions can also be carried out in a homogeneous system by using a proper solvent. There are, however, certain specific advantages offered by the heterogeneous system which are associated with the greater speed of operation, and the filtration of highly toxic material is avoided. Consider the reaction between dimethyl amine and $POCl_3$ and the subsequent reaction of the organic product with potassium fluoride (Hartley and West, 1969):

$$\begin{gathered}\text{POCl}_3 + 2(\text{CH}_3)_2\text{NH}(aq) + 2\text{NaOH} \rightarrow \\ ((\text{CH}_3)_2\text{N})_2\text{POCl}\,(chloroform) + 2\text{NaCl}(aq) \\ \downarrow \text{KF}(aq) \\ ((\text{CH}_3)_2\text{N})_2\text{POF}\,(chloroform) + \text{KCl}(aq)\end{gathered}$$

It is known that $POCl_3$ reacts with water but its reaction with $(CH_3)_2NH$ is very much faster than that with water, and hence the reaction can be conducted by adding $POCl_3$ to an agitated dispersion of chloroform and an aqueous solution of caustic soda. Further, both reactants partition much in favor of chloroform from water. Here the reaction between $POCl_3$ and $(CH_3)_2NH$ is expected to be instantaneous. Similarly, the reaction between dimethyl ester of phosphorodithionic acid and for instance, α-bromophenyl acetic acid (ethyl ester) to give the pesticide phenthoate is carried out in two-phase systems. The kinetics of these reactions have apparently not been established. It is expected that some of these reactions will fall in the category of instantaneous reactions (i.e., will conform to regime 4) and some sluggish reactions may fall in the category of slow or very slow reactions.

Scale-up

The scale-up of systems belonging to this regime would require a knowledge of $k_L a$ and the residence time distribution of the B phase.

3.8. REGIME BETWEEN 3 AND 4

Some of the important features of the depletion regime are as follows:

1. For a given value of $\sqrt{M}$ and q, the value of the enhancement factor is independent of the order of the reaction with respect to the solute (i.e., m). For example, for high values of $\sqrt{M}$, the curve of ϕ versus $\sqrt{M}$ with q as a parameter for $m, n = 3, 1$ lies within 0.5% of the curve for $m, n = 1, 1$.
2. For a given value of $\sqrt{M}$ and q, the value of the enhancement factor decreases with an increase in n, the order with respect to the dissolved reactant B.
3. The reactions that are zero order with respect to the dissolved reactant B ($n = 0$) have certain interesting features. For this case, as $\sqrt{M}$ is increased, the concentration of B at the interface becomes significantly less than that in the bulk liquid phase and finally it becomes zero. However, since the reaction is zero order with respect to the reactant B, the rate of chemical reaction is unaffected by the decrease in the concentration of B, until the latter becomes zero at the interface. Hence, the enhancement factor is given by

$$\phi = \sqrt{M}$$

until the reaction becomes instantaneous. In other words, the transition from regime 3 to regime 4 is very abrupt in the case of zero-order reactions ($n = 0$).

From Eqs. 2.44 (with $m = 1$, $n = 0$) and 2.97 we can find the value of $[B_o]$ at which the abrupt transition from regime 3 to 4 will occur at a specified value of k_L and $[A^*]$:

$$R_A = [A^*]\sqrt{D_A k_1} \tag{2.44}$$

$$R_A = \frac{k_L [B_o]}{Z}\sqrt{\frac{D_B}{D_A}} \tag{2.97}$$

At the transition point

$$[B_o] = \frac{Z[A^*]}{k_L}\left(\frac{D_A}{D_B}\right)^{1/2}(D_A k_1)^{1/2} \tag{3.14}$$

A system of this type can possibly be used for the simultaneous measurement of a and $k_L a$ and hence of the true k_L.

The specific rate of mass transfer is dependent on the value of the physical mass transfer coefficient k_L under otherwise uniform conditions. Thus in order to be able to predict the value of the enhancement factor, we must know the value of k_L. In most of the cases reported in the literature the k_L values were obtained for systems that contained no reactive species, but in other respects their properties were similar to the corresponding reacting solutions. It is presumed that the values of k_L for nonreacting systems are applicable to the corresponding reacting systems. It has now been established that this presumption may not be valid in many systems because of the occurrence of interfacial turbulence when mass transfer is accompanied by chemical reaction (see Section 3.13). The interfacial turbulence results in an increase in the k_L value; hence this factor should be taken into consideration while correlating the data. At present our knowledge in this field is inadequate to predict the increase in the value of k_L. From a practical point of view the predicted value of the specific rate of mass transfer, disregarding the existence of interfacial turbulence, will be on the conservative side, since interfacial turbulence will reduce the extent of depletion.

The literature provides limited information on the experimental verification of the predicted results for any specified system.

(A) Gas–Liquid Systems

3.8.1. Absorption of CO_2 in Aqueous Solutions of Caustic Alkalies and Amines

Nijsing et al. (1959), Hikita and Asai (1965), Emmert and Pigford (1962), Astarita (1961), Brian et al. (1967), and Kishinevskii et al. (1970) have studied absorption of CO_2 in aqueous solutions of either NaOH (or KOH) or monoethanolamine (MEA) under conditions such that the values of the terms on the left-hand and right-hand sides of expression 2.79 are comparable, so that depletion of the reactive species B occurs in the film. It appears that in the case of caustic soda solutions there is good agreement between the experimental and predicted values of the enhancement factors (Nijsing et al., 1959; Hikita and Asai, 1965). The experimental data indicate that there is no interfacial turbulence when CO_2 is absorbed in aqueous solutions of NaOH or KOH. In the case of the absorption of CO_2 in MEA solutions, however, interfacial turbulence sets in and hence the data should be correlated on the basis of the enhanced values of the physical mass transfer coefficient. Brian et al. (1967) have shown that there is good agreement between the experimental and theoretical values when the values of k_L in the presence of interfacial turbulence are used for correlation. This matter is discussed further in Section 3.13.

In industrial practice too, under certain conditions the absorption of CO_2 in aqueous MEA falls in the regime between 3 and 4 (Danckwerts and Sharma, 1966).

3.8.2. Absorption of O_2 in Aqueous Solutions of Sodium Dithionite

Jhaveri and Sharma (1969) have studied the absorption of O_2 in aqueous alkaline solutions of sodium dithionite under conditions such that a substantial depletion of dithionite occurred in the film. This system is interesting because in the part of the range of concentrations covered the reaction was second order in sodium dithionite and zero order in oxygen. The effect of depletion for this system will be much greater than in the case of a corresponding system where the reaction is first order with respect to the reactive species. Figure 3.17 shows that the data can be satisfactorily correlated by Eq. 2.114.

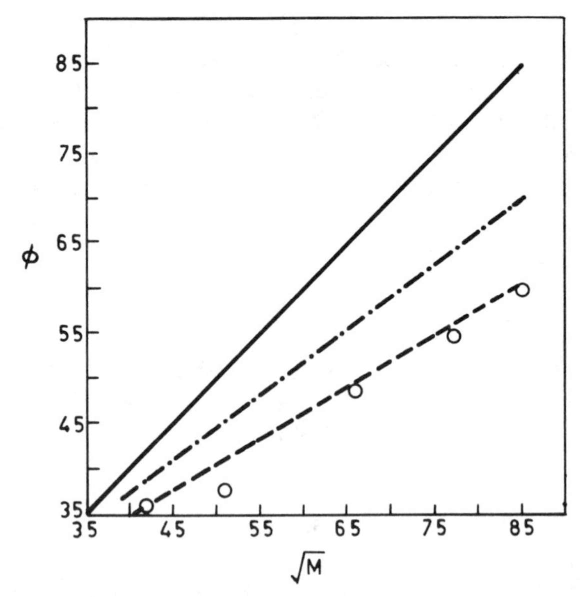

Figure 3.17. Absorption of O_2 in aqueous alkaline solutions of sodium dithionite under depletion conditions (——, pseudo-*n*th-order line; –·–, theoretical line for $m = 1$; ---, theoretical line for $m = 2$; ○, experimental points).

3.8.3. Absorption of O_2 in Aqueous Sodium Sulfite Solutions

Oishi et al. (1965) have studied the $CoSO_4$-catalyzed oxidation of sodium sulfite. The reaction was found to be first order in oxygen and 1.5 order in sodium sulfite under the set of conditions adopted by these authors. The experimental data of these workers are in good agreement with the theoretical predictions based on Eq. 2.114 over a wide range (from 4 to 50) of the values of ϕ_a.

3.8.4. Absorption of Oxygen in Alkaline Solutions Containing the Sodium Salt of 1, 4-Naphthaquinone-2-Sulfonic Acid (NQSA)

The Takahax process (Takeuchi et al., 1980) for the removal of H_2S via an absorption process and subsequent oxidation to sulfur uses alkaline liquors containing NQSA. The oxidation of reduced quinone (NHQSA) to NQSA is an important step in this process.

$$O_2 + 2NHQSA \rightarrow 2NQSA + 2H_2O$$

The kinetics of the absorption of O_2 in aqueous solutions of NHQSA was studied in a laminar jet apparatus at 25°C over a pH range of 9.8–12.6. Experiments were made in the fast pseudo-*m*th-order (regime 3) as well as in the depletion regime (regime between 3 and 4). The reaction was found to be first order in O_2 and NHQSA. Experimental data in the depletion regime agreed well with the predicted values.

The k_2 value at 25°C was found to be 4.5×10^9 $cm^3/mol\ sec$ for a pH greater than 11.5; the k_2 value was directly proportional to the pH in the range of 9.8–11.5.

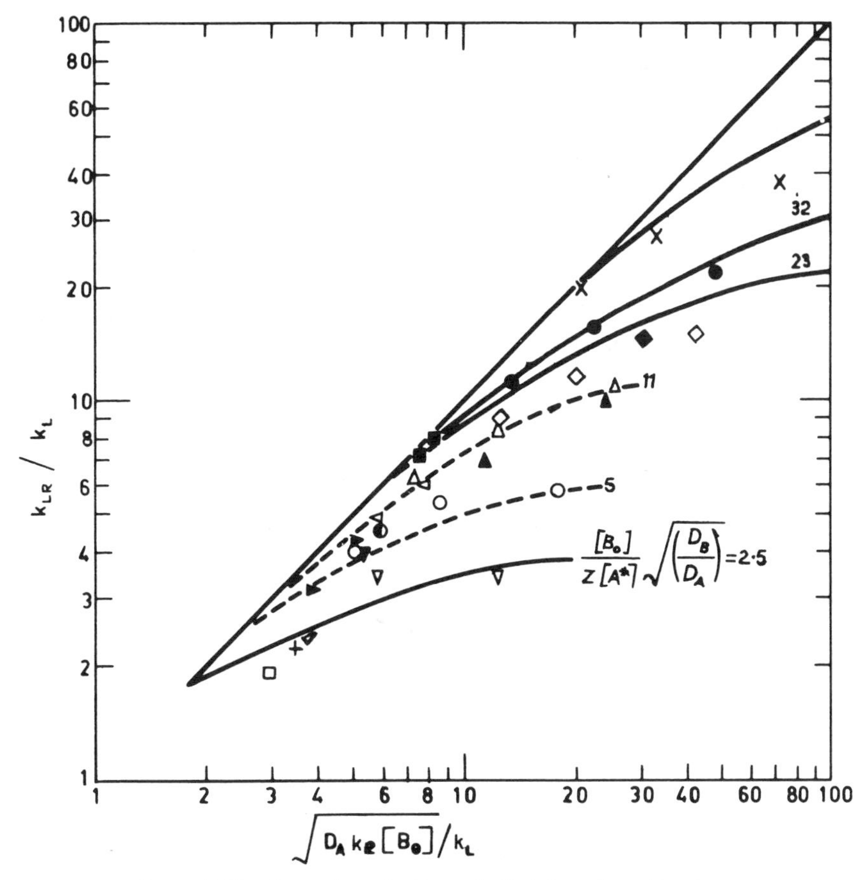

Figure 3.18. Extraction of chlorosubstituted acetic acid esters into aqueous NaOH under depletion conditions.

(B) Liquid–Liquid Systems

3.8.5. Extraction of Chlorosubstituted Acetic Acid Esters into Aqueous NaOH Solutions

The extraction of chlorosubstituted acetic acid esters into aqueous solutions of sodium hydroxide has been studied under conditions where the data conformed to the regime between 3 and 4 (Sharma and Nanda, 1968). Figure 3.18 shows that the experimental data for the extraction of chlorosubstituted acetic acid ester into aqueous sodium hydroxide solutions can be satisfactorily correlated by an equation similar to Eq. 2.114.

3.8.6. Extraction of Copper from Aqueous Solutions

Various aspects of the extraction of copper from aqueous solutions with a variety of extractants were covered in Section 3.7.15. Kondo et al. (1978) have studied the extraction of copper from aqueous solutions with benzene containing benzoyl acetone in a stirred contactor. These authors were able to vary the values of [A*], [B_o], k_L, and the speed of agitation over a wide range so that different controlling regimes—regimes 3 and 4 and the regime between 3 and 4—could be studied. The predicted values of the enhancement factor for the depletion regime agreed well with the experimental values.

Scale-up

The design of industrial equipment where the system belongs to the regime between 3 and 4 will require, besides the physicochemical data, a separate knowledge of k_L and a. In addition, it is necessary to know the residence time distribution of both phases.

3.9. CHEMICAL REACTIONS IN MOLTEN SALTS

A number of reactions that are catalyzed by solid catalysts can also be carried out in melts containing the active ingredients of the catalyst. For instance, the well-known reaction of the oxidation of SO_2 to SO_3 in the presence of a V_2O_5 catalyst can also be carried out in melts of potassium pyrosulfate containing V_2O_5. The problems associated with catalyst fouling would be practically absent in the molten system. Further, the relatively high heat transfer coefficients offered by molten salts facilitate the removal or supply of heat. This implies that the problems of hot spots and catalyst deactivation can perhaps be avoided. However, the molten-salt catalyst system is unlikely to be industrially attractive for common solid-catalyzed vapor-phase reactions because of the very low active areas provided by the system. Typically, in a sparged or mechanically agitated molten salt the maximum value of the effective interfacial area is unlikely to exceed 20 cm^2/cm^3. By contrast, a porous catalyst can easily offer areas in the range of $5-10 \times 10^4$ cm^2/cm^3 of catalyst. Thus the quantity of the catalyst required in the case of a molten-salt system will be relatively enormous compared to solid-catalyzed vapor-phase reactions. It then becomes attractive to distribute the melt in the pores of a porous catalyst. Kenney and Taylor (1971) and Kenney (1975) have discussed the various aspects of reactions in which the melt acts as a catalyst.

There are some situations where the process conditions demand contact between a gas and a molten salt. For instance, in the manufacture of phenol from toluene via benzoic acid, the air oxidation of acid is carried out under molten conditions with cuprous benzoate as a reactant.

In some situations the melt may simply act as a solvent for the reaction, and in other cases the melt may serve multiple purposes. Consider the case of the fluorination of CCl_4 with a molten fluoride:

$$CCl_4 + MF \rightleftharpoons CCl_3F + MCl$$

Here the melt can act as an effective fluorinating agent. However, if HF or F_2 is continuously passed through the melt, then a continuous process can be conceived. In such cases the melt may function in one or more of the following ways: as an exchanging medium, as a solvent, or as a catalyst, depending on the circumstances.

Sundermeyer (1965) has reviewed the field of fused salts and their use as reaction media. Table 3.5 lists some of the reactions that have been studied in molten-salt systems. (The fundamental aspects of gas absorption accompanied by chemical reaction in molten salts are practically the same as were discussed in Chapter 2.)

3.9.1. Processing of Spent Fuel from Nuclear Reactors

The processing of spent fuel from nuclear reactors is an important operation. In recent years a considerable amount of work has been directed at using high-temperature nonaqueous reprocessing methods. Here the molten mass is brought into contact with fluorine when the volatile UF_6 is removed; the fluorides of the fission product metals are relatively nonvolatile and remain in the molten system. Olander and Camahort (1966) studied this reaction by using chlorine instead of fluorine, since the former is relatively easy to handle in the laboratory. The model reaction studied was

$$Cl_2(g) + UCl_4(sol) \rightarrow UCl_6(sol)$$

UCl_4 was dissolved in the fused eutectic lithium chloride–potassium chloride mixture (59% LiCl). They found that the solubility of chlorine in the melt at temperatures in the range of 400–500°C was practically nil. (In any case, it was thought to be less than 4×10^{-9} mol/cm^3 atm.) A quartz wetted-rod contactor was used to study the kinetics of the reaction. (In principle, this apparatus is the same as the conventional wetted-wall columns.) The range of temperatures covered in their work was 400–700°C and the partial pressure of chlorine was varied from 0.25 to 1 atm. The UCl_4 concentration was varied from 1 to 3% w/w. Their studies show clearly that the reaction takes place at the gas–liquid interface, since neither reactant is soluble in the other phase. The production of UCl_6 appears to be controlled by the diffusion of U^{4+} in the liquid phase and the equilibrium of the reaction ($UCl_4 + Cl_2 \rightleftharpoons UCl_6$) at the interface.

3.9.2. Oxidation of HCl Gas (Deacon's Process)

The vapor-phase oxidation of HCl requires relatively high temperatures (400–500°C). Since this reaction is exothermic and limited by equilibrium factors, it would be better to work at lower temperatures. (It is usually desired to have as high a conversion of HCl as possible.) It is possible to convert HCl to Cl_2 in molten salts containing CuCl. Ruthven and Kenney (1967) have studied various aspects of this reaction. The transfer of oxygen could possibly be a limiting factor, and hence they studied the oxidation of CuCl in melts. A stirred contactor, which could be operated at a speed of agitation as high as 700 rev/min, was used, and the rate of absorption was followed manometrically. The transfer area was accurately

TABLE 3.5. Chemical Reactions in Melts

Reaction	Reference(s)
Chlorination of UCl_4 in $LiCl + KCl$ melt	Olander and Camahort (1966)
Oxidation of HCl in $CuCl + CuCl_2 + KCl + LiCl$ melt	Ruthven and Kenney (1967, 1968)
Oxidation of SO_2 in vanadium pentoxide–potassium pyrosulfate melt	Glueck and Kenney, (1968); Holroyd and Kenney (1971a, b)
Reaction between NH_3 and molten phthalic anhydride to give phthalimide	Bartholome et al. (1976)
Oxidation of cuprous and cobaltous benzoate in molten benzoic acid	Szonyi (1968); van Direndonck et al. (1974, 1975); Ghorpade et al. (1981)
Absorption of SO_2 and SO_3 in alkali metal carbonate melt; absorption of SO_2 in melts of borates and phosphates	Szonyi (1968); Mulder et al. (1972)
Chlorination of ethylene dichloride in chloride melts containing $AlCl_3$	Asinger (1968)
Manufacture of vinyl chloride from ethane (or ethylene), Cl_2 (or HCl), and air (oxygen) with $CuCl + CuCl_2 + KCl$ melt as the reaction medium (Transcat process)	Riegel et al. (1973); *Chem. Eng.* (1974); Hatt and Kerridge (1979)
Nitration of propane with molten $NaNO_3$–KNO_3	Coldiron et al. (1958)

known. The rate of absorption was found to be independent of the stirring speed over a wide range. Further, the rate of absorption was proportional to the transfer area (i.e., the specific rate of absorption was independent of the transfer area), and the specific rate of absorption was independent of the volume of the melt. It is obvious that no reaction occurs in the bulk of the melt and that the transfer area is important. The specific rate of absorption was proportional to the partial pressure of oxygen and square of the concentration of cuprous ions. If diffusion is accompanied by fast reaction in the film, then these data would imply that the order of the reaction with respect to cuprous ions would be four (from Eq. 2.44), which appears to be very unusual.

Ruthven and Kenney (1968) have also studied the kinetics of the oxidation of HCl over molten-salt catalysts ($CuCl + CuCl_2 + KCl + LiCl$). Their data indicate that the rate of reaction is controlled by the rate at which the melt can absorb oxygen, together with the assumption that the reaction

$$CuCl_2 \rightleftharpoons CuCl + \tfrac{1}{2}Cl_2$$

is always at the equilibrium (see also Sections 3.9.4 and 3.9.6).

3.9.3. Oxidation of SO_2 over Melts

Vanadium pentoxide–potassium pyrosulfate catalysts are universally used in sulfuric acid plants. The kinetics of this heterogeneous reaction has been studied by a number of workers in the course of the last four decades. There are conflicting opinions about the kinetics of this reaction. It also appears that under conditions of industrial importance the active catalyst exists in the melt phase. It would therefore be of interest to study independently the kinetics of absorption of SO_2 and O_2 in these melts.

Glueck and Kenney (1968) have studied the oxidation of SO_2 over molten potassium pyrosulfate containing vanadium pentoxide in the temperature range of 330–380°C. The reaction was found to be first order in SO_2 and zero order in oxygen.

Holroyd and Kenney (1971a) have studied the kinetics of the absorption of SO_2 into vanadium pentoxide–potassium pyrosulfate melts in the temperature range of 360–480°C. Here pentavalent vanadium is reduced to the tetravalent species. The reaction was found to be reasonably fast and the specific rate of absorption was found to be independent of the speed of stirring. Further, the rate of absorption was found to be directly proportional to the partial pressure of SO_2 and the 0.69th power of V_2O_5. Thus, the reaction conforms to regime 3 and the order of the reaction with respect to the solute gas is one. On the basis of the estimated values of the diffusivity and an approximate experimental value of the solubility, the value of the pseudo-first-order rate constant was found to be 4500 sec^{-1} at 450°C.

Holroyd and Kenney (1971b) have also studied the kinetics of the oxidation of tetravalent vanadium to the pentavalent vanadium species in potassium pyrosulfate melts in the temperature range of 390–612°C. The apparatus and the technique were the same as were used in their study of the absorption of SO_2 in pyrosulfate melts. The reaction was found to be very fast and confined to a surface layer in the melt approximately 900 Å thick. This reaction also conforms to regime 3. The specific rate of absorption was found to be proportional to the square root of the O_2 partial pressure and directly proportional to the mole fraction of the tetravalent vanadium species. Thus, according to Eq. 2.44, the order of the reaction with respect to O_2, m, is zero and that with respect to V^{4+}, n, is two.

The absorption of SO_2 into vanadium pentoxide–potassium pyrosulfate melts and the absorption of O_2 into melts containing tetravalent vanadium can be employed to obtain values of the effective interfacial area in sparged and mechanically agitated contactors. There are no published data in the literature on the effective interfacial area in such melts.

3.9.4. Phenol from Toluene by the Dow Process

In the new process of producing phenol from toluene via benzoic acid (Szonyi, 1968) the oxidation of benzoic acid is carried out in the presence of cuprous benzoate:

Overall reaction

$$O_2 + 2\,C_6H_5COOH \longrightarrow 2\,C_6H_5OH + 2CO_2$$

The following reaction is very important in this process:

$$O_2 + 4\,C_6H_5COOCu + 4\,C_6H_5COOH \longrightarrow 4Cu(OCOC_6H_5)_2 + 2H_2O$$

Cupric benzoate disproportionates to phenyl benzoate and cuprous benzoate; on hydrolysis, in the presence of magnesium benzoate as catalyst, phenyl benzoate gives phenol. The oxidation of cuprous benzoate to cupric benzoate appears to be the rate-controlling step. The oxidation reaction is carried out in bubble column reactors at temperatures around 250°C and the cuprous benzoate concentration is usually in the range of 5×10^{-5} to 2×10^{-4} mol/cm^3 (van Direndonck et al., 1974, 1975).

Van Direndonck et al. have reported that the oxidation of cuprous to cupric benzoate is fast and occurs completely in the film adjacent to the interface. The reaction was found to be first order with respect to oxygen and cuprous concentration. Thus the reaction conforms to regime 3. Ghorpade et al. (1981) have confirmed these findings. This system can also be used for the measurement of the effective interfacial area in a variety of contactors. In bubble column and mechanically agitated contactors the values of the effective interfacial area appear to be practically the same as those obtained with an air–water system under otherwise comparable conditions. Ghorpade et al. have also studied the kinetics of the oxidation of cobaltous benzoate in a molten benzoic acid medium, and here the reaction was found to conform to regime 3 and the reaction was zero order in O_2 and first order in the cobaltous benzoate. In addition, the analogous cases of cuprous salts of substituted benzoic acid melts (e.g., *o*-toluic acid and *p*-toluic acid) in the corresponding acid melts have also been studied.

3.9.5. Recovery of Sulfur Dioxide and Sulfur Trioxide from Emissions

In a process for the recovery of SO_2 and SO_3 from stack gases, the use of a carbonate melt consisting of a mixture of Li, Na, and K carbonates (percentage by weight: Li_2CO_3 = 32, Na_2CO_3 = 33, and K_2CO_3 = 35; m.p. = 397°C) has been suggested (Oldenkamp and Margolin, 1969). The following reactions are involved in the process:

Absorption step

$$SO_2 + M_2CO_3 \rightarrow M_2SO_3 + CO_2$$

$$SO_3 + M_2CO_3 \rightarrow M_2SO_4 + CO_2$$

$$\tfrac{1}{2}O_2 + M_2SO_3 \rightarrow M_2SO_4$$

Reduction and regeneration steps

A mixture of CO and H_2, obtained by the reforming of petroleum fractions, is used for the regeneration:

$$4H_2 + M_2SO_4 \rightarrow M_2S + 4H_2O$$

$$4CO + M_2SO_4 \rightarrow M_2S + 4CO_2$$

$$CO_2 + M_2S + H_2O \rightarrow M_2CO_3 + H_2S$$

H_2S obtained in the regeneration step is subsequently processed in the conventional way to recover sulfur.

The reaction of SO_2 and SO_3 with M_2CO_3 would be expected to be instantaneous.

3.9.6. Chlorination in Melts

Ethylene dichloride can be chlorinated in a molten chloride mixture consisting of Na, Ca, and Al chlorides, at 300–425°C, to give 1,1,2-trichloroethane or di- and trichloroethylenes (Asinger, 1968).

$$Cl_2 + C_2H_4Cl_2 \rightarrow Cl_2CH{-}CH_2Cl + HCl$$

$$\rightarrow \underset{\text{Cl}}{\text{CH}}{=}\underset{\text{Cl}}{\text{CH}} + HCl$$

$$\rightarrow CCl_2{=}CHCl + HCl$$

The mechanism of this reaction has not been studied.

Gorin et al. (1948) were probably the first authors who made a fairly systematic study of the chlorination in melts. The chlorination of methane in KCl—CuCl—$CuCl_2$ melts in the temperature range of 402–475°C was studied in a stirred contactor, where the interfacial area was known (i.e., the gas was not dispersed in the liquid) and in a 40-mm-i.d. and 40-cm-long wetted-wall column. The rate of reaction was found to be independent of the chlorine pressure in the range of about 0.08–30 atm. There was some effect of the speed of stirring on the rate of absorption in the stirred contactor. The rate of chlorination in a bubble reactor was found to vary with the cupric ion concentration. It is not clear from their work what the actual controlling mechanism is.

Kikkaw et al. (1975) have studied the chlorination of methyl cyclohexane in molten salt media. Both molecular types of melts (e.g., $ZnCl_2$ melts) and partially ionic melts (e.g., CuCl melts) were employed. The temperature was varied from 250 to 450°C. Kikkaw et al. found a substantial difference in the product distribution obtained with these types of melts. The reaction products essentially consisted of 1-, 2-, 3-, and 4-chloromethyl cyclohexanes and 1-, 3-, and 4-methyl cyclohexenes.

A recent process developed by Lummus (called the Transcat process) for the manufacture of vinyl chloride by the oxychlorination of C_2H_4/C_2H_6 with Cl_2/HCl and O_2/air is probably one of the most outstanding examples for the use of molten salts (Riegel et al. 1973; *Chem. Eng.*, 1974). Here CuCl + $CuCl_2$ + KCl melts are employed and at least three types of reactions occur: chlorination, dehydrochlorination, and regeneration of the catalyst.

$$C_2H_4 + Cl_2 \rightarrow ClCH_2CH_2Cl$$

$$C_2H_6 + Cl_2 \rightarrow C_2H_5Cl + HCl$$

$$C_2H_5Cl \rightarrow C_2H_4 + HCl$$

$$2HCl + \tfrac{1}{2}O_2 \rightarrow Cl_2 + H_2O$$

Hatt and Kerridge (1979) have also discussed some features of the Transcat process and have pointed out that a Cu_2Cl_2 + $CuCl_2$ + KCl melt is used in the temperature range of 370–450°C. The circulation of the melt is carried out by gas lift pumps, and trickle-bed reactors are used. In the first reactor air is contacted to convert CuCl to soluble $CuOCuCl_2$ and $CuCl_2$; in the second reactor hydrocarbon and HCl are brought into contact with the oxidized melt, and chlorination, oxychlorination, and dehydrochlorination reactions occur in this reactor. The reaction is carried out at about 7 atm.

3.9.7. Catalytic Reactions of Olefins

Homogeneous catalysts are employed for a variety of reactions of olefins. An important problem in this type of system is concerned with the separation of products from the catalyst and the solvent without decomposition. Parshall (1972) has suggested that tetraalkyl ammonium salts of $GeCl_3^-$ and $SnCl_3^-$ can be employed as solvents for catalytic reactions of olefins. These salts have a relatively low melting point ($< 100°C$) and are good solvents for olefins and complexes of the platinum metal. Thus, for instance, the solubility of ethylene at 84°C and 1 atm in $(C_2H_5)_4N(SnCl_3)$ is 1.3×10^{-5} mol/cm³ and this medium can dissolve as much as 7% w/w of $PtCl_2$. This catalytic system shows remarkable catalytic activity in the hydrogenation, hydroformylation, and so on of olefins. Some of the examples reported by Parshall are (1) the hydrogenation of methyl linoleate to methyl oleate; (2) the hydrogenation of 1,5,9-cyclododecatriene to cyclododecane; and (3) the carbonylation of ethylene to propionaldehyde and its aldol condensation product.

An important advantage offered by the molten salts is that in many cases the product can be easily separated by decantation or distillation.

3.9.8. Nitration of Propane

Nitropropane is required as an intermediate for drugs. For the manufacture of nitropropane the use of molten nitrates ($NaNO_3 + KNO_3$) in the temperature range of 372–444°C is likely to offer advantages over vapor-phase nitration because of the better temperature control achievable in the molten-salt medium (Coldiron et al., 1958). It is important to create conditions for uniform temperature, since these reactions are hazardous and may cause an explosion.

3.9.9. Oxidative Dehydrogenation and Coupling Reactions

It is well known that I_2 can dehydrogenate saturated hydrocarbons to unsaturated hydrocarbons (Adams et al., 1977). The oxidation of HI can be done *in situ* or separately. The use of I_2 circumvents equilibrium limitations encountered in straight dehydrogenation. HI acceptor can be a molten salt. The following steps are involved:

$$\begin{array}{llll} \tfrac{1}{2}O_2 + MI_2 + H_2O & \rightarrow M(OH)_2 & + I_2 \\ I_2 + C_nH_{2n+2} & \rightarrow C_nH_{2n} & + 2HI \\ 2HI + M(OH)_2 & \rightarrow MI_2 & + 2H_2O \\ \hline \tfrac{1}{2}O_2 + C_nH_{2n+2} & \rightarrow C_nH_{2n} & + H_2O \end{array}$$

LiI, PbI_2, and the like can be employed, and the temperature is usually in the range of 500–650°C.

Experiments were done in either a 2-cm-i.d. sparged reactor or a 5-cm (2-in.) baffled horizontal pipeline reactor where dehydrogenation and oxidation were conducted separately.

In the case of ethane, 70–80% conversion per pass was realized with a selectivity with respect to C_2H_4 greater than 90%. Similar experiments were conducted with butane to give butadiene. Ethyl benzene can be converted to styrene with a selectivity higher than 95%. *p*-Diisopropyl benzene can be converted to *p*-diisopropenyl benzene with 73% selectivity at 99% conversion.

Coupling reactions of hydrocarbons showed even more interesting results. Thus, 2-methyl propene can be converted to *p*-xylene and toluene to *trans*-stilbene. Further, naphthalene can be obtained from toluene and propene. Even nonhydrocarbons can be converted. Thus benzonitrile was obtained from aniline and toluene, and quinoline from aniline and propene.

The reactions studied in this work are of considerable practical value and can be adopted for other related chemicals (e.g., divinyl benzene from diethyl benzene).

3.9.10. Absorption of Butadiene in Molten Maleic Anhydride

Tetrahydrophthalic anhydride (THPA) is manufactured by the Diels–Alder reaction between butadiene and molten maleic anhydride:

```
 CH2              O          CH2           O
//             //           /   \        //
CH        CH— C           HC     CH—C
|     +   ||       O  →   ||     |      O
CH        CH— C           HC     CH—O
\\             \\           \   /        \\
 CH2              O          CH2           O
```

Gehlawat (1972) has studied the kinetics of the reaction in a 10-cm-i.d. mechanically agitated contactor provided with a 5-cm-diameter six-blade turbine impeller. Above a speed of agitation of about 600 rev/min the reaction was found to be kinetically controlled. The reaction was found to be first order in butadiene as well as maleic anhydride.

Consider the following case:

$$\text{Temperature} = 110°C$$

$$k_2 = 13.2 \text{ cm}^3/\text{mol sec}$$

Concentration of maleic anhydride $= [B_o] = 2 \times 10^{-3}$ mol/cm³ (in THPA)

$$l = 0.8$$

$$k_L a = 0.3 \text{ sec}^{-1}$$

$$k_L a = 0.3 \gg l k_2[\text{B}_o] = 0.026$$

Thus the necessary condition for regime 1 is satisfied.

3.10. EXAMPLES OF REVERSIBLE REACTIONS

We considered the salient features of reversible reactions in Section 2.10. Table 3.6 gives some examples of practical importance. A number of cases will be considered in Chapter 8, where we shall discuss desorption preceded by reaction. Many of these reactions are such that at lower temperatures the absorption process is favored and this may well tend to approach irreversible behavior. We have already covered some examples where the reversible nature of the reaction was pointed out. We shall briefly cover some typical cases in this section.

3.10.1. Absorption of CO_2 and H_2S in Aqueous Solutions of Amines and Alkalies

We have already covered various aspects of the absorption of CO_2 and H_2S in aqueous solutions of amines and alkalies. At moderately high temperatures and/or high gas loading, the equilibrium partial pressure of the solute gas becomes appreciable and then the reactions fall in the category of reversible reactions. The desorption of CO_2 from potash solutions, with or without a catalyst such as arsenite, will be covered in Chapter 8. Depending on circumstances, the absorption of CO_2 in aqueous solutions of mono- and diethanolamine and potash solutions containing arsenite may fall in the category of reversible pseudo-first-order reactions (see Section 2.10.1). In the case of H_2S, at high partial pressures the mechanism may conform to the reversible instantaneous reaction regime (see Section 2.10.2, where the reaction between H_2S and RNH_2 is discussed).

3.10.2. Absorption of Cl_2 in Water

The absorption of Cl_2 in water is important in several contexts. This step is also involved in the manufacture of chlorohydrines by reaction between olefins and water containing HOCl. The following reaction occurs when chlorine is absorbed in water:

$$Cl_2 + H_2O \rightleftharpoons H^+ + Cl^- + HOCl$$

TABLE 3.6. Examples of Gas Absorption with Reversible Chemical Reaction

Reaction	Reference(s)
Absorption of CO_2 in carbonated amine; and carbonate buffer solutions with or without catalysts at higher levels of carbonation	Danckwerts and Sharma (1966); Danckwerts (1968)
Absorption of H_2S in amine and carbonate buffer solutions	Danckwerts and Sharma (1966)
Absorption of CO in ammoniacal cuprous chloride solutions	van Krevelen and Baans (1950)
Absorption of Cl_2 in water	Brian et al. (1962)
Absorption of SO_2 in water and aqueous solutions of bisulfate	Danckwerts (1968)
Absorption of O_2 in blood	Ramachandran (1969)
Absorption of butadiene in aqueous cuprous ammonium acetate solutions	Morrel et al. (1946)
Deuterium exchange between H_2 and aminomethane	Kalra and Otto (1974)
Absorption of NO in aqueous solutions of ferrous sulfate	Hikita et al. (1977a)

Brian et al. (1962) have studied the reaction in a wetted-wall column and have shown that the reaction is reasonably fast and that the forward reaction follows pseudo-first-order kinetics; the pseudo-first-order rate constant at 25°C was found to be 13.7 sec^{-1}.

3.10.3. Manufacture of Isotopes

The manufacture of isotopes, based on a gas–liquid reaction, invariably involves a reversible reaction. Kalra and Otto (1974) have studied the rate of the isotope exchange reaction between H_2 and CH_3NH_2 catalyzed by potassium methylamine:

$$HD \rightleftharpoons CH_3NHD$$

This reaction has been found to be reasonably fast and first order with respect to HD as well as CH_3NHD. Thus the reaction falls in the category of Eq. 2.139 discussed in Section 2.10.1.

3.10.4. Absorption of Nitric Oxide in Aqueous Solutions of Ferrous Sulfate

Aqueous solutions of ferrous sulfate have been suggested for the removal of NO from gaseous streams. Hikita et al. (1977a) have studied the absorption of NO in aqueous solutions of ferrous sulfate in a laminar jet apparatus as well as a wetted-wall column. The reaction between NO and Fe^{2+} is reversible:

$$NO + Fe^{2+} \rightleftharpoons FeNO^{2+}$$

The theory of absorption with reversible reaction represented by this reaction has also been discussed. At a very high ratio of $[Fe^{2+}]$ to [NO] the reaction can be considered to be irreversible. The reaction was found to be first order in NO and Fe^{2+} and the values of the second-order rate constant at 25 and 35°C were found to be 8×10^8 and 10×10^8 cm^3/mol sec, respectively (ionic strength = 0.515 g ion/liter). The value of the rate constant at 25°C agrees reasonably well with that of Kustin et al. (1966) measured by the temperature jump method. Values of the equilibrium constant have also been reported.

3.11. EFFECT OF TEMPERATURE ON MASS TRANSFER ACCOMPANIED BY CHEMICAL REACTION

In this section we shall first consider the effect of the bulk temperature when a system conforms to any of the four regimes. It is assumed that at any specified temperature isothermal conditions prevail in the entire B phase.

3.11.1. Regime 1: Very Slow Reactions

In very slow reactions the effect of temperature will be dependent on two factors: (1) the solubility of A and (2) the rate constant. In the case of gas–liquid systems the value of the solubility of A generally decreases with an increase in the temperature. In the case of liquid–liquid systems, too, the solubility generally decreases with an increase in the temperature. There are, however, some cases where the solubility of some substances increases with an increase in the temperature. For instance, in the case of some esters, like benzilidene diacetate, dichloroethyl oxalate, and ethyl *p*-nitrobenzoate, the solubility increases considerably with an increase in the temperature (Sharma, 1969). Similarly, the solubility of toluene and chlorobenzene in aqueous sulfuric acid also increases with an increase in temperature (Cox and Strachan, 1971). In the case of gas–liquid systems too we sometimes have a situation where the solubility increases with an increase in temperature. The rate constant for the reaction, k_{mn}, increases with an increase in the temperature. Generally the value of the activation energy lies in the range of 8–15 kcal/mol.

The overall effect of these factors will depend on the relative magnitudes of the heat of solution of A and the activation energy. The overall rate should increase substantially with an increase in the temperature.

When volatile solvents are used, or alternatively when volatile reactants are involved, then the effect of temperature can be quite different. At any specified total pressure, the effective partial pressure of the solute gas A will be reduced very significantly. Consider a reaction in an aqueous phase at temperatures of 30, 60, and 90°C at a total pressure of 1 atm. Assume that the relative values of Henry's coefficient at these temperatures (taking 30°C as the datum) are 1, 0.7, and 0.4, respectively. Assume the reaction to be first order in A, and assume that the value of the activation energy for the reaction is 10 kcal/mol and that throughout this temperature range regime 1 prevails. The values of the vapor pressure of water at 30, 60, and 90°C are 31.8, 149.4, and 525.8 mm Hg, respectively. Thus the relative values of [A*] at a total pressure of 1 atm (with 30°C as the datum) will be 1, 0.587, and 0.129. The value of the rate constant will go up by a factor of about 16 when we go from a temperature of 30 to 90°C. The rate of reaction of A will, however, increase by a factor of only about 2.

It is very important to take the vapor pressure of the solvent or the reactant B into consideration for predicting the effect of temperature. Chandalia (1966, 1967, 1968a) has studied the Wacker-type processes for the conversion of ethylene, propylene, and butenes to the corresponding carbonyl compounds; the conversion of ethylene to vinyl acetate by reaction with acetic acid; and the conversion of ethylene to the corresponding acetals by reaction with methanol and ethanol. In these processes water or the organic reactant constitutes the B phase and all these species are volatile. If the reduction in the solubility of A due to the high vapor pressure of B is not taken into consideration, the results may not be properly interpreted. Chandalia (1968b) could rationally interpret his results by accounting for the reduction in the solubility due to the high vapor pressure of B. (The reduction in the solubility of A due to the vapor pressure of the solvent or the reactant is equally important in the case of regimes 2 and 3.)

In the case of the chlorination of a variety of volatile organic compounds higher temperatures are desirable. If heat removal can be ensured, then in these cases it is desirable to consider the advantages that are likely to be realized by using higher pressures. For instance, consider the chlorination of acetic acid in the presence of sulfur or acetic anhydride as a catalyst for the manufacture of chloroacetic acid. This reaction is usually carried out at 118°C, which is the boiling point of acetic acid at 760 mm Hg pressure. Let the heat be removed by refluxing acetic acid. In a typical case consider the partial pressure of chlorine to be 0.2 atm when the total pressure is 1 atm. In this case if we increase the total pressure to 3 atm and maintain the temperature at 118°C by external heat transfer, then the rate of absorption will increase by a factor of about 10 as a result of the increase in the partial pressure of chlorine.

It is conceivable that an increase in temperature might result in an increase in the value of k_{mn} to such an extent that the diffusion of A may become important and the system may conform to regime 2.

3.11.2. Regime 2: Slow Reactions

If the solubility of A decreases with an increase in temperature, then the overall effect of temperature will be to decrease the specific rate of mass transfer, since an increase of temperature marginally increases the value of k_L. In the case of mechanically agitated contactors there is even a possibility of a slight decrease in $k_L a$ values with an increase in the temperature. (The major change is due to the variation of a with the temperature; the viscosity of a solution decreases with an increase in the temperature and in general the value of a decreases with a decrease in the viscosity. The surface tension of the liquid or the interfacial tension in the case of liquid–liquid systems decreases with an increase in the temperature and a lower value of interfacial tension gives relatively higher values of interfacial area.)

It is likely that an increase of temperature might result in making the term $D_A k_{mn}[A^*]^{m-1}[B_o]^n$ (k_{mn} increases with temperature; D_A also increases with an increase in the temperature) greater than k_L^2 and the system might then conform to regime 3.

It is necessary to exercise care in interpreting the results covering the effect of temperature on the rate of the overall reaction. Thus, in the case of the nitration of aromatic compounds with mixed acid an increase in the temperature generally results in an increase in the solubility of the substance to be nitrated. In mechanically agitated contactors (which are commonly used for nitration) we may obtain an apparent activation energy of about 14–15 kcal/mol and incorrectly interpret the results by concluding that diffusional factors are unimportant (Albright and Hanson, 1969).

Groothuis (1961) has reported a systematic study of the effect of the important variables in the Shell air solutizer process for the sweetening of gasoline. Here the malodorous mercaptans present in the gasolines are oxidized to less pungent disulfides in an agitated reactor:

$$\tfrac{1}{2}O_2 + 2RSH \rightarrow R{-}S{-}S{-}R + H_2O$$

This is accomplished by contacting the gasoline, in which oxygen has been dissolved, with an aqueous solution of potassium hydroxide and certain organic compounds. These organic compounds help to emulsify, thereby increasing the interfacial area. It was found that the rate of oxidation was first order in O_2 and 0.25 order in the mercaptan. The rate-controlling step was found to be the transfer of O_2. The aqueous solution was always found to be saturated with the mercaptan. When the temperature was increased from 20 to 40°C the rate of extraction increased by a factor of 3. This may be because of the contribution of the term $D_A k_{mn}[A^*]^{m-1}[B_o]^n$ at higher temperatures. Thus, higher temperatures appear to be advantageous for increasing the rate of this reaction. In practice, however, the temperature is restricted to about 40°C to avoid undue discoloration of the product.

3.11.3. Regime 3: Fast Reactions

The specific rate of mass transfer for this regime is given by Eq. 2.44:

$$R_A = [A^*]\sqrt{\frac{2}{m+1} D_A k_{mn}[A^*]^{m-1}[B_o]^n} \tag{2.44}$$

The effect of temperature on D_A, k_{mn}, and $[A^*]$ has already been discussed. The net effect of all these factors is such that the overall effect of increasing the temperature is not very appreciable. In the case of the absorption of CO_2 in aqueous solutions of caustic soda an increase in the temperature from 25 to 45°C results in increasing the specific rate of absorption by only about 45%. [The ratio of rate constants at 45°C and 25°C is about 4 (Danckwerts and Sharma, 1966).] In the case of the absorption of CO_2 in potash buffer solutions containing arsenite as a catalyst an increase in the temperature from 40 to 60°C results in increasing the specific rate of absorption by about 50% (Sharma and Danckwerts, 1963).

In the case of extraction accompanied by a fast pseudo-first-order reaction Nanda and Sharma (1967) have shown that the specific rate of the extraction of ethyl dichloroacetate saturated with water into approximately 2 M NaOH increases by about 140% when the temperature is increased from 10 to 30°C. In this case, however, the solubility of the ester in water remains substantially constant in the temperature range of 0–30°C.

An increase in the temperature might result in increasing k_{mn} to such an extent that the condition given by expression 2.31 may no longer be valid, and the system might exhibit a behavior where the concentration of B at the interface is less than that in the bulk. In the case of gas absorption, however, the solubility generally decreases with an increase in temperature, so that for a given value of $[B_o]$, $[B_o]/[A^*]$ increases with an increase in temperature. On the left-hand side of the condition given by expression 2.31 k_{mn} appears as a square root, so that the net effect might be that at a higher temperature the same mechanism holds. This is illustrated by an example.

$$\text{Temperatures} = 25 \text{ and } 45°\text{C}$$

$$k_L = 0.03 \text{ cm/sec}$$

Carbon dioxide at a partial pressure of 0.25 atm is absorbed in an aqueous solution of monoisopropanolamine containing 1×10^{-3} mol/cm³ of the amine ($Z = 2$).

At 25°C,

$$[A^*] = 0.25 \times 3.30 \times 10^{-5} \text{ mol/cm}^3$$

$$k_2 = 6.62 \times 10^6 \text{ cm}^3\text{/mol sec}$$

$$\frac{\sqrt{D_A k_2 [B_o]}}{k_L} (\simeq 10) \ll \frac{[B_o]}{Z[A^*]}\sqrt{\frac{D_B}{D_A}} \quad (= 46)$$

At 45°C

$$[A^*] = 0.25 \times 1.95 \times 10^{-5} \text{ mol/cm}^3$$

$$k_2 = 1.95 \times 10^7 \text{ cm}^3\text{/mol sec}$$

$$\frac{\sqrt{D_A k_2 [B_o]}}{k_L} (\simeq 23) \ll \frac{[B_o]}{Z[A^*]}\sqrt{\frac{D_B}{D_A}} \quad (\simeq 77.7)$$

Thus an increase in the temperature from 25 to 45°C in this case does not result in a change in the regime.

(In the foregoing calculation, as an approximation, the value of the diffusivity of monoisopropanolamine has been taken as the same as that of monoethanolamine.)

3.11.4. Regime 4: Instantaneous Reactions

The specific rate of mass transfer in instantaneous reactions will not be significantly affected by an increase in the temperature. This is because the k_L value is only marginally affected by temperature. However, if the type of contactor is such that a significantly decreases with an increase in temperature, then the output of a given reactor may even decrease with an increase in the temperature.

3.12. TEMPERATURE AT THE FLUID–FLUID INTERFACE

We shall now consider the problem where the bulk B phase has a uniform temperature but there may be a temperature gradient close to the interface.

3.12.1. Pseudo-*m*th-Order Reactions (Regime 3)

In general, any reacting system is either exothermic or endothermic. It is therefore likely that the interface temperature is significantly different from that in the bulk B phase. Danckwerts (1952, 1967), Carberry (1966), Clegg and Mann (1969), Cook and Moore (1972), and Shah (1972) have considered this problem. Danckwerts has shown, on the basis of the penetration theory, that when gas absorption is accompanied by a pseudo-first-order reaction, the following equation holds:

$$\frac{\rho_L \sigma}{\Delta H[A^*]}\sqrt{\frac{\alpha}{D_A}}\,\Delta T' = 2\sqrt{\frac{k_1 t_E}{\pi}} \qquad (3.15)$$

provided that $k_1 t_E \gg 5$, where

$$\Delta H = \Delta H_A + \Delta H_S$$

ΔH_A = heat of reaction, cal/mol

ΔH_S = heat of physical dissolution, cal/mol

(both taken as positive when heat is evolved). (Film theory cannot be used for the calculation of the temperature rise at the surface, since the film thickness for mass and heat transfer are not the same.)

It is assumed, in the derivation of Eq. 3.15, that $\alpha/(\alpha - D_A) \simeq 1$. This assumption is justified, since the values of the thermal diffusivity are an order of magnitude greater than the molecular diffusivity values. This assumption is equivalent to considering the heat flux due to the reaction as a boundary heat flux. The equation derived by Danckwerts is in general applicable to solutes with low solubility. It is further assumed that the liquid is nonvolatile and there is no gas-side resistance. In addition, the physicochemical properties are assumed to be invariant and taken to be the same as that of the datum temperature.

It can be seen from Eq. 3.15 that the change in the surface temperature will be a function of the solubility of the solute, the heat of the reaction, and the reaction rate constant. The other factors, in general, do not show marked variation with temperature. In the case of systems with moderate solubility and heat of solution, the effect of the increase in temperature at the surface may be insignificant.

Clegg and Mann (1969) have given a penetration theory solution of the problem of gas absorption with a fast pseudo-first-order reaction resulting in considerable evolution of heat. It is also implicit in the theoretical development of the problem that convection currents are absent. Clegg and Mann considered the problem of the absorption of chlorine in toluene where the solubility of chlorine is relatively high ($\simeq$ 60 cm^3/cm^3 of toluene atm, heat of solution = 5.5 kcal/mol, and heat of reaction = 30 kcal/mol). They have shown that under certain conditions, which may sometimes be encountered in practice, the absorption rate decreases as a result of the rise in temperature at the interface even to the extent where it falls below the rate obtainable for absorption in the absence of chemical reaction. (The example considered is of the type where the isothermal enhancement factor is rather low.)

Shah (1972) has relaxed the assumptions made in the analysis of Danckwerts and has accounted for the variation in diffusivity, solubility, and rate constant due to the change in temperature.

Example

Consider the absorption of oxygen by 24% (by weight) *n*-butyraldehyde in *n*-butyric acid in the presence of manganese acetate as a catalyst. The absorption of O_2 is carried out in a stirred cell (Ladhabhoy, 1970). The following values at 20°C are known for the terms in

Eq. 3.15:

$$[A^*] = 10.45 \times 10^{-6} \text{ mol/cm}^3$$
$$D_A = 1.80 \times 10^{-5} \text{ cm}^2\text{/sec}$$
$$\Delta H = (140.6 + 1.6) \times 10^3 \text{ cal/mol}$$
$$= 141.2 \times 10^3 \text{ cal/mol}$$
$$k_1 = 38.3 \text{ sec}^{-1}$$
$$\rho_L = 0.912 \text{ g/cm}^3$$
$$\sigma = 0.472 \text{ cal/g°C}$$
$$\alpha = 82.5 \times 10^{-5} \text{ cm}^2\text{/sec}$$
$$k_L = 3.6 \times 10^{-3} \text{ cm/sec at 40 rev/min in the stirred cell}$$

The estimated value of t_E is 1.77 sec. The substitution of these values in Eq. 3.15 gives $\Delta T' = 4.8$°C.

In this example the values of ΔH and t_E are very high, and hence the temperature rise at the interface is very significant. In common examples the value of $\Delta T'$ is around 0.1–0.3°C.

3.12.2. Instantaneous Reactions (Regime 4)

For instantaneous reactions (regime 4) da Silva and Danckwerts (1968) have shown that the following equation holds for the temperature change at the interface, irrespective of the time of exposure or k_L:

$$\Delta T' = \frac{[A^*] + [B_o]/Z}{\rho_L \sigma}(\Delta H_A + \Delta H_S)\sqrt{\frac{D_A}{\alpha}} \tag{3.16}$$

Example

Consider the absorption of pure H_2S in aqueous ammonia under conditions such that

$$[A^*] = 1 \times 10^{-5} \text{ mol/cm}^3$$
$$[B_o] = 2 \times 10^{-4} \text{ mol/cm}^3$$
$$\rho_L \sigma = 1 \text{ cal/cm}^3\text{°C for water}$$
$$\Delta H_S = 4.7 \times 10^3 \text{ cal/mol}$$
$$\Delta H_A = 6.3 \times 10^3 \text{ cal/mol}$$
$$\alpha = 1.5 \times 10^{-3} \text{ cm}^2\text{/sec for water}$$
$$D_A = 1.34 \times 10^{-5} \text{ cm}^2\text{/sec}$$

The temperature rise calculated from Eq. 3.16 works out to be 0.2°C.

Ikemizu et al. (1978) have measured the temperature rise at the interface in jets of liquid by means of a traversing thermocouple with a 20-μm-thick tip when SO_2 was absorbed in aqueous solutions of sodium hydroxide and ammonia was absorbed in aqueous solutions of HNO_3, HCl, and H_2SO_4. The measured rise in temperature at the interface agreed with the theoretical prediction based on the assumption that the heats of solution and reaction are released at the interface and the reaction plane, respectively. The temperature rise at the interface was found to be independent of the distance from the jet nozzle tip.

Chiang and Toor (1964) have considered the problem associated with gas absorption accompanied by a large heat effect and volume change of the liquid phase. Such a situation is likely to be encountered, for instance, in the absorption of ammonia or methylamines in water. When the solubility of the gas is relatively high there will be a significant volume change on absorption. In the theoretical development by Chiang and Toor (1964) it was assumed *inter alia* that the heat transfer between the gas and the liquid surface is negligible. Pure ammonia was absorbed in jets of water at a temperature of 22.2°C and the contact time was varied from 0.001 to 0.02 sec. It was found that the predicted rates of absorption based on isothermal conditions were practically the same as those based on both the heat and volume change of the liquid phase and they agreed very closely with the experimental data. However, if predictions are based on only temperature change, then the experimental values are approximately 12% higher than the predicted values. At first it appears rather intriguing that predicted data under isothermal conditions agree with the experimental data. Theoretical calculations predict a rise in the surface temperature of the order of 17°C. (This apparently has been verified experimentally.) It so happens in this case that the effect of ΔH is nullified partly by the volume change and partly as a result of the decrease in the solubility of ammonia with an increase in the temperature.

The effect of temperature in any practical situation is likely to be quite complicated. Thus, for instance, when CO_2 diluted with an inert gas (e.g., H_2) is absorbed in aqueous amine solutions, the temperature of the incoming gas is about 100–150°C. The absorbent enters the column at about 35–40°C. The inert gas will have a tendency to pick up water, thereby causing the liquid to cool. At the bottom of the column there will be an exchange of heat between the hot gas and relatively cold absorbent. Kohl and Riesenfeld (1974) have reported some data from in-

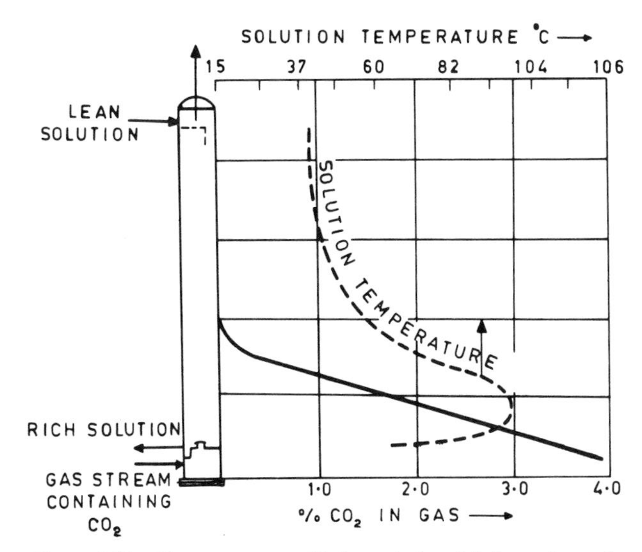

Figure 3.19. Temperature profile in an industrial absorption column (absorption of CO_2 in an aqueous solution of an alkanolamine).

dustrial columns, and the temperature distribution is shown in Figure 3.19. Bourne et al. (1974) and Coggan and Bourne (1969a, b) have considered the design of plate absorbers where a large quantity of heat is evolved and the solvent is volatile.

3.13. EFFECT OF INTERFACIAL TURBULENCE

Gas absorption

When the rate of gas absorption accompanied by a chemical reaction is dependent on the physical mass transfer coefficient, the interfacial turbulence would be expected to affect the specific rate of absorption as it influences the value of the physical mass transfer coefficient. Brian et al. (1967) have demonstrated the importance of this factor by absorbing CO_2 in aqueous solutions of monoethanolamine (MEA) in a short wetted-wall column under conditions such that the specific rate of absorption was dependent on k_L. (There was depletion of MEA and the system was between regimes 3 and 4.) Since the hydrodynamics of the liquid flow over the wetted-wall column is properly understood, the value of k_L for any solute gas can be predicted with a fair degree of confidence for any specified conditions. Brian et al. (1967) dissolved propylene in aqueous solutions of MEA, and its rate of desorption while CO_2 was being absorbed was noted. (Mixtures of CO_2 and air were passed continuously through the wetted-wall column, and the concentrations of propylene in the outlet gas as well as in the liquid leaving the column were determined. Blank experiments were made with only air in the gas phase.) This method enables an accurate determination of k_L when interfacial turbulence may be expected to be present. The experimental data show clearly that when CO_2 was absorbed in aqueous MEA, the prevailing k_L value increased by a factor of 1.7–2.3, depending on the liquid flow rate, the concentration of MEA, and so forth. The effect of the increase in k_L would be to increase the specific rate of mass transfer of CO_2. It would be reasonable to attribute this increase in k_L to the convection currents caused by the absorption of CO_2 in MEA. In a similar work, Furmer et al. (1971) studied the desorption of dissolved N_2O from aqueous solutions containing 2.3 M MEA and 2 M NaOH while CO_2 was being absorbed in falling films (wavy as well as turbulent film regimes). The k_L value for N_2O increased by as much as a factor of 3 when CO_2 was absorbed in aqueous MEA as compared to the situation when the gas phase contained no CO_2.

Sada et al. (1977a, b) have made measurements of rates of absorption of CO_2 in aqueous jets of monoethanolamine, ethylenediamine, and monoisopropanolamine. They have also carried out experiments in the presence of a surface active agent. Simultaneous measurements of the rate of desorption of C_2H_4 dissolved in aqueous solutions were made. It is also clear from this work that interfacial turbulence exists in these systems, and actual values of k_L measured along with the measurement of the rate of CO_2 absorption accompanied by chemical reaction correlate the data well. In the presence of a surface active agent there was no interfacial turbulence and experimental data agreed with the predicted values based on calculated values of k_L.

Hikita et al. (1977b) have shown that when pure SO_2 is absorbed in jets of aqueous sodium hydroxide, interfacial turbulence is encountered and measured rates of absorption are higher than the predicted values. By use of a surface active agent interfacial turbulence can be suppressed almost completely, and then experimental results agree with predictions based on absorption accompanied by instantaneous reaction.

Imaishi and Fujinawa (1978) have made an optical study of the interfacial behavior when CO_2 was absorbed in a wetted-wall column in aqueous solutions of mono- and diethanolamines, NH_3, and n-butylamine. It was found that interfacial turbulence very much exists and is a secondary flow, induced by the Marangoni effect, whose structure is rather a longitudinal roll cell than a transverse one. Further, the induced flow grows to observable limits within less than 2×10^{-2} sec. The concentration distribution of the reaction products changes the surface tension to induce flow; the surface tension at the interface tends to be higher as a result of the higher local concentration of products. The concept of a critical Marangoni number has also been discussed.

Danckwerts and da Silva (1967) contacted pure CO_2 with a drop of 1 *M* MEA at atmospheric pressure on a microscopic slide and observed its behavior. It was found that after about 1 sec convection currents could be seen, and these currents stopped when the MEA was completely carbonated. Danckwerts and da Silva also experimentally determined the surface tension of the fresh and the carbonated 1 *M* MEA solution. The surface tension of the carbonated 1 *M* MEA solution at 19°C was found to be 2% higher than that of the uncarbonated solution.

Thomas and Nicholl (1967) used an interferometric technique to study the convection currents. The concentration of MEA was varied and the time for the onset of convection was noted. Their results suggest that the time varies up to 20 sec or more for 0.1 *M* amine solution. In a subsequent paper Thomas and Nicholl (1969) have described the use of a wave-front-shearing interferometer, in conjunction with a specially designed gas–liquid diffusion cell, for the study of this problem. Their experimental data indicate that in a stagnant pool a minimum time of 4.5 sec (in 2.5 *M* MEA solution) elapses before interfacial turbulence can be observed. These authors are of the opinion that interfacial turbulence is not important in jets and wetted-wall columns. In the case of packed columns, however, the relatively stagnant pools of liquids at the packing junctions may show interfacial turbulence.

The foregoing observations raise a doubt as to whether instabilities can set in at short exposure times (less than 0.3 sec) in a wetted-wall column and laminar jet apparatus. Brian (1968) has considered this problem, and has indicated that insofar as a wetted-wall column is concerned, the falling liquid is basically unstable in the absence of any surface tension gradients.

Extraction

Bakker et al. (1967) have carried out extraction with an instantaneous chemical reaction. For this purpose acetic acid was extracted from isobutanol into water that contained sodium hydroxide in a wetted-wall column. The mass transfer coefficient increased by a factor of 2–3 as a result of interfacial turbulence. At high reagent concentrations, however, the value of the enhancement factor becomes unity because under these conditions the concentration of the solute at the interface becomes zero, so that the essential conditions for the occurrence of microscale interfacial movement, which require a difference in concentration at the surface, cannot be satisfied.

Conclusions

It is likely that interfacial turbulence is far more important on the laboratory scale, where the concentration differences are large and the surface is often undisturbed, than in industrial contactors, where the concentration differences are usually relatively small and vigorous agitation is provided. In any case, for systems conforming to regime 3 there will be no effect of interfacial turbulence on the specific rate of mass transfer, and in other cases it has a somewhat favorable influence on the rate of mass transfer.

3.14. STABILITY OF TWO-PHASE REACTORS

We have covered a variety of examples of gas–liquid and liquid–liquid reactions in this chapter. We have also seen that many reactions, such as oxidation, alkylation, chlorination, and nitration, are exothermic reactions. In Volume 1, Chapter 12, we showed that for single-phase exothermic reactors multiple steady states can exist because the heat generation function is not linear (it is usually a sigmoid function) with respect to temperature, and therefore the heat consumption function, which is linear with respect to temperature, can intersect the heat generation function at multiple points, resulting in a multiplicity of steady states. Thus the problem of multiple steady states can arise only in the case of exothermic reactors operated adiabatically; isothermal backmix reactors would be expected to be stable.

In Sections 3.11 and 3.12 we discussed the effect of bulk temperature and that of the temperature rise at the interface, respectively, on the specific rate of mass transfer. Here also it is desirable to consider the possibilities of multiple steady states for different regimes separately, since a completely general case would be very complex and we are most unlikely to get simple criteria for multiple steady states. Ding et al. (1974), Hoffman et al. (1975), Sharma et al. (1976), Raghuram and Shah (1977), and Raghuram et al.

(1979) have discussed various aspects of multiple steady states in mechanically agitated gas–liquid reactors operated adiabatically. As will be shown later, in principle, five steady states can be realized in certain circumstances (Hoffman et al., 1975).

We shall consider the following reaction, which is conducted in an adiabatically operated mechanically agitated contactor (CSTR):

$$A(g) + B(l) \rightarrow C(l) + D(g)$$

A number of assumptions have been made in order to analyze this problem (Hoffman et al., 1975):

1. The gas-phase resistance is negligible and the liquid feed does not contain any dissolved volatile species.
2. The reactant as well as the solvent are nonvolatile, so there is no loss of material and heat with the gas leaving the reactor. This assumption is also relevant in liquid–liquid systems, since one of the reactants may vaporize if it is volatile. In many practical situations both B and the solvent may be volatile, and care should be exercised while considering such systems.
3. The physical properties of the gas and the liquid, $k_L a$, and the volumetric flow rate of the liquid leaving the reactor are independent of temperature. This is a reasonable assumption provided that the range of temperature is limited.
4. D_A and D_B are the same and are unaffected by temperature changes or the composition of the liquid. We have already considered the question of the comparative values of D_A and D_B, and in Section 3.7 it was pointed out that there are some systems of industrial importance where D_B is substantially different from D_A.
5. The heat capacities of the gas as well as of the liquid and ΔH_s are independent of the temperature and composition of the liquid. This is a reasonable assumption.
6. Henry's law holds and solubility is independent of the conversion. The temperature dependence of Henry's constant can be correlated by an Arrhenius-type equation. The gaseous product D is stripped from the liquid phase.
7. The temperature of the gas and liquid phases inside the reactor is the same.
8. The total pressure of the gas bubbles is independent of position in the reactor. Further, the value of a and the gas holdup are independent of position, conversion, and temperature in the reactor.

Assumptions 1–8 can be considered reasonable for well-agitated contactors. The theoretical aspects of this problem have been considered in detail by Ding et al. (1974), Hoffman et al. (1975), Sharma et al. (1976), and Raghuram et al. (1979) and these papers should be referred to for further details. We shall summarize the important findings:

As pointed out in Section 3.11, the solubility of the gas A generally decreases with an increase in temperature and the value of ϕ increases with an increase in temperature. Because of these interactions, five steady states can be realized in some special cases (Figure 3.20). The specific case considered by Hoffman et al. is concerned with the chlorination of n-decane. This system is not a typical gas–liquid reaction, since the value of the solubility of Cl_2 in n-decane is relatively high. It is most interesting that under certain conditions up to seven steady states may be encountered.

Special Case of Stability in Gas–Liquid Reactors

So far we have considered the temperature stability of exothermic gas–liquid reactors. Under certain special conditions, however, we may have a situation that involves pressure stability. Hancock and Kenney

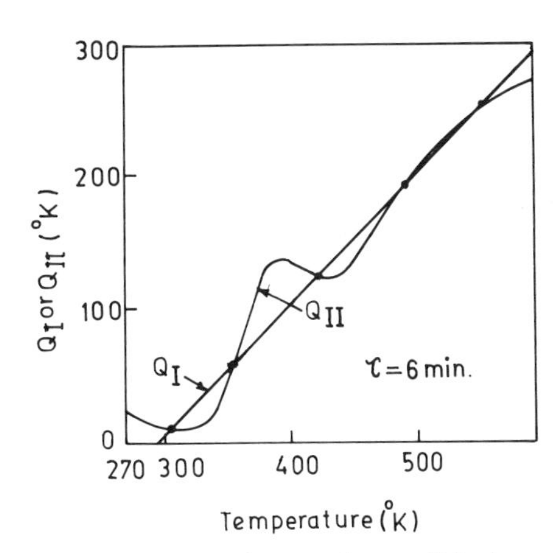

Figure 3.20. Multiple steady states in an adiabatic continuously stirred tank reactor for gas–liquid reaction: Q_I, heat removal function; Q_{II}, heat generation function. τ, mean residence time.

(1972) have studied the reaction between methanol and HCl in a sparged reactor by passing their vapors through a concentrated solution of $ZnCl_2$ at 160°C ($ZnCl_2$ acts as a catalyst for this reaction) to give vapors of CH_3Cl and H_2O.

$$CH_3OH(g) + HCl(g) \xrightarrow[\substack{160°C \\ \text{(liquid)}}]{\text{aqueous } ZnCl_2} CH_3Cl(g) + H_2O(g)$$

This reaction conforms to the slow reaction regime (regime 2) (Shah and Sharma, 1976).

Hancock and Kenney have found that at an inlet methanol pressure between 0.05 and 0.2 atm there exist continuous oscillations in the rate of production of methyl chloride even under isothermal conditions. These oscillations are characteristic of an unstable steady state. Above 0.2 atm and below 0.05 atm partial pressure of methanol a unique steady state is obtained.

There is a strong effect of HCl vapor pressure on the vapor pressure of water over concentrated $ZnCl_2$ solutions. The slope of the curve of product vapor pressure versus reactant pressure is a major factor that determines this instability.

REFERENCES

Abramzon, A. A., and Ostrovskit, M. V. (1961), *J. Appl. Chem. USSR (Engl. Transl.)*, **34**, 2226.

Abramzon, A. A., and Ostrovskit, M. V. (1962), *J. Appl. Chem. USSR (Engl. Transl.)*, **35**, 2328.

Abramzon, A. A., and Ostrovskit, M. V. (1963), *J. Appl. Chem. USSR (Engl. Transl.)*, **36**, 380.

Adams, C. T., Brandenberger, S. G., Dubois, J. B., Mill, G. S., Nager, M., and Richardson, D. B. (1977), *J. Org. Chem.*, **42**, 1.

Albright, L. F., and Hanson, C. (1969), *Loss Prev.*, **3**, 26.

Albright, L. F., and Hanson, C. (1975), *Industrial and Laboratory Nitration* (Am. Chem. Soc. Symp. Ser. No. 22), American Chemical Society, Washington, D.C.

Albright, L. F., Schiefferle, D. F., and Hanson, C. (1976), *J. Appl. Chem. Biotechnol.*, **26**, 522.

Allenbach, U., Wirges, H.-P., and Deckwer, W.-D. (1977), *Verfahrenstechnik*, **11**(12), 751.

Alper, E. (1973), *Trans. Inst. Chem. Eng.*, **51**, 159.

Andrew, S. P. S., and Hanson, D. (1961), *Chem. Eng. Sci.*, **14**, 105.

Asinger, F. (1968), *Paraffin Chemistry and Technology*, Pergamon, London.

Astarita, G. (1961), *Chem. Eng. Sci.*, **16**, 202.

Astarita, G., Marrucci, G., and Coleti, L. (1964), *Chim. Ind. (Milan)*, **46**, 1021.

Augugliaro, V., and Rizzuti, L. (1978), *Chem. Eng. Sci.*, **33**, 1441.

Bailes, P. J., Hanson, C., and Hughes, M. A. (1976), *Chem. Eng.*, **83**(18), 86.

Bakker, C. A. P., van Vlissingen, F. H. F., and Beek, W. J. (1967), *Chem. Eng. Sci.*, **22**, 1349.

Balyanski, G. V., Selin, M. E., and Kolychev, V. B. (1972), *J. Appl. Chem. USSR (Engl. Transl.)*, **45**(10), 2261.

Barron, C. H., and O'Hern, H. A. (1966), *Chem. Eng. Sci.*, **21**, 397.

Bartholome, E., Hetzel, E., Horn, H. Ch., Molzahn, M., Rotermund, G. W., and Vogel, L. (1976), *Chem.-Ing.-Tech.*, **48**, 355; [English translation in *Int. Chem. Eng.* (1978), **18**, 381].

Baveja, K. K. (1979), Studies in Gas–Liquid Reactions, Ph.D. thesis, I.I.T., Delhi, India.

Baveja, K. K., Subba Rao, D., and Sarkar, M. K. (1979), *J. Chem. Eng. Japan*, **12**(4), 322.

Beenackers, A. A. C. M., and van Swaaij, W. P. M. (1978), *Chem. Eng. J.*, **15**, 25, 39.

Bekhli, E. Yu, Nesterov, O. V., and Entelis, S. G. (1967), *J. Polymer Sci.*, Part C, No. 16, 209.

Bell, R. P., and Yates, K. (1962), *J. Chem. Soc.*, p. 1927.

Bender, M. L., and Jones, J. M. (1962), *J. Org. Chem.*, **27**, 3771.

Bengtsson, S., and Bjerle, I. (1975), *Chem. Eng. Sci.*, **30**, 1429.

Bhargava, R. K., and Sharma, M. M. (1978), *Chem. Eng. Sci.*, **33**, 525.

Bhave, R. R., and Sharma, M. M. (1981), *J. Chem. Tech. Biotechnol.*, **31**, 93.

Bidner, M. S., and de Santiago, M. (1971), *Chem. Eng. Sci.*, **26**, 1484.

Bishnoi, P. R., Sharma, M. M., and Shah, K. H. (1961), in Chari, S. A. (Ed.), *Chemical Process Design*, CSIR, New Delhi, India.

Bossier, J. A., Farritor, R. E., Hughmark, G. A., and Kao, J. T. F. (1973), *AIChE J.*, **19**, 1065.

Bourne, J. R., von Stockar, U., and Coggan, G. C. (1974), *Ind. Eng. Chem. Process Design Dev.*, **13**, 115.

Bratchley, R., and Green, M. (1970), *Chem. Ind. (London)*, p. 926.

Brian, P. L. T. (1968), *Chem. Eng. Sci.*, **23**, 1513.

Brian, P. L. T., Vivian, J. E., and Habib, A. G. (1962), *AIChE J.*, **8**, 205.

Brian, P. L. T., Vivian, J. E., and Matiatos, D. C. (1967), *AIChE J.*, **13**, 28.

Broström, A. (1975), *Trans. Inst. Chem. Eng.*, **53**, 29.

Brown, H. C. (1975), *Organic Syntheses via Boranes*, Wiley, New York.

Brown, H. C., Garg, C. P., and Liu, K.-T. (1971), *J. Org. Chem.*, **36**, 387.

Caldin, E. F. (1964), *Fast Reactions in Solutions*, Blackwell, Oxford.

Carberry, J. J. (1966), *Chem. Eng. Sci.*, **21**, 951.

Carleton, A. J., Rennie, J., and Valentin, F. H. H. (1969), *Chim. Ind. (Paris)*, **101**(10), 1439.

Carlson, K. D., Sohns, V. E., Perkins, R. B., and Huffman, E. L. (1977), *Ind. Eng. Chem. Prod. Res. Dev.*, **6**, 95.

Carr, N. L., and Shah, Y. T. (1979), *Can. J. Chem. Eng.*, **57**, 35.

Carraher, C. E., Jr. (1969), *J. Polymer Sci.*, **7**, Part A-1, 2359.

Cerfontain, H. (1968), *Mechanistic Aspects in Aromatic Sulfonation and Desulfonation*, Wiley-Interscience, New York.

Chandalia, S. B. (1966), *Indian J. Technol.*, **4**, 260.

Chandalia, S. B. (1967), *Indian J. Technol.*, **5**, 218.

Chandalia, S. B. (1968a), *Indian J. Technol.*, **6**, 88.

Chandalia, S. B. (1968b), *Indian J. Technol.*, **6**, 249.

Chandalia, S. B. (1970), *Chem. Process. Eng. (India)*, **4**(4), 19.

Chandalia, S. B. (1977), *Oxidation of Hydrocarbons*, Sevak, Bombay.

Chandrasekaran, K., and Sharma, M. M. (1974), *Chem. Eng. Sci.*, **29**, 2130.

Chandrasekaran, K., and Sharma, M. M. (1977), *Chem. Eng. Sci.*, **32**, 275.

Chandrasekaran, K., and Sharma, M. M. (1978), *Chem. Eng. Sci.*, **33**, 1294.

Chapman, J. W., Cox, P. R., and Strachan, A. N. (1974), *Chem. Eng. Sci.*, **29**, 1247.

Chapman, J. W., and Strachan, A. N. (1974), *J. Chem. Soc., Chem. Commun.*, p. 293.

Chaudhari, R. V., and Doraiswamy, L. K. (1974), *Chem. Eng. Sci.*, **29**, 129.

Chem. Eng. (1972), **79**(8), 50.

Chem. Eng. (1974), **81**(13), 114.

Chen, T.-I., and Barron, C. H. (1972), *Ind. Eng. Chem. Fundam.*, **11**, 466.

Chhabria, M. C. (1972), Kinetics of Heterogeneous Reactions, Ph.D. (Tech.) thesis, University of Bombay.

Chhabria, M. C., and Sharma, M. M. (1974), *Chem. Eng. Sci.*, **29**, 993.

Chiang, S. H., and Toor, H. L. (1964), *AIChE J.*, **10**, 398.

Chock, P. B., and Halpern, J. (1966), *J. Am. Chem. Soc.*, **88**, 3511.

Clarke, J. K. A. (1964), *Ind. Eng. Chem. Fundam.*, **3**, 239.

Clegg, G. T., and Mann, R. (1969), *Chem. Eng. Sci.*, **24**, 321.

Clippinger, E. (1964), *Ind. Eng. Chem. Prod. Res. Dev.*, **3**, 3.

Coffey, R. S. (1970), in Ugo, R. (Ed.), *Aspects of Homogeneous Catalysis*, D. Reidel, Dordrecht, p. 5.

Coggan, G. C., and Bourne, J. R. (1969a), *Trans. Inst. Chem. Eng.*, **47**, T96.

Coggan, C. G., and Bourne, J. R. (1969b), *Trans. Inst. Chem. Eng.*, **47**, 160.

Coldiron, D. C., Albright, L. F., and Alexander, L. G. (1958), *Ind. Eng. Chem.*, **50**, 991.

Cook, A. E., and Moore, E. (1972), *Chem. Eng. Sci.*, **27**, 605.

Coombes, R. G., Moodie, R. B., and Schofield, K. (1968), *J. Chem. Soc.*, p. 800.

Counce, R. M., and Perona, J. J. (1979), *Ind. Eng. Chem. Fundam.*, **18**, 400.

Cowdrey, W. A., and Davies, D. S. (1949), *J. Chem. Soc.*, p. 1871.

Cox, P. R., and Strachan, A. N. (1971), *Chem. Eng. Sci.*, **26**, 1013.

Cox, P. R., and Strachan, A. N. (1972a), *Chem. Eng. Sci.*, **27**, 457.

Cox, P. R., and Strachan, A. N. (1972b), *Chem. Eng. J.*, **4**, 253.

Danckwerts, P. V. (1952), *Appl. Sci. Res.*, **A3**, 385.

Danckwerts, P. V. (1967), *Chem. Eng. Sci.*, **22**, 472.

Danckwerts, P. V. (1968), *Chem. Eng. Sci.*, **23**, 1045.

Danckwerts, P. V. (1979), *Chem. Eng. Sci.*, **34**, 4453.

Danckwerts, P. V., and da Silva, A. T. (1967), *Chem. Eng. Sci.*, **22**, 1513.

Danckwerts, P. V., and Gillham, A. J. (1966), *Trans. Inst. Chem. Eng.*, **44**, T42.

Danckwerts, P. V., and Rizvi, S. F. (1971), *Trans. Inst. Chem. Eng.*, **49**, 124.

Danckwerts, P. V., and Sharma, M. M. (1966), *Chem. Eng., Inst. Chem. Eng.*, No. 202, CE244.

da Silva, A. T., and Danckwerts, P. V. (1968), *Proc. Symp. Tripartite Chem. Eng. Conf.* (Montreal), p. 48.

Datta, R. L., and Mitter, H. K. (1919), *J. Am. Chem. Soc.*, **41**, 2028.

Deckwer, W.-D. (1976), *J. Chem. Eng. Data*, **21**, 176.

Deckwer, W.-D. (1977), *Chem. Eng. Sci.*, **32**, 51.

Deckwer, W.-D., Allenbach, U., and Bretschneider, H. (1977), *Chem. Eng. Sci.*, **32**, 43.

Deckwer, W.-D., and Puxbaumer, H. H. (1975), *Chem. Ing.-Tech.*, **47**, 163.

Dehmlow, E. V. (1974), *Angew. Chem. Int. Ed. Engl.*, **13**, 170.

Dehmlow, E. V., and Dehmlow, S. S. (1980), *Phase Transfer Catalysis* (Monographs in Modern Chemistry, Vol. 11), Verlag Chemie, Weinheim, West Germany.

de Waal, K. J. A., and Okeson, J. C. (1966), *Chem. Eng. Sci.*, **21**, 559.

Ding, J. S. Y., Sharma, S., and Luss, D. (1974), *Ind. Eng. Chem. Fundam.*, **13**, 76.

Dixon, J. K., and Saunders, K. W. (1954), *Ind. Eng. Chem.*, **46**, 652.

Eigen, M., and Kustin, K. (1962), *J. Am. Chem. Soc.*, **84**, 1355.

Emmert, R. E., and Pigford, R. L. (1962), *AIChE J.*, **8**, 171 (erratum, p. 702).

Fendler, J. H., and Fendler, E. J. (1977), *Catalysis in Micellar and Macromolecular Systems*, Academic Press, New York.

Finkelstein, N. P., and Fleming, C. A. (1976), Report No. 1793, The Kinetics and Mechanism of Solvent Extraction of Copper by LIX64N and Kelex100, National Institute for Metallurgy, South Africa.

Flett, D. S., Hartlage, J. A., Spink, D. R., and Okuhara, D. N. (1975), *J. Inorg. Nucl. Chem.*, **37**, 1967.

Floyd, M. B., and Boozer, C. E. (1963), *J. Am. Chem. Soc.*, **85**, 984.

Fukushima, S., Uyama, A., Yamaguchi, Y., Tsuji, E., and Mezaki, S. (1978), *J. Chem. Eng. Japan*, **11**(4), 283.

Furmer, Yu. V., Akesl'rod, Yu. V., Dil'man, V. V., and Lashakov, A. L. (1971), *Theoret. Found. Chem. Eng. USSR (Engl. Transl.)*, **5**, 115.

Ganguli, K. L., and van den Berg, H. J. (1978), *Chem. Eng. Sci.*, **33**, 27.

Gehlawat, J. K. (1972), *Indian Chem. Engr. (Trans.)*, **14**, 22.

Gehlawat, J. K., and Sharma, M. M. (1968), *Chem. Eng. Sci.*, **23**, 1173.

Gehlawat, J. K., and Sharma, M. M. (1970), *J. Appl. Chem.*, **20**, 93.

Ghorpade, A. K., Chipalkatti, S. V., and Sharma, M. M. (1981), *Chem. Eng. Sci.*, **36**, 1227.

Gilliland, E. R., and Seebold, J. E. (1941), *Ind. Eng. Chem.*, **33**, 1143.

Glueck, A. R., and Kenney, C. N. (1968), *Chem. Eng. Sci.*, **23**, 1257.

Gorin, E., Fontana, C. M., and Kidder, G. A. (1948), *Ind. Eng. Chem.*, **40**, 2128; 2135.

Gregory, D. P., Martens, R. J., Stubbs, C. E., and Wagner, J. D. (1976), *J. Appl. Chem. Biotechnol.*, **26**, 623.

Griskey, R. G., Hudia, S. R., and Siskovic, N. (1974), *J. Appl. Polymer Sci.*, **18**, 3057.

Grobler, A., Simon, A., Kada, T., and Fazakas, L. (1967), *J. Organometal. Chem.*, **7**, 3.

Groothuis, H. (1961), *Chem. Eng. Sci.*, **14**, 176.

Grummitt, O. (1942), *J. Am. Chem. Soc.*, **64**, 1811.

Gupta, R. K., and Sharma, M. M. (1967), *Indian Chem. Engr.* (*Trans.*), **9**(3), 100.

Haase, D. J., and Waker, D. G. (1974), *Chem. Eng. Prog.*, **70**(5), 74.

Hague, D. N. (1971), *Fast Reactions*, Wiley, New York.

Halpern, J., Harrod, J. F., and James, B. R. (1966), *J. Am. Chem. Soc.*, **88**, 5150.

Hancock, E. G. (1975), *Benzene and Its Industrial Derivatives*, Ernest Benn, London.

Hancock, M. D., and Kenney, C. N. (1972), *Proc. 5th European / 2nd Int. Symp. Chem. React. Eng.*, pp. B 3–47.

Hanson, C., and Ismail, H. A. M. (1976), *J. Appl. Chem. Biotechnol.*, **26**, 111.

Hanson, C., Marsland, J. G., and Wilson, G. (1971), *Chem. Eng. Sci.*, **26**, 1513.

Hanson, C., Hughes, M. A., and Marsland, J. G. (1974), *Mass Transfer with Chemical Reaction in Liquid–Liquid Systems*, Society of Chemical Industry, London, p. 2401.

Hanson, C., Hughes, M. A., and Whewell, R. J. (1978), *J. Appl. Chem. Biotechnol.*, **28**, 426.

Harada, M., Nomura, M., Eguchi, W., and Nagata, S. (1971), *J. Chem. Eng. Japan*, **4**(1), 54.

Hardwick, W. H., and Wace, P. F. (1965), *Chem. Process Eng.*, **46**, 283.

Harnisch, H. (1980), *Pure Appl. Chem.*, **52**, 809.

Hartley, G. S., and West, T. F. (1969), *Chemicals for Pest Control*, Pergamon, Oxford.

Hatcher, W. J., and Hart, D. R. (1980), *Chem. Eng. Sci.*, **35**, 90.

Hatt, B. W., and Kerridge, D. H. (1979), *Chem Brit.*, **15**(2), 78.

Hikita, H., and Asai, S. (1965), *J. Chem. Eng. Japan*, **3**, 115.

Hikita, H., Asai, S., Ishikawa, H., and Hirano, S. (1977a), *J. Chem. Eng. Japan*, **10**, 120.

Hikita, H., Asai, S., and Tsuji, T. (1977b), *AIChE J.*, **23**, 538.

Hikita, H., Asai, S., Ishikawa, H., and Honda, M. (1977c) *Chem. Eng. J.*, **13**, 7.

Hikita, H., Asai, S., Ishikawa, H., Okamoto, T., Sakamoto, S., and Kitagawa, M. (1978), *J. Chem. Eng. Japan*, **11**, 360.

Hikita, H., Asai, S., Ishikawa, H., and Uku, J. (1980), *Chem. Eng. Commun.*, **5**, 315.

Hjortkjaer, J., and Jensen, V. W. (1976), *Ind. Eng. Chem. Prod. Res. Dev.*, **15**, 46.

Hobbs, C. C., Drew, E. H., van't Hof, H. A., Mesich, F. G., and Onore, M. J. (1972), *Ind. Eng. Chem. Prod. Res. Dev.*, **11**, 220.

Hoffman, L. A., Sharma, S., and Luss, D. (1975), *AIChE J.*, **21**, 318.

Hoffmann, U., and Emig, G. (1979), *Ger. Chem. Eng.*, **2**, 282.

Hofmann, H. (1961), *Chem. Eng. Sci.*, **14**, 193.

Holroyd, F. P. B., and Kenney, C. N. (1971a), *Chem. Eng. Sci.*, **26**, 1963.

Holroyd, F. P. B., and Kenney, C. N. (1971b), *Chem. Eng. Sci.*, **26**, 1971.

Hughes, M. A. (1975), *Chem. Ind.* (*London*), No. 24, 1042.

Hughes, M. A., Preston, J. S., and Whewell, R. J. (1976), *J. Inorg. Nucl. Chem.*, **38**, 2067.

Ikemizu, K., Morroka, S., and Kato, Y. (1978), *Kagaku Kogaku, Ronbunshu*, **4**, 496.

Imaishi, N., and Fujinawa, K. (1978), *Kagaku Kogaku, Ronbunshu*, **4**, 484, 490.

Jahan, S. (1978), Kinetics of Heterogeneous Reactions, M.Sci. (Tech.) thesis, University of Bombay.

Jagirdar, G. C., and Sharma, M. M. (1980), *J. Separ. Process. Technol.*, **1**(2), 40.

James, B. R. (1973), *Homogeneous Hydrogenation*, Wiley, New York.

Jhaveri, A. S., and Sharma, M. M. (1967), *Chem. Eng. Sci.*, **22**, 1.

Jhaveri, A. S., and Sharma, M. M. (1968), *Chem. Eng. Sci.*, **23**, 1.

Jhaveri, A. S., and Sharma, M. M. (1969), *Chem. Eng. Sci.*, **24**, 189.

Johnson, G. R., and Crynes, B. L. (1974), *Ind. Eng. Chem. Process Design Dev.*, **13**, 6.

Joosten, G. E. H., Maatman, H., Prins, W., and Stamhuis, E. J. (1980), *Chem. Eng. Sci.*, **35**, 223.

Juvekar, V. A., and Sharma, M. M. (1973), *Chem. Eng. Sci.*, **28**, 976.

Kaloshin, V. M. (1971), *J. Appl. Chem. USSR* (*Engl. Transl.*), **44**, 669.

Kalra, H., and Otto, F. D. (1974), *Can. J. Chem. Eng.*, **52**, 258.

Kameoka, Y., and Pigford, R. L. (1977), *Ind. Eng. Chem. Fundam.*, **16**, 163.

Kane, P. G. (1975), Kinetics of Heterogeneous Reactions, M.Sci. (Tech.) thesis, University of Bombay.

Kataoka, T., Nishiki, T., and Ueyama, K. (1971), *Kagaku Kogaku*, **35**(10), 1157.

Kataoka, T., Nishiki, T., and Ueyama, K. (1975), *Chem. Eng. J.*, **10**, 189.

Kenney, C. N. (1975), *Catal. Rev. Sci. Eng.*, **11**(2), 197.

Kenney, C. N., and Taylor, R. F. (1971), in Roberts, F., Taylor, R. F., and Jenkins, T. R. (Eds.), *High Temperature Chemical Reaction Engineering, Solids Conversion Processes*, Institution of Chemical Engineers, London.

Kikkaw, S., Hayashi, T. Nomura, M., and Otsu, N. (1975), *Bull. Chem. Soc. Japan*, **48**, 90.

Kishinevskii, M. Kh., Kornienko, T. S., and Popa, T. M. (1970), *Theoret. Found. Chem. Eng. USSR* (*Engl. Transl.*), **5**, 671.

Kohl, A. L., and Riesenfeld, F. C. (1974), *Gas Purification*, 2nd ed., McGraw-Hill, New York.

Komasawa, I., Inoue, T., and Otake, T. (1972), *J. Chem. Eng. Japan*, **5**, 34.

Komiyama, H., and Inoue, H. (1975), *J. Chem. Eng. Japan*, **8**, 310.

Komiyama, H., and Inoue, H. (1980), *Chem. Eng. Sci.*, **35**, 154.

Kondo, K., Takahashi, S., Tsuneyuki, T., and Nakashio, F. (1978), *J. Chem. Eng. Japan*, **11**, 193.

Kothari, P. J., and Sharma, M. M. (1966a), *Chem. Eng. Sci.*, **21**, 391.

Kothari, P. J., and Sharma, M. M. (1966b), *Indian Chem. Engr. (Trans.)*, **8**, 98.

Kramers, H., Blind, M. P. P., and Snoeck, E. (1961), *Chem. Eng. Sci.*, **14**, 115.

Krueger, K. H., and Schmitz, P. (1970), Ger. Offen. 1,916,271 (8 October); *Chem. Abstr.* (1971), **73**, 133823z.

Kulkarni, A. A. (1979), Kinetics of Heterogeneous Reactions: Oxidation of Diisopropylbenzene Isomers, M.Chem. Eng. thesis, University of Bombay.

Kuo, C. H., Li, K. Y., Wen, C. P., and Weeks, J. L., Jr. (1977), *Am. Inst. Chem. Eng. Symp. Ser.*, **73**, No. 166 (Water—1976, I: Physical, Chemical Wastewater Treatment), p. 230.

Kuo, C. H., and Wen. C. P. (1977), *Am. Inst. Chem. Eng. Symp. Ser.*, **73**, No. 166 (Water—1976; I: Physical, Chemical Wastewater Treatment), p. 272.

Kustin, K., Taub, I. A., and Weinstock, E. (1966), *Inorg. Chem.*, **5**, 1079.

Ladhabhoy, M. E. (1970), Kinetics of Oxidation of Organic Compounds: *n*-Butylaldehyde to *n*-Butyric Acid and 2-Ethylhexaldehyde to 2-Ethylhexanoic Acid, Ph.D. (Tech.) thesis, University of Bombay.

Ladhabhoy, M. E., and Sharma, M. M. (1969), *J. Appl. Chem.*, **19**, 267.

Ladhabhoy, M. E., and Sharma, M. M. (1970), *J. Appl. Chem.*, **20**, 274.

Lahiri, R. N. (1981), *Ind. Chem. Eng. Trans.*, **23**, 44.

Larson, R. A., and Rockwell, A. L. (1979), *J. Environ. Sci. Technol.*, **13**(3), 325.

Laudry, J. E. (1967), The Effect of a Second Order Chemical Reaction on the Absorption of Methyl Mercaptan in a Laminar Jet Apparatus, Ph.D. thesis, Louisiana State University, 1966; *Diss. Abstr.*, **27B**, No. 9, 3091.

Laurent, A., Charpentier, J. C., and Prost, C. (1974), *J. Chim. Phys.*, **71**(4), 613.

Lawless, J. J., and Searle, H. T. (1962), *J. Chem. Soc.*, p. 4200.

Lee, L. M., and Harriott, P. (1977), *Ind. Eng. Chem. Process Design Dev.*, **16**, 282.

Lefebvre, G., and Chauvin, Y. (1970), in Ugo, R. (Ed.), *Aspects of Homogeneous Catalysis*, D. Reidel, Dordrecht, p. 108.

Lefers, J. B., de Boks, F. C., van den Bleek, C. M., and van den Berg, P. J. (1980), *Chem. Eng. Sci.*, **35**, 145.

Linek, V. (1966), *Chem. Eng. Sci.*, **21**, 777.

Linek, V., and Mayrhoferova, J. (1970), *Chem. Eng. Sci.*, **25**, 787.

Linek, V., and Sobotka, M. (1973), *Collect. Czech. Chem. Commun.*, **38**, 2819.

Lira, E. P., and Anderson, R. F. (1977), in Hickson, J. L., (Ed.), *Sucrochemistry* (Am. Chem. Soc. Symp. Ser. No. 41), American Chemical Society, Washington, D.C., p. 223.

Low, D. I. R. (1967), *Can. J. Chem. Eng.*, **45**, 166.

McNeil, K. M. (1970), *Can. J. Chem. Eng.*, **48**, 252.

Manogue, W. H., and Pigford, R. L. (1960), *AIChE J.*, **6**, 494.

Mashelkar, R. A., and Sharma, M. M. (1970), *Trans. Inst. Chem. Eng.*, **48**, T162.

Mehta, V. D., and Sharma, M. M. (1971), *Chem. Eng. Sci.*, **26**, 461.

Melnyk, P. B., Judkins, D., and Netzer, A. (1977), *Tappi*, **60**(3), 97.

Menger, F. M. (1979), *Pure Appl. Chem.*, **51**, 999.

Menger, F. M., Rhee, J. U., and Rhee, H. K. (1975), *J. Org. Chem.*, **40**, 3803.

Millich, F., and Carraher, C. E., Jr. (1977), *Interfacial Synthesis*, Vol. 1, *Fundamentals*, Marcel Dekker, New York.

Mirviss, S. B. (1961), *J. Am. Chem. Soc.*, **83**, 3051.

Mishra, G. C., and Srivastava, R. D. (1975), *Chem. Eng. Sci.*, **30**, 1387.

Mishra, G. C., and Srivastava, R. D. (1976), *Chem. Eng. Sci.*, **31**, 969.

Morgan, J. P., and Murray, F. E. (1971), *Tappi*, **54**(9), 1500.

Morgan, P. W. (1965), *Condensation Polymers: By Interfacial and Solution Methods*, Wiley-Interscience, New York, pp. 22, 66.

Morrel, C. E., Paltz, W. J., Packie, J. W., Asbury, W. C., and Brown, C. L. (1946), *Trans. Am. Inst. Chem. Eng.*, **42**, 473.

Mulder, A. J., Naber, J. E., and Ploeg, J. E. G. (1972), Brit. Pat. 1,279,053; *Chem. Abstr.* (1972), **77**, 117856.

Murray, F. E. (1968), *Pulp Paper Mag. Can.*, **69** (5 January), 3.

Nanda, A. K., and Sharma, M. M. (1966), *Chem. Eng. Sci.*, **21**, 707.

Nanda, A. K., and Sharma, M. M. (1967), *Chem. Eng. Sci.*, **22**, 769.

Nardhani, K. M., and Chandalia, S. B. (1969), *Indian Chem. Engr. (Trans.)*, **11**(3), 101.

Naworski, J. S., and Harriott, P. (1969), *Ind. Eng. Chem. Fundam.*, **8**, 397.

Neelkantan, J., and Gehlawat, J. K. (1980), *Ind. Eng. Chem. Fundam.*, **19**, 36.

Nijsing, R. A. T. O., Handriksz, R. H., and Kramers, H., (1959), *Chem. Eng. Sci.*, **10**, 88.

Nyvlt, V., and Kastanek, F. (1975), *Collect. Czech. Chem. Commun.*, **40**, 1853.

Oishi, T., Yamaguchi, I., and Nagata, S. (1965), *Mem. Fac. Eng. Kyoto Univ.*, **27**, 317.

Olander, D. R., and Camahort, J. L. (1966), *AIChE J.*, **12**, 693.

Oldenkamp, R. D., and Margolin, E. D. (1969), *Chem. Eng. Prog.*, **65**(11), 73.

Onda, K., Takeuchi, H., and Maeda, Y. (1972), *Chem. Eng. Sci.*, **27**, 449.

Osborn, J. A., Jardine, F. H., Young, J. F., and Wilkinson, G. (1966), *J. Chem. Soc.*, (Part A), p. 1711.

Palko, A. A., Landau, L., and Drury, J. S. (1971), *Ind. Eng. Chem. Process Design Dev.*, **10**, 79.

Pangarkar, V. G., and Sharma, M. M. (1974), *Chem. Eng. Sci.*, **29**, 2297.

Parshall, G. W. (1972), *J. Am. Chem. Soc.*, **94**, 8716.

Piret, E. L., Penney, W. H., and Trambouze, P. J. (1960), *AIChE J.*, **6**, 394.

Pocker, Y., Stevens, K. D., and Champoux, J. J. (1969), *J. Am. Chem. Soc.*, **91**, 4199.

Pogrebnaya, U. L., Usov, A. P., Baranov, A. V., Nestrenko, A. I., and Bezyazychnyi, P. I. (1975), *J. Appl. Chem. USSR (Engl. Transl.)*, **48**, 1105.

Pohorecki, R. (1968), *Chem. Eng. Sci.*, **23**, 1447.

Pohorecki, R. (1976), *Chem. Eng. Sci.*, **31**, 637.

Popovic, M., and Deckwer, W.-D. (1975), *Chem. Eng. Sci.*, **30**, 913.

Prengle, H. W., Jr., and Barona, N. (1970), *Hydrocarbon Process. Petrol. Refiner*, **49**(11), 159.

Prengle, H. W., Mauk, C. E., Legan, R. W., and Hewes, C. G. (1975), *Hydrocarbon Process. Petrol. Refiner*, **54**(10), 82.

Pruden, B. B., and Le, H. (1976), *Can. J. Chem. Eng.*, **54**, 319.

Puranik, S. A., and Sharma, M. M. (1970a), *Chem. Eng. Sci.*, **25**, 257.

Puranik, S. A., and Sharma, M. M. (1970b), *Indian Chem. Engr. (Trans.)*, **12**, 49.

Raghuram, S., and Shah, Y. T. (1977), *Chem. Eng. J.*, **13**, 81.

Raghuram, S., Shah, Y. T., and Tierney, J. W. (1979), *Chem. Eng. J.*, **17**, 63.

Ramachandran, P. A. (1969), *Chem Process. Eng. (India)*, **3**(1), 23.

Razumovskii, S. D., Shatokhina, E. J., Malievskii, A. D., and Zaikov, G. E. (1975), *Bull. Acad. Sci. USSR, Chem. Ser. (Engl. Transl.)*, **24**(3), 469.

Reith, T., and Beek, W. J. (1973), *Chem. Eng. Sci.*, **28**, 1331.

Richards, G. M., Ratcliff, G. A., and Danckwerts, P. V. (1964), *Chem. Eng. Sci.*, **19**, 325.

Richardson, F. D. (1975), in Dahl, W., Lange, K. W., and Papamantellos, D. (Eds.), *Kinetics of Metallurgical Processes in Steel Making*, Verlag Stahleisen M. B. H., Dusseldorf, West Germany, p. 279.

Richardson, J. A. (1977), *Diss. Abstr.*, **38B**, 2289.

Richardson, J. A., and Rase, H. F. (1978), *Ind. Eng. Chem. Prod. Res. Dev.*, **17**, 287.

Riegel, H. Schindler, H. D., and Sze, M. C. (1973), *Chem. Eng. Prog.*, **69**(10), 89.

Rizzuti, L., Augugliaro, V., and Marrucci, G. (1976), *Chem. Eng. Sci.*, **31**, 877.

Roberts, D., and Danckwerts, P. V. (1962), *Chem. Eng. Sci.*, **17**, 961.

Rod, V., and Rychnovsky, L. (1975), Mass Transfer with a Very Fast Chemical Reaction in Two-Phase Liquid Systems, Overall Rate of Cu(II) Extraction by 8-Hydroxy Quinoline, Paper presented at 5th CHISA Congress, Prague, August 1975.

Rosenbaum, J. B., George, D. R., and May. J. T. (1971), Metallurgical Application of Solvent Extraction, 2: Practice and Trends, U.S. Department of the Interior, Bureau of Mines Information Circular 8502.

Rossi, P. P., Magnoni, F., and Dall'Asta, G. (1979), *Hydrocarbon Process. Petrol. Refiner*, **58**(8), 93.

Roth, J. F., Craddock, J. H., Hershman, A., and Paulik, F. E. (1971), *Chemtech.*, **1**, 600.

Roughton, F. J. W. (1959), in Butler, J. A. V., and Randall, J. T. (Eds.), *Progress in Biophysics and Biophysical Chemistry*, Pergamon, London, Vol. 9, p. 55.

Roughton, F. J. W., and Rossi-Bernardi, L. (1966), *Proc. Roy. Soc. (London)*, **B164**(996), 381.

Ruthven, D. M., and Kenney, C. N. (1967), *Chem. Eng. Sci.*, **22**, 1561.

Ruthven, D. M., and Kenney, C. N. (1968), *Chem. Eng. Sci.*, **23**, 981.

Rylander, P. N. (1973), *Organic Syntheses with Noble Metal Catalysts*, Academic Press, New York, p. 62.

Rylander, P. N., and Greenfield, H. (1976), *Catalysis in Organic Synthesis*, Academic Press, New York.

Sada, E., Kumazawa, H., and Butt, M. A. (1976), *Can. J. Chem. Eng.*, **54**, 421.

Sada, E., Kumazawa, H., Butt, M. A., and Lozano, J. E. (1977a), *Can. J. Chem. Eng.*, **55**, 293.

Sada, E., Kumazawa, H., Butt, M. A., and Lozano, J. E. (1977b), *J. Chem. Eng. Japan*, **10**, 487.

Sada, E., Kumazawa, H., Yamanaka, Y., Kudo, I., and Kondo, T. (1978), *J. Chem. Eng. Japan*, **11**, 290.

Sada, E., Kumazawa, H., Kudo, I., and Kondo, T. (1979a), *Ind. Eng. Chem. Process Design Dev.*, **18**, 275.

Sada, E., Kumazawa, H., Kudo, I., and Kondo, T. (1979b), *Chem. Eng. Sci.*, **34**, 719.

Sankholkar, D. S., and Sharma, M. M. (1973), *Chem. Eng. Sci.*, **28**, 49.

Satyamurthy, N. (1976), A Study in Mass Transfer (Absorption of Oxygen by Aqueous Sodium Sulphite Solutions), Ph.D. thesis, University of Madras, India.

Satyamurthy, N., Degaleesan, T. E., Chandrasekharan, K., and Laddha, G. S. (1979), *Can. J. Chem. Eng.*, **57**, 145.

Saunby, J. B., and Kiff, B. W. (1976), *Hydrocarbon Process. Petrol. Refiner*, **55**(11), 247.

Sawicki, J. E., and Barron, C. H. (1973), *Chem. Eng. J.*, **5**, 153.

Scher, M., Gill, W. N., and Jelinek, R. V. (1963), *Ind. Eng. Chem. Fundam.*, **2**, 107.

Shaffer, D. L., Jones, J. H., and Daubert, T. E. (1974), *Ind. Eng. Chem. Process Design Dev.*, **13**, 14.

Shah, Y. T. (1972), *Chem. Eng. Sci.*, **27**, 1469.

Shah, Y. T. (1979), *Gas–Liquid–Solid Reactor Design*, McGraw-Hill, New York.

Shah, Y. T., and Sharma, M. M. (1976), *Trans. Inst. Chem. Eng.*, **54**, 1.

Sharma, M. M. (1964), Kinetics of Gas Absorption, Ph.D. thesis, Cambridge University, England.

Sharma, M. M. (1965), *Trans. Faraday Soc.*, **61**, 681.

Sharma, M. M., and Danckwerts, P. V. (1963), *Chem. Eng. Sci.*, **18**, 729.

Sharma, M. M., and Danckwerts, P. V. (1970), *Brit. Chem. Eng.*, **15**, 522.

Sharma, M. M., and Mashelkar, R. A. (1968), *Proc. Symp. Tripartite Chem. Eng. Conf.* (Montreal), p. 10.

Sharma, M. M., and Nanda, A. K. (1968), *Trans. Inst. Chem. Eng.*, **46**, T44.

Sharma, R. C. (1969), Kinetics of Alkaline Hydrolysis of Esters, Ph.D. thesis, University of Bombay.

Sharma, R. C., and Sharma, M. M. (1969), *J. Appl. Chem.*, **19**, 162.

Sharma, R. C., and Sharma, M. M. (1970a), *Bull. Chem. Soc. Japan*, **43**, 642.

Sharma, R. C., and Sharma, M. M. (1970b), *Bull. Chem. Soc. Japan*, **43**, 1282.

Sharma, S., Hoffman, L. A., and Luss, D. (1976), *AIChE J.*, **22**, 324.

Sherwood, T. K., Pigford, R. L., and Wilke, C. R. (1975), *Mass Transfer*, McGraw-Hill, New York.

Sheth, M. N. (1977), Kinetics of Heterogeneous Reactions, M.Chem.Eng. thesis, University of Bombay.

Shropshire, J. A., and Eustace, D. J. (1978), U.S. 4,124,693.

Singh, D. K., Sharma, R. N., and Srivastava, R. D. (1978), *AIChE J*, **24**, 232.

Sohrabi, M., Kaghazchi, T., and Hanson, C. (1977), *J. Appl. Chem. Biotechnol.*, **27**, 453.

Sokolov, L. B. (1977), in Millich, F., and Carraher, C. E., Jr. (Eds.), *Interfacial Synthesis*, Vol. I, *Fundamentals*, Marcel Dekker, New York, p. 141.

Sokolov, L. B., and Nikonov, V. Z. (1977), in Millich, F., and Carraher, C. E., Jr. (Eds.) *Interfacial Synthesis*, Vol. I., *Fundamentals*, Marcel Dekker, New York, p. 167.

Sprow, F. B., (1969), *Ind. Eng. Chem. Process Design Dev.*, **8**, 254.

Sridharan, K., and Sharma, M. M. (1976), *Chem. Eng. Sci.*, **31**, 767.

Srivastava, R. D., McMillan, A. F., and Harris, I. J. (1968), *Can. J. Chem. Eng.*, **46**, 181.

Starks, C. M. (1980), *Chemtech.*, **10**, 110.

Starks, C. M., and Owens, R. M. (1973), *J. Am. Chem. Soc.*, **95**, 3613.

Subramanian, K. N., and Richardson, F. D. (1968), *J. Iron Steel Inst. (London)*, **206**, 576.

Sundermeyer, W. (1965), *Angew. Chem. Int. Ed. Engl.*, **4**, 222.

Szekely, J. (1967), *Chem. Eng. (London)*, **206**, CE41.

Szekely, J., and Themelis, N. J. (1971), *Rate Phenomena in Process Metallurgy*, Wiley, New York.

Szonyi, G. (1968), in Gould, R. F. (Ed.), *Homogeneous Catalysis* (Adv. Chem. Ser. No. 70) American Chemical Society, Washington, D.C., p. 53.

Takeuchi, H., and Yamanaka, Y. (1978), *Ind. Eng.Chem. Proc.ss Design Dev.*, **17**, 389.

Takeuchi, H., Takahashi, K., Hoshino, T., and Takahashi, M. (1980), *Chem. Eng. Commun.*, **4**, 181.

Teramoto, M., Ikeda, M., and Teranishi, H. (1976a), *Kagaku Kogaku, Ronbunshu*, **2**, 86; *Int. Chem. Eng.* (1977), **17**, 265.

Teramoto, M., Ikeda, M., and Teranishi, H. (1976b), *Kagaku Kogaku, Rombunshu*, **2**, 637.

Teramoto, M., Ito, T., and Teranishi, H. (1977), *J. Chem. Eng. Japan*, **10**, 218.

Thomas, W. J. (1963), *Trans. Inst. Chem. Eng.*, **41**, T289.

Thomas, W. J., and Nicholl, E. McK. (1967), *Chem. Eng. Sci.*, **22**, 1877.

Thomas, W. J., and Nicholl, E. McK. (1969), *Trans. Inst. Chem. Eng.*, **47**, T-325.

Throckmorton, P. E., Hansen, L. I., Christenson, R. C., and Pryde, E. H. (1968), *J. Am. Oil Chem. Soc.*, **45**, 59.

Throckmorton, P. E., and Pryde, E. H. (1972), *J. Am. Oil Chem. Soc.*, **49**, 643.

Tiwari, R. K. (1976), Studies in Alkylation and Oxidation of Aromatic Hydrocarbons, Ph.D. (Tech.) thesis, University of Bombay.

Tiwari, R. K., and Sharma, M. M. (1977), *Chem. Eng. Sci.*, **32**, 1253.

Trambouze, P. (1961), *Chem. Eng. Sci.*, **14**, 161.

Trambouze, P., Trambouze, M. T., and Piret, E. L. (1961), *AIChE J.*, **7**, 1338.

Trushanov, V. N., Tsirlin, A. M., Nikitenko, A. M., and Khodov, G. Ya. (1975), *Zh. Prikl. Khim.*, **48**(2), 297 (in Russian).

van Direndonck, L., De Jong, P., von Denhoff, J., Vonken, H., and Vermijs, R. (1974), *Practical Model of the Benzoic Acid Oxidation Step as a Means Towards Optimization of the Phenol Process* (Adv. Chem. Ser. No. 133), American Chemical Society, Washington, D.C., p. 432.

van Direndonck, L., de Jong, P., Vermijs, R., and von Denhoff, J. (1975), Optimization of the Benzoic Acid Oxidation Step in the Toluene Route towards Phenol, Paper presented at the 5th International Chisa Congress, Prague, August 1975.

van Krevelen, D. W., and Baans, C. M. E. (1950), *J. Phys. Chem.*, **54**, 370.

Vasudevan, T. V., and Sharma, M. M. (1983a), *Ind. Eng. Chem. Process Design Dev.*, **22**, 161.

Vasudevan, T. V., and Sharma, M. M. (1983b), *Ind. Eng. Chem. Process Design Dev.*, in press.

Wesselingh, J. A., and van't Hoog, A. C. (1970), *Trans. Inst. Chem. Eng.*, **48**, T-69.

Westerterp, K. R., van Dierendonck, L. L., and De'Kraa, J. A. (1963), *Chem. Eng. Sci.*, **18**, 157.

Whewell, R. J., Hughes, M. A., and Hanson, C. (1975), *J. Inorg. Nucl. Chem.*, **37**, 2303.

Whewell, R. J., Hughes, M. A., and Hanson, C. (1976), *J. Inorg. Nucl. Chem.*, **38**, 2071.

Whewell, R. J., Hughes, M. A., and Hanson, C. (1977), Aspects of the Kinetics and Mechanism of the Extraction of Copper with Hydroxyoximes, Paper presented at the International Solvent Extraction Conference, Toronto, Canada, September 1977.

Whiteway, S. G. (1979), *Can. J. Chem. Eng.*, **57**, 78.

Wielgosz, Z., Dobkowski, Z., and Krajewski, B. (1972), *European Polymer J.*, **8**(9), 1113.

Wild, J. D., and Potter, O. E. (1968), *Proc. Symp. Mass Transfer Chem. React.*, p. 30.

Wilke, C. R., and Chang, P. (1955), *AIChE J.*, **1**, 264.

Williamson, D. G., and Cvetanovic, R. J. (1968), *J. Am. Chem. Soc.*, **90**, 3668; 4248.

Wittbecker, E. L., and Katz, M. (1959), *J. Polymer Sci.*, **40**, 367.

Yadav, G. D. (1975), *Chem. Ind. Dev. (India)*, **9**(6), 16.

Yadav, G. D. (1980), Heterogeneous Reactions: Chlorination of Aqueous Phenols and Aromatic Sulfonic Acids; Effect of Diffusivity on True Gas-Side Mass Transfer Coefficient; Phase Transfer Catalysis, Ph.D. (Tech.) thesis, University of Bombay.

Yadav, G. D., and Sharma, M. M. (1981), *Chem. Eng. Sci.*, **36**, 599.

Yagi, S., and Inoue, H. (1962), *Chem. Eng. Sci.*, **17**, 411.

Yagodin, G. Ya., Tarasov, V. V., and Yurtov, E. V. (1974), *Dokl. Akad. Nauk SSSR*, **218**(B), 647; *Chem. Abstr.* (1975) **82**, 45843m.

Yakushkin, M. I. (1969), *Khim. Prom.*, **45**, 504.

Yano, T., Suetaka, T., Umehara, T., and Shiotani, S. (1974), *Nippon Kogaku Kaishi*, No. 8, 1577.

CHAPTER FOUR

Mass Transfer Accompanied by Consecutive and Two-Step Reactions

4.1. CONSECUTIVE REACTIONS

Consecutive reactions are very commonly encountered in organic process industries. The substitution-chlorination and alkylation of aromatic compounds involve consecutive reactions. In a typical case of chlorination of phenol, mono-(*o*- and *p*-) and dichlorophenols and the like are formed. Here the objective may be to get high yields of mono- or dichlorophenols. Similarly, in the alkylation of phenol with isobutylene when mono- (*o*- and *p*-) and di-*tert*-butyl phenol derivatives are formed, our objective may be to get high yields of *p*-*tert*-butyl phenol. Table 4.1 gives some examples of industrial importance.

The problem of consecutive reactions in a homogeneous system has been extensively discussed in textbooks (see e.g., Frost and Pearson, 1961; Levenspiel, 1967; Rodiguin and Rodiguina, 1964). However, when heterogeneous reactions are involved and the diffusion of the solute is important, then an additional factor of mass transfer has to be considered. The basic problem is concerned with the role of diffusion in affecting the selectivity with respect to the intermediate product. This problem has received attention only in the course of the last few years (van de Vusse, 1966; Gehlawat and Sharma, 1970; Harriott, 1970; Chua and Ratcliffe, 1970; Teramoto et al., 1969, 1970; Nakao et al., 1972; and Pangarkar and Sharma, 1974).

Consider a system that can be represented by the following equations:

$$A + Z_1B \xrightarrow{k_2'} C \tag{4.1}$$

$$A + Z_2C \xrightarrow{k_2''} D \tag{4.2}$$

(Stoichiometric factors Z_1 and Z_2 for these steps will be taken as unity.) For the sake of simplicity, we shall assume that the reactions follow second-order kinetics; first order with respect to A and first order with respect to B or C. It is a common observation that in most cases the value of the rate constant for the second step is considerably smaller than that for the first step. For instance, in the case of the alkylation of *p*-cresol with isobutylene in the presence of sulfuric acid as a catalyst, the values of the second-order rate constant at 70°C for the first and second steps are 620 and 40 cm^3/mol sec, respectively (Gehlawat and Sharma, 1970). Similarly, in the case of chlorination of *p*-cresol dissolved in 1,2,4-trichlorobenzene, the values of the second-order rate constant for the first and the second steps at 100°C are 1.9×10^5 and 1.5×10^4 cm^3/mol sec, respectively (Pangarkar and Sharma, 1974). However, there are certain special situations where the rate constant for the second step can be very much greater than that for the first step. Thus, in the case of the reaction between ethylenedichloride and aqueous ammonia, the rate constant for the reaction of ethylenediamine (product of the first step) and ethylenedichloride is expected to be much greater than that for the reaction between ethylenedichloride and ammonia. This observation is based on the fact that there is a close analogy between the rate constants for the reactions of amines and a variety of substrates like alkyl halides, alkene oxides, CO_2, COS, and CS_2 (see, e.g., Sharma, 1965).

For convenience, we shall consider the following specific cases and discuss the effect of mass transfer on the rate of absorption of A and the *selectivity* with respect to the formation of C. The selectivity index is defined as the ratio of the rates of reaction of A with B and C. We shall use the film theory throughout Section 4.1.

1. Both reactions are in the slow or very slow reaction regime (regime 2 or 1).

TABLE 4.1. Industrially Important Examples of Mass Transfer Accompanied by Consecutive Reaction

System	Reference(s)
Chlorination of benzene; side-chain chlorination of toluene	Ratcliffe (1966)
Chlorination of phenol and *p*-cresol	Nakao et al. (1972); Inoue and Kobayashi (1968); Teramoto et al. (1969); Pangarkar and Sharma (1974)
Chlorination of ethylene dichloride	Chua and Ratcliffe (1970)
Chlorination of *n*-decane and other paraffins	van de Vusse (1966)
Hydrochlorination of acetylene	Goldstein and Waddams (1967)
Reaction between C_2H_2 and HF	Kirk and Othmer (1966)
Oligomerization of isobutylene to di- and triisobutylene	Guterbock (1959)
Alkylation of phenol, *p*-cresol, and catechol with isobutylene	Gehlawat and Sharma (1970)
Alkylation of benzene with ethylene with $AlCl_3$ as a catalyst	Goldstein and Waddams (1967)
Nitration of aromatic compounds	Albright (1966, 1967)
Reaction between ethylene dichloride and aqueous ammonia	Leszezynski et al. (1967)

2. The first-step reaction is between regimes 2 and 3 or in regime 3; the second-step reaction is in the slow reaction regime (regime 2).
3. Both reactions are fast pseudo-first-order (regime 3).
4. Fast reactions are accompanied by depletion of B and C in the film (regime between 3 and 4).
5. The first-step reaction is instantaneous (regime 4).

It will be assumed in the following discussion that the rate constant for the second reaction is substantially less than that for the first reaction.

4.1.1. Both Reactions in the Slow or Very Slow Reaction Regime (Regime between 1 and 2)

When both reactions are in the slow or very slow reaction regime, there is no reaction of A while it is diffusing in the film. Both reactions occur in the bulk liquid. The concentration profiles for the various species are shown in Figure 4.1. The following condition should be satisfied:

$$\sqrt{M_{1,\mathrm{o}}} = \frac{\sqrt{D_A k_2'[B_o]}}{k_L} \ll 1 \qquad (4.3)$$

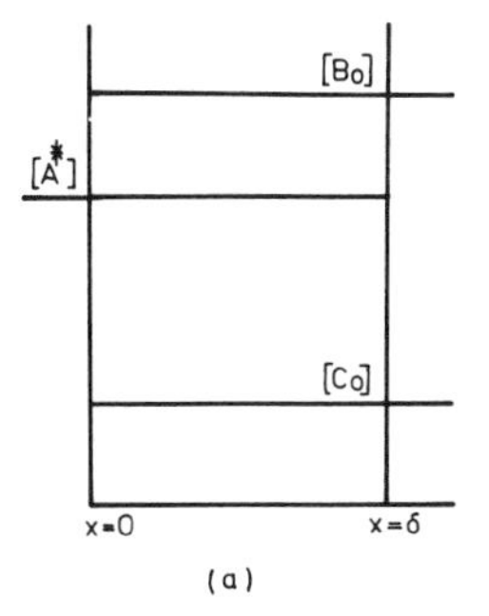

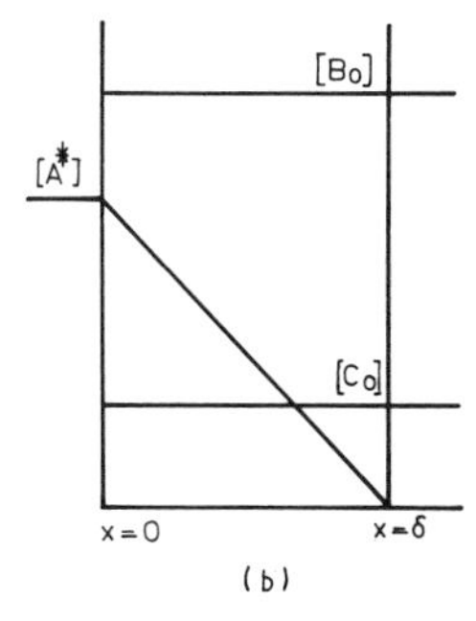

Figure 4.1. Typical concentration profiles for the case when both reactions are (*a*) very slow; (*b*) slow.

Since $k_2'' \ll k_2'$, it follows that

$$\sqrt{M_{2,o}} = \sqrt{D_A k_2'' C_o}/k_L \ll 1$$

The concentration of dissolved A in the bulk would be a finite quantity or 0, depending on whether the reaction occurring in the bulk liquid is rapid. First, let us assume that the concentration of A in the bulk liquid is some finite quantity $[A_o]$. Then, the relative rates of reaction of A with B and C would be

$$\frac{R_B a}{R_C a} = \frac{lk_2'[B_o][A_o]}{lk_2''[C_o][A_o]} = \frac{k_2'[B_o]}{k_2''[C_o]} \quad (4.4)$$

The total amount of A reacting in the bulk liquid would be

$$R_A a = R_B a + R_C a = (lk_2'[B_o] + lk_2''[C_o])[A_o] \quad (4.5)$$

At steady state, the amount of A reacting in the bulk liquid is equal to the amount of A transported through diffusion in the film. Hence,

$$R_A a = k_L a([A^*] - [A_o]) \quad (4.6)$$

Elimination of the unknown term $[A_o]$ in Eqs. 4.5 and 4.6 gives the following equation for the rate of absorption of A:

$$R_A a = \frac{(lk_2'[B_o] + lk_2''[C_o])k_L a}{(lk_2'[B_o] + lk_2''[C_o]) + k_L a}[A^*] \quad (4.7)$$

Since the relative rate of reaction of A with B and C is given by the ratio $k_2'[B_o]/k_2''[C_o]$, it appears that although mass transfer affects the rate of reaction of A, it does not significantly affect the selectivity with respect to C. The amount of B and C reacting with A would be as follows:

$$R_B a = \frac{(lk_2'[B_o])k_L a}{(lk_2'[B_o] + lk_2''[C_o]) + k_L a}[A^*] \quad (4.8)$$

and

$$R_C a = \frac{(lk_2''[C_o])k_L a}{(lk_2'[B_o] + lk_2''[C_o]) + k_L a}[A^*] \quad (4.9)$$

Since the term $[B_o]/[C_o]$ is lower in a continuous backmix reactor than in a continuous plug flow reactor, the selectivity with respect to C would be poorer in the backmix unit. In the case of a batch unit, the concentration of C increases with time and hence the yield of C starts decreasing with time. In such cases it is advisable to restrict the level of conversion with respect to B to a low value so that the maximum selectivity with respect to C can be realized, if desired.

The effect of temperature on the selectivity with respect to the intermediate substance C will be insignificant unless the difference between the activation energy for the two steps is significant and there exists a finite concentration of A in the bulk liquid phase.

4.1.2. First-Step Reaction Is Fast Pseudo-First-Order (Regime 3) or between Regimes 2 and 3; Second-Step Is in the Slow Reaction Regime (Regime 2)

First step between Regimes 2 and 3

Here a considerable amount of A reacts with B in the film but a part of the reaction between A and B occurs in the bulk. There is, however, no free A in the bulk. The reaction between A and C does not occur in the film and takes place only in the bulk. Since a part of A leaves the film unreacted, it will undergo reactions with B as well as with C in the bulk. Figure 4.2 shows the concentration profiles. Our objective is to find the amounts of A that react with species B and C.

This mechanism will be valid when the following

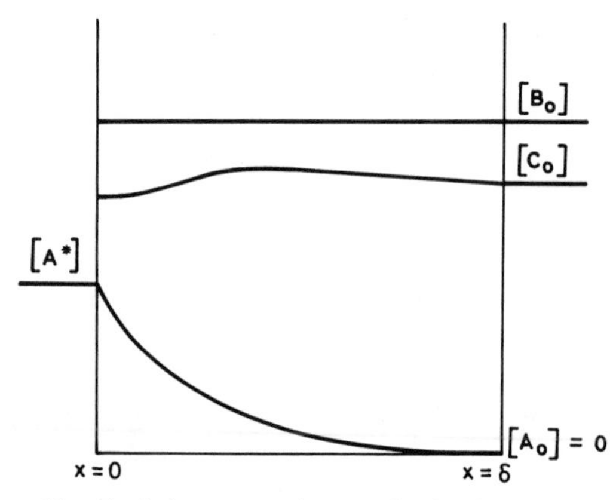

Figure 4.2. Typical concentration profiles for the case when the first-step reaction is fast pseudo-first-order and the second-step reaction is slow or very slow.

conditions hold:

$$\frac{\sqrt{D_A k_2'[B_o]}}{k_L} \geqslant 1 \qquad (4.10a)$$

$$\ll \frac{[B_o]}{[A^*]}\sqrt{\frac{D_B}{D_A}} \qquad (4.10b)$$

$$\frac{\sqrt{D_A k_2''[C_o]}}{k_L} \ll 1 \qquad (4.10c)$$

It would be expected that the selectivity with respect to C would be very high for this mechanism, particularly when all of A reacts in the film.

The basic differential equation governing the transport of A for this case is

$$D_A \frac{d^2[A]}{dx^2} = k_2'[B_o][A] \qquad (4.11)$$

where it has been assumed that there is no depletion of B in the film ($[B_i] \simeq [B_o]$).

The boundary conditions are as follows.

$$x = 0: \quad [A] = [A^*], \quad [B] = [B_o], \quad \frac{d[B]}{dx} = 0$$

$$x = \delta: \quad [A] = 0$$

The total specific rate of absorption of A is given by Eq. 4.12, which is obtained from the solution of Eq. 4.11 and noting that

$$R_A = -D_A\left(\frac{d[A]}{dx}\right)_{x=0}$$

$$R_A = \frac{[A^*]\sqrt{D_A k_2'[B_o]}}{\tanh\left(\dfrac{\sqrt{D_A k_2'[B_o]}}{k_L}\right)} \qquad (4.12)$$

The flux of A at the point x equal to δ is given by

$$-D_A\left(\frac{d[A]}{dx}\right)_{x=\delta} = \frac{[A^*]\sqrt{D_A k_2'[B_o]}}{\sinh\left(\dfrac{\sqrt{D_A k_2'[B_o]}}{k_L}\right)} \qquad (4.13)$$

This will be the sum of the rates of B and C reacting with A in the bulk liquid. The relative rates of reaction in the bulk would be given by the ratio $k_2'[B_o]/k_2''[C_o]$. Hence the amount of C reacting would be

$$R_C = \frac{[A^*]\sqrt{D_A k_2'[B_o]}}{\sinh\left(\dfrac{\sqrt{D_A k_2'[B_o]}}{k_L}\right)} \frac{k_2''[C_o]}{k_2'[B_o] + k_2''[C_o]} \qquad (4.14)$$

The amount of B reacting by difference is

$$R_B = \frac{[A^*]\sqrt{D_A k_2'[B_o]}}{\sinh\left(\dfrac{\sqrt{D_A k_2'[B_o]}}{k_L}\right)} \times\left[\cosh\left(\frac{\sqrt{D_A k_2'[B_o]}}{k_L}\right) - \frac{k_2''[C_o]}{k_2'[B_o] + k_2''[C_o]}\right] \qquad (4.15)$$

Equation 4.15 assumes that no C reacts in the film. From the foregoing equations it is seen that a decrease in k_L marginally decreases the rate of absorption of A but would improve the selectivity with respect to C.

First Step in Regime 3

When all of A is consumed in the film, no free dissolved A reaches the bulk liquid phase and the selectivity with respect to C is very high. The necessary condition for all of A to react in the film is given by the following expression:

$$\frac{\sqrt{D_A k_2'[B_o]}}{k_L} > 3 \qquad (4.16)$$

Example

Consider the following example of the chlorination of *p*-cresol dissolved in 1,2,4-trichlorobenzene at 100°C (Pangarkar and Sharma, 1974)

$$D_{Cl_2} = 3 \times 10^{-5}\ \text{cm}^2/\text{sec}$$

Concentration of *p*-cresol

$$= [\mathrm{B_o}]$$

$$= 4.2 \times 10^{-3}\ \mathrm{mol/cm^3}$$

$$k_2' = 1.9 \times 10^5\ \mathrm{cm^3/mol\ sec}$$

Concentration of monochloro-*p*-cresol

$$= [\mathrm{C_o}]$$

$$= 1.5 \times 10^{-3}\ \mathrm{mol/cm^3}$$

$$k_2'' = 1.5 \times 10^4\ \mathrm{cm^3/mol\ sec}$$

$$\frac{D_\mathrm{B}}{D_\mathrm{A}} = 0.72$$

The value of the liquid-side mass transfer coefficient, k_L, in a bubble column at a gas velocity of 15 cm/sec is expected to be around 4×10^{-2} cm/sec. Thus, the values of the various parameters are

$$\frac{\sqrt{D_\mathrm{A} k_2' [\mathrm{B_o}]}}{k_\mathrm{L}} = 3.86, \qquad \frac{\sqrt{D_\mathrm{A} k_2'' [\mathrm{C_o}]}}{k_\mathrm{L}} = 0.65$$

For a partial pressure of chlorine of 0.8 atm, the value of $[\mathrm{B_o}]/[\mathrm{A^*}]\sqrt{D_\mathrm{B}/D_\mathrm{A}}$ can be shown to be approximately 17. Thus, the conditions given by expressions 4.10b, 4.10c, and 4.16 are satisfied. These conditions will favor very high selectivity with respect to monochloro-*p*-cresol and the experimental data of Pangarkar and Sharma (1974) confirm this prediction.

An increase in the value of k_L may shift the regime of the first step from regime 3 to regime 2 in which no A would react in the film. Under these conditions, the selectivity with respect to C will be adversely affected.

4.1.3. Both Reactions Fast Pseudo-First-Order (Regime 3)

In certain circumstances the reaction of A with both B and C may occur entirely in the film and yet the concentrations of B and C at the interface may be equal to their respective bulk concentrations. Typical concentration profiles for this case are shown in Figure 4.3a.

The necessary conditions for this situation are given by expressions 4.10b, 4.16, and 4.17.

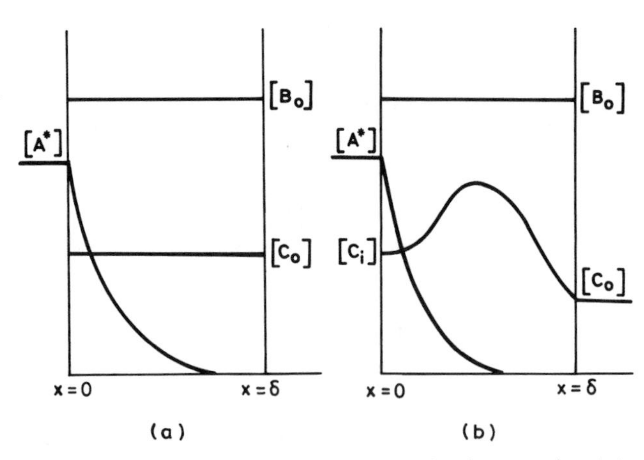

Figure 4.3. Typical concentration profiles for the case when (*a*) both reactions are fast pseudo-first-order; (b) the second-step reaction becomes second order because of the generation of species C.

$$1 \ll \frac{\sqrt{D_\mathrm{A} k_2'' [\mathrm{C_o}]}}{k_\mathrm{L}} \ll \frac{[\mathrm{C_o}]}{[\mathrm{A^*}]}\sqrt{\frac{D_\mathrm{C}}{D_\mathrm{A}}} \tag{4.17}$$

The following differential equation is valid:

$$D_\mathrm{A}\frac{d^2[\mathrm{A}]}{dx^2} = (k_2'[\mathrm{B_o}] + k_2''[\mathrm{C_o}])[\mathrm{A}] \tag{4.18}$$

The boundary conditions are as follows:

$$x = 0: \quad [\mathrm{A}] = [\mathrm{A^*}], \quad [\mathrm{B}] = [\mathrm{B_o}], \quad [\mathrm{C}] = [\mathrm{C_o}],$$

$$\frac{d[\mathrm{B}]}{dx} = \frac{d[\mathrm{C}]}{dx} = 0, \quad R_\mathrm{A} = -D_\mathrm{A}\frac{d[\mathrm{A}]}{dx} \tag{4.19}$$

$$x = \delta: \quad [\mathrm{A}] = 0 \tag{4.20}$$

The solution of Eq. 4.18 can be obtained by standard techniques. The specific rate of absorption of A is given by

$$R_\mathrm{A} = [\mathrm{A^*}]\sqrt{D_\mathrm{A}(k_2'[\mathrm{B_o}] + k_2''[\mathrm{C_o}])} \tag{4.21}$$

The rates of reaction of the species B and C are given by the following equations, respectively:

$$R_\mathrm{B} = R_\mathrm{A}\frac{k_2'[\mathrm{B_o}]}{k_2'[\mathrm{B_o}] + k_2''[\mathrm{C_o}]} \tag{4.22}$$

$$R_C = R_A \frac{k_2'[C_o]}{k_2'[B_o] + k_2''[C_o]} \quad (4.23)$$

The quantity $k_2'[B_o]/k_2''[C_o]$ will determine the selectivity, and mass transfer factors have no effect on the selectivity.

In a general case where the initial bulk liquid concentration of the intermediate species C is low or negligible, this regime is unlikely to hold. The intermediate species is generated as a result of the first-step reaction. Thus, when the first-step reaction occurs in the film, the concentration of the intermediate species in the film will be significantly different from the bulk liquid concentration and will vary from point to point in the film (see Figure 4.3b). The assumption of a constant concentration equal to $[C_o]$ will probably not be valid. However, in these cases where the bulk liquid concentration of the intermediate is relatively high and the solute-gas partial pressure is relatively low, the distortion of the C profile may not be significant and the concentration of C at all the points in the film may be practically the same as $[C_o]$.

In some cases, an increase in the value of k_L can result in a situation where the first step continues to be in regime 3 but the second step is shifted to regime 2. In such situations, the selectivity with respect to C will improve with an increase in the value of k_L. Consider the following case:

$$D_A = D_B = D_C = 1 \times 10^{-5}\ \text{cm}^2/\text{sec}$$

$$[A^*] = 5 \times 10^{-5}\ \text{mol/cm}^3$$

$$Z_1 = Z_2 = 1$$

$$k_2' = 1 \times 10^5\ \text{cm}^3/\text{mol sec}$$

$$k_2'' = 5 \times 10^3\ \text{cm}^3/\text{mol sec}$$

$$[B_o] = 3 \times 10^{-3}\ \text{mol/cm}^3$$

$$[C_o] = 1 \times 10^{-3}\ \text{mol/cm}^3$$

We shall consider two values of k_L, 2×10^{-3} cm/sec and 1.4×10^{-2} cm/sec. The values of the parameters $\sqrt{D_A k_2'[B_o]}/k_L$ and $\sqrt{D_A k_2''[C_o]}/k_L$ are 27.5 and 3.5, respectively, when $k_L = 2 \times 10^{-3}$ cm/sec. The value of $[B_o]/[A^*]$ and $[C_o]/[A^*]$ are 60 and 20, respectively. Thus we find that both steps conform to regime 3 and A is consumed in the film. Both B and C react with A in the film and the selectivity with respect to C will be poor.

For k_L equal to 1.4×10^{-2} cm/sec, the value of $\sqrt{D_A k_2'[B_o]}/k_L$ is 3.93, which indicates that the reaction of B with A is still in regime 3. However, the value of $\sqrt{D_A k_2''[C_o]}/k_L$ is now only 0.5 and hence practically no A will react with C in the film. The selectivity with respect to C will be remarkably good for this case, because the concentration of dissolved A in bulk is now negligible and the reaction between A and C occurs in the bulk only.

4.1.4. Fast Reactions Accompanied by Depletion of Reactant B and Intermediate C in the Film (Regime between 3 and 4 for Both Steps)

An interesting case arises when there is depletion of reactant B in the film (Figure 4.4). Because of the depletion, the concentration of reactant B varies from point to point and is substantially different from the bulk liquid concentration. The ratio $k_2'[B]/k_2''[C]$ will determine the relative rates of reaction of B and C. Since the concentration of B in the film is substantially lower than that in the bulk, the ratio $[B]/[C]$ will always be lower than $[B_o]/[C_o]$. Therefore, the selectivity with respect to C will be adversely affected as a result of the depletion of B.

Pangarkar and Sharma (1974) have considered this problem. The relevant differential equations are as follows:

$$D_A \frac{d^2[A]}{dx^2} = k_2'[A][B] + k_2''[A][C] \quad (4.24)$$

$$D_B \frac{d^2[B]}{dx^2} = k_2'[A][B] \quad (4.25)$$

$$D_C \frac{d^2[C]}{dx^2} = k_2''[A][C] - k_2'[A][B] \quad (4.26)$$

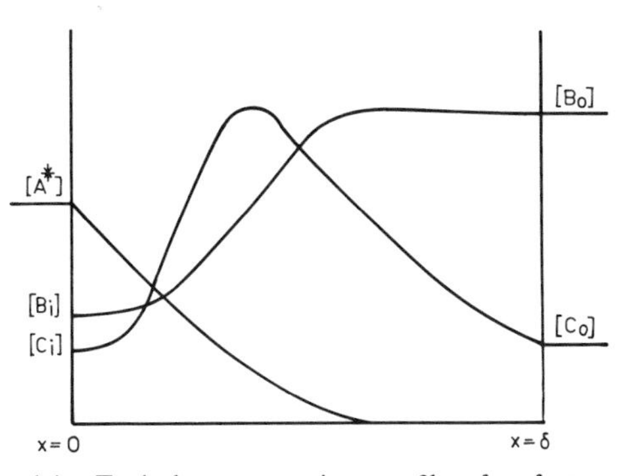

Figure 4.4. Typical concentration profiles for fast reactions accompanied by depletion of reactant B.

The boundary conditions for these equations are

$$x = 0: \quad [A] = [A^*], \quad [B] = [B_i], \quad [C] = [C_i],$$

$$-D_A\left(\frac{d[A]}{dx}\right) = R_A,$$

$$\frac{d[B]}{dx} = \frac{d[C]}{dx} = 0 \tag{4.27}$$

$$x = \delta: \quad [A] = 0, \quad [B] = [B_o], \quad [C] = [C_o] \tag{4.28}$$

The solution of Eq. 4.24 can be obtained by a procedure similar to that used by Hikita and Asai (1964) for gas absorption with a single reaction. The solution is given by

$$[A] = \frac{[A^*]\sinh\left[\sqrt{\dfrac{k'}{D_A}}(\delta - x)\right]}{\sinh\left(\sqrt{\dfrac{k'}{D_A}}\,\delta\right)} \tag{4.29}$$

where

$$k' = k_2'[B_i] + k_2''[C_i] \tag{4.30}$$

The specific rate of mass transfer is now obtained as follows:

$$R_A = -D_A\left(\frac{d[A]}{dx}\right)_{x=0} = \frac{[A^*]\sqrt{D_A k'}}{\tanh\left(\dfrac{\sqrt{D_A k'}}{k_L}\right)} \tag{4.31}$$

Since for this case $\sqrt{D_A k'}/k_L$ is greater than 3 we have

$$R_A = [A^*]\sqrt{D_A k'} \tag{4.32}$$

The amounts of A reacting with B and C are, respectively

$$R_B = R_A \frac{k_2'[B_i]}{k'} \tag{4.33}$$

and

$$R_C = R_A \frac{k_2''[C_i]}{k'} \tag{4.34}$$

The selectivity with respect to the intermediate species C is indicated by a selectivity index, S, defined as the ratio of the rate of reaction of A with B to the rate of reaction of A with C. The selectivity index S is therefore given by

$$S = \frac{R_B}{R_C} = \frac{k_2'[B_i]}{k_2''[C_i]} \tag{4.35}$$

or

$$S = \frac{M_{1,i}}{M_{2,i}} \tag{4.36}$$

where

$$M_{1,i} = \frac{D_A k_2'[B_i]}{k_L^2} \tag{4.36a}$$

$$M_{2,i} = \frac{D_A k_2''[C_i]}{k_L^2} \tag{4.36b}$$

Equation 4.35 (or Eqs. 4.36a, b) contains the unknown concentration terms $[B_i]$ and $[C_i]$. The procedure employed for predicting $[B_i]$ and $[C_i]$ is as follows.

We first replace the variable concentration terms [B] and [C] in Eqs. 4.24, 4.25, and 4.26 by $[B_i]$ and $[C_i]$. Equation 4.25 is then subtracted from Eq. 4.24 to give

$$D_A\frac{d^2[A]}{dx^2} = D_B\frac{d^2[B]}{dx^2} + k_2''[C_i][A] \tag{4.37}$$

The concentration term [A] in Eq. 4.37 is now replaced by the value given by Eq. 4.29. Thus,

$$D_A\frac{d^2[A]}{dx^2} = D_B\frac{d^2[B]}{dx^2} + \frac{k_2''[C_i][A^*]\sinh\left[\sqrt{\dfrac{k'}{D_A}}(\delta - x)\right]}{\sinh\left(\sqrt{\dfrac{k'}{D_A}}\,\delta\right)} \tag{4.38}$$

Equation 4.38 is now integrated twice using the boundary conditions given by Eqs. 4.27 and 4.28. On simplifying we get

$$\frac{M_{1,i}}{M_{1,o}} = \frac{1}{\phi_{a,1} - 1} \times \left(\phi_{a,1} - \frac{M_{1,i}}{\sqrt{M_{1,i} + M_{2,i}}} - \frac{M_{2,i}}{M_{1,i} + M_{2,i}}\right) \tag{4.39}$$

where $M_{1,i}$ and $M_{2,i}$ are defined by Eqs. 4.36a and 4.36b, respectively;

$$\phi_{a,1} = 1 + \frac{[B_o]}{[A^*]}\frac{D_B}{D_A} = 1 + q_1 \quad (4.39a)$$

and

$$\sqrt{M_{1,o}} = \frac{\sqrt{D_A k_2' [B_o]}}{k_L} \quad (4.39b)$$

Similar operations with Eqs. 4.24 and 4.26 yield the following result:

$$\frac{M_{2,i}}{M_{2,o}} = \frac{1}{\phi_{a,2} - 1}\left[\phi_{a,2} - \sqrt{M_{1,i} + M_{2,i}} + \frac{2M_{1,i}}{\sqrt{M_{1,i} + M_{2,i}}} \times \left(1 - \frac{1}{\sqrt{M_{1,i} + M_{2,i}}}\right)\right] \quad (4.40)$$

where

$$\phi_{a,2} = 1 + \frac{[C_o]}{[A^*]}\frac{D_C}{D_A} = 1 + q_2 \quad (4.40a)$$

and

$$\sqrt{M_{2,o}} = \frac{\sqrt{D_A k_2'' [C_o]}}{k_L} \quad (4.40b)$$

Equations 4.39 and 4.40 can be solved simultaneously for $M_{1,i}$ and $M_{2,i}$.

The selectivity index S can now be calculated from Eq. 4.36. The total specific rate of mass transfer can be obtained by writing Eq. 4.32 in the following form:

$$R_A = k_L [A^*]\sqrt{M_{1,i} + M_{2,i}} \quad (4.41)$$

Example

For the chlorination of a mixture of *p*-cresol and monochloro-*p*-cresol dissolved in 1,2,4-trichlorobenzene the following data are available (Pangarkar, 1972):

$$\text{Temperature} = 100^\circ\text{C}$$

$$k_2' = 1.9 \times 10^5 \text{ cm}^3/\text{mol sec}$$

$$k_2'' = 1.5 \times 10^4 \text{ cm}^3/\text{mol sec}$$

$$[p\text{-cresol}] = 4 \times 10^{-3} \text{ mol/cm}^3$$

$$[\text{monochloro-}p\text{-cresol}] = 1.8 \times 10^{-3} \text{ mol/cm}^3$$

$$D_{Cl_2} = 3.10 \times 10^{-5} \text{ cm}^2/\text{sec}$$

$$\text{Pressure} = 1 \text{ atm}$$

$$[A^*] = 1.32 \times 10^{-4} \text{ mol/cm}^3$$

$$k_L = 5.1 \times 10^{-3} \text{ cm/sec}$$

$$\frac{D_{p\text{-cresol}}}{D_{Cl_2}} = 0.72; \qquad \frac{D_{\text{monochloro-}p\text{-cresol}}}{D_{Cl_2}} = 0.63$$

Calculate the selectivity index for monochloro-*p*-cresol formation and obtain the relative rate of formation of mono- and dichloro-*p*-cresol.

In order to determine the regime for the first- and second-step reactions, the values of $\sqrt{M_{1,o}}$, $\sqrt{M_{2,o}}$, and $\phi_{a,1}$ and $\phi_{a,2}$ should be known.

$$\frac{\sqrt{D_A k_2' [B_o]}}{k_L} = \frac{\sqrt{3.1 \times 10^{-5} \times 1.9 \times 10^5 \times 4 \times 10^{-3}}}{5.1 \times 10^{-3}} = 30$$

$$\frac{[B_o]}{[A^*]}\sqrt{\frac{D_B}{D_A}} = 25.7$$

Since the values of $\sqrt{M_{1,o}}$ and $([B_o]/[A^*])\sqrt{D_B/D_A}$ are comparable, the first-step reaction will occur in the depletion regime. Similarly, for the second-step reaction, the values of $\sqrt{M_{2,o}}$ and $([C_o]/[A^*])\sqrt{D_C/D_A}$ are found to be 5.67 and 10.8, respectively. Thus, since $\sqrt{M_{2,o}}$ is less than $([C_o]/[A^*])\sqrt{D_C/D_A}$, the second-step reaction should be in the pseudo-first-order regime. However, as a result of the generation of the species C in the film, the concentration of species C varies from point to point in the film and $[C_i]$ is substantially different from $[C_o]$. Therefore, the second-step reaction has also to be treated as a second-order reaction.

From the foregoing discussion it is clear that both the first- and second-step reactions occur in the regime between 3 and 4 and the treatment given in Section 4.1.4 should be applicable.

For the calculation of the selectivity index S and the relative rates of formation of species C and D, the values of $\sqrt{M_{1,i}}$ and $\sqrt{M_{2,i}}$ are required. Equations 4.39 and 4.40 can be solved simultaneously for this purpose.

Let $\sqrt{M_{1,i}}$ and $\sqrt{M_{2,i}}$ be equal to 19.5 and 7.9, respectively. With these values, and $\phi_{a,1}$ and $\phi_{a,2}$ equal to 31 and 13.6 (in calculating $\phi_{a,1}$ and $\phi_{a,2}$, we have assumed that $D_A = D_B = D_C$), respectively, the left-hand side of Eq. 4.39 is

$$\frac{M_{1,i}}{M_{1,o}} = \frac{380}{900} = 0.422$$

The right-hand side of Eq. 4.39 is equal to 0.422. Since the values of two sides of Eq. 4.39 agree, this set of values of $\sqrt{M_{1,i}}$ and $\sqrt{M_{2,i}}$ is accepted as a preliminary estimate to be tested in Eq. 4.40. The left-hand side of Eq. 4.40 is

$$\frac{M_{2,i}}{M_{2,o}} = \frac{62.5}{29.1} = 2.14$$

The right-hand side of Eq. 4.40 is 2.13. Here also, the two sides of Eq. 4.40 agree. Therefore, the values of $\sqrt{M_{1,i}}$ and $\sqrt{M_{2,i}}$ are

$$\sqrt{M_{1,i}} = 19.5, \qquad \sqrt{M_{2,i}} = 7.9$$

This value of $\sqrt{M_{2,i}}$ (i.e., 7.9) is much greater than that of $\sqrt{M_{2,o}}$ (i.e., 5.67). Thus, it is apparent that the generation of species C in the film increases the concentration of C in the film and $[C_i]$ is much greater than $[C_o]$. This increase in the concentration adversely affects the selectivity, as $M_{2,i}$ appears in the denominator of Eq. 4.36. The selectivity index S is now obtained from Eq. 4.36:

$$S = \frac{M_{1,i}}{M_{2,i}} = \frac{380}{62.5} = 6.08$$

The rate of absorption of Cl_2 is given by Eq. 4.41:

$$R_A = k_L[A^*]\sqrt{M_{1,i} + M_{2,i}}$$

$$= 5.1 \times 10^{-3} \times 1.32 \times 10^{-4}\sqrt{380 + 62.5}$$

$$= 1.42 \times 10^{-5} \text{ mol/cm}^2 \text{ sec}$$

The specific rate of reaction of A with B, R_B, is

$$R_B = R_A \frac{M_{1,i}}{M_{1,i} + M_{2,i}}$$

$$= 1.42 \times 10^{-5} \times \frac{380}{442.5}$$

$$= 1.22 \times 10^{-5} \text{ mol/cm}^2 \text{ sec}$$

Similarly, the specific rate of reaction of A with C, R_C is

$$R_C = R_A \frac{M_{2,i}}{M_{1,i} + M_{2,i}}$$

$$= 1.42 \times 10^{-5} \times \frac{62.5}{442.5}$$

$$= 2 \times 10^{-6} \text{ mol/cm}^2 \text{ sec}$$

4.1.5. First-Step Reaction Instantaneous (Regime 4)

Here the reaction between A and B is so fast that both species are completely consumed by the reaction at a reaction plane, λ, close to the interface. The condition required to be satisfied for the first-step reaction to be instantaneous is given by

$$\frac{\sqrt{D_A k_2'[B_o]}}{k_L} \gg \frac{[B_o]}{[A^*]}\sqrt{\frac{D_B}{D_A}} \tag{4.42}$$

The concentration of the species A is zero beyond the reaction plane (see Figure 4.5). The reaction between A and C, therefore, has to occur in the region between the interface and the reaction plane.

As explained in Section 4.1.4, when the first-step reaction occurs in the film, the concentration of species C varies from point to point in the film, even when the conditions for the second-step reaction to be pseudo-first-order are satisfied. (Under certain conditions, the variation in [C] may be neglected; see Section 4.1.4.)

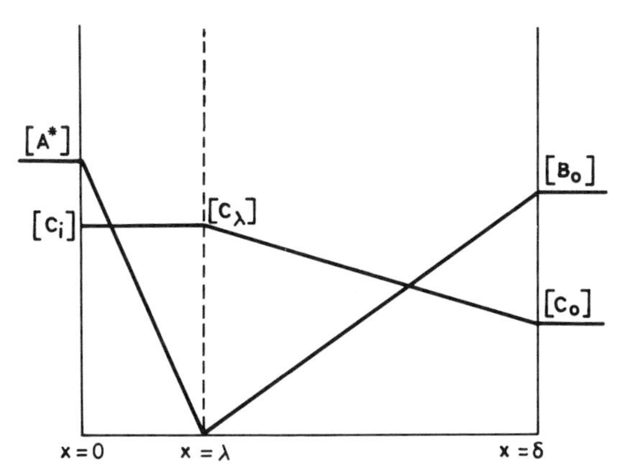

Figure 4.5. Typical concentration profiles for the case when the first-step reaction is instantaneous.

In general the differential equations for this case are

$$0 < x < \lambda; \qquad D_A \frac{d^2[\mathrm{A}]}{dx^2} = k_2''[\mathrm{A}][\mathrm{C}] \quad (4.43)$$

$$\lambda < x < \delta; \qquad D_B \frac{d^2[\mathrm{B}]}{dx^2} = 0 \quad (4.44)$$

The boundary conditions for these equations are

$$x = 0: \qquad [\mathrm{A}] = [\mathrm{A}^*], \quad [\mathrm{C}] = [\mathrm{C_i}], \quad \frac{d[\mathrm{C}]}{dx} = 0 \quad (4.45)$$

$$x = \lambda: \qquad [\mathrm{A}] = [\mathrm{B}] = 0, \quad [\mathrm{C}] = [\mathrm{C}_\lambda],$$

$$-D_A \frac{d[\mathrm{A}]}{dx} = D_B \frac{d[\mathrm{B}]}{dx} \quad (4.46)$$

$$x = \delta: \qquad [\mathrm{B}] = [\mathrm{B_o}], \quad [\mathrm{C}] = [\mathrm{C_o}] \quad (4.47)$$

When the variable [C] term is replaced by $[\mathrm{C_i}]$, Eq. 4.43 becomes

$$D_A \frac{d^2[\mathrm{A}]}{dx^2} = k_2''[\mathrm{C_i}][\mathrm{A}] \quad (4.48)$$

The solution of Eq. 4.48 is

$$[\mathrm{A}] = \frac{[\mathrm{A}^*]\sinh\left[\sqrt{\dfrac{k_2''[\mathrm{C_i}]}{D_A}}(\lambda - x)\right]}{\sinh\left(\sqrt{\dfrac{k_2''[\mathrm{C_i}]}{D_A}}\,\lambda\right)} \quad (4.49)$$

The rate of absorption is now obtained, noting that

$$R_A = -D_A\left(\frac{d[\mathrm{A}]}{dx}\right)_{x=0}$$

Thus,

$$R_A = \frac{[\mathrm{A}^*]\sqrt{D_A k_2''[\mathrm{C_i}]}}{\tanh\left[\dfrac{\sqrt{D_A k_2''[\mathrm{C_i}]}}{k_L}\left(\dfrac{\lambda}{\delta}\right)\right]} \quad (4.50)$$

or

$$R_A = \frac{[\mathrm{A}^*]\sqrt{D_A k_2''[\mathrm{C_i}]}}{\tanh\left(\dfrac{\sqrt{D_A k_2''[\mathrm{C_i}]}}{k_L'}\right)} \quad (4.51)$$

where $k_L' = k_L(\delta/\lambda)$. An approximate estimate of δ/λ can be obtained by assuming that there is no second step (see sec. 2.6)

$$\frac{\delta}{\lambda} \approx \frac{[\mathrm{B_o}]}{[\mathrm{A}^*]}\frac{D_B}{D_A}$$

$$\approx \phi_{a,1}$$

(provided that $[\mathrm{B_o}] \gg [\mathrm{A}^*]$). Therefore, $k_L' \approx k_L \phi_{a,1}$ and

$$R_A \approx \frac{[\mathrm{A}^*]\sqrt{D_A k_2''[\mathrm{C_i}]}}{\tanh\left(\dfrac{\sqrt{D_A k_2''[\mathrm{C_i}]}}{k_L \phi_{a,1}}\right)} \quad (4.52)$$

The case of particular interest is discussed next: As $\phi_{a,1}$ increases, k_L' increases and $\sqrt{D_A k_2''[\mathrm{C_i}]}/k_L'$ decreases. In the limit as $\sqrt{D_A k_2''[\mathrm{C_i}]}/k_L' \to 0$,

$$\tanh\left(\frac{\sqrt{D_A k_2''[\mathrm{C_i}]}}{k_L'}\right) \to \frac{\sqrt{D_A k_2''[\mathrm{C_i}]}}{k_L'}$$

or

$$\tanh\left(\frac{\sqrt{D_A k_2''[\mathrm{C_i}]}}{k_L'}\right) \to \frac{\sqrt{D_A k_2''[\mathrm{C_i}]}}{k_L \phi_{a,1}} \quad (4.53)$$

noting that $k'_L \approx k_L \phi_{a,1}$. Substituting from Eq. 4.53 into Eq. 4.51, we get

$$R_A \approx k_L \phi_{a,1}[A^*] \tag{4.54}$$

This equation is the same as that for the specific rate of mass transfer for the case when the first-step reaction is instantaneous and no C is present. Thus, when $\phi_{a,1}$ is very much greater than 1, the reaction between A and C will be negligible and a very high selectivity with respect to the intermediate can be obtained.

For a quantitative estimate of the selectivity index S for the general case, λ/δ and $[C_i]$ must be known. From the foregoing discussion it is evident that because of the high k'_L values, the value of $\sqrt{D_A k''_2 [C_i]}/k'_L$ is substantially lower than that of $\sqrt{D_A k''_2 [C_i]}/k_L$. Also, because of the generation of species C in the film, the concentration of species C at any point in the film is likely to be substantially greater than that in the bulk liquid phase, $[C_o]$. Therefore, the quantity $[C_i]/[A^*]$ will be much greater than $[C_o]/[A^*]$. Thus, the following inequality is likely to hold:

$$\frac{\sqrt{D_A k''_2 [C_i]}}{k'_L} \ll \frac{[C_i]}{[A^*]}\sqrt{\frac{D_C}{D_A}} \tag{4.55}$$

The condition given by expression 4.55 indicates that there is no depletion of species C in the region between the interface and the reaction plane. In other words, the concentration of species C at the interface, $[C_i]$, and that at the reaction plane, $[C_\lambda]$, are practically the same. Therefore, Eq. 4.51 can be written as

$$R_A = \frac{[A^*]\sqrt{D_A k''_2 [C_\lambda]}}{\tanh\left(\dfrac{\sqrt{D_A k''_2 [C_\lambda]}}{k'_L}\right)} \tag{4.56}$$

$[C_\lambda]$ is obtained as follows: A mass balance for the species C (when $\delta \gg \lambda$) gives

rate of generation = rate of transport from the reaction plane into the bulk liquid phase (4.57)

or

$$\frac{D_B}{(\delta - \lambda)}[B_o] = \frac{D_C}{\delta - \lambda}([C_\lambda] - [C_o]) \tag{4.58}$$

Therefore,

$$[C_\lambda] = [C_o] + [B_o]\frac{D_B}{D_C} \tag{4.59}$$

When $\lambda \ll \delta$, λ/δ is obtained by taking a mass balance at the reaction plane:

$$-D_A\left(\frac{d[A]}{dx}\right)_{x=\lambda} = \frac{D_B[B_o]}{\delta - \lambda} \tag{4.60}$$

or

$$\frac{[A^*]\sqrt{D_A k''_2 [C_\lambda]}}{\sinh\left[\sqrt{M_{2,\lambda}}(\lambda/\delta)\right]} = \frac{D_B[B_o]}{\delta - \lambda} \tag{4.61}$$

where

$$\sqrt{M_{2,\lambda}} = \frac{\sqrt{D_A k''_2 [C_\lambda]}}{k_L} \tag{4.62}$$

On simplification Eq. 4.61 yields the following equation:

$$\frac{1 - \lambda/\delta}{\sinh\left[\sqrt{M_{2,\lambda}}(\lambda/\delta)\right]} = \frac{\phi_{a,1} - 1}{\sqrt{M_{2,\lambda}}} \tag{4.63}$$

Equation 4.63 can be solved for λ/δ by a trial-and-error procedure.

The specific rate of the second step reaction, R_C is

$$R_C = R_A - R_B$$

The selectivity index S is then obtained as

$$S = \frac{R_B}{R_A - R_B}$$

Example

It is desired to estimate the selectivity index for the following conditions:

$$[B_o] = 2.2 \times 10^{-3}\ \text{mol/cm}^3$$

$$[C_o] = 1.4 \times 10^{-3}\ \text{mol/cm}^3$$

$$[A^*] = 2.5 \times 10^{-4}\ \text{mol/cm}^3$$

$$D_A = 3.1 \times 10^{-5}\ \text{cm}^2\text{/sec}$$

$$k_L = 3 \times 10^{-3}\ \text{cm/sec}$$

$$Z_1 = Z_2 = 1$$

$$k''_2 = 1.5 \times 10^4\ \text{cm}^3\text{/mol sec}$$

The reaction between A and B is instantaneous. For the purpose of calculation the diffusivities of the species A, B, and C may be assumed to be equal.

The value of $[C_\lambda]$ is given by Eq. 4.59. Thus,

$$[C_\lambda] = [C_o] + [B_o]$$

$$= (1.4 + 2.2) \times 10^{-3}\ \text{mol/cm}^3$$

$$= 3.6 \times 10^{-3}\ \text{mol/cm}^3$$

$$\phi_{a,1} = 1 + \frac{[B_o]}{[A^*]}$$

$$= 1 + \frac{2.2 \times 10^{-3}}{2.5 \times 10^{-4}}$$

$$= 9.8$$

$$\sqrt{M_{2,\lambda}} = \frac{\sqrt{D_A k_2''[C_\lambda]}}{k_L}$$

$$= \frac{\sqrt{3.1 \times 10^{-5} \times 1.5 \times 10^4 \times 3.6 \times 10^{-3}}}{3 \times 10^{-3}}$$

$$= 13.6$$

The value of λ/δ is obtained from Eq. 4.63 by a trial-and-error procedure. Let λ/δ be equal to 0.084. Now the right-hand side of Eq. 4.63 is

$$\frac{\phi_{a,1} - 1}{\sqrt{M_{2,\lambda}}} = \frac{9.8 - 1}{13.6} = 0.647$$

The left-hand side of Eq. 4.63 is

$$\frac{1 - \lambda/\delta}{\sinh\left[\sqrt{M_{2,\lambda}}\,(\lambda/\delta)\right]} = \frac{1 - 0.084}{\sinh(13.6 \times 0.084)}$$

$$= 0.649$$

Since the agreement between the two sides is reasonably good, we accept the value of λ/δ as 0.084.

The specific rate of reaction of A with B is

$$R_B = \frac{k_L[B_o]}{1 - \lambda/\delta} = \frac{3 \times 10^{-3} \times 2.2 \times 10^{-3}}{1 - 0.084}$$

$$= 7.2 \times 10^{-6}\ \text{mol/cm}^2\ \text{sec}$$

The specific rate of mass transfer for the solute A is given by Eq. 4.56:

$$R_A = \frac{[A^*]\sqrt{D_A k_2''[C_\lambda]}}{\tanh\left[\sqrt{M_{2,\lambda}}\,(\lambda/\delta)\right]}$$

$$= \frac{2.5 \times 10^{-4}\sqrt{3.1 \times 10^{-5} \times 1.5 \times 10^4 \times 3.6 \times 10^{-3}}}{\tanh(13.6 \times 0.084)}$$

$$= 12.55 \times 10^{-6}\ \text{mol/cm}^2\ \text{sec}$$

Now,

$$S = \frac{R_B}{R_A - R_B} = \frac{7.2 \times 10^{-6}}{(12.55 - 7.2) \times 10^{-6}} = 1.345$$

The selectivity with respect to species C for this case may be favorably affected by an increase in the value of k_L, since the rate of the first-step reaction is directly proportional to k_L, whereas the rate of the second step is marginally affected by an increase in k_L. Actually, if the value of the bracketed term in the denominator of Eq. 4.56 is greater than 3, then k_L will not influence the rate of the second-step reaction.

Example

Consider the following data:

$$k_2' = 2.4 \times 10^6\ \text{cm}^3/\text{mol sec}$$

$$k_2'' = 2.5 \times 10^4\ \text{cm}^3/\text{mol sec}$$

$$D_A = 3 \times 10^{-5}\ \text{cm}^2/\text{sec}$$

$$[A^*] = 2 \times 10^{-4}\ \text{mol/cm}^3$$

$$[B_o] = 2 \times 10^{-3}\ \text{mol/cm}^3$$

$$[C_o] = 2 \times 10^{-3}\ \text{mol/cm}^3$$

The stoichiometric factors for both reactions are equal to 1 and the diffusivities of the species A, B, and C may be assumed to be equal.

We shall consider two contactors (Nos. 1 and 2) which provide k_L values of 2×10^{-3} and 1×10^{-2} cm/sec, respectively. We shall now find the selectivity for the two cases.

It was pointed out earlier in this section that an increase in the value of k_L may favorably affect the selectivity when the first-step reaction is instantaneous. The condition to be satisfied in order for the first step to be instantaneous is given by expression 4.42.

Contactor 1. The condition required for the first-step reaction to be instantaneous is given by

$$\frac{\sqrt{D_A k_2'[B_o]}}{k_L} \gg \frac{[B_o]}{[A^*]}\sqrt{\frac{D_B}{D_A}}$$

$$\frac{\sqrt{3 \times 10^{-5} \times 2.4 \times 10^{6} \times 2 \times 10^{-3}}}{2 \times 10^{-3}} \gg \frac{2 \times 10^{-3}}{2 \times 10^{-4}}$$

$$190 \gg 10$$

Since the left-hand side is much greater than the right-hand side, the first-step reaction is instantaneous.

For the second-step reaction, the relevant value of $\sqrt{M}$ is $\sqrt{M_{2,\lambda}}(\lambda/\delta)$. Now,

$$[C_\lambda] = [C_o] + [B_o]$$

$$= (2 + 2) \times 10^{-3}\ \mathrm{mol/cm^3}$$

$$= 4 \times 10^{-3}\ \mathrm{mol/cm^3}$$

Therefore,

$$\sqrt{M_{2,\lambda}} = \frac{\sqrt{D_A k_2''[C_\lambda]}}{k_L}$$

$$= \frac{\sqrt{3 \times 10^{-5} \times 2.5 \times 10^{4} \times 4 \times 10^{-3}}}{2 \times 10^{-3}}$$

$$= 27.47$$

The value of $[C_\lambda]/[A^*]$ is 20. Thus, the second-step reaction would be fast second order, since $\sqrt{M_{2,\lambda}}$ and $[C_\lambda]/[A^*]$ are comparable. Thus, at the foregoing concentration of C if the reaction were conducted separately, the system would conform to the depletion regime.

The value of λ/δ is not known, but for purposes of checking the regime for the second-step reaction, λ/δ may be taken as approximately equal to $(1 + [B_o]/[A^*])^{-1} \simeq 1/11$. Thus,

$$\sqrt{M_{2,\lambda}}\left(\frac{\lambda}{\delta}\right) = \frac{27.47}{11} = 2.497$$

It is therefore evident that the second-step reaction has been shifted from the fast second-order regime (between 3 and 4) to the regime between 2 and 3 because the first-step reaction is instantaneous.

For this contactor, the following mechanism is therefore valid.

First-step reaction: regime 4

Second-step reaction: regime between 2 and 3

To calculate the selectivity index, we require the value of λ/δ. Equation 4.63 can be used for this purpose and a trial-and-error procedure has to be followed.

$$\frac{1 - \lambda/\delta}{\sinh\left[\sqrt{M_{2,\lambda}}(\lambda/\delta)\right]} = \frac{\phi_{a,1} - 1}{\sqrt{M_{2,\lambda}}} \tag{4.63}$$

Let λ/δ be equal to 0.061. The left-hand side of Eq. 4.63 is

$$\frac{1 - 0.061}{\sinh(27.47 \times 0.061)} = 0.3639$$

The right-hand side of Eq. 4.63 is

$$\frac{11 - 1}{27.47} = 0.364$$

Since the agreement between the calculated values is reasonably close, the assumed value of λ/δ is accepted. Now,

$$R_B = \frac{k_L[B_o]}{1 - \lambda/\delta} = \frac{2 \times 10^{-3} \times 2 \times 10^{-3}}{0.939}$$

$$= 4.25 \times 10^{-6}\ \mathrm{mol/cm^2\ sec}$$

$$R_A = \frac{[A^*]\sqrt{D_A k_2''[C_\lambda]}}{\tanh\left[\sqrt{M_{2,\lambda}}(\lambda/\delta)\right]}$$

$$= \frac{2 \times 10^{-4}\sqrt{3 \times 10^{-5} \times 2.5 \times 10^{4} \times 4 \times 10^{-3}}}{\tanh(27.47 \times 0.061)}$$

$$= 11.76 \times 10^{-6}\ \mathrm{mol/cm^2\ sec}$$

$$R_C = R_A - R_B$$

$$= (11.76 - 4.25) \times 10^{-6}$$

$$= 7.51 \times 10^{-6}\ \mathrm{mol/cm^2\ sec}$$

Therefore,

$$S = \frac{R_B}{R_C} = \frac{4.25 \times 10^{-6}}{7.51 \times 10^{-6}} = 0.565$$

It is evident that selectivity is rather poor.

Contactor 2. The values of $\phi_{a,1}$ and $\phi_{a,2}$ would be the same as in contactor 1.

$$\frac{\sqrt{D_A k_2'[B_o]}}{k_L} = \frac{\sqrt{3 \times 10^{-5} \times 2.4 \times 10^{6} \times 2 \times 10^{-3}}}{1 \times 10^{-2}}$$

$$= 38$$

Now,

$$\frac{\sqrt{D_A k_2'[B_o]}}{k_L} \gg \frac{[B_o]}{[A^*]} \qquad (D_B = D_A)$$

$$38 \gg 10$$

Therefore, the first-step reaction is instantaneous. For the second step reaction

$$\sqrt{M_{2,\lambda}} = \frac{\sqrt{3 \times 10^{-5} \times 2.5 \times 10^{4} \times 4 \times 10^{-3}}}{1 \times 10^{-2}}$$

$$= 5.48$$

Assume a tentative value of λ/δ as $1/11$.

$$\sqrt{M_{2,\lambda}}\left(\frac{\lambda}{\delta}\right) = \frac{5.48}{11} = 0.498$$

The second-step reaction is slow, since $\sqrt{M_{2,\lambda}}(\lambda/\delta)$ is much less than 1.

To calculate λ/δ we again use Eq. 4.63. Let λ/δ be equal to 0.086; then right-hand side of Eq. 4.63 is

$$\frac{10}{5.48} = 1.82$$

The left-hand-side term is

$$\frac{1 - 0.086}{\sinh(5.48 \times 0.086)} = 1.86$$

The values agree and therefore the assumed value of λ/δ is accepted. Now,

$$R_B = \frac{k_L[B_o]}{1 - \lambda/\delta} = \frac{1 \times 10^{-2} \times 2 \times 10^{-3}}{0.914}$$

$$= 2.18 \times 10^{-5} \text{ mol/cm}^2 \text{ sec}$$

$$R_A = \frac{[A^*]\sqrt{D_A k_2''[C_\lambda]}}{\tanh\left[\sqrt{M_{2,\lambda}}(\lambda/\delta)\right]}$$

$$= \frac{2 \times 10^{-4}\sqrt{3 \times 10^{-5} \times 2.5 \times 10^{4} \times 4 \times 10^{-3}}}{\tanh(5.48 \times 0.086)}$$

$$= 2.504 \times 10^{-5} \text{ mol/cm}^2 \text{ sec}$$

$$R_C = R_A - R_B$$

$$= 0.324 \times 10^{-5} \text{ mol/cm}^2 \text{ sec}$$

$$S = \frac{R_B}{R_C} = \frac{2.18 \times 10^{-5}}{0.324 \times 10^{-5}} = 6.72$$

It can be seen that the selectivity for the intermediate species in contactor 2 is very high as compared to that for contactor 1. It is possible to obtain a product from contactor 2 that will contain practically no product of the second-step reaction if the k_L value is sufficiently increased. It should also be noted that any further increase in k_L may shift the first-step reaction to the fast pseudo-first-order regime (regime 3), whereas the second step would be in the slow reaction regime (regime 2). It was pointed out in Section 4.1.3 that the maximum selectivity is obtained for this scheme.

4.1.6. Effect of Temperature on Selectivity

If gas absorption is accompanied by an exothermic reaction, a large temperature rise may occur at the interface. This may alter the selectivity considerably. For example, the rate of the second step may become quite high, creating a situation where the second step also occurs in the film (the conditions may be such that in the absence of the temperature rise, the second step might have occurred in the bulk). The problem may also be important if the first step is instantaneous while the second step is in regime 2. The temperature rise at the interface may shift the second step of the reaction from regime 2 to regime 3.

4.1.7. Examples

1. Alkylation of Phenols with Isobutylene

Gehlawat and Sharma (1970) have studied the kinetics of the alkylation of phenol, *p*-cresol, and catechol with isobutylene in the presence of 1–5% w/w H_2SO_4 as a catalyst. Here, consecutive reactions are involved. For instance, consider the alkylation of *p*-cresol:

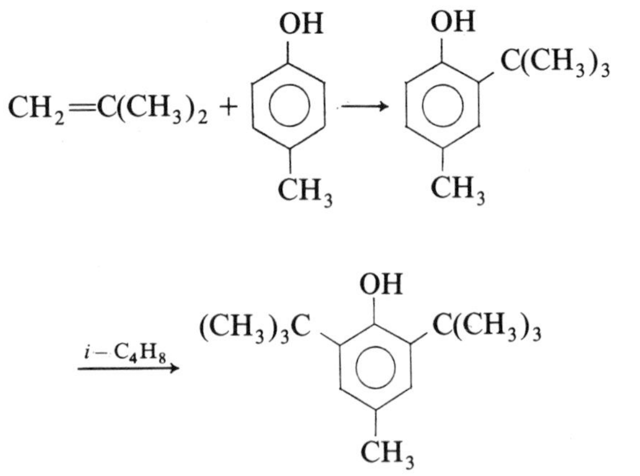

$$CH_2{=}C(CH_3)_2 + \text{(p-cresol: OH, ring, }CH_3) \longrightarrow \text{(2-}C(CH_3)_3\text{-p-cresol: OH, ring, }C(CH_3)_3, CH_3)$$

$$\xrightarrow{i-C_4H_8} \text{(2,6-di-}C(CH_3)_3\text{-p-cresol: OH, }(CH_3)_3C\text{, ring, }C(CH_3)_3, CH_3)$$

The kinetics of the first and second steps were separately studied in a stirred cell and the experiments were also carried out in a bubble column. From the experimental data, it is clear that the diffusional factors are important for both steps. In the case of the bubble column, both steps, assuming some representative concentrations of B and C, conform to regime 2; that is, no alkylation occurs in the film and no free isobutylene exists in the bulk liquid. It is thus clear that the superficial velocity of the gas would influence the rate of the alkylation reaction since the $k_L a$ value increases as about the 0.7 power of the gas velocity (Sharma and Mashelkar, 1968). Further, the effect of the gas velocity on the selectivity with respect to the intermediate product would be expected to be insignificant, since the $k_L a$ values for both steps increase in the same proportion. Experimental data clearly show that the gas velocity has a profound effect on the rate of reaction but that there is practically no effect on the selectivity with respect to the intermediate product. If this reaction is carried out in a packed column the situation may be different, since then the first step might be in the regime between 2 and 3 and the selectivity with respect to C would be higher and would be affected by the liquid flow rate. However, in view of the high melting point of *p*-cresol and alkylated cresols, a packed column is not recommended.

2. Chlorination of n-Decane

van de Vusse (1966) has studied the chlorination of *n*-decane with and without a solvent. (The solvent used was dichlorobenzene.) Most of the experiments were carried out at about 100°C in a 120-cm^3 glass reactor provided with a magnetic stirrer. The following conclusions can be drawn:

1. The method of initiation, which can be thermal or by ultraviolet light, has no effect on the selectivity for monochlorides.
2. At low levels of conversion, it is not possible to clearly discern the effect of stirring on the selectivity with respect to monochlorides. It was observed that the yield of monochlorides was generally lower in the unstirred reactor than in the stirred reactor, particularly at higher *n*-decane conversions. This is presumably because under the unstirred conditions the k_L value is relatively low and the second-step reaction may occur in the film thereby lowering the yield of monochlorides.
3. The presence of a solvent can change the regime of the first step, since it would change the concentration of *n*-decane (see the conditions given by expressions 4.3 and 4.10a).

3. Chlorination of 1,2-Dichloroethane

The chlorination of 1,2-dichloroethane to tri- and tetrachloroethane is industrially important:

$$Cl_2 + ClCH_2CH_2Cl(l) \longrightarrow CH_2ClCHCl_2 \xrightarrow{Cl_2} CH_2ClCCl_3 + CHCl_2CHCl_2$$

Chua and Ratcliffe (1970) have studied liquid-phase chlorination in a glass bubble column reactor at 55°C. The reaction was catalyzed by light from 100-W incandescent lamp. These authors found that the rate of chlorination was controlled by diffusional factors but that chlorine did not react in the film. In other words, the reaction occurred in the bulk. As discussed in Section 4.1, mass transfer should not affect the selectivity in this case. The experimental data of Chua and Ratcliffe show that diffusional factors did not affect the selectivity.

4. Chlorination of p-Cresol

Teramoto et al. (1969) have studied the chlorination of *p*-cresol, dissolved in CCl_4, in 9-cm-i.d. glass reactor (500-cm^3 capacity) provided with a suitable agitator. Chlorine was not dispersed in the liquid and the agitation speed was kept in a restricted range (140–300 rev/min), so that no vortex was formed. Thus, the gas–liquid interfacial area was accurately known. The relevant reactions are as follows:

$$Cl_2 + \text{[p-cresol: OH, CH}_3\text{]} \xrightarrow{k_2'} \text{[OH, Cl, CH}_3\text{]} \xrightarrow{k_2''} \text{[Cl, OH, Cl, CH}_3\text{]}$$

The reaction was found to be first order with respect to the Cl_2 as well as the cresol. The kinetics of each step was studied in a homogeneous system. The value of the ratio of the rate constants for the first and second steps was found to be 110.

The available physicochemical data as well as typical k_L values in the stirred cell indicate that the first step conforms to the regime between 2 and 3, and depending on the concentrations of *p*-cresol and chlorine, and the value of k_L, it may conform to regime 3. However, the second step is likely to conform to regime 2 or the regime between 1 and 2, if carried out independently. The solubility of chlorine is very high (equal to 3.5×10^{-3} mol/cm^3 atm at 25°C) and the necessary conditions for the validity of fast pseudo-first-order reactions were probably not satisfied in the reported work. Thus the system might have been in the depletion regime (between regimes 3 and 4), and in these circumstances the interfacial concentration of *p*-cresol will increase with an increase in the speed of stirring and tend to approach the bulk concentration. If the second step conforms to regime 1 or to the regime between 1 and 2, then the yield of the monochlorinated product would increase with an increase in the speed of stirring. Further, with a decrease in the partial pressure of chlorine, the first step will tend to conform to the fast pseudo-first-order reaction regime (regime 3) and hence the yield of intermediate product should improve. The experimental data of Teramoto et al. confirm these predictions. (Since the solubility of Cl_2 in CCl_4 is relatively high, it is likely that there was a significant gas-side resistance when lean mixtures of Cl_2 were used.)

Pangarkar and Sharma (1974) have also carried out some work on the chlorination of *p*-cresol. Since the solubility of Cl_2 in CCl_4 is relatively high and the value of the second-order rate constant for the first step is relatively low, it was decided to work with 1,2,4-trichlorobenzene as a solvent at 100°C. The values of the second-order rate constant for the first and second steps at 100°C were found to be 1.9×10^5 and 1.5×10^4 cm^3/mol sec, respectively. Further, by using contactors such as a bubble column and a stirred cell and by varying the partial pressure of chlorine, different regimes could be covered. It was found possible to work with the first step in regime 3, the regime between 3 and 4, and regime 4. In all the cases the agreement between the experimental results and predicted values was found to be reasonably good. Figure 4.6 shows a typical plot of the selectivity index S versus k_L. It can be seen that the selectivity is significantly affected by a change in the k_L value. (See also the examples in Sections 4.1.4 and 4.1.5.)

Teramoto et al. (1970) have also studied the effect of bubble size on the selectivity of the intermediate product in the chlorination of *p*-cresol. It is well known that small bubbles (say, less than 2 mm in diameter) behave as rigid spheres and that larger bubbles (diameter > 3 mm) give higher k_L values than do smaller bubbles. Teramoto et al. found that by using a variety of gas distributors, the bubble size could be varied from 0.3 to 6 mm (the superficial gas velocity was relatively low—0.27–0.6 cm/sec). At low values of k_L the necessary condition for regime 3 may not be satisfied and there may be depletion of *p*-cresol at the interface. Consequently, the yield of the intermediate product should increase with an increase in the bubble size, which in turn increases k_L. (It was independently checked by the authors that k_L increases with an increase in the bubble size.) Experimental data show that the larger bubble size gives a higher yield of intermediate product. In the case of the depletion regime (the regime between 3

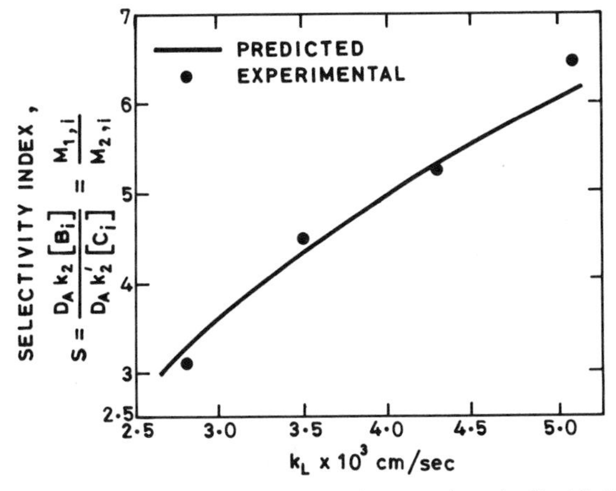

Figure 4.6. Plot of the selectivity index S against the liquid-side mass transfer coefficient k_L for second-order reactions.

and 4) the first-step reaction occurs in the film and there is a significant drop in the concentration of species B. On the other hand, the first-step reaction generates the intermediate species C in the film, and therefore at all points in the film the concentration of species C is likely to be greater than that in the bulk liquid phase. An increase in [C] is likely to enhance the rate of the second-step reaction. The overall effect of these changes is then to lower the selectivity.

5. *Chlorination of Phenol*

The reaction scheme for the case of chlorination of phenol follows a parallel-cum-consecutive type of reaction mechanism:

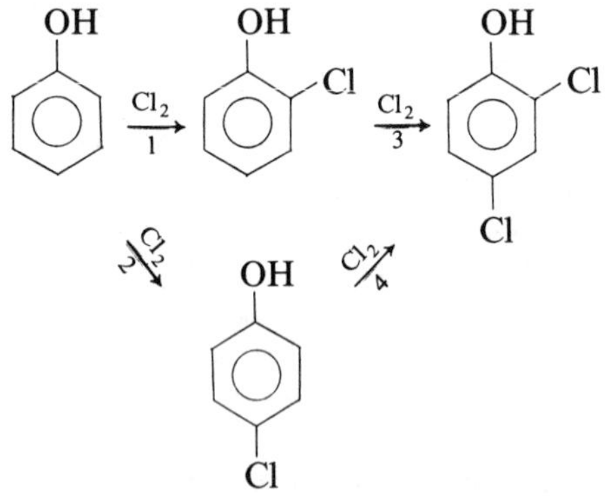

Further, the chlorination of 2,4-dichlorophenol to 2,4,6-trichlorophenol is relatively slow. Nakao et al. (1972) studied the kinetics of this reaction in a stirred cell and in a bubble column. At 27°C the values of the second-order rate constants for the various steps marked in this reaction scheme were found to be as follows:

Step 1 = 1.1×10^4 cm^3/mol sec

Step 2 = 3.5×10^3 cm^3/mol sec

Step 3 = 0.46 cm^3/mol sec

Step 4 = 2.5×10^{-4} cm^3/mol sec

The experimental study of Nakao et al. (1972) covered the following set of variables:

Range of concentration of phenol dissolved in CCl_4 as a solvent	= 0.2–4.3 × 10^{-3} mol/cm^3
Partial pressure of chlorine	= 0.2–1 atm
Superficial gas velocity	= 1–2 cm/sec

The reaction mechanism for the first step may conform to regime 3 or 2 or to the regime between 2 and 3, depending on the value of k_L.

4.1.8. Selectivity Disguised by Mixing in Homogeneous Systems

Rys (1977) has shown how mixing can affect the selectivity of consecutive reactions carried out in the liquid phase (homogeneous system). Homogeneous nitration of durene (1,2,4,5-tetramethyl benzene) gives a dinitro derivative and unconverted durene but *no* mononitro derivative, even though the second-step nitration is very much slower than the first-step nitration. In another case involving equimolar bromination of resorcinol in methanol, not only monobromo isomers but also dibromo isomers and 2,4,6-tribromoresorcinol were formed. In this case of bromination, the degree of substitution decreased when the rate of stirring was increased. Further, the relative proportion of the 2,4-isomer increased with increasing intensity of mixing. A new model has been suggested that can explain these observations.

The foregoing information is concerned with homogeneous systems but it is very likely that similar phenomena may be observed in heterogeneous systems where for a specified level of conversion of B we may well get a different product distribution, depending on the local and global intensity of mixing.

4.2. MASS TRANSFER ACCOMPANIED BY A TWO-STEP CHEMICAL REACTION

The problem of mass transfer accompanied by a two-step chemical reaction is represented by the following equations:

$$A + B \xrightarrow{k_2} C \tag{4.64}$$

$$C + B \xrightarrow{k_2^*} \text{products} \tag{4.65}$$

The bulk liquid concentration of nonvolatile reacting species B is denoted by $[B_o]$ and the interfacial concentrations of the diffusing species A and the intermediate are denoted by $[A^*]$ and $[C_i]$, respectively. Reaction 4.64 is first order in A and B. Likewise, reaction 4.65 is first order in C and B. The rate constants for reactions 4.64 and 4.65 are represented by k_2 and k_2^*, respectively.

The problem of mass transfer accompanied by a

two-step reaction is not commonly encountered in practice, particularly those cases where the reaction between A and B occurs in the film. Some examples of interest are given at the end of this section. This problem brings out some interesting features.

If no reaction between A and B occurs in the film, the problem can be readily analyzed, since it reduces to the case of reaction in the bulk phase. Further, in the case of systems where the transfer of A is accompanied by a pseudo-first-order reaction the second step will have no influence on the specific rate of transfer of A except through the stoichiometric reduction in the concentration of B in the bulk phase. However, complications arise when the reactions between A and B and between B and C occur in the film and there is depletion of B in the film, since in this case the concentration profile of B in the film will be affected by the second step.

4.2.1. Fast to Instantaneous Reactions (Regime between 3 and 4 and Regime 4)

Brian and Beaverstock (1965) have studied fast and instantaneous reactions on the basis of the film and penetration theories. The relevant differential equations for depletion conditions cannot be solved analytically and hence numerical methods are employed. The solution of these authors brings out certain unique aspects of this system. A typical plot of the enhancement factor ϕ against the parameter $\sqrt{M}$ is shown in Figure 4.7.

When the second step is instantaneous ($k_2^* \to \infty$), species C will be consumed as soon as it is formed. Thus 2 moles of species B will react with each mole of species A at every point within the liquid phase, and the overall equation

$$\text{A} + 2\text{B} \rightarrow \text{products} \tag{4.66}$$

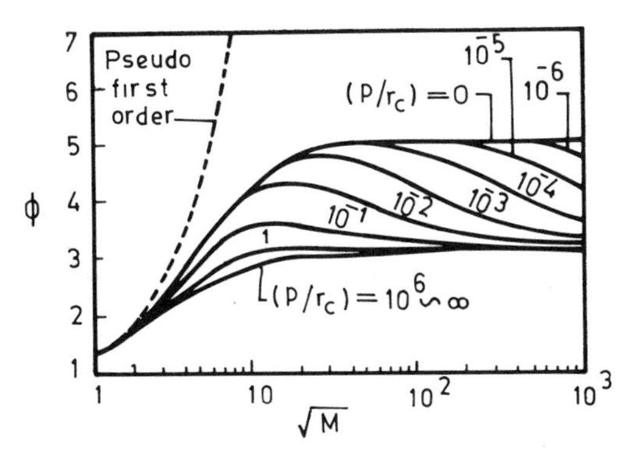

Figure 4.7. Plot of the enhancement factor, ϕ, against the parameter $\sqrt{M}$. $P = k_2^*/k_2$; $r_C = D_C/D_A$.

will adequately describe the process. Thus the bottommost curve ($P/r_C = 10^6$) in Figure 4.7 gives the value of the enhancement factor for this case. The asymptotic value of the enhancement factor will be given by the following equation:

$$\phi_a = 1 + \frac{[B_o]}{2[A^*]} \tag{4.67}$$

for $k_2^* \to \infty$ and equal diffusivities of A and B.

Similarly, when the second reaction is extremely slow ($k_2^* \to 0$), the intermediate C formed can diffuse into the bulk without undergoing appreciable reaction in the liquid film. Thus the reaction

$$\text{A} + \text{B} \rightarrow \text{products} \tag{4.68}$$

will represent the reactions taking place in the film. The uppermost curve ($P/r_C = 0$) in Figure 4.7 gives the value of ϕ for this case and the enhancement factor will be given by

$$\phi_a = 1 + \frac{[B_o]}{[A^*]} \tag{4.69}$$

for $k_2^* \to 0$ and equal diffusivities of A and B.

For a finite value of the ratio of reaction rate constants k_2/k_2^*, the enhancement factor initially increases as $\sqrt{M}$ increases until it reaches a maximum value. As $\sqrt{M}$ is further increased, the enhancement factor starts decreasing until it finally approaches the asymptotic value given by Eq. 4.67. Thus the asymptotic value of ϕ is approached after a maxima for a given value of the ratio of k_2/k_2^*. (See Figure 4.7, $P/r_C = 10^{-1}$.) Hence, it follows that the relatively long-lived intermediate species augments the rate of mass transfer. The effect of increasing $\sqrt{M}$ in any specified system can be explained as follows.

At low values of $\sqrt{M}$, the rate of the second reaction is so slow compared to the diffusion rate of C that the effect of the second reaction is not significant. But as $\sqrt{M}$ is progressively increased through a reduction in the value of k_L, the rate of transport of C into the bulk liquid becomes less, with the result that an appreciable amount of C reacts in the film itself. This reaction distorts the concentration profile of B, thereby lowering the rate of mass transfer. In the limiting case of very large values of $\sqrt{M}$, the system behaves as if both reactions were taking place instantaneously, irrespective of the ratio of the reaction rate constants.

The reported numerical solutions of Brian and

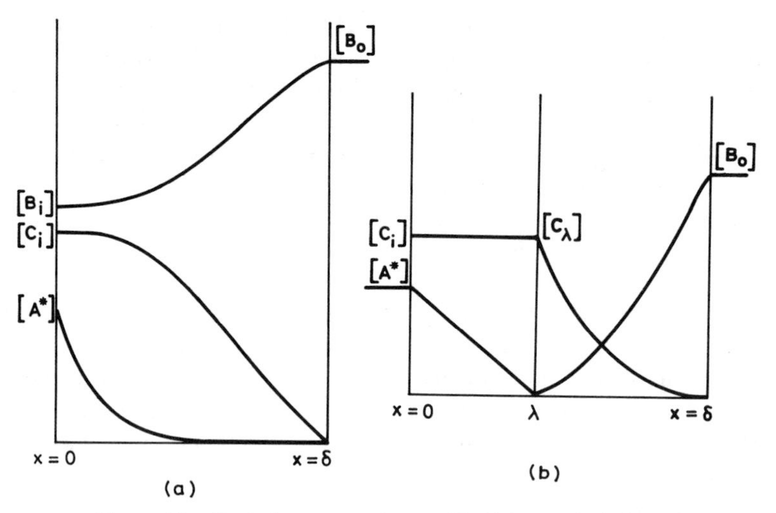

Figure 4.8. Typical concentration profiles for (*a*) depletion of reactant B in the film, (*b*) instantaneous reaction.

Beaverstock are applicable to a limited range of operating variables. It is possible to obtain analytical solutions on the basis of the film theory with some simplifying assumptions (Ramachandran, 1972). As regards analytical solutions based on film theory, we shall consider two possible regimes: the depletion of reactant B in the film (regime between 3 and 4), and instantaneous reactions (regime 4). The concentration profiles are shown in Figure 4.8.

4.2.2. Depletion of Reactant B in the Film (Regime between 3 and 4)

For this case, the differential equations are as follows for a second-order reaction:

$$D_A \frac{d^2[A]}{dx^2} = k_2[B][A] \tag{4.70}$$

$$D_B \frac{d^2[B]}{dx^2} = k_2[B][A] + k_2^*[B][C] \tag{4.71}$$

$$D_C \frac{d^2[C]}{dx^2} = k_2^*[B][C] - k_2[B][A] \tag{4.72}$$

The boundary conditions are, at

$$x = 0: \quad [A] = [A^*], \quad \frac{d[B]}{dx} = \frac{d[C]}{dx} = 0,$$

$$[C] = [C_i], \quad [B] = [B_i] \tag{4.73}$$

and at

$$x = \delta \quad [A] = 0,$$

$$[B] = [B_o], \quad [C] = 0 \tag{4.74}$$

The rate of absorption is given by

$$R_A = -D_A \left(\frac{d[A]}{dx} \right)_{x=0}$$

These differential equations cannot be solved analytically. However, we can make some simplifying assumptions (Ramachandran, 1972). The reaction terms in Eq. 4.71 can be eliminated by combining with Eqs. 4.70 and 4.72. The resulting equation can be integrated to obtain a relation for $[B_i]$. This equation, however, also contains another unknown, $[C_i]$. To obtain the value of $[C_i]$ the concentration profile of C is required. This can be obtained by the procedure suggested by Hikita and Asai (1964) for nonvolatile reactants. Thus, $[B_i]$ replaces [B] in Eqs. 4.70 and 4.72. Equation 4.70 can be directly integrated by using the boundary conditions given earlier to yield the profile for [A] as well as R_A. The profile for [A] is then substituted in Eq. 4.72, along with the substitution of $[B_i]$ for [B] to facilitate the integration. The resulting equation gives the profile of [C], which can be used to obtain $[C_i]$ for use in evaluating $[B_i]$. The reaction terms in Eq. 4.71 can be eliminated with the help of Eq. 4.70 and 4.72 and we get

$$D_B \frac{d^2[B]}{dx^2} = D_C \frac{d^2[C]}{dx^2} + 2D_A \frac{d^2[A]}{dx^2} \tag{4.75}$$

If Eq. 4.75 is integrated twice with the above boundary conditions, the following equation for the interfacial concentration of B is obtained:

$$[B_i] = [B_o] + \frac{D_C}{D_B}[C_i] + 2\frac{D_A}{D_B}[A^*] - \frac{2R_A}{k_L}\frac{D_A}{D_B} \quad (4.76)$$

This equation alone is not sufficient to predict R_A, since it involves two unknowns, $[B_i]$ and $[C_i]$. Hence we assume that the concentration profile of [B] is flat in the vicinity of the interface. This assumption reduces Eqs. 4.70 and 4.72 to the following form, which can be integrated.

$$D_A\frac{d^2[A]}{dx^2} = k_2[B_i][A] \quad (4.77)$$

$$D_C\frac{d^2[C]}{dx^2} = k_2^*[B_i][C] - k_2[B_i][A] \quad (4.78)$$

The solution is more conveniently expressed in terms of dimensionless variables, as discussed next.

The enhancement factor for second-order fast reactions can be represented as follows (see Section 2.7):

$$\phi = \frac{\sqrt{M}\cdot\eta}{\tanh(\sqrt{M}\cdot\eta)} \qquad \text{where } \sqrt{M} = \frac{\sqrt{D_A k_2[B_o]}}{k_L} \quad (4.79)$$

and η is a correction factor ($\eta < 1$) to account for the depletion of the reactant B at the interface.

$$\eta = \sqrt{\frac{[B_i]}{[B_o]}} \quad (4.80)$$

From this set of differential equations, the following expression for η can be obtained:

$$\eta^2 = 1 + \frac{2}{q} + \frac{1}{q}\left[\frac{r_C/P}{(r_C/P) - 1}\right] \times \left[\sqrt{\frac{r_C}{P}}\,\frac{\tanh\left[\sqrt{(MP/r_C)}\,\eta\right]}{\tanh(\sqrt{M}\eta)} - 1\right] - \frac{2}{q}\left[\frac{\sqrt{M}\eta}{\tanh(\sqrt{M}\eta)}\right] \quad (4.81)$$

(provided $r_C/P \neq 1$) where

$$P = \frac{k_2^*}{k_2}, \qquad q = \frac{[B_o]D_B}{[A^*]D_A}, \qquad r_C = \frac{D_C}{D_A}$$

Similar expressions for η for a third-order reaction (1, 2) and a first-order reaction (1, 0) can be obtained.

Consider the limiting cases of Eq. 4.81 for $P \to 0$ (second reaction very slow) and $P \to \infty$ (second reaction extremely rapid).

For $P \to 0$, Eq. 4.81 reduces to

$$\eta^2 = 1 + \frac{1}{q} - \frac{1}{q}\left[\frac{\sqrt{M}\cdot\eta}{\tanh(\sqrt{M}\eta)}\right] \quad (4.82)$$

This can be shown to be the expression for $[B_i]/[B_o]$ for gas absorption accompanied by a simple second-order reaction with a stoichiometric factor of 1.

For $P \to \infty$, Eq. 4.81 reduces to

$$\eta^2 = 1 + \frac{2}{q} - \frac{2}{q}\left[\frac{\sqrt{M}\eta}{\tanh(\sqrt{M}\eta)}\right] \quad (4.83)$$

This is the expression for η^2 or $[B_i]/[B_o]$ for the case of absorption with reaction with a stoichiometric factor of 2.

Special Case of Reactions That Are Zero Order in B

Reactions that are zero order with respect to B have certain special features. For this case, at low values of $\sqrt{M}$ (when $\sqrt{M} \ll q$) the reaction becomes pseudo-first-order and the enhancement factor is given by

$$\phi = \frac{\sqrt{M}}{\tanh\sqrt{M}} \quad (4.84)$$

As $\sqrt{M}$ is increased, the concentration of B at the interface becomes significantly less than that in the bulk, and finally $[B_i]$ becomes equal to zero. However, since the reactions are zero order with respect to the concentration of B, the rate of chemical reaction is unaffected by the variation in the concentration of B at the interface until $[B_i]$ becomes equal to zero. Hence the enhancement factor for zero-order reactions is given by Eq. 4.84 *even for depletion conditions*. The equation ceases to be valid when $\sqrt{M}$ reaches a value for which $[B_i]$ equals zero. Further increase in $\sqrt{M}$ results in a decrease in the enhancement factor. Thus the highest value of the enhancement factor for a given system occurs when $\sqrt{M}$ is such that $[B_i]$ equals to zero. This value of $\sqrt{M}$ is given by the following equation:

$$\sqrt{M} = 1 + \frac{[B_o]}{2[A^*]}\frac{D_B}{D_A} + \frac{\left(\dfrac{k_2}{k_2^*}\right)}{2\left(\dfrac{D_C}{D_A}\dfrac{k_2}{k_2^*} - 1\right)} \times \left[\frac{\sqrt{\dfrac{k_2}{k_2^*}\dfrac{D_C}{D_A}}\tanh\left(\sqrt{\dfrac{D_C k_2^*}{k_L}\dfrac{D_A}{D_C}}\right)}{\tanh\left(\dfrac{\sqrt{D_A k_2}}{k_L}\right)} - 1\right]\frac{D_C}{D_A} \quad (4.85)$$

Thus the film theory model is capable of predicting the maximum value of ϕ for this case.

4.2.3. Instantaneous Reaction (Regime 4)

If the values of the physicochemical parameters are such that the following condition is satisfied:

$$\frac{\sqrt{D_A k_2 [B_o]}}{k_L} \gg \frac{[B_o]}{[A^*]}\sqrt{\frac{D_B}{D_A}} \quad (4.86)$$

then reaction 4.64 becomes instantaneous. The kinetics of reaction 4.64 is no longer important for this case.

From Eqs. 4.67 and 4.69 it is seen that the asymptotic value of the enhancement factor corresponds to a case of gas absorption with instantaneous reaction with a stoichiometric factor of 1 and 2 for $P \to 0$ and $P \to \infty$, respectively. For an intermediate value of P, the notional stoichiometric factor will be between 1 and 2. Ramachandran (1972) has shown that the rate of absorption can be correlated by an effective stoichiometric factor Z ($1 < Z < 2$) defined by the following equation:

$$R_A = \frac{D_A[A^*]}{\lambda} = \frac{1}{Z}\frac{D_B[B_o]}{(\delta - \lambda)} \quad (4.87)$$

An analytical expression can be derived for the value of Z. Thus, for a particular case of $[B_o]$ very much greater than $[A^*]$, we have

$$Z = \frac{1 + \dfrac{1}{6}\dfrac{MP}{r_C}}{1 + \dfrac{1}{12}\dfrac{MP}{r_C}} \quad (4.88)$$

where the term MP/r_C is defined as $D_C k_2^*[B_o]/k_L^2$. A similar equation can be used to predict the rate of absorption for the case where the intermediate is fairly volatile. Thus for this case we have

$$Z = \frac{1 + \dfrac{1}{6}\dfrac{MP}{r_C}\left(\dfrac{1}{1+\mu}\right)}{1 + \dfrac{1}{12}\dfrac{MP}{r_C}\left(\dfrac{1}{1+\mu}\right)} \quad (4.89)$$

where

$$\mu = \frac{k_{G_C}}{k_L H_C} = \text{stripping factor} \quad (4.90)$$

REFERENCES

Albright, L. F. (1966), *Chem. Eng.*, **73**(9), 169.

Albright, L. F. (1967), in Kirk, R. E., and Othmer, D. F. (Eds.), *Encyclopedia of Chemical Technology*, 2nd ed., Vol. 13, Wiley-Interscience, New York, p. 784.

Brian, P. L. T., and Beaverstock, M. C. (1965), *Chem. Eng. Sci.*, **20**, 47.

Chua, Y. H., and Ratcliffe, J. S. (1970), *Mech. Chem. Eng. Trans.*, **6**(2), 35.

Frost, A. A., and Pearson, R. G. (1961), *Kinetics and Mechanism: A Study of Homogeneous Chemical Reactions*, 2nd ed., Wiley, New York.

Gehlawat, J. K., and Sharma, M. M. (1970), *J. Appl. Chem.*, **20**, 93.

Goldstein, R. F., and Waddams, A. L. (1967), *The Petroleum Chemicals Industry*, 3rd ed., Spon, London, pp. 321, 237.

Guterbock, H. (1959), *Polyisobutylene*, Springer-Verlag, Berlin.

Harriott, P. (1970), *Can. J. Chem. Eng.*, **48**, 109.

Hikita, H., and Asai, S. (1964), *J. Chem. Eng. Japan*, **2**, 77.

Inoue, H., and Kobayashi, T. (1968), *Proc. 4th European Symp. Chem. React. Eng.* (Suppl. *Chem. Eng. Sci.*), p. 147.

Kirk, R. E., and Othmer, D. F. (Eds.) (1966), *Encyclopedia of Chemical Technology*, 2nd ed., Vol. 9, Wiley-Interscience, New York, 742.

Leszezynski, A., Kubica, J., Pilc, A., and Bacia, W. (1967), *Przemysl Chem.*, **46**(4); *Chem. Abstr.* (1967), **67**, 32273.

Levenspiel, O. (1967), *Chemical Reaction Engineering*, 2nd ed., Wiley, New York.

Nakao, K., Hashimoto, K., and Otake, T. (1972), *J. Chem. Eng. Japan*, **5**, 264.

Pangarkar, V. G. (1972), Mass Transfer with Chemical Reaction, Ph.D. (Tech.) thesis, University of Bombay.

Pangarkar, V. G., and Sharma, M. M. (1974), *Chem. Eng. Sci.*, **29**, 561.

Ramachandran, P. A. (1972), *Chem. Eng. Sci.*, **27**, 1807.

Ratcliffe, J. S. (1966), *Brit. Chem. Eng.*, **11**(12), 1535.

Rodiguin, N. M., and Rodiguina, E. N. (1964), *Consecutive Chemical Reactions—Mathematical Analysis and Development* (translated from the Russian by R. F. Schneider), Van Nostrand Reinhold, Florence, Kentucky.

Rys, P. (1977), *Angew. Chem. Int. Ed. Engl.*, **16**, 807.

Sharma, M. M. (1965), *Trans. Faraday Soc.*, **61**, 681.

Sharma, M. M., and Mashelkar, R. A. (1968), *Proc. Symp. Tripartite Chem. Eng. Conf.* (Montreal), p. 10.

Teramoto, M., Nagayasu, T., Matsui, T., Hashimoto, K., and Nagata, S. (1969), *J. Chem. Eng. Japan*, **2**, 186.

Teramoto, M., Fugita, S., Kataoka, M., Hashimoto, K., and Nagata, S. (1970), *J. Chem. Eng. Japan*, **3**, 79.

van de Vusse, J. G. (1966), *Chem. Eng. Sci.*, **21**, 631, 1239.

CHAPTER FIVE

Absorption of a Gas into a Solution Containing Two Reactants

In this chapter the theory of absorption accompanied by the chemical reaction of a gas, A, in a solution containing two reactive species, B_1 and B_2, will be considered. The reaction scheme is as follows:

$$A + Z_1B_1 \rightarrow \text{products}$$

$$A + Z_2B_2 \rightarrow \text{products}$$

where Z_1 and Z_2 are the stoichiometric factors.

This problem is of some industrial importance. Thus, for instance, carbon dioxide may be absorbed in aqueous solutions containing a mixture of alkanolamines or a mixture of carbonate buffer and an alkanolamine. Table 5.1 gives some examples of industrial importance. Some liquid–liquid reactions also conform to this scheme (see Section 5.8.5).

The reaction between A and B_1 is assumed to be first order with respect to A and first order with respect to B_1. Also, it is assumed that the reaction between A and B_2 is first order with respect to A and first order with respect to B_2. This problem will be considered in a way similar to that presented for a single reactant in Chapter 2. The film theory will be used throughout this chapter.

5.1. VERY SLOW REACTIONS

For very slow reactions the rate of mass transfer of A is much greater than the rate at which it reacts with B_1 and B_2, and the bulk B phase shows a concentration of A equal to the saturation concentration. Figure 5.1 shows the concentration profiles.

The following condition should be satisfied:

$$k_L a \gg lk' \tag{5.1}$$

where

$$k' = k_{A-B_1}[B_{1,o}] + k_{A-B_2}[B_{2,o}] \tag{5.2}$$

TABLE 5.1. Examples of Absorption of a Gas into a Solution Containing Two Reactants

System	Reference(s)
Absorption of CO_2 in a solution containing two amines; an aqueous solution of carbonate buffer and an amine	Danckwerts and Sharma (1966); Ramachandran and Sharma (1971); Shrier and Danckwerts (1969); Leder (1971)
Absorption of H_2S in a solution of two amines	Danckwerts and Sharma (1966)
Absorption of ethylene (or propylene) in an aqueous solution containing free Cl_2 and HOCl for the manufacture of chlorohydrin	Saeki et al. (1972)
Co-oxidation of organic compounds (e.g., cyclohexane and acetaldehyde) with air (or O_2)	Ohi and Ai (1970)
Alkylation of mixed cresols with isobutylene	Gehlawat and Sharma (1970)
Chlorination of mixed cresols or mixed xylenols	Sheth (1977)

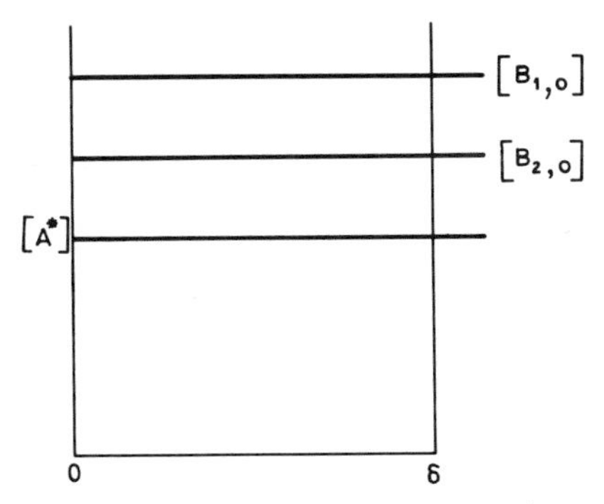

Figure 5.1. Concentration profiles for one gas and two reactants: both very slow reactions (regime 1).

Here the rate of reaction, $R_A a$ in mol per cubic centimeters per second (mol/cm^3 sec) will be given by

$$R_A a = lk'[A^*] \tag{5.3}$$

The amounts of A that react with B_1 and B_2 are given by the following equations, respectively:

$$R_{A-B_1} = R_A \frac{k_{A-B_1}[B_{1,o}]}{k'} \tag{5.4}$$

$$R_{A-B_2} = R_A \frac{k_{A-B_2}[B_{2,o}]}{k'} \tag{5.5}$$

5.2. SLOW REACTIONS

For slow reactions the rate of mass transfer of the solute A is much less than the rate at which A reacts with B_1 and B_2. Further, the reaction is fast enough to keep the concentration of the dissolved A in the bulk at practically zero concentration, but is not fast enough to manifest in the film. Figure 5.2 shows the typical concentration profiles.

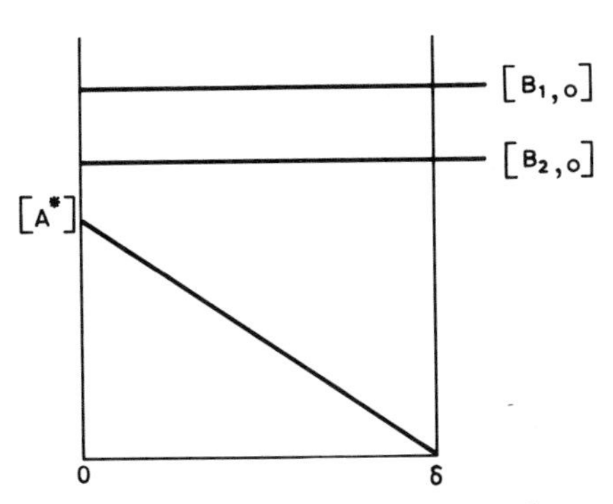

Figure 5.2. Concentration profiles for one gas and two reactants: both slow reactions (regime 2).

In this case the specific rate of absorption is unaffected by the concentration of B_1 and B_2, and Eq. 5.6 holds

$$R_A = k_L[A^*] \tag{5.6}$$

(Equation 5.6 is the same as Eq. 2.7.) The necessary conditions for the validity of regime 2 should be satisfied:

$$k_L a \ll lk' \tag{5.7}$$

$$\frac{D_A k'}{k_L^2} \ll 1 \tag{5.8}$$

The amounts of A that react with B_1 and B_2 are given by Eqs. 5.4 and 5.5, respectively.

5.3. REGIME BETWEEN 2 AND 3 AND FAST PSEUDO-FIRST-ORDER REACTIONS (REGIME 3)

When the concentrations of B_1 and B_2 at the interface are practically the same as that in the bulk the reaction between A and B_1 and A and B_2 can be treated as pseudo-first-order. Here the reaction is fast enough to occur in the film. Figure 5.3 shows the concentration profiles of solute A and reactants B_1 and B_2. Jhaveri (1969) has considered this case. The necessary conditions for the validity of the pseudo-first-order mechanism (regime between 2 and 3) are as follows:

$$1 < \frac{\sqrt{D_A k_{A-B_1}[B_{1,o}]}}{k_L} \ll \frac{[B_{1,o}]}{Z_1[A^*]}\sqrt{\frac{D_{B_1}}{D_A}} \tag{5.9}$$

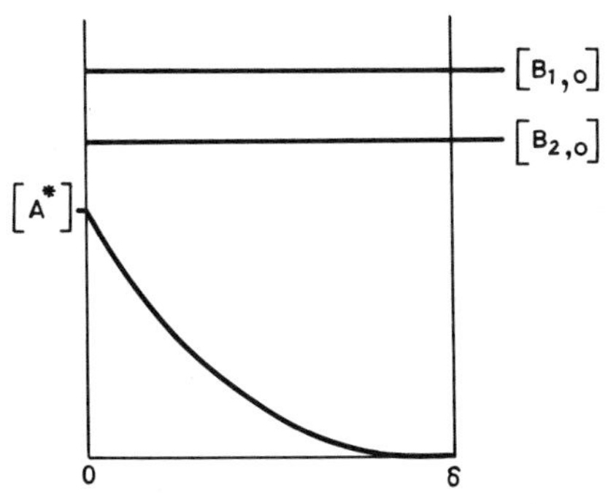

Figure 5.3. Concentration profiles for one gas and two reactants: both fast pseudo-first-order reactions.

and

$$1 < \frac{\sqrt{D_A k_{A-B_2}[B_{2,o}]}}{k_L} \ll \frac{[B_{2,o}]}{Z_2[A^*]}\sqrt{\frac{D_{B_2}}{D_A}} \tag{5.10}$$

The differential equation for the absorption of A is

$$D_A \frac{d^2A}{dx^2} = k'[A] \tag{5.11}$$

The boundary conditions are as follows:

$$x = 0: \quad [A] = [A^*] \tag{5.12}$$

$$x = \delta: \quad [A] = 0 \tag{5.13}$$

The specific rate of absorption of A is given by

$$R_A = -D_A\left(\frac{d[A]}{dx}\right)_{x=0} \tag{5.14}$$

The solution of Eq. 5.11 along with Eq. 5.14 gives

$$R_A = \frac{[A^*]\sqrt{D_A k'}}{\tanh\left(\sqrt{D_A k'}/k_L\right)} \tag{5.15}$$

$$\phi = \frac{R_A}{k_L[A^*]} = \frac{\sqrt{D_A k'}/k_L}{\tanh\left(\sqrt{D_A k'}/k_L\right)} \tag{5.16}$$

For $\sqrt{D_A k'/k_L^2}$ greater than 3, $\tanh(\sqrt{D_A k'}/k_L)$ is approximately equal to unity and Eq. 5.15 simplifies to

$$R_A = [A^*]\sqrt{D_A k'} \tag{5.17}$$

Under these conditions the reactions of A occur entirely in the film (regime 3). (The penetration theory solution will also give Eq. 5.17.) The amounts of A chemically combined with B_1 and B_2 are given by the following equations:

$$R_{A-B_1} = R_A \frac{k_{A-B_1}[B_{1,o}]}{k'} \tag{5.18}$$

$$R_{A-B_2} = R_A \frac{k_{A-B_2}[B_{2,o}]}{k'} \tag{5.19}$$

Example 1

Consider the absorption of CO_2 in an aqueous solution containing a mixture of monoethanolamine (MEA) and diethanolamine (DEA).

Data

Temperature = 30°C

$$k_{MEA} = 9.95 \times 10^6 \text{ cm}^3/\text{mol sec}$$

$$k_{DEA} = 1.93 \times 10^6 \text{ cm}^3/\text{mol sec}$$

$$[MEA] = 5 \times 10^{-4} \text{ mol/cm}^3$$

$$[DEA] = 1 \times 10^{-3} \text{ mol/cm}^3$$

Diffusivity of CO_2 in water at 30°C = 2.2×10^{-5} cm²/sec

$$\frac{(\text{Viscosity of } 1\,M \text{ DEA} + 0.5\,M \text{ MEA solution})}{(\text{Viscosity of water})} \text{ at } 25°\text{C} \; \frac{1.25}{0.9} = 1.39$$

(The viscosity of the mixture is assumed to be equal to the viscosity of a DEA solution having the same weight percent of DEA as a mixture of MEA and DEA.)

Diffusivity of CO_2 in the reaction solution at 30°C $= \frac{2.2}{1.39} \times 10^{-5}$

$= 1.58 \times 10^{-5}$ cm²/sec

(It is assumed that the ratio of the viscosity of the alkanolamine solution to that of water is the same at 25 and 30°C.)

Partial pressure of CO_2 = 0.1 atm

Interfacial concentration of CO_2 in water at 30°C = [A*]

$= 2.8 \times 10^{-6}$ mol/cm³

Physical mass transfer coefficient $= 10^{-2}$ cm/sec

$$Z_1 = Z_2 = 2$$

Conditions given by expressions 5.9 and 5.10 are satisfied for MEA and DEA.

For MEA

$$\frac{\sqrt{D_{CO_2}k_{MEA}[MEA]}}{k_L} \ll \frac{[MEA]}{Z_1[A^*]}\sqrt{\frac{D_{MEA}}{D_{CO_2}}}$$

$$\frac{\sqrt{1.58 \times 10^{-5} \times 9.95 \times 10^6 \times 5 \times 10^{-4}}}{10^{-2}}$$

$$\ll \frac{5 \times 10^{-4}}{2 \times 2.8 \times 10^{-6}}\sqrt{\frac{1.1}{1.92}}$$

$$29 < 67.5$$

(It is assumed that the ratio of diffusivity of MEA (or DEA) to that of CO_2 at infinite dilution and at the specified concentration of alkanolamines are the same. The diffusivities of CO_2, MEA, and DEA at 25°C and at infinite dilution are 1.92×10^{-5}, 1.1×10^{-5}, and 0.68×10^{-5} cm^2/sec respectively.)

For DEA

$$\frac{\sqrt{D_{CO_2}k_{DEA}[DEA]}}{k_L} \ll \frac{[DEA]}{Z_2[A^*]}\sqrt{\frac{D_{DEA}}{D_{CO_2}}}$$

$$\frac{\sqrt{1.58 \times 10^{-5} \times 1.93 \times 10^6 \times 1 \times 10^{-3}}}{10^{-2}}$$

$$\ll \frac{1 \times 10^{-3}}{2 \times 2.8 \times 10^{-6}}\sqrt{\frac{0.68}{1.92}}$$

$$17.5 \ll 106$$

$$k' = k_{MEA}[MEA] + k_{DEA}[DEA]$$

$$= 4975 + 1930 \text{ sec}^{-1}$$

$$= 6905 \text{ sec}^{-1}$$

$$\frac{\sqrt{D_A k'}}{k_L} = \frac{\sqrt{1.58 \times 10^{-5} \times 6905}}{10^{-2}} = 33$$

$$\tanh\frac{\sqrt{D_A k'}}{k_L} = 1$$

Equation 5.17 gives

$$R_A = [A^*]\sqrt{D_A k'} = 2.8 \times 10^{-6} \times 0.33$$

$$= 9.25 \times 10^{-7} \text{ mol/cm}^2 \text{ sec}$$

The amounts of A that have reacted with B_1 and B_2 are given by Eqs. 5.18 and 5.19, respectively.

$$R_{A-B_1} = R_A \frac{k_{MEA}[MEA]}{k'}$$

$$= 9.25 \times 10^{-7} \times \frac{4980}{6910} \text{ mol/cm}^2 \text{ sec}$$

$$= 6.67 \times 10^{-7} \text{ mol/cm}^2 \text{ sec}$$

$$R_{A-B_2} = R_A \frac{k_{DEA}[DEA]}{k'}$$

$$= 9.25 \times 10^{-7} \times \frac{1930}{6910} \text{ mol/cm}^2 \text{ sec}$$

$$= 2.58 \times 10^{-7} \text{ mol/cm}^2 \text{ sec}$$

Example 2: Simultaneous Absorption of NH_3 and CO_2 in Water

Another example that can be treated on the basis of the equations developed in Section 5.3 is that of the simultaneous absorption of ammonia and carbon dioxide in aqueous solutions of amine. This problem is relevant in the manufacture of urea where the mixture of NH_3 and CO_2 coming from the carbamate decomposer has to be separated before recycling. The composition of the mixture is (2 mol NH_3: 1 mol CO_2) such that the absorption of NH_3 is gas film controlled. The concentration of dissolved NH_3 can therefore be predicted from the interfacial partial pressure of NH_3. This problem belongs to the category of simultaneous absorption of two gases (Chapter 6), but because of the particular situation noted above it reduces to the case of absorption into a medium containing two reactants, namely, the amine and NH_3. The objective here is to selectively absorb CO_2. The amine (MEA or DEA), which is faster reacting than NH_3, binds most of the CO_2 absorbed and the bulk of the absorbed NH_3 remains as free dissolved NH_3. To illustrate the advantage of employing aqueous amine solutions, the following data pertaining to the simultaneous absorption of NH_3 and CO_2 in aqueous MEA and DEA in a bubble column may be considered. It will be useful to see how the selectivity, defined by the following equation, is affected by the choice of the amine:

$$S = \frac{R_{CO_2-\text{amine}}}{R_{CO_2-NH_3}}$$

(i) *Absorption in Aqueous* MEA *Solution*

Temperature = 46°C

$$[\text{MEA}] = 1.6 \times 10^{-3}\ \text{mol/cm}^3$$

$$[NH_3] = 1 \times 10^{-3}\ \text{mol/cm}^3$$

$$[A^*]_{CO_2} = 3.43 \times 10^{-6}\ \text{mol/cm}^3$$

$$D_{CO_2} = 2.42 \times 10^{-5}\ \text{cm}^2/\text{sec}$$

$$k_{CO_2-\text{MEA}} = 2.23 \times 10^7\ \text{cm}^3/\text{mol sec}$$

$$k_{CO_2-NH_3} = 2 \times 10^6\ \text{cm}^3/\text{mol sec}$$

$$k_L = 3 \times 10^{-2}\ \text{cm/sec}$$

Since MEA reacts at a rate that is faster than NH_3, it would suffice if the necessary conditions for the reactions to conform to the pseudo-first-order reaction regime were checked for MEA only. (The value of $\sqrt{M}$ for the CO_2–NH_3 reaction is greater than 3.)

$$\sqrt{M}_{CO_2-\text{MEA}} = \frac{\sqrt{D_{CO_2} k_{CO_2-\text{MEA}}[\text{MEA}]}}{k_L}$$

$$= \frac{\sqrt{2.42 \times 10^{-5} \times 2.23 \times 10^7 \times 1.6 \times 10^{-3}}}{3 \times 10^{-2}}$$

$$= 31$$

$$q_{CO_2-\text{MEA}} = \frac{[\text{MEA}]}{Z[A^*]_{CO_2}} \sqrt{\frac{D_{\text{MEA}}}{D_{CO_2}}}$$

$$= \frac{1.6 \times 10^{-3}}{2 \times 3.43 \times 10^{-6}} \sqrt{\frac{1.1 \times 10^{-5}}{1.92 \times 10^{-5}}}$$

$$= 176$$

The ratio of D_{MEA}/D_{CO_2} is taken to be the same as at 25°C. Thus, $\sqrt{M}_{CO_2-\text{MEA}}$ is much less than $q_{CO_2-\text{MEA}}$ and equations developed in Section 5.3 can be employed.

The total specific rate of absorption of CO_2, R_{CO_2}, is given by Eq. 5.17:

$$R_{CO_2} = [A^*]_{CO_2} \sqrt{D_{CO_2}(k_{\text{MEA}}[\text{MEA}] + k_{NH_3}[NH_3])}$$

$$= 3.43 \times 10^{-6} \sqrt{(2.42 \times 10^{-5})}$$

$$\times \sqrt{(2.23 \times 10^7 \times 1.6 \times 10^{-3} + 2 \times 10^6 \times 1 \times 10^{-3})}$$

$$= 3.27 \times 10^{-6}\ \text{mol/cm}^2\ \text{sec}$$

$$R_{CO_2-\text{MEA}} = R_{CO_2} \times \frac{(k_{\text{MEA}}[\text{MEA}])}{(k_{\text{MEA}}[\text{MEA}] + k_{NH_3}[NH_3])} \qquad \text{(Eq. 5.18a)}$$

$$= (3.27 \times 10^{-6}) \times \frac{(2.23 \times 10^7 \times 1.6 \times 10^{-3})}{(2.23 \times 10^7 \times 1.6 \times 10^{-3} + 2 \times 10^6 \times 1 \times 10^{-3})}$$

$$= 3.1 \times 10^{-6}\ \text{mol/cm}^2\ \text{sec}$$

$$R_{CO_2-NH_3} = R_{CO_2} \times \frac{(k_{NH_3}[NH_3])}{(k_{\text{MEA}}[\text{MEA}] + k_{NH_3}[NH_3])} \qquad \text{(Eq. 5.19a)}$$

$$= (3.27 \times 10^{-6}) \times \frac{(2 \times 10^6 \times 1 \times 10^{-3})}{(2.23 \times 10^7 \times 1.6 \times 10^{-3} + 2 \times 10^6 \times 1 \times 10^{-3})}$$

$$= 1.73 \times 10^{-7}\ \text{mol/cm}^2\ \text{sec}$$

The selectivity index S is given by

$$S = \frac{R_{CO_2-\text{MEA}}}{R_{CO_2-NH_3}}$$

$$= \frac{3.1 \times 10^{-6}}{1.73 \times 10^{-7}}$$

$$= 17.9$$

(ii) *Absorption in Aqueous* DEA *Solution.* The data are the same as in Example (i) for MEA with the following additions.

$$[DEA] = 1.6 \times 10^{-3} \text{ mol/cm}^3$$

$$k_{CO_2-DEA} = 4.15 \times 10^6 \text{ cm}^3/\text{mol sec}$$

Since the rate constant for DEA is less than that for MEA, under otherwise similar conditions, the reaction between CO_2 and DEA will also conform to the pseudo-first-order reaction regime.

The relevant specific rates of absorption are as follows.

$$R_{CO_2} = [A^*]_{CO_2}\sqrt{D_{CO_2}(k_{DEA}[DEA] + k_{NH_3}[NH_3])}$$

$$= 3.43 \times 10^{-6}\sqrt{(2.42 \times 10^{-5})}$$

$$\times \sqrt{(4.15 \times 10^6 \times 1.6 \times 10^{-3} + 2 \times 10^6 \times 1 \times 10^{-3})}$$

$$= 1.58 \times 10^{-6} \text{ mol/cm}^2 \text{ sec}$$

$$R_{CO_2-DEA} = R_{CO_2}$$

$$\times \frac{(k_{DEA}[DEA])}{(k_{DEA}[DEA] + k_{NH_3}[NH_3])}$$

$$= (1.58 \times 10^{-6})$$

$$\times \frac{(4.15 \times 10^6 \times 1.6 \times 10^{-3})}{(4.15 \times 10^6 \times 1.6 \times 10^{-3} + 2 \times 10^6 \times 1 \times 10^{-3})}$$

$$= 1.21 \times 10^{-6} \text{ mol/cm}^2 \text{ sec}$$

$$R_{CO_2-NH_3} = R_{CO_2}$$

$$\times \frac{(k_{NH_3}[NH_3])}{(k_{DEA}[DEA] + k_{NH_3}[NH_3])}$$

$$= (1.58 \times 10^{-6})$$

$$\times \frac{(2 \times 10^6 \times 1 \times 10^{-3})}{(4.15 \times 10^6 \times 1.6 \times 10^{-3} + 2 \times 10^6 \times 1 \times 10^{-3})}$$

$$= 3.65 \times 10^{-7} \text{ mol/cm}^2 \text{ sec}$$

The selectivity index S is then obtained from

$$S = \frac{R_{CO_2-DEA}}{R_{CO_2-NH_3}} = \frac{1.21 \times 10^{-6}}{3.65 \times 10^{-7}} = 3.31$$

From these two cases it is clear that the faster-reacting MEA gives higher selectivity with respect to CO_2 than DEA.

5.4. INSTANTANEOUS REACTIONS

In instantaneous reactions the reactions between A and B_1 as well as A and B_2 are instantaneous compared to diffusion rates, and the reactions occur at a plane that is close to the interface and where the concentrations of all the species are zero. Figure 5.4 shows the concentration profiles of the reactants A, B_1, and B_2. Conditions given by expressions 5.20 and 5.21 should be satisfied:

$$\frac{\sqrt{D_A k_{A-B_1}[B_{1,o}]}}{k_L} \gg \frac{[B_{1,o}]}{Z_1[A^*]}\sqrt{\frac{D_{B_1}}{D_A}} \quad (5.20)$$

$$\frac{\sqrt{D_A k_{A-B_2}[B_{2,o}]}}{k_L} \gg \frac{[B_{2,o}]}{Z_2[A^*]}\sqrt{\frac{D_{B_2}}{D_A}} \quad (5.21)$$

By taking the material balance across the reaction plane we get (see Figure 5.4)

$$\frac{D_A[A^*]}{\lambda} = \frac{D_{B_1}[B_{1,o}]}{Z_1(\delta - \lambda)} + \frac{D_{B_2}[B_{2,o}]}{Z_2(\delta - \lambda)} \quad (5.22)$$

Elimination of λ from Eq. 5.22 and noting that $k_L = D_A/\delta$, gives (Jhaveri, 1969)

$$R_A = k_L[A^*]\left(1 + \frac{[B_{1,o}]}{Z_1[A^*]}\frac{D_{B_1}}{D_A} + \frac{[B_{2,o}]}{Z_2[A^*]}\frac{D_{B_2}}{D_A}\right) \quad (5.23)$$

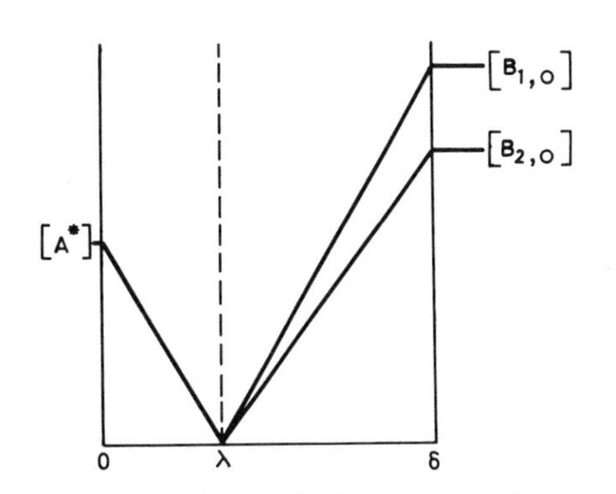

Figure 5.4. Concentration profiles for one gas and two reactants: both instantaneous reactions.

When the second reactant B_2 is not present in the system, Eq. 5.23 will reduce to Eq. 2.83.

The amounts of A chemically combined with B_1 and B_2 are given by these equations:

$$R_{A-B_1} = R_A \times \frac{\dfrac{[B_{1,o}]}{Z_1[A^*]}\dfrac{D_{B_1}}{D_A}}{\dfrac{[B_{1,o}]}{Z_1[A^*]}\dfrac{D_{B_1}}{D_A} + \dfrac{[B_{2,o}]}{Z_2[A^*]}\dfrac{D_{B_2}}{D_A}} \quad (5.24)$$

$$R_{A-B_2} = R_A \times \frac{\dfrac{[B_{2,o}]}{Z_2[A^*]}\dfrac{D_{B_2}}{D_A}}{\dfrac{[B_{1,o}]}{Z_1[A^*]}\dfrac{D_{B_1}}{D_A} + \dfrac{[B_{2,o}]}{Z_2[A^*]}\dfrac{D_{B_2}}{D_A}} \quad (5.25)$$

provided that

$$\frac{[B_{1,o}]}{Z_1[A^*]}\frac{D_{B_1}}{D_A} \gg 1$$

and

$$\frac{[B_{2,o}]}{Z_2[A^*]}\frac{D_{B_2}}{D_A} \gg 1$$

We showed in Sections 2.6 and 2.7 that when D_B is very different from D_A the penetration theory solution is closer to the experimental observations than are solutions based on the film theory. Therefore, in Eqs. 5.23, 5.24, and 5.25 the diffusivity ratio terms should be replaced by square root of this ratio.

Example

Consider the absorption of CO_2 in an aqueous solution containing MEA and DEA.

$$\text{Temperature} = 30°C$$

$$k_{MEA} = 9.95 \times 10^6 \text{ cm}^3/\text{mol sec}$$

$$k_{DEA} = 1.93 \times 10^6 \text{ cm}^3/\text{mol sec}$$

$$[MEA] = 5 \times 10^{-4} \text{ mol/cm}^3$$

$$[DEA] = 1 \times 10^{-3} \text{ mol/cm}^3$$

$$D_{CO_2} = 1.58 \times 10^{-5} \text{ cm}^2/\text{sec}$$

$$p_A = 1 \text{ atm}$$

$$[A^*] = 2.8 \times 10^{-5} \text{ mol/cm}^3$$

$$k_L = 3 \times 10^{-3} \text{ cm/sec}$$

$$Z_1 = Z_2 = 2$$

The necessary conditions given by expressions 5.20 and 5.21 for MEA and DEA are satisfied.

For MEA

$$\frac{\sqrt{D_{CO_2}k_{MEA}[MEA]}}{k_L} \gg \frac{[MEA]}{Z_1[A^*]}\sqrt{\frac{D_{MEA}}{D_{CO_2}}}$$

$$\frac{\sqrt{1.58 \times 10^{-5} \times 9.95 \times 10^6 \times 5 \times 10^{-4}}}{3 \times 10^{-3}}$$

$$\gg \frac{5 \times 10^{-4}}{2 \times 2.8 \times 10^{-5}}\sqrt{\frac{1.1}{1.92}}$$

$$93.4 \gg 6.8$$

For DEA

$$\frac{\sqrt{D_{CO_2}k_{DEA}[DEA]}}{k_L} \gg \frac{[DEA]}{Z_2[A^*]}\sqrt{\frac{D_{DEA}}{D_{CO_2}}}$$

$$\frac{\sqrt{1.58 \times 10^{-5} \times 1.93 \times 10^6 \times 1 \times 10^{-3}}}{3 \times 10^{-3}}$$

$$\gg \frac{1 \times 10^{-3}}{2 \times 2.8 \times 10^{-5}}\sqrt{\frac{0.68}{1.92}}$$

$$58.1 \gg 10.6$$

From Eq. 5.23

$$R_A = (3 \times 10^{-3} \times 2.8 \times 10^{-5})(1 + 6.8 + 10.6)$$

$$= 8.4 \times 18.4 \times 10^{-8} \text{ mol/cm}^2 \text{ sec}$$

$$= 1.55 \times 10^{-6} \text{ mol/cm}^2 \text{ sec}$$

The amount of A chemically combined with B_1 is

given by Eq. 5.24:

$$R_{A-B_1} = 1.55 \times 10^{-6} \times \frac{6.8}{17.4}$$

$$= 6.05 \times 10^{-7} \text{ mol/cm}^2 \text{ sec}$$

The amount of A chemically combined with B_2 is given by Eq. 5.25

$$R_{A-B_2} = 1.55 \times 10^{-6} \times \frac{10.6}{17.4}$$

$$= 9.44 \times 10^{-7} \text{ mol/cm}^2 \text{ sec}$$

5.5. ONE REACTION INSTANTANEOUS AND THE OTHER BETWEEN REGIMES 2 AND 3

We will assume that the reaction between A and B_2 is instantaneous compared to the diffusion rates of A and B_2 and that the reaction between A and B_1 is between regimes 2 and 3. Figure 5.5 shows the typical concentration profiles. The condition for the reaction between A and B_2 to be instantaneous is given by Eq. (5.21):

$$\sqrt{M_{2,o}} = \frac{\sqrt{D_A k_{A-B_2}[B_{2,o}]}}{k_L} \gg \frac{[B_{2,o}]}{Z_2[A^*]}\sqrt{\frac{D_{B_2}}{D_A}}$$

The condition for the reaction between A and B_1 to be fast pseudo-first-order is given by the following expression:

$$\sqrt{M_{1,o}} = \frac{\sqrt{D_A k_{A-B_1}[B_{1,o}]}}{k_L} \ll \frac{[B_{1,o}]}{Z_1[A^*]}\sqrt{\frac{D_{B_1}}{D_A}} \quad (5.9)$$

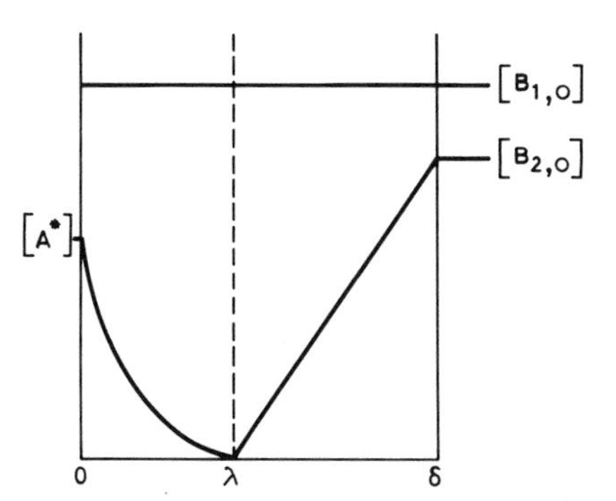

Figure 5.5. Concentration profiles for one gas and two reactants: one instantaneous reaction and one fast pseudo-first-order reaction.

The differential equations for this case are as follows:

$$D_A \frac{d^2[A]}{dx^2} = k_1'[A] \quad \text{for} \quad 0 < x < \lambda \quad (5.26)$$

where

$$k_1' = k_{A-B_1}[B_{1,o}] \quad (5.27)$$

$$D_{B_2}\frac{d^2[B_2]}{dx^2} = 0 \quad \text{for} \quad \lambda < x < \delta \quad (5.28)$$

and

$$-D_A\left(\frac{d[A]}{dx}\right)_{x=\lambda} = \frac{D_{B_2}}{Z_2}\left(\frac{d[B_2]}{dx}\right)_{x=\lambda} \quad (5.29)$$

The boundary conditions are as follows:

$$x = 0: \quad [A] = [A^*], \quad [B_1] = [B_{1,o}], \quad [B_2] = 0 \quad (5.30)$$

$$x = \lambda: \quad [A] = 0, \quad [B_1] = [B_{1,o}], \quad [B_2] = 0 \quad (5.31)$$

$$x = \delta: \quad [A] = 0, \quad [B_1] = [B_{1,o}], \quad [B_2] = [B_{2,o}] \quad (5.32)$$

The rate of absorption is obtained by solving Eq. 5.26 for A and noting that

$$R_A = -D_A\left(\frac{d[A]}{dx}\right)_{x=0}$$

Thus,

$$R_A = \frac{[A^*]\sqrt{D_A k_{A-B_1}[B_{1,o}]}}{\tanh\left(\frac{\sqrt{D_A k_{A-B_1}[B_{1,o}]}}{k_L} \cdot \frac{\lambda}{\delta}\right)} \quad (5.33)$$

The value of λ/δ required in Eq. 5.33 is obtained as follows. At the reaction plane by stoichiometry we have

$$-D_A\left(\frac{d[A]}{dx}\right)_{x=\lambda} = \frac{D_{B_2}}{Z_2}\frac{[B_{2,o}]}{(\delta - \lambda)} \quad (5.34)$$

or

$$\frac{[A^*]\sqrt{D_A k_{A-B_1}[B_{1,o}]}}{\sinh\left(\frac{\sqrt{D_A k_{A-B_1}[B_{1,o}]}}{k_L}\frac{\lambda}{\delta}\right)} = \frac{D_{B_2}}{Z_2}\frac{[B_{2,o}]}{(\delta - \lambda)} \tag{5.35}$$

Simplifying, we get

$$\frac{1 - (\lambda/\delta)}{\sinh\left(\frac{\sqrt{D_A k_{A-B_1}[B_{1,o}]}}{k_L}\frac{\lambda}{\delta}\right)} = \frac{\phi_{a,A-B_2} - 1}{\frac{\sqrt{D_A k_{A-B_1}[B_{1,o}]}}{k_L}} \tag{5.36}$$

where

$$\phi_{a,A-B_2} = 1 + \frac{[B_{2,o}]}{Z_2[A^*]}\frac{D_{B_2}}{D_A} \tag{5.36a}$$

The value of λ/δ can be obtained from Eq. 5.36 by a *trial-and-error* procedure and using this value in Eq. 5.33, we can calculate R_A.

Equation 5.33 has two values in the limiting cases. Thus, when $\sqrt{D_A k_{A-B_1}[B_{1,o}]}/k'_L$ is very much less than unity [here $k'_L = k_L(\delta/\lambda)$],

$$\tanh\frac{\sqrt{D_A k_{A-B_1}[B_{1,o}]}}{k'_L} \to \frac{\sqrt{D_A k_{A-B_1}[B_{1,o}]}}{k'_L}$$

Equation 5.33 therefore reduces to

$$R_A = k'_L[A^*] \tag{5.37}$$

But

$$k'_L = k_L\frac{\delta}{\lambda}$$

$$= k_L\phi_{a,A-B_2}$$

Therefore,

$$R_A = k_L\phi_{a,A-B_2}[A^*] \tag{5.38}$$

Equation 5.38 is the same as that derived for gas absorption with instantaneous reaction with a single reactant B. It is therefore evident that for the case when $\sqrt{D_A k_{A-B_1}[B_{1,o}]}/k'_L$ is very much less than unity, the rate of reaction of A with B_1 will be negligible. (See the next example.) For the case when $\sqrt{D_A k_{A-B_1}[B_{1,o}]}/k'_L$ is greater than 3 Eq. 5.33 gives

$$R_A = [A^*]\sqrt{D_A k_{A-B_1}[B_{1,o}]} \tag{5.39}$$

Example

Consider the absorption of CO_2 (A) in an aqueous solution containing diethanolamine (B_1) and methylaminoethanol, MAE (B_2), under the following conditions:

$$\text{Temperature} = 25°C$$

$$[DEA] = 2 \times 10^{-3}\ \text{mol/cm}^3$$

$$[MAE] = 3 \times 10^{-4}\ \text{mol/cm}^3$$

Interfacial concentration of CO_2 in the solution

$$[A^*]_{CO_2} = 9 \times 10^{-6}\ \text{mol/cm}^3.$$

True liquid-side mass transfer coefficient

$$k_L = 1 \times 10^{-2}\ \text{cm/sec}$$

$$Z_1 = Z_2 = 2$$

$$k_{CO_2-DEA} = 1.48 \times 10^6\ \text{cm}^3/\text{mol sec}$$

$$k_{CO_2-MAE} = 3.16 \times 10^7\ \text{cm}^3/\text{mol sec}$$

The diffusivity of CO_2 in the reacting solution is calculated by a procedure similar to that outlined in the example in Section 5.3.

$$D_{CO_2} = 1.3 \times 10^{-5}\ \text{cm}^2/\text{sec}$$

$$\sqrt{\frac{D_{B_1}}{D_A}} = 0.6$$

It will be assumed that

$$\sqrt{\frac{D_{B_2}}{D_A}} = 0.75$$

To determine the regimes of absorption with respect to both reactants, the corresponding values of $\sqrt{M}$ and q are required. For this purpose, in the evaluation of q values the square roots of the diffusivity ratios are used (see Section 2.7).

For DEA

$$\sqrt{M_{1,o}} = \frac{\sqrt{D_{CO_2} k_{DEA-CO_2}[DEA]}}{k_L}$$

$$= \frac{\sqrt{1.3 \times 10^{-5} \times 1.48 \times 10^6 \times 2 \times 10^{-3}}}{1 \times 10^{-2}}$$

$$= 19.6$$

$$q_{A-B_1} = \frac{[DEA]}{Z_1[A^*]_{CO_2}} \sqrt{\frac{D_{B_1}}{D_A}}$$

$$= \frac{2 \times 10^{-3}}{2 \times 9 \times 10^{-6}} \times 0.6 = 66.67$$

Since $\sqrt{M_{1,o}} \ll q_{A-B_1}$, the reaction between A and B_1 would be fast pseudo-first-order in A if B_1 alone were present.

For MAE

$$\sqrt{M_{2,o}} = \frac{\sqrt{D_{CO_2} k_{CO_2-MAE}[MAE]}}{k_L}$$

$$= \frac{\sqrt{1.3 \times 10^{-5} \times 3.16 \times 10^7 \times 3 \times 10^{-4}}}{1 \times 10^{-2}}$$

$$= 35.1$$

$$q_{A-B_2} = \frac{[MAE]}{Z_2[A^*]_{CO_2}} \sqrt{\frac{D_{B_2}}{D_A}}$$

$$= \frac{3 \times 10^{-4}}{2 \times 9 \times 10^{-6}} \times 0.75$$

$$= 12.5$$

Here, $\sqrt{M_{2,o}} \gg q_{A-B_2}$ and therefore the reaction between A and B_2 is instantaneous.

The value of λ/δ is obtained from Eq. 5.36 by a trial-and-error procedure. However, since the expression derived is based on the film model, the value of $\phi_{a,A-B_2}$ to be used is that pertaining to the film model:

$$\phi_{a,A-B_2} = 1 + \frac{[MAE]}{Z_2[A^*]_{CO_2}} \frac{D_{B_2}}{D_A}$$

$$= 1 + \frac{3 \times 10^{-4}}{2 \times 9 \times 10^{-6}} \times 0.562$$

$$= 10.47$$

$$\frac{\phi_{a,A-B_2} - 1}{\dfrac{\sqrt{D_{CO_2} k_{DEA}[DEA]}}{k_L}} = \frac{10.47 - 1}{19.6} = \frac{9.47}{19.6} = 0.483$$

Now, let $\lambda/\delta = 0.072$. The left-hand side of Eq. 5.36 is then given by

$$\frac{1 - (\lambda/\delta)}{\sinh\left[\sqrt{M_{1,o}}(\lambda/\delta)\right]} = \frac{1 - 0.072}{\sinh(19.6 \times 0.072)}$$

$$= 0.481$$

Since both sides tally well, the value of λ/δ is taken as 0.072. The specific rate of absorption of CO_2 is given by Eq. 5.33:

$$R_{CO_2} = \frac{[A^*]_{CO_2}\sqrt{D_{CO_2} k_{DEA}[DEA]}}{\tanh\left[\sqrt{M_{1,o}}(\lambda/\delta)\right]}$$

$$= \frac{9 \times 10^{-6}\sqrt{1.3 \times 10^{-5} \times 1.48 \times 10^6 \times 2 \times 10^{-3}}}{\tanh(19.6 \times 0.072)}$$

$$= 1.99 \times 10^{-6} \text{ mol/cm}^2 \text{ sec}$$

The amount of CO_2 chemically combined with MAE (B_2) is given by the flux of MAE at the reaction plane:

$$R_{CO_2-MAE} = \frac{D_{MAE}}{\delta Z_2} \frac{[MAE]}{1 - (\lambda/\delta)}$$

$$= \frac{7.3 \times 10^{-6} \times 3 \times 10^{-4}}{1.3 \times 10^{-3} \times 2(1 - 0.072)}$$

$$= 9.08 \times 10^{-7} \text{ mol/cm}^2 \text{ sec}$$

Therefore, the amount of CO_2 that has reacted with DEA (B_1) is

$$1.99 \times 10^{-6} - 9.08 \times 10^{-7} = 1.08 \times 10^{-6} \text{ mol/cm}^2 \text{ sec}$$

The specific rates of absorption of CO_2 when either B_1 or B_2 is present alone are

$$R_{CO_2-B_1} = [A^*]_{CO_2}\sqrt{D_{CO_2} k_{DEA}[DEA]}$$

$$= 9 \times 10^{-6}\sqrt{1.3 \times 10^{-5} \times 1.48 \times 10^6 \times 2 \times 10^{-3}}$$

$$= 1.76 \times 10^{-6} \text{ mol/cm}^2 \text{ sec}$$

and

$$R_{CO_2-B_2} = k_L[A^*]_{CO_2}\left(1 + \frac{[B_{2,o}]}{Z_2[A^*]_{CO_2}}\frac{D_{B_2}}{D_A}\right)$$

$$= 1 \times 10^{-2} \times 9 \times 10^{-6}$$

$$\times\left(1 + \frac{3 \times 10^{-4}}{2 \times 9 \times 10^{-6}} \times 0.562\right)$$

$$= 9.32 \times 10^{-7} \text{ mol/cm}^2 \text{ sec}$$

It can be seen that the specific rates of absorption of A, R_{A-B_1} and R_{A-B_2}, when B_1 and B_2 are present alone are higher than those when B_1 and B_2 are present together. Thus, the presence of the second reactant has a lowering effect on the rate of absorption with respect to the other reactant.

5.6. BOTH REACTIONS IN THE DEPLETION REGIME (REGIME BETWEEN 3 AND 4)

Under certain conditions, the reactions of the solute with the reactants B_1 and B_2 may fall in the depletion regime. Figure 5.6 shows the typical concentration profiles. The necessary conditions are given by the following expressions:

$$\frac{\sqrt{D_A k_{A-B_1}[B_{1,o}]}}{k_L} \approx \frac{[B_{1,o}]}{Z_1[A^*]}\sqrt{\frac{D_{B_1}}{D_A}} \quad (5.40)$$

$$\frac{\sqrt{D_A k_{A-B_2}[B_{2,o}]}}{k_L} \approx \frac{[B_{2,o}]}{Z_2[A^*]}\sqrt{\frac{D_{B_2}}{D_A}} \quad (5.41)$$

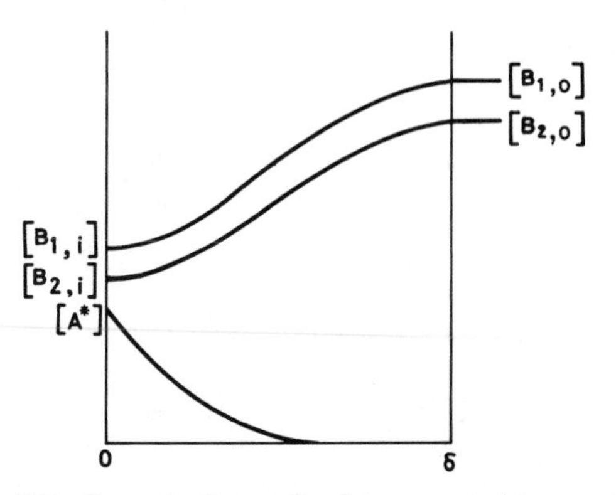

Figure 5.6. Concentration profiles for one gas and two reactants: both second-order reactions (depletion regime).

Jhaveri (1969) and Alper (1972) have considered this problem. Alper has pointed out that the procedure followed by Jhaveri is not correct. However, an analytical solution can be obtained for this case by adopting the following procedure.

The following differential equations hold:

$$D_A\frac{d^2[A]}{dx^2} = k_{A-B_1}[A][B_1] + k_{A-B_2}[A][B_2] \quad (5.42)$$

$$D_{B_1}\frac{d^2[B_1]}{dx^2} = Z_1 k_{A-B_1}[A][B_1] \quad (5.43)$$

$$D_{B_2}\frac{d^2[B_2]}{dx^2} = Z_2 k_{A-B_2}[A][B_2] \quad (5.44)$$

The boundary conditions are as follows.

$$x = 0: \quad [A] = [A^*], \quad [B_1] = [B_{1,i}], \quad [B_2] = [B_{2,i}]$$

$$R_A = -D_A\frac{d[A]}{dx},$$

$$\frac{d[B_1]}{dx} = \frac{d[B_2]}{dx} = 0 \quad (5.45)$$

$$x = \delta: \quad [A] = 0, \quad [B_1] = [B_{1,o}], \quad [B_2] = [B_{2,o}] \quad (5.46)$$

Equation 5.42 can be solved on the lines suggested by Hikita and Asai (1964). The solution obtained is as follows:

$$[A] = \frac{[A^*]\sinh\sqrt{\dfrac{k_{A-B_1}[B_{1,i}] + k_{A-B_2}[B_{2,i}]}{D_A}}(\delta - x)}{\sinh\sqrt{\dfrac{k_{A-B_1}[B_{1,i}] + k_{A-B_2}[B_{2,i}]}{D_A}}\delta} \quad (5.47)$$

The specific rate of mass transfer of the solute A is given by

$$R_A = -D_A\left(\frac{d[A]}{dx}\right)_{x=0}$$

$$= \frac{[A^*]\sqrt{D_A(k_{A-B_1}[B_{1,i}] + k_{A-B_2}[B_{2,i}])}}{\tanh\dfrac{\sqrt{D_A(k_{A-B_1}[B_{1,i}] + k_{A-B_2}[B_{2,i}])}}{k_L}} \tag{5.48}$$

For the case when

$$\sqrt{\frac{D_A(k_{A-B_1}[B_{1,i}] + k_{A-B_2}[B_{2,i}])}{k_L}} > 3,$$

the specific rate of mass transfer is given by

$$R_A = [A^*]\sqrt{D_A(k_{A-B_1}[B_{1,i}] + k_{A-B_2}[B_{2,i}])} \tag{5.49}$$

Equation 5.49 contains two unknown concentrations $[B_{1,i}]$ and $[B_{2,i}]$. The procedure adopted for calculating $[B_{1,i}]$ and $[B_{2,i}]$ is as follows.

The variable concentration terms for the two reactants B_1 and B_2 are replaced by $[B_{1,i}]$ and $[B_{2,i}]$ in Eqs. 5.42, 5.43, and 5.44.

$$D_A\frac{d^2[A]}{dx^2} = k_{A-B_1}[B_{1,i}][A] + k_{A-B_2}[B_{2,i}][A] \tag{5.50}$$

$$D_{B_1}\frac{d^2[B_1]}{dx^2} = Z_1 k_{A-B_1}[B_{1,i}][A] \tag{5.51}$$

$$D_{B_2}\frac{d^2[B_2]}{dx^2} = Z_2 k_{A-B_2}[B_{2,i}][A] \tag{5.52}$$

Subtracting Eq. 5.51 from Eq. 5.50 and rearranging, we get

$$D_A\frac{d^2[A]}{dx^2} = D_{B_1}\frac{d^2[B_1]}{dx^2} + (k_{A-B_1}[B_{1,i}](1 - Z_1) + k_{A-B_2}[B_{2,i}])[A] \tag{5.53}$$

We now substitute Eq. 5.47 for the concentration term for species A. Therefore, Eq. 5.53 becomes

$$D_A\frac{d^2[A]}{dx^2} = D_{B_1}\frac{d^2[B_1]}{dx^2} + (k_{A-B_1}[B_{1,i}](1 - Z_1) + k_{A-B_2}[B_{2,i}]) \times \frac{[A^*]\sinh\sqrt{\dfrac{k_{A-B_1}[B_{1,i}] + k_{A-B_2}[B_{2,i}]}{D_A}}(\delta - x)}{\sinh\sqrt{\dfrac{k_{A-B_1}[B_{1,i}] + k_{A-B_2}[B_{2,i}]}{D_A}}\,\delta} \tag{5.54}$$

Equation 5.54 is now integrated twice using the boundary conditions given by Eqs. 5.45 and 5.46. The following equation is obtained on simplifying:

$$\frac{M_{1,i}}{M_{1,o}} = \frac{1}{\phi_{a,A-B_1} - 1}\left\{\phi_{a,A-B_1} - \sqrt{M_{1,i} + M_{2,i}} + \frac{M_{1,i}(1 - Z_1) + M_{2,i}}{\sqrt{M_{1,i} + M_{2,i}}} \times \left(1 - \frac{1}{\sqrt{M_{1,i} + M_{2,i}}}\right)\right\} \tag{5.55}$$

where

$$\sqrt{M_{1,o}} = \frac{\sqrt{D_A k_{A-B_1}[B_{1,o}]}}{k_L}$$

$$\sqrt{M_{2,o}} = \frac{\sqrt{D_A k_{A-B_2}[B_{2,o}]}}{k_L}$$

$$\phi_{a,A-B_1} = 1 + \frac{[B_{1,o}]}{Z_1[A^*]}\frac{D_{B_1}}{D_A}$$

$$\sqrt{M_{1,i}} = \frac{\sqrt{D_A k_{A-B_1}[B_{1,i}]}}{k_L}$$

$$\sqrt{M_{2,i}} = \frac{\sqrt{D_A k_{A-B_2}[B_{2,i}]}}{k_L}$$

Similar operations on Eqs. 5.52 and 5.50 yield the following result on simplification:

$$\frac{M_{2,i}}{M_{2,o}} = \frac{1}{\phi_{a,A-B_2} - 1}\left\{\phi_{a,A-B_2} - \sqrt{M_{1,i} + M_{2,i}} + \frac{M_{1,i} + M_{2,i}(1 - Z_2)}{\sqrt{M_{1,i} + M_{2,i}}}\left(1 - \frac{1}{\sqrt{M_{1,i} + M_{2,i}}}\right)\right\} \quad (5.56)$$

where

$$\phi_{a,A-B_2} = 1 + \frac{[B_{2,o}]}{Z_2[A^*]}\frac{D_{B_2}}{D_A}$$

Equation 5.49 can be written in the following form:

$$R_A = k_L[A^*]\sqrt{M_{1,i} + M_{2,i}} \quad (5.57)$$

The amounts of A chemically combined with B_1 and B_2 are, respectively,

$$R_{A-B_1} = R_A\frac{M_{1,i}}{M_{1,i} + M_{2,i}} \quad (5.58)$$

$$R_{A-B_2} = R_A\frac{M_{2,i}}{M_{1,i} + M_{2,i}} \quad (5.59)$$

Thus, to calculate R_A, we should know $M_{1,i}$ and $M_{2,i}$. $M_{1,i}$ and $M_{2,i}$ can be obtained by solving Eqs. 5.55 and 5.56 simultaneously.

Example

To illustrate the procedure for calculating the amounts of the gas A chemically combined with reactants B_1 and B_2, the following data for the absorption of CO_2 in aqueous solutions of MEA and DEA may be considered:

Temperature = 30°C

$k_{MEA} = 9.95 \times 10^6$ cm³/mol sec

$k_{DEA} = 1.93 \times 10^6$ cm³/mol sec

$[MEA] = 8 \times 10^{-4}$ mol/cm³

$[DEA] = 4 \times 10^{-4}$ mol/cm³

Partial pressure of CO_2

= 0.3 atm

Interfacial concentration of CO_2 in the solution at 30°C

$= 8.4 \times 10^{-6}$ mol/cm³

Physical mass transfer coefficient

$= 9 \times 10^{-3}$ cm/sec

$$Z_1 = Z_2 = 2$$

The diffusivity of CO_2 in the reacting solution is calculated by a procedure similar to that given in the example in Section 5.3.

$$D_{CO_2} = 1.6 \times 10^{-5}\ \text{cm}^2/\text{sec}$$

The conditions given by expressions 5.40 and 5.41 are satisfied.

For MEA

$$\sqrt{M_{1,o}} = \frac{\sqrt{D_{CO_2}k_{MEA}[MEA]}}{k_L} \approx \frac{[MEA]}{Z_1[CO_2^*]}\sqrt{\frac{D_{MEA}}{D_{CO_2}}} \quad (\text{i.e., } q_{A-B_1})$$

$$\frac{\sqrt{1.6 \times 10^{-5} \times 9.95 \times 10^6 \times 8 \times 10^{-4}}}{9 \times 10^{-3}} \approx \frac{8 \times 10^{-4}}{2 \times 8.4 \times 10^{-6}}\sqrt{\frac{1.1 \times 10^{-5}}{1.92 \times 10^{-5}}}$$

$$39.65 \approx 36.1$$

For DEA

$$\sqrt{M_{2,o}} = \frac{\sqrt{D_{CO_2}k_{DEA}[DEA]}}{k_L} \approx \frac{[DEA]}{Z_2[CO_2^*]}\sqrt{\frac{D_{DEA}}{D_{CO_2}}} \quad (\text{i.e., } q_{A-B_2})$$

$$\frac{\sqrt{1.6 \times 10^{-5} \times 1.93 \times 10^6 \times 4 \times 10^{-4}}}{9 \times 10^{-3}} \approx \frac{4 \times 10^{-4}}{2 \times 8.4 \times 10^{-6}}\sqrt{\frac{6.8 \times 10^{-6}}{1.92 \times 10^{-5}}}$$

$$12.4 \approx 14.2$$

We assume tentative values of $\sqrt{M_{1,i}}$ and $\sqrt{M_{2,i}}$. Let $\sqrt{M_{1,i}} = 17.2$ and $\sqrt{M_{2,i}} = 8.8$. Therefore,

$$\sqrt{M_{1,i} + M_{2,i}} = \sqrt{295 + 77.5} = 19.3$$

Since $\sqrt{M_{1,i} + M_{2,i}} \gg 1$, Eqs. 5.55 and 5.56 can be written (neglecting $1/\sqrt{M_{1,i} + M_{2,i}}$ in the term (1 −

$1/\sqrt{M_{1,i} + M_{2,i}}$) as

$$\frac{M_{1,i}}{M_{1,o}} = \frac{1}{q_{A-B_1}}\left(\phi_{a,A-B_1} - \frac{Z_1 M_{1,i}}{\sqrt{M_{1,i} + M_{2,i}}}\right) \tag{5.55a}$$

$$\frac{M_{2,i}}{M_{2,o}} = \frac{1}{q_{A-B_2}}\left(\phi_{a,A-B_2} - \frac{Z_2 M_{2,i}}{\sqrt{M_{1,i} + M_{2,i}}}\right) \tag{5.56a}$$

Using the assumed values of $M_{1,i}$ and $M_{2,i}$ in Eq. 5.55a, we have as the left-hand side

$$\frac{295}{1572} = 0.187$$

and as the right-hand side

$$\frac{1}{36.2}\left(37.2 - \frac{2 \times 295}{\sqrt{295 + 77.5}}\right) = \frac{6.63}{36.2} = 0.183$$

Since the sides are nearly equal, the assumed values of $M_{1,i}$ and $M_{2,i}$ are accepted as preliminary estimates to be tried again in Eq. 5.56a. The left-hand side of Eq. 5.56a is

$$\frac{M_{2,i}}{M_{2,o}} = \frac{77.5}{153.2} = 0.506$$

The right-hand side of Eq. 5.56a is

$$\frac{1}{q_{A-B_2}}\left(\phi_{a,A-B_2} - \frac{Z_2 M_{2,i}}{\sqrt{M_{1,i} + M_{2,i}}}\right)$$

$$= \frac{1}{14.2}\left(15.2 - \frac{2 \times 77.5}{\sqrt{295 + 77.5}}\right)$$

$$= \frac{1}{14.2}(15.2 - 8.06) = 0.507$$

Here also, the two sides are nearly equal. Therefore, the assumed values are correct and can be used for further calculations.

The amount of CO_2 chemically combined with MEA and with DEA is given by Eqs. 5.58 and 5.59, respectively.

$$R_{CO_2-MEA} = k_L[CO_2^*]\left\{\sqrt{M_{1,i} + M_{2,i}} \times \left(\frac{M_{1,i}}{M_{1,i} + M_{2,i}}\right)\right\}$$

$$= 9 \times 10^{-3} \times 8.4 \times 10^{-6} \times \left(19.3 \times \frac{295}{295 + 77.5}\right)$$

$$= 1.158 \times 10^{-6} \text{ mol/cm}^2 \text{ sec}$$

$$R_{CO_2-DEA} = k_L[CO_2^*]\left\{\sqrt{M_{1,i} + M_{2,i}} \times \left(\frac{M_{2,i}}{M_{1,i} + M_{2,i}}\right)\right\}$$

$$= 9 \times 10^{-3} \times 8.4 \times 10^{-6} \times \left(19.3 \times \frac{77.5}{295 + 77.5}\right)$$

$$= 3.03 \times 10^{-7} \text{ mol/cm}^2 \text{ sec}$$

5.7. KINETICS OF REACTIONS INVOLVING ONE GAS AND TWO REACTANTS

Our discussions in Section 5.1–5.6 clearly indicate that only when we are in the very slow reactions regime (Section 5.1) or pseudo-first-order reactions regime (Section 5.3) can we deploy the pertinent theory to obtain the value of the rate constant. Thus if we know the rate constant for one of the reactants (say B_1), the rate constant for the second reactant (B_2) can be calculated from the overall rate of absorption of A.

5.8. EXAMPLES

5.8.1. Manufacture of Ethylene and Propylene Chlorohydrin

Saeki et al. (1972) have studied some aspects of the absorption of ethylene in water containing dissolved Cl_2 and HOCl. In the old established process, ethylene oxide was manufactured from ethylene chlorohydrin (ECH), which in turn was made by the absorption of ethylene and chlorine in water. In practically all the new plants ethylene oxide is made by the direct oxidation of ethylene. It appears that most of the old ethylene oxide plants have been converted to propylene oxide, for which the direct oxidation process has not been found to be successful. It is therefore expected that the basic mechanism reported in the paper by Saeki et al. will be useful for the design of a propylene chlorohydrin reactor.

Experiments were made in a 7.6-cm(3-in.)-i.d. 91.5-cm(36-in.)-long glass bubble column reactor. The effect of baffles in the form of eight perforated plates was also studied. The value of the physical mass transfer coefficient was obtained from data pertaining to the absorption of ethylene in water. The backmixing data were obtained by using KCl as a tracer. The effects of backmixing on the performance of the bubble column reactor were also studied. The basic reactions are as follows:

$$C_2H_4 + HOCl \rightarrow ClC_2H_4OH$$

$$C_2H_4 + Cl_2 \rightarrow ClC_2H_4Cl$$

In practice, ethylene dichloride is an undesirable product.

On the basis of the previous work of Johnson and co-workers it can be concluded that the absorption of ethylene is accompanied by instantaneous reactions with Cl_2 and HOCl. Equations 5.23, 5.24, and 5.25 (Section 5.4) hold and experimental data agree well with the theoretical predictions.

5.8.2 Absorption of CO_2 in Aqueous Solutions Containing Two Amines

Alper and Danckwerts (1976) have studied the absorption of CO_2 in aqueous solutions containing two amines in a 10.2-cm-i.d. packed column provided with 1.27-cm ceramic Raschig rings up to a height of 158 cm. The superficial liquid velocity was 0.4 cm/sec. Mixtures of monoethanolamine (MEA) and diisopropanolamine (DIPA), MEA and methylaminoethanol (MAE), MEA and monoisopropanolamine, MEA and diethanolamine (DEA), and DEA and DIPA were used. Pure CO_2 was used and under their experimental conditions the controlling regime was either absorption accompanied by instantaneous reaction with both the reactants (Section 5.4) or absorption accompanied by instantaneous reaction with one reactant and by the depletion regime with respect to the second reactant. These authors have also carried out experiments in a string of spheres column (sphere diameter = 3.72 cm) with a view to using this as a model contactor. (See Section 10.1.2.)

In all cases the modeling experiments gave the expected results. In the cases above the total rate of absorption of CO_2 in the packed column cannot be theoretically predicted, since the liquid flows in the plug flow manner and the concentrations of B_1 and B_2 at different locations in the column are interdependent.

5.8.3. Absorption of NO_2/N_2O_4 in Aqueous Alkaline Solutions of Sodium Sulfite

We discussed some aspects of the absorption of NO_2/N_2O_4 in water in Section 3.4.5, where it was pointed out that the absorption of N_2O_4 in water is accompanied by a fast pseudo-first-order reaction. Absorption of lean NO_2/N_2O_4 and SO_2 is relevant in pollution abatement. Aqueous alkaline solutions are used for the removal of SO_2. It was therefore thought desirable to consider the absorption of lean N_2O_4 in aqueous solutions of Na_2SO_3 (Kameoka and Pigford, 1977). Experiments were carried out in a string of spheres column that consisted of five stainless steel spheres 3.8 cm (1.5 in.) in diameter.

Since lean mixtures of NO_2 ($< 2\%$) were used, the necessary conditions for a fast pseudo-first-order reaction would be expected to be well satisfied. Since N_2O_4 can react with water, OH^- and SO_3^{2-}—an equation of the type 5.17 will hold.

$$R_A = [N_2O_4^*] \times \sqrt{D_{N_2O_4}\left(k_{H_2O} + k_{OH^-}[OH^-] + k_{SO_3^{2-}}[SO_3^{2-}]\right)}$$

The value of the second-order rate constant for SO_3^{2-} (first order in N_2O_4 and first order in SO_3^{2-}) was found to be 8.69×10^6 cm^3/mol sec at 25°C.

Takeuchi et al. (1977) have also studied the absorption of NO_2 in aqueous solutions of sodium sulfite and bisulfite. It was observed that absorption of NO_2 is accompanied by a fast pseudo-first-order reaction ($m = 1$, $n = 1$). The values of the second-order rate constant at 25°C were found to be 6.6×10^8 cm^3/mol sec and 1.5×10^7 cm^3/mol sec for sulfite and bisulfite, respectively. The rate constant for sulfite differs from that obtained by Kameoka and Pigford (1977).

These authors have found that at low partial pressures of NO_2, the hydrolysis of NO_2 is accompanied by a fast pseudo-second-order reaction ($m = 2$) and therefore the following equation will hold for the absorption of NO_2 in aqueous solutions of sulfite (or bisulfite):

$$R_A = [A^*]\left\{ D_A\left(\tfrac{2}{3}k_{NO_2-H_2O}[A^*] + k_2[B_o]\right)\right\}^{1/2}$$

5.8.4. Chlorination of Aqueous Buffered Solutions of Phenolic Substances

We considered in Section 3.4.12 the kinetics of aqueous-phase chlorination of phenolic substances such as *o*- and *p*-chlorophenol, *p*-nitrophenol, and *m*-aminophenol hydrochloride. Here the absorption of lean Cl_2 was found to be accompanied by a fast pseudo-first-order reaction. (The reaction is first order in the phenolic substance as well.) Yadav and Sharma (1981) and Yadav (1980) have studied the absorption of lean Cl_2 in aqueous hydrogen phthalate, acetate, and phosphate buffers (pH range 2.6–6.7) containing *o*- and *p*-chlorophenol in a stirred contactor with independent stirrers for gas and liquid phases. The absorption of lean Cl_2 in aqueous buffered solutions is also by itself accompanied by a fast pseudo-first-order reaction. (Actually, the hydrolysis reaction $Cl_2 + H_2O \rightarrow H^+ + Cl^- + HOCl$ is greatly catalyzed by these buffer anions.) In the case of *p*-chlorophenol in acetate and hydrogen phthalate buffers the system conformed to absorption accompanied by a fast pseudo-first-order reaction with both the dissolved species; the data correlated well with Eq. 5.17. (Independent measurements were made with the buffer solutions as well as solutions of chlorophenols to obtain the values of the rate constant.) With phosphate buffer the hydrolysis reaction conformed to the depletion regime, but that of *p*-chlorophenol conformed to the fast pseudo-first-order reaction regime. Yadav (1980) has analyzed this problem theoretically and successfully used this theory to correlate the experimental data.

5.8.5. Interfacial Copolycondensation

In Section 3.7.16 we discussed the subject of interfacial polycondensation. This method can be extended to copolycondensation. Consider the case of polyamides. Here instead of one diacylchloride and one diamine we may use two diacylchlorides and one diamine or vice versa. Polymers of certain distinctive properties can thus be produced. We pointed out in Section 3.7.16 that these polyamide reactions are unique in that the reaction occurs in the organic phase. Thus if one diamine were to be reacted with two diacylchlorides dissolved in an organic solvent immiscible with water, then we might well have a situation where the controlling resistance would be that associated with the diffusion of the two diacylchlorides to the reaction plane (regime 4). Sokolov and Nikonov (1977) have discussed this subject in detail and have pointed out the different situations that arise. (Regime 1 or 2 or 3 or 4 can possibly exist, depending on the circumstances.)

If two amines and only one diacylchloride are used, then the example will fall in the category of the simultaneous absorption of two gases accompanied by chemical reaction (Chapter 6).

REFERENCES

Alper, E. (1972), *Chem. Eng. Sci.*, **27**, 649.

Alper, E., and Danckwerts, P. V. (1976), *Chem. Eng. Sci.*, **31**, 599.

Danckwerts, P. V., and Sharma, M. M. (1966), *Chem. Eng., Inst. Chem. Eng.*, No 202, CE244.

Gehlawat, J. K., and Sharmá, M. M. (1970), *J. Appl. Chem.*, **20**, 93.

Hikita, H., and Asai, S. (1964), *J. Chem. Eng. Japan*, **2**, 77.

Jhaveri, A. S. (1969), *Chem. Eng. Sci.*, **24**, 1738.

Kameoka, Y., and Pigford, R. L. (1977), *Ind. Eng. Chem. Fundam.*, **16**, 163.

Leder, F. (1971), *Chem. Eng. Sci.*, **26**, 1381.

Ohi, T., and Ai, M. (1970), *Kogyo Kogaku Zasshi*, **73**, 2156; *Chem. Abstr.* (1971), **74**, 75827.

Ramachandran, P. A., and Sharma, M. M. (1971), *Trans. Inst. Chem. Eng.*, **49**, 253.

Saeki, G., Weng, P. K. J., and Johnson, A. I. (1972), *Can. J. Chem. Eng.*, **50**, 730.

Sheth, M. N. (1977), Kinetics of Heterogeneous Reactions, M. Chem. Eng. thesis, University of Bombay.

Shrier, A. L., and Danckwerts, P. V. (1969), *Ind. Eng. Chem. Fundam.*, **8**, 415.

Sokolov, L. B., and Nikonov, V. Z. (1977), in Millich, F., and Carraher, C. E., Jr. (Eds.), *Interfacial Syntheses*, Vol. 1, *Fundamentals*, Marcel Dekker, New York, p. 167.

Takeuchi, H., Ando, M., and Kizawa, N. (1977), *Ind. Eng. Chem. Process Design Dev.*, **16**, 303.

Yadav, G. D. (1980), Heterogeneous Reactions: Chlorination of Aqueous Phenols and Aromatic Sulfonic Acids; Effect of Diffusivity on True Gas-Side Mass Transfer Coefficient; Phase Transfer Catalysis, Ph.D. (Tech.) thesis, University of Bombay.

Yadav, G. D., and Sharma, M. M. (1981), *Chem. Eng. Sci.*, **36**, 599.

CHAPTER SIX

Simultaneous Absorption and Reaction of Two Gases

The absorption of two or more gases into a liquid is industrially important in several contexts (Ramachandran and Sharma, 1971). The objective of the operation may be (1) to recover one or more components present in a gas mixture; (2) to remove selectively one of the components; (3) to manufacture some specific chemical formed by the interaction of two dissolved gases in the liquid phase. The various industrial processes involving the absorption of two gases may be classified into four categories.

1. Absorption of two or more gases in a nonreacting medium.
2. Absorption of two gases in a reacting liquid.
3. Absorption of two gases accompanied by complex chemical reactions.
4. Absorption of two gases that react with each other.

Tables 6.1 and 6.2 summarize some industrially important examples of the absorption and reaction of two gases.

6.1. ABSORPTION OF TWO GASES IN A NONREACTING MEDIUM

Aspects of multicomponent physical absorption are discussed extensively in the literature (Sherwood and Pigford, 1952; Treybal, 1968). Ramachandran and Sharma (1971) have also discussed some aspects of this problem. In the case of multicomponent physical absorption, the presence of one gas does not, in general, directly affect the rate of absorption of the other gas because the gases do not compete for a common liquid-phase reactant. When the solute gases are dilute, the absorption of each gas can be considered separately, as though the other soluble components were absent. When the concentration of the soluble components in the gas phase becomes large, however, there is an appreciable decrease in the gas flow rate from the bottom to the top of the column. Added complications arise as a result of changes in the liquid flow rate within the column and heat effects accompanying absorption. In certain cases the solubility of one gas may be enhanced by the other component. Thus, the knowledge of solubility data in the actual system is an essential prerequisite for the design of these absorbers. The following data would be required for design purposes:

1. Physical solubility of the components in the liquid solvent in presence of one another;
2. Diffusivities of the solutes in a multicomponent gas mixture;
3. Diffusivities of the solutes in the liquid phase;
4. Gas-side and liquid-side mass transfer coefficients in the type of equipment envisaged;
5. Gas–liquid interfacial area in the contactor to be used.

6.2. ABSORPTION OF TWO GASES IN A REACTING LIQUID

In this section, absorption accompanied by single-step irreversible chemical reactions will be considered. The reaction scheme can be formulated as

$$\mathrm{A_1} + Z_{\mathrm{A_1}}\mathrm{B} \rightarrow \text{products} \quad \text{(i)}$$

$$\mathrm{A_2} + Z_{\mathrm{A_2}}\mathrm{B} \rightarrow \text{products} \quad \text{(ii)}$$

Here, A_1 and A_2 are the two gases being absorbed; they react with a nonvolatile reactive species

TABLE 6.1. Industrially Important Examples of the Absorption and Reaction of Two Gases

Gases Being Absorbed	Absorbent	Reference(s)
CO_2, H_2S and CO_2, H_2S, COS	a. Aqueous potassium carbonate solutions	Garnell et al. (1958) Gioia (1967)
	b. Aqueous potassium phosphate solutions	Gioia and Marrucci (1970)
	c. Aqueous sodium hydroxide solutions	Astarita and Gioia (1965)
	d. Aqueous diglycolamine solutions	Dingman and Moore (1968)
	e. Solutions of diisopropanolamine	Ouwerkerk (1978)
Isobutylene, butenes	Aqueous sulfuric acid	Davis and Schuler (1930) Gehlawat and Sharma (1968)
$COCl_2$, CO_2	Water, aqueous carbonate solution, or caustic soda	Manogue and Pigford (1960) Ramachandran and Sharma (1970)
CO, CO_2	Ammoniacal cuprous chloride	van Krevelen and Baans (1950)
HCN, CO_2	Alkalis	Taylor (1969)
SO_2, CO_2	Aqueous carbonate solution or caustic soda	Goettler and Pigford (1968)
SO_2, O_2	Water containing $MnSO_4$ as a catalyst	Coughanowr and Krause (1965) Gunn and Saleem (1970)

B present in the liquid phase. The products of the reaction are also nonvolatile. The terms Z_{A_1} and Z_{A_2} are the stoichiometric coefficients of A_1 and A_2, respectively, in reactions (i) and (ii). We define the following dimensionless parameters to characterize the process of absorption and reaction of two gases:

$$M_{A_1} = \frac{[2/(m+1)] D_{A_1} k_{A_1} [B_o]^n [A_1^*]^{m-1}}{k_L^2}$$

$$M_{A_2} = \frac{[2/(m'+1)] D_{A_2} k_{A_2} [B_o]^{n'} [A_2^*]^{m'-1}}{k_L^2}$$

$$q_{A_1} = \frac{[B_o]}{Z_{A_1}[A_1^*]} \frac{D_B}{D_{A_1}}, \qquad q_{A_2} = \frac{[B_o]}{Z_{A_2}[A_2^*]} \frac{D_B}{D_{A_2}}$$

$$q_{A_1A_2} = \frac{[B_o]}{Z_{A_1}[A_1^*](D_{A_1}/D_B) + Z_{A_2}[A_2^*](D_{A_2}/D_B)}$$

Here m, n denote the order of the reaction of A_1 with B and m', n' denote the order of reaction of gas A_2 and B.

6.2.1. Mechanism of Absorption

Depending on the relative magnitudes of the various dimensionless groups listed above, the absorption and reaction of two gases will follow different mechanisms. The various cases are summarized below and the corresponding concentration profiles are shown in Figure 6.1.

Fast Pseudo-mth-Order Reaction

Here the concentration of the reactive species B in the neighborhood of the interface and bulk of the liquid are nearly the same; that is, there is no "depletion" of B in the film. The condition under which this

Table 6.2. Industrially Important Examples of the Absorption of Two Gases that React with Each Other in the Liquid Medium

Gases Being Absorbed	Product Formed	Liquid Medium Employed	Reference(s)
NH_3, CO_2	Ammonium carbamate	Water, aqueous MEA, aqueous urea nitrate	Hatch and Pigford (1962) Schmidt (1970) Teramoto (1973) Hegner and Molzahn (1979)
C_2H_4, Cl_2	Dichloroethane	Dichloroethane	Balasubramanian et al. (1966) Chua and Ratcliffe (1970, 1971)
Acetylene, chlorine	Tetrachloroethane	Tetrachloroethane	FIAT-843
SO_2, H_2S	Sulfur	a. Molten sulfur	*Chem. Engg. News* (1970) Wiewiorowski (1969)
		b. Triethylene glycol solution	Goar (1968)
		c. Diethylene glycol with amine as catalyst	
CO_2, H_2S	Thiourea	Calcium cynamide solution	Hahn (1970)
C_2H_4, O_2	Acetaldehyde	Solutions of $CuCl/CuCl_2$ containing $PdCl_2$ as catalyst	Chandalia (1968) Hatch (1970)
C_2H_4, HCl, O_2	Dichloroethane	Aqueous $CuCl_2$	Friend et al. (1968)
SO_2, Cl_2, H_2O	H_2SO_4, HCl	Water	Sadek et al. (1977)
Ethylene, propylene	Copolymer	Non-Newtonian solution of copolymer	Jordan (1968)

mechanism would be valid is

$$\frac{\sqrt{M_{A_1}}}{q_{A_1}} + \frac{\sqrt{M_{A_2}}}{q_{A_2}} \ll 1 + \frac{1}{q_{A_1A_2}} \tag{6.1}$$

Absorption of Two Gases under Depletion Conditions

When the condition given by expression 6.1 is not satisfied and the terms on the left-hand side and those on the right-hand side are comparable, the absorption of two gases will be under depletion conditions. The term *depletion* signifies that the concentration of the reactive species B at the interface is substantially lower than that in the bulk (the concentration of B varies significantly in the liquid film).

Absorption of Two Gases, One of Which Reacts Instantaneously in the Liquid Phase

When the rate of chemical reaction of one gas, say A_1, is very much faster than the rate of diffusion of A_1, then absorption of that gas will be accompanied by an instantaneous reaction. Under these conditions, the species A_1 and B cannot coexist in the liquid. They diffuse toward one another and react at a reaction plane located a distance λ below the interface. The concentration of both A_1 and B is zero at

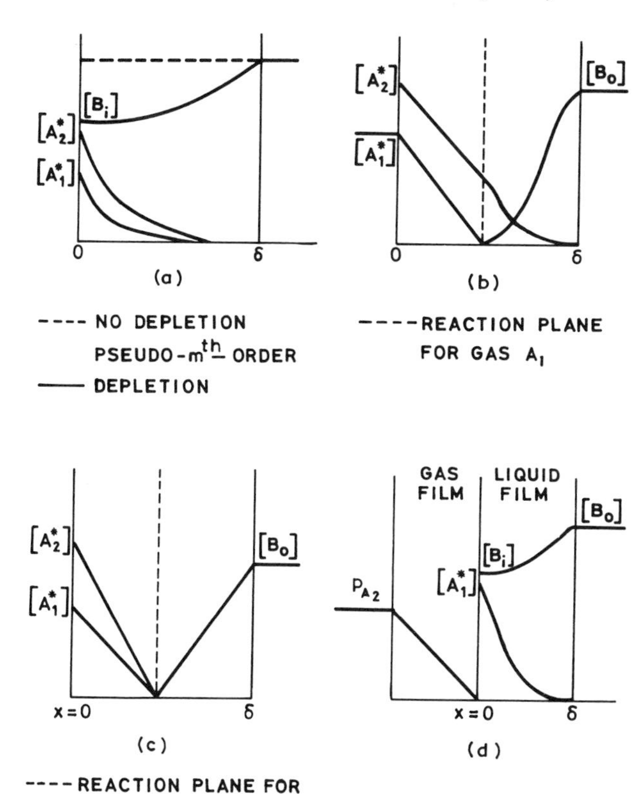

Figure 6.1. Simultaneous absorption of two gases accompanied by chemical reaction: concentration profiles of reactant and dissolved gases according to the film theory. (*a*) General case; (*b*) reaction between A_1 and B instantaneous; (*c*) both reactions instantaneous; (*d*) absorption of gas A_2 entirely gas-film-controlled.

this reaction plane. The condition under which this mechanism is likely to be valid is

$$\sqrt{M_{A_1}} \gg q_{A_1} \tag{6.2}$$

The liquid film may then be thought to be composed of two regions: (1) a region between 0 and λ where the concentration of the reactive species, B, is zero; (2) a region between λ and δ (the film thickness) where the concentration of B is finite. It is evident that no reaction of the second gas, A_2, can take place in the region from 0 to λ. If the rate of reaction of A_2 in the film is negligible when compared with the rate of diffusion of A_2 in the film (when $\sqrt{M_{A_2}} \ll 1$), the reaction of A_2 will take place in the bulk liquid. On the other hand, if the value of the parameter $\sqrt{M_{A_2}}$ is comparable to or greater than unity, the reaction of A_2 may take place in the liquid film in the region between λ and δ.

Absorption of Both Gases Accompanied by Instantaneous Reactions

If the condition given by expression 6.2 is valid for gas A_2 as well (i.e., $\sqrt{M_{A_2}} \gg q_{A_2}$), the absorption of both gases will be accompanied by instantaneous reactions. Here both A_1 and A_2 diffuse toward a common reaction plane where they react with B. The concentration of A_1, A_2, and B is zero at the reaction plane.

In some circumstances, the resistance of absorption of one or both the gases may be entirely on the gas side. This case is discussed in Section 6.2.3.

6.2.2. Rate of Absorption for Various Mechanisms

Fast Pseudo-mth-Order Reactions

For the pseudo-*m*th(or *m*′th)-order regime, the presence of one gas does not affect the rate of absorption of the other gas, and the rate of absorption of each gas can be calculated as though the gases were present individually. Thus, the equations given in Section 2.4 may be used here. The enhancement factors for the gases A_1 and A_2 are given as

$$\phi_{A_1} = \frac{R_{A_1}}{k_L[A_1^*]} = \frac{\sqrt{M_{A_1}}}{\tanh\sqrt{M_{A_1}}} \tag{6.3a}$$

and

$$\phi_{A_2} = \frac{R_{A_2}}{k_L[A_2^*]} = \frac{\sqrt{M_{A_2}}}{\tanh\sqrt{M_{A_2}}} \tag{6.3b}$$

If the values of $\sqrt{M_{A_1}}$ and $\sqrt{M_{A_2}}$ are greater than 3, the hyperbolic terms in the denominator are approximately unity and the specific rate of absorption of each gas is given by the familiar equation for absorption accompanied by a fast pseudo-mth-order reaction.

Example: Absorption of Isobutylene and Butene-2 in Aqueous H_2SO_4

Calculate the rates of absorption of isobutylene and butene-2 in 70% w/w (11.5 *M*) sulfuric acid under the following conditions:

Partial pressure of isobutylene

$$= 0.5 \text{ atm}$$

Partial pressure of butene-2

$$= 0.5 \text{ atm}$$

Henry's constant for isobutylene (A_1) in 70% H_2SO_4

$$= 4.62 \times 10^{-7} \text{ mol/cm}^3 \text{ atm}$$

Henry's constant for butene-2 (A_2) in 70% H_2SO_4

$$= 3.78 \times 10^{-7} \text{ mol/cm}^3 \text{ atm}$$

Temperature

$$= 30°\text{C}$$

True liquid-side mass transfer coefficient,

$$k_L = 2 \times 10^{-4} \text{ cm/sec}$$

The regime of absorption for both gases can be found by employing expression 6.1. For this purpose the values of $\sqrt{M_{A_1}}$, $\sqrt{M_{A_2}}$, q_{A_1}, and q_{A_2} are required. The relevant data are

$$[A_1^*]\left(\sqrt{D_{A_1} k_{A_1}}\right)$$

$$= 4.27 \times 10^{-7} \text{ mol/cm}^2 \text{ sec} \quad \text{(Gehlawat, 1969)}$$

$$[A_2^*]\left(\sqrt{D_{A_2} k_{A_2}}\right)$$

$$= 1.1 \times 10^{-8} \text{ mol/cm}^2 \text{ sec} \quad \text{(Sankholkar, 1974)}$$

$$\sqrt{M_{A_1}} = \frac{\sqrt{D_{A_1} k_{A_1}}}{k_L} = 9242,$$

$$\sqrt{M_{A_2}} = \frac{\sqrt{D_{A_2} k_{A_2}}}{k_L} = 291$$

$$q_{A_1} = \frac{[B_o]}{Z_{A_1}[A_1^*]} = \frac{11.5 \times 10^{-3}}{2.3 \times 10^{-7}} = 5 \times 10^4$$

$$q_{A_2} = \frac{[B_o]}{Z_{A_2}[A_2^*]} = \frac{11.5 \times 10^{-3}}{1.89 \times 10^{-7}} = 6 \times 10^4$$

(For the purpose of checking the conditions given by expression 6.1, D_B has been assumed to be equal to D_{A_1} and D_{A_2}.)

$$q_{A_1A_2} = \frac{[B_o]}{Z_{A_1}[A_1^*] + Z_{A_2}[A_2^*]}$$

$$= \frac{11.5 \times 10^{-3}}{4.19 \times 10^{-7}} = 2.74 \times 10^4$$

Applying expression 6.1, we get

$$\frac{\sqrt{M_{A_1}}}{q_{A_1}} + \frac{\sqrt{M_{A_2}}}{q_{A_2}} = 0.184 + 0.47 \times 10^{-2} = 0.188$$

$$1 + \frac{1}{q_{A_1A_2}} = 1 + \frac{1}{2.74 \times 10^4} \simeq 1$$

Comparing these two values, we can see that the conditions for the fast pseudo-first-order reaction regime are satisfied. The specific rates of absorption are then given by

$$R_{A_1} = [A_1^*]\sqrt{D_{A_1} k_{A_1}} = 4.27 \times 10^{-7} \text{ mol/cm}^2 \text{ sec}$$

$$R_{A_2} = [A_2^*]\sqrt{D_{A_2} k_{A_2}} = 1.1 \times 10^{-8} \text{ mol/cm}^2 \text{ sec}$$

Depletion regime

The differential equations based on the film theory for the case of absorption accompanied by fast chemical reaction of two gases are similar to those for the single gas absorption given in Section 2.7. Thus, for a general-order (m, n and m', n') chemical reaction the following equations will be valid:

$$D_{A_1} \frac{d^2[A_1]}{dx^2} = k_{A_1}[A_1]^m[B]^n \quad (6.4)$$

$$D_{A_2} \frac{d^2[A_2]}{dx^2} = k_{A_2}[A_2]^{m'}[B]^{n'} \quad (6.5)$$

$$D_B \frac{d^2[B]}{dx^2} = Z_{A_1} k_{A_1}[A_1]^m[B]^n + Z_{A_2} k_{A_2}[A_2]^{m'}[B]^{n'} \quad (6.6)$$

The boundary conditions are, at

$$x = 0: \quad [A_1] = [A_1^*], \quad [A_2] = [A_2^*],$$

$$[B] = [B_i], \frac{d[B]}{dx} = 0 \qquad (6.7)$$

and at

$$x = \delta: \quad [A_1] = [A_2] = 0, \quad [B] = [B_o] \quad (6.8)$$

The required absorption rates are given by

$$R_{A_1} = -D_{A_1}\left(\frac{d[A_1]}{dx}\right)_{x=0} \qquad (6.9)$$

$$R_{A_2} = -D_{A_2}\left(\frac{d[A_2]}{dx}\right)_{x=0} \qquad (6.10)$$

These equations have been formulated on the basis of the film theory. Similar equations can be formulated on the basis of the penetration theory. Numerical solutions to this problem based on the penetration theory have been obtained by Goettler and Pigford (1964). Analytical solutions based on the film theory have been derived independently by Onda et al. (1970a), and Ramachandran and Sharma (1968). The film theory solution is obtained by employing a procedure similar to that employed by Hikita and Asai (1964) for the absorption of a single gas (see Section 2.7). Thus by eliminating the kinetic terms in Eq. 6.6 by means of Eqs. 6.4 and 6.5 we obtain

$$D_B\frac{d^2[B]}{dx^2} = Z_{A_1}D_{A_1}\frac{d^2[A_1]}{dx^2} + Z_{A_2}D_{A_2}\frac{d^2[A_2]}{dx^2} \qquad (6.11)$$

Integrating this equation twice and using the boundary conditions 6.7 to 6.10, we get an equation for the interfacial concentration of the reactive species B:

$$[B_i] = [B_o] + Z_{A_1}[A_1^*]\frac{D_{A_1}}{D_B} + Z_{A_2}[A_2^*]\frac{D_{A_2}}{D_B} - \frac{Z_{A_1}R_{A_1}}{k_L}\frac{D_{A_1}}{D_B} - \frac{Z_{A_2}R_{A_2}}{k_L}\frac{D_{A_2}}{D_B} \qquad (6.12)$$

The values of R_{A_1} and R_{A_2} are now calculated by using the value of the interfacial concentration of B in the pseudo-first-order equation. Thus we have

$$\phi_{A_1} = \sqrt{M_{A_1}}\left(\frac{[B_i]}{[B_o]}\right)^{n/2} \qquad (6.13)$$

$$\phi_{A_2} = \sqrt{M_{A_2}}\left(\frac{[B_i]}{[B_o]}\right)^{n'/2} \qquad (6.14)$$

provided that $\sqrt{M_{A_1}}$ and $\sqrt{M_{A_2}}$ are greater than 3. Equation 6.12 can also be written in the dimensionless form in terms of the parameters $\sqrt{M_{A_1}}$ and $\sqrt{M_{A_2}}$ to facilitate calculations. Thus for a second-order reaction (1—1) Eq. 6.12 reduces to the following form:

$$\frac{[B_i]}{[B_o]} + \left(\frac{\sqrt{M_{A_1}}}{q_{A_1}} + \frac{\sqrt{M_{A_2}}}{q_{A_2}}\right)\sqrt{\frac{[B_i]}{[B_o]}} - \left(1 + \frac{1}{q_{A_1A_2}}\right) = 0 \qquad (6.15)$$

provided that $\sqrt{M_{A_1}}, \sqrt{M_{A_2}} > 3$.

When the second gas A_2 is not present, Eq. 6.15 reduces to the following equation:

$$\frac{[B_i]}{[B_o]} + \frac{\sqrt{M_{A_1}}}{q_{A_1}}\sqrt{\frac{[B_i]}{[B_o]}} - \left(1 + \frac{1}{q_{A_1}}\right) = 0 \qquad (6.15a)$$

provided that $\sqrt{M_{A_1}} > 3$; Eq. 6.15a is applicable to the case of a single gas absorption under depletion conditions (Eq. 6.15a is the same as Eq. 2.110). It has been shown that this analytical solution and the numerical solutions derived by Goettler and Pigford (1964) agree well (Ramachandran and Sharma, 1971).

Example: Absorption of CO_2 and COS in Aqueous Methylaminoethanol

Calculate the specific rate of absorption of CO_2 (A_1) and COS (A_2) when absorbed in a 1 *M* aqueous solution of methylaminoethanol (MAE):

Temperature

$= 25°C$

Partial pressure of CO_2 (A_1)

$= 0.4$ atm

Partial pressure of COS (A_2)

$= 0.2$ atm

Henry's constant for CO_2

$= 3.35 \times 10^{-5}$ mol/cm^3 atm

Henry's constant for COS

$= 2.09 \times 10^{-5}$ mol/cm^3 atm

Diffusivity of CO_2 in the solution

$= 1.47 \times 10^{-5}$ cm^2/sec

Diffusivity of COS in the solution

$= 1.47 \times 10^{-5}$ cm^2/sec

Values of D_B/D_{A_1} and D_B/D_{A_2}

$= 0.61$

$$k_{CO_2-MAE} = 3.162 \times 10^7 \text{ cm}^3/\text{mol sec}$$

$$k_{COS-MAE} = 2.09 \times 10^5 \text{ cm}^3/\text{mol sec}$$

$$k_L = 0.01 \text{ cm/sec}$$

$$Z_{CO_2} = Z_{COS} = 2$$

To determine the regime of absorption, the values of $\sqrt{M_{A_1}}$, $\sqrt{M_{A_2}}$, q_{A_1}, q_{A_2}, and $q_{A_1A_2}$ for both gases are required.

$$\sqrt{M_{A_1}} = \frac{\sqrt{(1.47 \times 10^{-5})(3.162 \times 10^7)(1 \times 10^{-3})}}{1 \times 10^{-2}}$$

$$= 68.17$$

$$\sqrt{M_{A_2}} = \frac{\sqrt{(1.47 \times 10^{-5})(2.09 \times 10^5)(1 \times 10^{-3})}}{1 \times 10^{-2}}$$

$$= 5.54$$

$$q_{A_1} = \frac{1 \times 10^{-3}}{2 \times 0.4 \times (3.35 \times 10^{-5})}\sqrt{0.61}$$

$$= 29.14$$

$$q_{A_2} = \frac{1 \times 10^{-3}}{2 \times 0.2 \times (2.09 \times 10^{-5})}\sqrt{0.61}$$

$$= 93.42$$

$$\frac{\sqrt{M_{A_1}}}{q_{A_1}} + \frac{\sqrt{M_{A_2}}}{q_{A_2}} = \frac{68.17}{29.14} + \frac{5.54}{93.42}$$

$$= 2.398$$

$$\frac{1}{q_{A_1A_2}} = \frac{2(0.4 \times 3.35 + 0.2 \times 2.09) \times 10^{-5} \times \sqrt{0.61}}{1 \times 10^{-3}}$$

$$= 0.02747$$

Using these values in expression 6.1, we see that

$$\frac{\sqrt{M_{A_1}}}{q_{A_1}} + \frac{\sqrt{M_{A_2}}}{q_{A_2}} \text{ and } 1 + \frac{1}{q_{A_1A_2}}$$

are comparable and thus the condition for the depletion regime is satisfied. To obtain R_{A_1} and R_{A_2} we need the value of $[B_i]$. For this purpose the value of $[B_i]/[B_o]$ is obtained from the positive root of Eq. 6.15.

$$\eta = \sqrt{\frac{[B_i]}{[B_o]}} = 0.371$$

The values of R_{A_1} and R_{A_2} are then obtained as

$$R_{A_1} = k_L[A_1^*]\sqrt{M_{A_1}}\,\eta$$

$$= (1 \times 10^{-2})$$

$$\times (1.34 \times 10^{-5}) \times 68.17 \times 0.371$$

$$= 3.389 \times 10^{-6} \text{ mol/cm}^2 \text{ sec}$$

$$R_{A_2} = k_L[A_2^*]\sqrt{M_{A_2}}\,\eta$$

$$= (1 \times 10^{-2})$$

$$\times (4.18 \times 10^{-6}) \times 5.54 \times 0.371$$

$$= 8.59 \times 10^{-8} \text{ mol/cm}^2 \text{ sec}$$

The rate of absorption of A_2 when present alone is

$$R_{A_2} = [A_2^*]\sqrt{D_{A_2}k_{A_2}[B_o]} = k_L[A_2^*]\sqrt{M_{A_2}}$$

$$= (1 \times 10^{-2}) \times (4.18 \times 10^{-6}) \times 5.6$$

$$= 2.34 \times 10^{-7} \text{ mol/cm}^2 \text{ sec}$$

The value of $\sqrt{[B_i]/[B_o]}$ when A_1 is present alone is obtained by solving Eq. 6.15a.

$$\eta = \sqrt{\frac{[B_i]}{[B_o]}} = 0.380$$

Therefore,

$$R_{A_1} = k_L[A_1^*]\sqrt{M_{A_1}}\,\eta$$

$$= (1 \times 10^{-2})$$

$$\times (1.34 \times 10^{-5}) \times 68.17 \times 0.380$$

$$= 3.471 \times 10^{-6} \text{ mol/cm}^2 \text{ sec}$$

It can be seen that the rate of absorption of A_1 is practically unaffected by the presence of A_2, whereas that of A_2 is significantly affected by the presence of A_1. While computing q_{A_1} and q_{A_2} we have taken the ratio of diffusivities as the square root, in line with comments made in Sections 2.7 and 3.4.1.

Absorption of Two Gases, One of Which Reacts Instantaneously in the Liquid Phase

Under certain conditions (when $\sqrt{M_{A_1}} \gg q_{A_1}$) the absorption of gas A_1 is accompanied by an instantaneous reaction. The species A_1 and B cannot coexist in the liquid in these circumstances and the concentration of B is zero if the concentration of A_1 is finite, and vice versa. The reaction of gas A_1 occurs at a reaction plane λ. The second gas (A_2) diffuses beyond λ and reacts in the zone from λ to δ. The concentration profiles for various reaction regimes for A_2 are shown in Figure 6.2. The rate of absorption of A_1 is given by the diffusional flux of A_1 at the point $x = \lambda$:

$$R_{A_1} = \frac{D_{A_1}[A_1^*]}{\lambda} \tag{6.16}$$

The following differential equations govern the transport of species A_2 and B in the region from λ to δ:

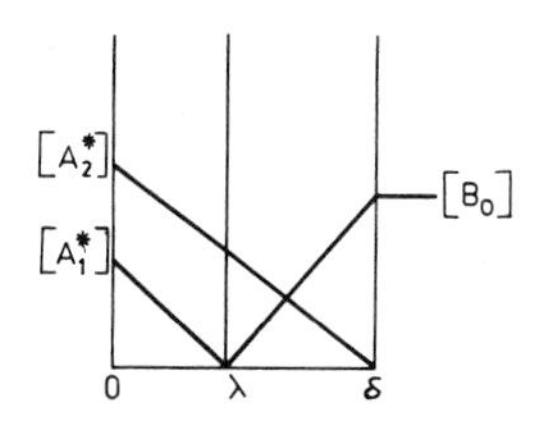

(a) ABSORPTION OF GAS A_2 ACCOMPANIED BY A SLOW REACTION

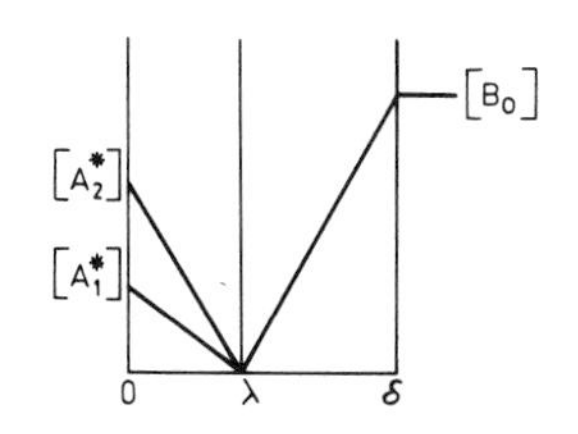

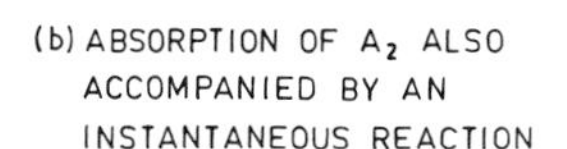
(b) ABSORPTION OF A_2 ALSO ACCOMPANIED BY AN INSTANTANEOUS REACTION

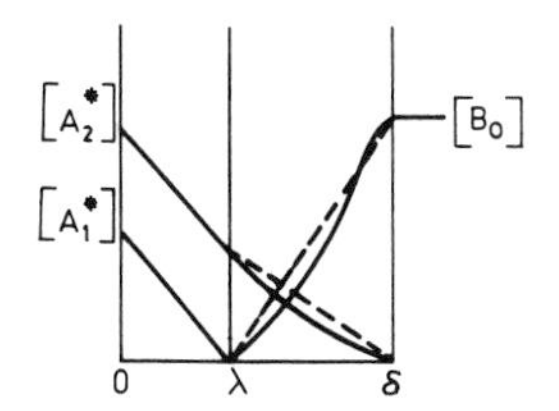

(c) ABSORPTION OF A_2 ACCOMPANIED BY A FAST SECOND ORDER REACTION

---- ASSUMED LINEAR PROFILE FOR ANALYTICAL SOLUTION.

Figure 6.2. Simultaneous absorption of two gases: concentration profiles for the cases when the absorption of gas A_1 is accompanied by an instantaneous reaction.

$$D_{A_2}\frac{d^2[A_2]}{dx^2} = k_{A_2}[A_2][B] \tag{6.17}$$

$$D_B\frac{d^2[B]}{dx^2} = Z_{A_2}k_{A_2}[A_2][B] \tag{6.18}$$

Species A_2 does not undergo any chemical reaction in the zone from 0 to λ because the concentration of the reactive species B is zero in this zone. Hence, the following differential equation governs the transport of A_2 in the zone from 0 to λ:

$$D_{A_2}\frac{d^2[A_2]}{dx^2} = 0 \qquad \text{for } 0 < x < \lambda \tag{6.19}$$

The boundary conditions can be stipulated as usual, and the rates of absorption of A_1 and A_2 are given by the diffusional fluxes of the respective gases at the interface. In addition, we have a relation for the balance of fluxes at the reaction plane λ:

$$-Z_{A_1}D_{A_1}\left(\frac{d[A_1]}{dx}\right)_{x=\lambda} = D_B\left(\frac{d[B]}{dx}\right)_{x=\lambda} \tag{6.20}$$

The equations are nonlinear and cannot be solved analytically. Ramachandran and Sharma (1971) have obtained an analytical solution to the problem based on the assumption of a linearized concentration profile for A_2 and B in the zone from λ to δ. Goettler and Pigford (1968) and Ouwerkerk (1968) have also obtained approximate analytical solutions to the problem on the basis of somewhat similar assumptions. The solution proposed by Ramachandran and Sharma for predicting the rate of absorption consists of a trial-and-error procedure using the following steps.

1. Assume a value for the specific rate of absorption of the instantaneously reacting gas A_1. Calculate the position of the reaction plane for A_1 by Eq. 6.16:

$$\lambda = \frac{D_{A_1}[A_1^*]}{R_{A_1}}$$

2. Check the assumed value of R_{A_1} by using the following equation:

$$R_{A_1} = \frac{D_B[B_o]}{Z_{A_1}(\delta - \lambda)} - \frac{k_{A_2}[B_o](\delta - \lambda)}{12 Z_{A_1}} \times \left\{ Z_{A_2}\frac{D_{A_2}}{D_B}[A_2^*] + Z_{A_1}\frac{D_{A_1}}{D_B}[A_1^*] - \frac{\lambda}{\delta}\left([B_o] + Z_{A_1}\frac{D_{A_1}}{D_B}[A_1^*] + Z_{A_2}\frac{D_{A_2}}{D_B}[A_2^*] \right) \right\} \tag{6.21}$$

3. The value of R_{A_1} can be used to calculate the value of the rate of absorption of the second gas R_{A_2} as follows:

$$Z_{A_2}R_{A_2} = \frac{D_B}{\delta}\left([B_o] + Z_{A_1}[A_1^*]\frac{D_{A_1}}{D_B} + Z_{A_2}[A_2^*]\frac{D_{A_2}}{D_B} \right) - Z_{A_1}R_{A_1} \tag{6.22}$$

Absorption of Both Gases Accompanied by Instantaneous Reactions

Under certain conditions (when $\sqrt{M_{A_1}} \gg q_{A_1}$ and $\sqrt{M_{A_2}} \gg q_{A_2}$) the absorption of both gases will be accompanied by instantaneous reactions. Roper et al. (1962) have given a theoretical treatment to this case based on the penetration theory. Astarita (1967) has given a film theory solution to the problem that is based on a stoichiometric balance of fluxes at the reaction plane (see Figure 6.1*c*).

$$D_B\frac{[B_o]}{\delta - \lambda} = Z_{A_1}\frac{D_{A_1}[A_1^*]}{\lambda} + Z_{A_2}\frac{D_{A_2}[A_2^*]}{\lambda} \tag{6.23}$$

The specific rates of absorption are given by

$$R_{A_1} = \frac{D_{A_1}[A_1^*]}{\lambda} \tag{6.24}$$

$$R_{A_2} = \frac{D_{A_2}[A_2^*]}{\lambda} \tag{6.25}$$

Elimination of λ from Eqs. 6.23–6.25 gives

$$R_{A_1} = k_L[A_1^*]\left(1 + \frac{\dfrac{[B_o]}{Z_{A_1}[A_1^*]}\dfrac{D_B}{D_{A_1}}}{1 + \dfrac{Z_{A_2}[A_2^*]}{Z_{A_1}[A_1^*]}\dfrac{D_{A_2}}{D_{A_1}}} \right) \tag{6.26}$$

A similar equation holds for the rate of absorption of gas A_2.

The solution of Roper et al. (1962) based on the penetration model is similar to expression 6.26 except that the various diffusivity ratios appear as square roots. Their solution is as follows:

$$R_{A_1} = k_L[A_1^*]\left(\sqrt{\frac{D_{A_1}}{D_B}} + \frac{\dfrac{[B_o]}{Z_{A_1}[A_1^*]}\sqrt{\dfrac{D_B}{D_{A_1}}}}{1 + \dfrac{Z_{A_2}[A_2^*]D_{A_2}}{Z_{A_1}[A_1^*]D_{A_1}}} \right) \tag{6.27}$$

provided that $q_{A_1} > 3$. A similar equation holds for

R_{A_2}. The solutions based on the film and penetration theories agree exactly for the case of equal diffusivities.

6.2.3. Absorption of Two Gases, One of Which Is Absorbed under Gas-Film-Controlled Conditions

Under certain conditions the resistance to the transfer of one gas, say A_1, might be entirely on the gas side. The species A_1 then diffuses through the gas film and reacts at a reaction plane that is very close to the interface. The specific rate of absorption of A_1 is then given by

$$R_{A_1} = k_{G_{A_1}} p_{A_1} \tag{6.28}$$

The conditions under which Eq. 6.28 is likely to be valid are as follows:

$$Z_{A_1} k_{G_{A_1}} p_{A_1} \ll k_L [B_o]$$

and

$$\sqrt{M_{A_1}} > \frac{[B_o]}{Z_{A_1} H_{A_1} p_{A_1}} \tag{6.29}$$

or

$$k_{G_{A_1}} \ll H_{A_1} \sqrt{M_{A_1}} \tag{6.29a}$$

The reaction of species A_2 occurs at a finite rate in the region from 0 to δ. The rate of absorption of A_2 can be predicted by using a modified pseudo-first-order reaction equation (Ramachandran and Sharma, 1971).

Example: Absorption of H_2S _and_ CO_2 _in Aqueous_ MAE

Consider the simultaneous absorption of H_2S (A_1) and CO_2 (A_2) in aqueous 1 M methylaminoethanol (MAE) under the following conditions:

$$k_L = 1 \times 10^{-2} \text{ cm/sec}$$

$$k_{CO_2-MAE} = 3.16 \times 10^7 \text{ cm}^3\text{/mol sec}$$

Interfacial concentration of H_2S

$$= 3 \times 10^{-4} \text{ mol/cm}^3$$

Concentration of MAE

$$= 1 \times 10^{-3} \text{ mol/cm}^3$$

Interfacial concentration of CO_2

$$= 5.0 \times 10^{-5} \text{ mol/cm}^3$$

$$D_{H_2S} = D_{CO_2} = 1.6 \times 10^{-5} \text{ cm}^2\text{/sec}$$

$$\frac{D_{\text{amine}}}{D_{H_2S}} = \frac{D_{\text{amine}}}{D_{CO_2}} = 0.56$$

$$Z_{H_2S} = 1$$

$$Z_{CO_2} = 2$$

Assume that gas-side resistance is absent. The reaction between H_2S and the amines is instantaneous (Danckwerts and Sharma, 1966). To prove that the absorption of CO_2 is accompanied by an instantaneous reaction we can compare the values of $\sqrt{M_{A_2}}$ and q_{A_2}

$$\sqrt{M_{A_2}} = \frac{\sqrt{D_{CO_2} k_{CO_2-MAE} [\text{MAE}]}}{k_L}$$

$$= \frac{\sqrt{(1.6 \times 10^{-5})(3.16 \times 10^7)(1 \times 10^{-3})}}{1 \times 10^{-2}}$$

$$= 71.06$$

$$q_{A_2} = \frac{[\text{MAE}]}{Z_{CO_2} [A^*]_{CO_2}} \sqrt{\frac{D_{\text{amine}}}{D_{CO_2}}}$$

$$= \frac{1 \times 10^{-3}}{2 \times (5.0 \times 10^{-5})} \times 0.75$$

$$= 7.5$$

Since $\sqrt{M_{A_2}} \gg q_{A_2}$, the absorption of CO_2 is accompanied by an instantaneous reaction even when present alone. Thus, in the presence of H_2S also, the absorption of CO_2 will be accompanied by an instantaneous reaction with the amine.

The specific rates of absorption of the two gases when absorbed simultaneously are given by Eq. 6.27

with the proper subscript of A_1 or A_2. Thus,

$$R_{A_1} = k_L[A_1^*]\left(\sqrt{\frac{D_{A_1}}{D_B}} + \frac{\dfrac{[B_o]}{Z_{A_1}[A_1^*]}\sqrt{\dfrac{D_B}{D_{A_1}}}}{1 + \dfrac{Z_{A_2}[A_2^*]D_{A_2}}{Z_{A_1}[A_1^*]D_{A_1}}}\right)$$

$$= (1 \times 10^{-2}) \times (3 \times 10^{-4})$$

$$\times\left[1.33 + \frac{\dfrac{1 \times 10^{-3}}{1 \times (3 \times 10^{-4})} \times 0.75}{1 + \dfrac{2 \times (5 \times 10^{-5}) \times (1.6 \times 10^{-5})}{1 \times (3 \times 10^{-4}) \times (1.6 \times 10^{-5})}}\right]$$

$$= 9.63 \times 10^{-6} \text{ mol/cm}^2 \text{ sec}$$

$$R_{A_2} = k_L[A_2^*]\left(\sqrt{\frac{D_{A_2}}{D_B}} + \frac{\dfrac{[B_o]}{Z_{A_2}[A_2^*]}\sqrt{\dfrac{D_B}{D_{A_2}}}}{1 + \dfrac{Z_{A_1}[A_1^*]D_{A_1}}{Z_{A_2}[A_2^*]D_{A_2}}}\right)$$

$$= (1 \times 10^{-2}) \times (5 \times 10^{-5})$$

$$\times\left[1.33 + \frac{\dfrac{1 \times 10^{-3}}{2 \times (5 \times 10^{-5})} \times 0.75}{1 + \dfrac{1 \times (3 \times 10^{-4}) \times (1.6 \times 10^{-5})}{2 \times (5 \times 10^{-5}) \times (1.6 \times 10^{-5})}}\right]$$

$$= 1.60 \times 10^{-6} \text{ mol/cm}^2 \text{ sec}$$

The rates of absorption of the two gases when present alone are

$$R_{A_1} = k_L[A_1^*]\left(\sqrt{\frac{D_{A_1}}{D_B}} + \frac{[B_o]}{Z_{A_1}[A_1^*]}\sqrt{\frac{D_B}{D_{A_1}}}\right)$$

$$= (1 \times 10^{-2}) \times (3 \times 10^{-4})$$

$$\times\left(1.33 + \frac{1 \times 10^{-3}}{1 \times (3 \times 10^{-4})} \times 0.75\right)$$

$$= 1.149 \times 10^{-5} \text{ mol/cm}^2 \text{ sec}$$

$$R_{A_2} = k_L[A_2^*]\left(\sqrt{\frac{D_{A_2}}{D_B}} + \frac{[B_o]}{Z_{A_2}[A_2^*]}\sqrt{\frac{D_B}{D_{A_2}}}\right)$$

$$= (1 \times 10^{-2}) \times (5 \times 10^{-5})$$

$$\times\left(1.33 + \frac{1 \times 10^{-3}}{2 \times (5 \times 10^{-5})} \times 0.75\right)$$

$$= 4.41 \times 10^{-6} \text{ mol/cm}^2 \text{ sec}$$

It can be seen that the rates of absorption of the two gases when present alone are considerably higher than those when the gases are present together.

6.2.4. Absorption of Two Gases Accompanied by Reaction in the Bulk Liquid

The foregoing treatment is applicable to reactions occurring in the diffusion film surrounding the gas–liquid interface. In some cases, the absorption of two gases may be accompanied by reaction in the bulk liquid. This will be the case if the rate of chemical reaction of one or both of the gases is not fast enough to manifest in the liquid film. The condition under which this occurs, say for species A_1, is

$$\sqrt{M_{A_1}} \ll 1$$

The rate of absorption of A_1 when this condition is satisfied is given by

$$R_{A_1} = k_L[A_1^*] \tag{6.30}$$

provided the concentration of dissolved A_1 in the bulk liquid is zero. This will be the case when

$$lk_{A_1}[A_1^*]^m[B_o]^n \gg k_L a[A_1^*] \tag{6.31}$$

When the reaction of the gas A_1 occurs in the bulk liquid, the concentration profile of species B is unaffected by the presence of A_1. Thus, the species A_1 will not affect the rate of absorption of A_2 under these conditions.

6.3. SOME EXAMPLES OF THE ABSORPTION AND REACTION OF TWO GASES

6.3.1. Simultaneous Absorption of Hydrogen Sulfide and Carbon Dioxide

The simultaneous absorption of H_2S and CO_2 is often encountered in natural gas processing plants and in synthetic ammonia plants. It may be necessary to remove hydrogen sulfide selectively from the gas mixture. The absorbents generally employed are as follows:

1. Carbonate solutions (Garnell et al., 1958; Gioia, 1967);
2. Triethanolamine solutions (Danckwerts and Sharma, 1966);
3. Phosphate buffer solutions (Gioia and Marrucci, 1970);
4. Solutions of mono-, di-, or triethanolamines or aqueous ammonia (Danckwerts and Sharma, 1966; Sada et al., 1976a) or diglycolamine (Dingman and Moore, 1968) or solutions of diisopropanolamine (Ouwerkerk, 1978);
5. Aqueous caustic soda (Astarita and Gioia, 1965).

The absorption of H_2S is accompanied by an instantaneous reaction in these absorbents. In some cases (when the condition given by expression 6.29a is valid) the absorption of H_2S may be controlled entirely by gas-side resistance. In most cases the absorption of CO_2 is accompanied by reactions in the bulk liquid (regime 2) when the absorbent used is carbonate, phosphate buffer, or triethanolamine solutions. Hence, the selectivity of these solutions with respect to the absorption of H_2S is very high. On the other hand, CO_2 reacts much faster in solutions of caustic soda, mono- or diethanolamine solutions, and diglycolamine solutions. The selectivity of these solutions for absorbing H_2S will be relatively poor. In some cases, it may be possible to absorb H_2S selectively by employing hydrodynamic conditions that give a large value of k_L. For example, if aqueous solutions of ammonia or diisopropanolamine are employed to absorb a mixture of H_2S and CO_2, the use of a plate column can be recommended. This is due to the high value of k_L in the plate column, which causes the reaction of CO_2 to occur predominantly in the bulk. On the other hand, in a packed column, the value of $\sqrt{M}$ for CO_2 would be higher and an appreciable amount of CO_2 would react in the film itself, thereby reducing the selectivity with respect to H_2S. For example, at a temperature of 20°C the rate constant for the absorption of CO_2 in ammonia is 3.05×10^5 cm^3/mol sec. Hence the value of $\sqrt{D_{CO_2} k_2 [B_o]}$ would be 3.0×10^{-2} cm/sec for an amine concentration of 2×10^{-4} mol/cm^3. In a packed column, where the typical value of k_L is around 6×10^{-3} cm/sec, the value of $\sqrt{M}$ is 5. In a plate column, on the other hand, for a typical k_L value of 6×10^{-2} cm/sec, the value of $\sqrt{M}$ is 0.5, which indicates that most of the reaction of CO_2 occurs in the bulk. Ouwerkerk (1978) has shown, with experimental data from 11-cm- and 45-cm-diameter plate columns, that high selectivity is realized with solutions of diisopropanolamine in plate columns. He also made measurements in a stirred cell with individual gases, and the experimental values of specific rate of mass transfer agreed with the predicted values. In the laboratory plate columns, values of k_G, k_L, and the effective interfacial area were measured by employing chemical methods. An 8.5-m-diameter plate column was designed on the basis of these data and the theory of simultaneous absorption with reaction of two gases.

Oloman et al. (1969) describe a process in which a solution of Na_2CO_3 and $NaHCO_3$ at equilibrium at the prevalent CO_2 concentration in the gas was used as a scrubbing reagent. This mixture, having a pH of about 9, would not absorb CO_2 but would absorb H_2S. The reaction of H_2S would be to some extent reversible at this pH:

$$H_2S + CO_3^{2-} \rightleftharpoons HS^- + HCO_3^-$$

To make the reaction proceed entirely to the right, NaHS was oxidized with air or oxygen to $Na_2S_2O_3$ in the presence of an iron salt that acted as an oxidation catalyst:

$$2NaHS + 2O_2 \rightarrow Na_2S_2O_3 + H_2O$$

6.3.2. Absorption of C_4 Fractions in Sulfuric Acid

A typical C_4 fraction from a refinery stream and a naphtha cracker contains 13–25% isobutylene along with varying proportions of butene-1, *cis*- and *trans*-butene-2, and butadiene. The mixture, after the recovery of butadiene, is absorbed in a 50–55% w/w aqueous sulfuric acid with a view to recovering the isobutylene. High selectivity with respect to isobutylene may be required in these cases. The sulfuric acid concentration of 50–55% is very selective for isobutylene. For this concentration range, the transfer of isobutylene is under a fast pseudo-first-order mechanism and the transfer of butenes is diffusion controlled (regime 2). The relative rates of absorption of these gases in aqueous sulfuric acid have been studied by Davis and Schuler (1930). The kinetics of absorption of isobutylene in sulfuric acid solutions has been studied by Gehlawat and Sharma (1968) (see Section 3.4.7.) The kinetics of the absorption of

2-butene and 2-methyl-2-butene in various concentrations of sulfuric acid has been studied by Sankholkar and Sharma (1973).

6.3.3. Absorption of a Mixture of Mercaptans and Carbon Dioxide in Alkaline Solutions

Lites et al. (1968) have performed a study of the absorption of a mixture of mercaptans and carbon dioxide in an alkaline solution in a wetted-wall column. The reaction of mercaptans with the OH^- ion is instantaneous. For low partial pressures of mercaptans and relatively high OH^- concentrations the process of the absorption of mercaptans becomes entirely gas film controlled.

6.3.4. Absorption of a Mixture of Hydrogen Cyanide and Carbon Dioxide in Alkaline Solutions

This situation is encountered in the manufacture of hydrogen cyanide by ammoxidation of methane. Taylor (1969) has studied experimentally the absorption of a mixture of these substances in aqueous alkaline solutions. Under the experimental conditions a plate efficiency of 66% was obtained for HCN and a plate efficiency of 4–5% for the absorption of CO_2. The hydrodynamic conditions in these experiments were such that in the absence of HCN, the absorption of CO_2 was under pseudo-first-order conditions. In the presence of HCN, however, the absorption of CO_2 changes to a depletion condition (there is a significant drop in the OH^- ion concentration in the film), with a consequent drop in efficiency. The experimental results of Taylor agree broadly with the theory discussed earlier.

6.3.5. Simultaneous Absorption of NO_2 and NO and NO / NO_2 and SO_2 in Aqueous Alkaline Solutions

A mixture of NO_2 and NO is absorbed in aqueous solutions of sodium hydroxide and/or sodium carbonate and carbonated ammonia for the manufacture of sodium nitrite and ammonium nitrite, respectively. The composition of the product with respect to nitrite–nitrate content depends on the ratio of NO_2 and NO; with a stoichiometric mixture, essentially pure nitrite may be produced. There is very limited information on the kinetics of absorption in this system. Ninomiya and Fuji (1978) have reported that in a packed column operated in a cocurrent downflow manner, the selectivity with respect to nitrate formation when a rich mixture of NO_2 and NO is absorbed in carbonated ammonia solutions depends on the flow regime (see Section 13.2 for different flow regimes). This presumably arises out of large differences in the value of k_L and a in different flow regimes. The importance of the gas-phase reaction has not been adequately covered in the literature.

Simultaneous absorption of lean SO_2 and NO_x in stack gases in aqueous alkaline solutions is of some practical relevance in pollution abatement. The specific rate of absorption of lean NO_2 in aqueous alkaline sulfite solution is reasonably good (see Section 3.4.5, under gas–liquid reactions). The specific rate of absorption of lean NO_2 in aqueous solutions of sodium hydroxide increases in the presence of SO_2 in the gas phase as sodium sulfite, formed as a product of the reaction between SO_2 and OH^-, reacts with NO_2 at a higher rate as compared to NaOH (Takeuchi and Yamanaka, 1978). If an aqueous solution of sodium sulfite is employed, then the specific rate of absorption of NO_2 decreases in the presence of SO_2 as the latter reacts with SO_3^{2-} to give HSO_3^-, which reacts at a lower rate with NO_2 as compared to SO_3^{2-}.

Sada et al. (1978) have studied the simultaneous absorption of SO_2 and NO in aqueous mixed solutions of sodium chlorite and sodium hydroxide. The presence of SO_2 substantially reduces the specific rate of absorption of NO.

6.3.6. Simultaneous Nitration of Benzene and Toluene

Hanson et al. (1971) and Hanson and Ismail (1977) have considered the simultaneous nitration of benzene and toluene from an equimolar mixture of the two. Under the conditions employed by these authors, the extraction of both benzene and toluene is accompanied by a fast pseudo-first-order reaction. Thus Eqs. 6.3a and 6.3b should hold, and the ratio of the specific rate of nitration of toluene (R_{A_2}) to that of benzene (R_{A_1}) should be given by

$$\frac{R_{A_2}}{R_{A_1}} = \frac{[A_2^*]\sqrt{D_{A_2}k_{A_2}}}{[A_1^*]\sqrt{D_{A_1}k_{A_1}}}$$

(The hyperbolic tangent values in the denominator are equal to unity.)

The substitution of the available physicochemical data from independent sources gives the value of

R_{A_2}/R_{A_1} as in the range of 1.5–2.5, which is in good agreement with the experimental value of 2.

A study of the competitive rates of nitration is sometimes employed in laboratory practice even under heterogeneous conditions. It should be realized that the ratio of the rate constants for the two reactants can be obtained only if both steps conform to either regime 1 or regime 3 (or to the regime between 2 and 3). Thus, for instance, let us say that the nitration of benzene was in regime 2 while that of toluene was in regime 3; then a study of the competitive rate of nitration of these two substances under heterogeneous conditions would not give us the value of k_{A_2}/k_{A_1}.

6.4. ABSORPTION OF TWO GASES FOLLOWED BY COMPLEX CHEMICAL REACTIONS

In Section 6.2 we considered a case of the absorption of two gases accompanied by single-step irreversible reactions. In some cases, the absorption of two gases may be followed by complex reactions. The problem may be of importance in some industrial processes. Some of the cases likely to be encountered are as follows:

1. Product of reaction of first gas acting as a reactant for the second gas (Onda et al., 1970b; Ramachandran and Sharma, 1971; da Silva and Danckwerts, 1973);
2. Reaction of the first gas yielding the second gas as a product (Ramachandran and Sharma, 1970);
3. Absorption of one or both the gases accompanied by reversible reactions (Ramachandran, 1971).

6.4.1. Reaction Product of the First Gas Acting as a Reactant for the Second Gas

The reaction scheme when the product of the reaction of one gas acts as a reactant or catalyst for the second gas can be represented as follows:

$$A_1 + B \rightarrow S$$

$$A_2 + S \rightarrow \text{products}$$

or

$$A_2 \xrightarrow{S} \text{products}$$

An example of a system of this type occurs when a mixture of chlorine and carbon dioxide is absorbed in caustic soda. Here the hypochlorite ions formed in the reaction of Cl_2 and OH^- ions act as a catalyst for the hydration reaction of CO_2.

In some cases, the reactive species B is regenerated as a consequence of the liquid-phase reaction of the gas A_2.

$$A_1 + B \rightarrow C + \text{products}$$

$$A_2 + C \rightarrow B$$

The theoretical aspects of the problem have been discussed by Onda et al. (1970b) and Ramachandran and Sharma (1971). Some examples of industrial processes to which this reaction scheme is probably applicable are given next.

Liquid-phase oxychlorination of C_2H_4 *to* $C_2H_4Cl_2$

$$C_2H_4 + 2CuCl_2 \rightarrow 2CuCl + C_2H_4Cl_2$$

$$\tfrac{1}{2}O_2 + 2CuCl + 2HCl \rightarrow 2CuCl_2 + H_2O$$

Wacker process for conversion of olefin into corresponding carbonyl compound

$$C_2H_4 + PdCl_2 + H_2O \rightarrow CH_3CHO + 2H^+ + 2Cl^- + Pd$$

$$Pd + 2CuCl_2 \rightarrow PdCl_2 + 2CuCl$$

$$\tfrac{1}{2}O_2 + 2CuCl + 2HCl \rightarrow 2CuCl_2 + H_2O$$

Shah and Kenney (1972) have developed a theoretical model for a reaction scheme of this type that takes into account the reversibility of the reaction. The proposed scheme is applicable to the case of the oxidation of sulfur dioxide in an ionic melt containing V_2O_5–pyrosulfate:

$$SO_2(g) + V_2O_5 \rightleftharpoons SO_3(g) + V_2O_4$$

$$\tfrac{1}{2}O_2(g) + V_2O_4 \rightleftharpoons V_2O_5$$

Some of the implications of the analytical solution to this problem proposed by Shah and Kenney are as follows:

1. The rates of absorption of SO_2 and O_2 are stronger functions of the D_{O_2}/D_{SO_2} ratio than

of the $D_{V_2O_5}/D_{SO_2}$ ratio.

2. The rate of desorption of SO_3 affects the overall rate.
3. An increase in the ratio of O_2 to SO_2 increases the enhancement factor for SO_2 absorption.

6.4.2. Absorption of Two Gases, A_1 and A_2, Where the Reaction of A_1 Results in the Formation of A_2

In some industrially important examples of the simultaneous absorption of two gases, A_1 and A_2, the gaseous species A_2 may be formed as a result of the liquid-phase reaction of gas A_1. Some examples of such systems are as follows:

1. Simultaneous absorption of $COCl_2$ and CO_2 in water and sodium carbonate buffer solutions:

$$COCl_2 + H_2O \rightarrow CO_2 + 2H^+ + 2Cl^-$$

2. Simultaneous absorption of SO_2 and CO_2 in carbonate–bicarbonate buffer solutions:

$$SO_2 + CO_3^{2-} \rightarrow CO_2 + SO_3^{2-}$$

3. Absorption of CO and O_2 in highly oxygenated hemoglobin solutions (La Force, 1966):

$$CO + O_2Hb \rightleftharpoons O_2 + COHb$$

where O_2Hb and COHb denote oxyhemoglobin and carboxyhemoglobin, respectively. This is a case where gas A_2 is formed as a result of the reversible reaction of gas A_1.

Ramachandran and Sharma (1970) have considered theoretical aspects of this problem for various cases. Consider a simple reaction scheme, formulated as

$$A_1 + B \rightarrow A_2 + C$$

where the reaction is assumed to be irreversible. In such systems, the rate of absorption of A_1 is not affected by the presence of A_2 and can be predicted by the usual equations for the absorption of a single gas, which were discussed in Chapter 2. When some reaction of A_1 occurs in the film the local concentration of A_2 at any point is increased. This reduces the concentration driving force for the transport of species A_2 and hence reduces the rate of absorption of A_2. It can be shown that the specific rate of absorption of gas A_2 is given by

$$R_{A_2} = k_L([A_2^*] - [A_{2,o}]) - R_{A_1} + k_L[A_1^*] \tag{6.32}$$

From Eq. 6.32 it is seen that the decrease in the rate of absorption of A_2 is given by the term $R_{A_1} - k_L[A_1^*]$. It can be shown that when the reaction of A_1 occurs entirely in the bulk (when $\sqrt{M_{A_1}} \ll 1$, $R_{A_1} = k_L[A_1^*]$) there will be no decrease in the rate of absorption of A_2 except through a stoichiometric increase in the bulk concentration of A_2. On the other hand, if the reaction of A_1 occurs entirely in the film, the rate of absorption of gas A_2 will be drastically reduced. As an illustration, consider the case of the absorption of a mixture of phosgene and carbon dioxide at 25°C in a bubble cap plate column.

Rate constant for the hydrolysis of phosgene,

$$k_{A_1} = 6\ \text{sec}^{-1}$$

$$D_{A_1} = 2 \times 10^{-5}\ \text{cm}^2/\text{sec}$$

$$k_L = 3 \times 10^{-2}\ \text{cm/sec}$$

Hence

$$\frac{\sqrt{D_{A_1} k_{A_1}}}{k_L} = 0.37$$

Thus, we find that most of the reaction of phosgene would occur in the bulk and there would be practically no decrease in the rate of absorption of carbon dioxide as a result of the presence of phosgene. On the other hand, consider the absorption at 35°C in a packed column. We have $k_{A_1} = 22\ \text{sec}^{-1}$, $k_L = 6 \times 10^{-3}$ cm/sec, $\sqrt{D_{A_1} k_{A_1}}/k_L = 3.5$. It is seen that the hydrolysis reaction of phosgene occurs in the film and the concentration of CO_2 in the liquid film is increased because of the hydrolysis reaction of phosgene. As a consequence, the rate of absorption of carbon dioxide is reduced.

A similar situation occurs when a mixture of phosgene and carbon dioxide is absorbed in sodium carbonate buffer solutions. Here, under certain conditions no CO_2 will be absorbed, even though the concentration of CO_2 in the bulk liquid may be zero. This is again due to the formation of CO_2 in the film as a result of the hydrolysis of phosgene (CO_2 does not react in the film).

6.4.3. Absorption of Two Gases Accompanied by Reversible Chemical Reactions

The absorption of a single gas accompanied by a reversible chemical reaction was discussed in Section 2.10. Likewise, the absorption of two gases may be accompanied by a reversible reaction. This problem can be represented as

$$A_1 + B \rightleftharpoons C_1 + C_2 \qquad \text{(i)}$$

$$A_2 + B \rightleftharpoons E_1 + E_2 \qquad \text{(ii)}$$

The species C_1 and E_1 may be the same in some cases. Reactions (i) and (ii) may be instantaneous or may proceed according to a finite rate. Some examples of the absorption of two gases accompanied by a reversible reaction follow.

Simultaneous absorption of H_2S *and* CO_2 *in amine solutions*

$$H_2S + RNH_2 \rightleftharpoons RNH_3^+ + HS^-$$

$$CO_2 + 2RNH_2 \rightleftharpoons RNH_3^+ + RNHCOO^-$$

Simultaneous absorption of O_2 *and* CO *in hemoglobin solutions*

$$O_2 + Hb \rightleftharpoons O_2Hb$$

$$CO + Hb \rightleftharpoons COHb$$

Simultaneous absorption of CO *and* CO_2 *in ammoniacal cuprous chloride*

$$CO + Cu(NH_3)_2^+ + NH_3 \rightleftharpoons Cu(NH_3)_3CO$$

$$CO_2 + 2NH_3 \rightleftharpoons NH_2COO^- + NH_4^+$$

Ramachandran (1971) has considered the theoretical aspects of the problem of the simultaneous absorption of two gases accompanied by a reversible instantaneous chemical reaction. Consider a reaction scheme represented as

$$A_1 + B \rightleftharpoons Z_1C_1 + Z_1'C_2 + \cdots$$

$$A_2 + B \rightleftharpoons Z_2E_1 + Z_2'E_2 + \cdots$$

It can be shown that the rate of absorption of gas A_1 is given by the following equation:

$$R_{A_1} = k_L\left([A_1^*] - [A_{1,o}] + \frac{[C_{1,i}]}{Z_1} - \frac{[C_{1,o}]}{Z_1}\right) \qquad (6.33)$$

where C_1 is a species that is formed in the reaction of gas A_1 only, $[C_{1,i}]$ is the concentration of C_1 at the interface, and $[C_{1,o}]$ is the concentration of C_1 in the bulk liquid. Similarly, the rate of absorption of the gas A_2 is given by

$$R_{A_2} = k_L\left([A_2^*] - [A_{2,o}] + \frac{[E_{1,i}]}{Z_2} - \frac{[E_{1,o}]}{Z_2}\right) \qquad (6.34)$$

where E_1 represents a species that occurs in the reaction of gas A_2 only.

The problem of the simultaneous absorption of two gases accompanied by reversible reactions of finite rate is also amenable to analytical treatment (Ramachandran, 1971).

Ramachandran (1971) has also considered a problem of simultaneous absorption of two gases represented by the following scheme:

$$A_1 + B \xrightarrow{\text{instantaneous}} \text{products} \qquad \text{(i)}$$

$$A_2 + B \rightleftharpoons E \text{ (reversible and finite rate)} \qquad \text{(ii)}$$

Here, gas A_1 reacts irreversibly and instantaneously with the dissolved liquid-phase species B, while gas A_2 undergoes a reversible reaction of finite rate with B. Since reaction (i) is instantaneous, the solute A_1 and the species B cannot coexist in the same region of the liquid. Thus, at any point in the liquid film $B = 0$ if $A_1 \neq 0$, and vice versa. The liquid film may then be considered to be composed of two regions: (a) the region from the interface to the reaction plane, 0 to λ—here the concentration of A_1 is positive while the concentration of B is zero; (b) the region from the reaction plane λ to δ, the film thickness—here the concentration of the dissolved gas A_1 is zero while the concentration of B is positive (see Figure 6.3).

Consider the region between 0 and λ. Here, since the concentration of B is zero, reaction (ii) tends to proceed in the backward direction, resulting in the formation of B. The B formed will instantaneously

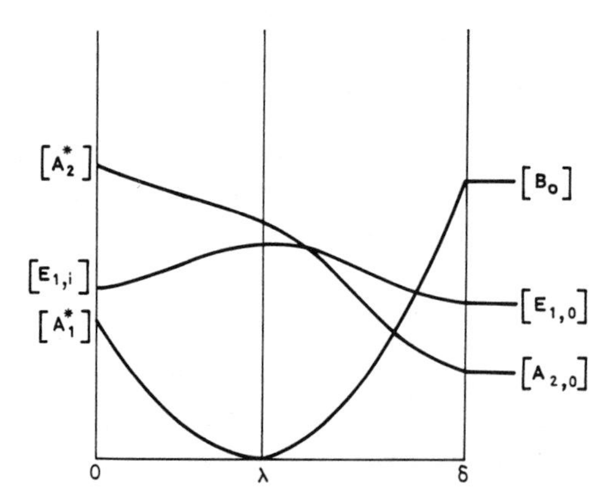

Figure 6.3. Concentration profiles for the problem $A_1 + B \rightarrow$ products; $A_2 + B \rightleftharpoons E$ based on the film theory.

react with the gas A_1 present in the zone. The reactions taking place in this zone of the liquid film are as follows:

$$E \rightarrow A_2 + B$$

$$A_1 + B \rightarrow \text{products}$$

Thus, species A_2 is formed in the region from 0 to λ, which reduces the concentration driving force for the transport of A_2. In the region from λ to δ, the reaction of gas A_2 with B takes place:

$$A_2 + B \rightleftharpoons E$$

Thus, the mechanism of absorption of two gases where one reacts reversibly and the other irreversibly is complex. An analytical solution for the rate of absorption can be obtained on the assumption of a linear concentration profile of B in the region from λ to δ.

6.5. ABSORPTION OF TWO GASES THAT REACT WITH EACH OTHER

There are many industrially important cases where gases A_1 and A_2 are absorbed in a solvent in which a reaction takes place between dissolved A_1 and A_2 (Ramachandran and Sharma, 1971; Teramoto et al., 1973), that is, there is no indigenous reactive species present in the liquid phase. An example is the absorption of a mixture of ammonia and carbon dioxide in water—a system encountered in urea plants. Here dissolved ammonia and carbon dioxide react to form ammonium carbamate. In some cases, the liquid-phase reaction of the dissolved gases may involve consecutive steps. For example, when ethylene and chlorine are absorbed together in a liquid medium of an organic solvent (dichloroethane) they react to form dichloroethane. The latter can undergo a substitution reaction with chlorine to form trichloroethane.

In industrial practice, the two reactive gases A_1 and A_2 may be present in a mixture or may be introduced separately in the liquid phase. The dynamics of the two cases differ in the following respects:

1. When the two gases are introduced separately and if the mixing in the gas phase is insignifi cant, the two gases dissolve at different sites and the concentration profiles in the liquid film are different from that which would exist if the two gases dissolved at the same site.
2. There might be some gas-side resistance for the transport of one or both of the gases if the two gases are present together in a mixture. The concentration profiles for the two cases are shown in Figures 6.4 and 6.5.

The two cases are considered separately below. In all the cases, the reaction between A_1 and A_2 is assumed to be fast. This implies that the entire reaction of the two gases occurs in the liquid film itself.

6.5.1. Gases A_1 and A_2 Present in a Mixture

The following differential equations, based on the film theory, are applicable to the case where gases A_1

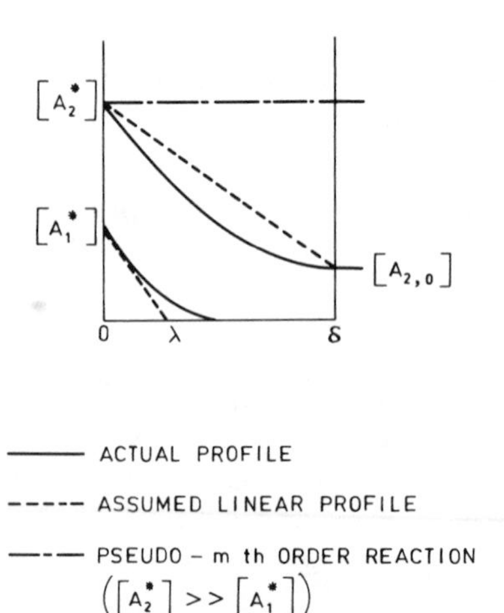

Figure 6.4. Concentration profiles for the case of the simultaneous absorption of two gases that react with each other for the case where the gases are present together in a mixture.

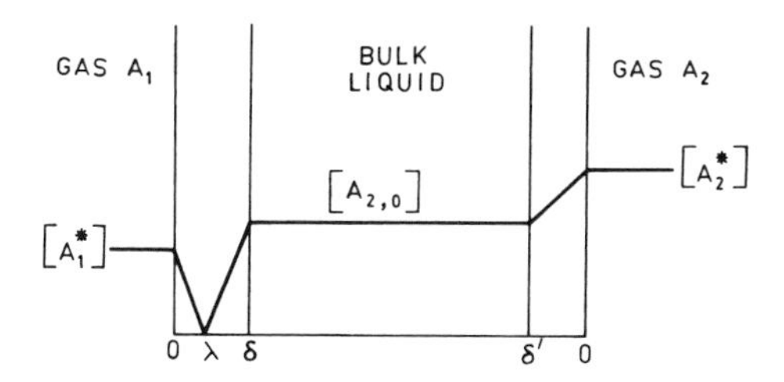

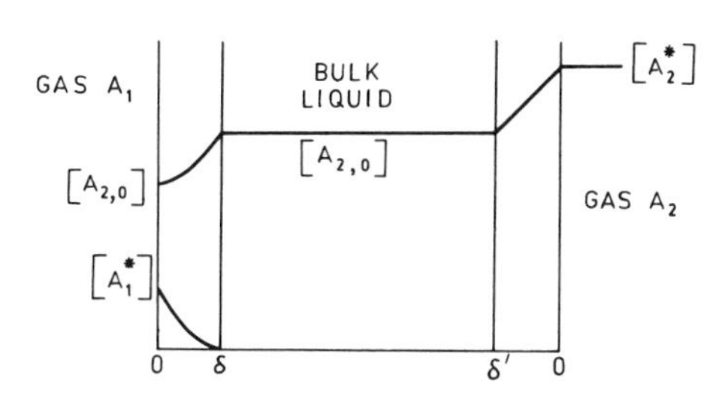

Figure 6.5. Concentration profiles for the case of the simultaneous absorption of two gases that react with each other for the case where the gases are introduced separately.

and A_2 react in the liquid phase according to the reaction scheme

$$A_1 + ZA_2 \rightarrow \text{products}$$

$$D_{A_1}\frac{d^2[A_1]}{dx^2} = k_{A_1A_2}[A_1]^m[A_2]^n \quad (6.35)$$

$$D_{A_2}\frac{d^2[A_2]}{dx^2} = Zk_{A_1A_2}[A_1]^m[A_2]^n \quad (6.36)$$

Here, $k_{A_1A_2}$ is the rate constant for the reaction of A_1 and A_2 and the order of reaction is m and n with reference to species A_1 and A_2, respectively. The boundary conditions are, at

$$x = 0: \quad [A_1] = [A_1^*], \quad [A_2] = [A_2^*] \quad (6.37a)$$

and at

$$x = \delta: \quad [A_1] = 0, \quad [A_2] = [A_{2,o}] \quad (6.37b)$$

Here, $[A_2^*]$ is assumed to be greater than $[A_1^*]$ and hence there may be some finite concentration of the dissolved species A_2 in the bulk.

The specific rates of absorption are given by

$$R_{A_1} = -D_{A_1}\left(\frac{d[A_1]}{dx}\right)_{x=0} \quad (6.38a)$$

$$R_{A_2} = -D_{A_2}\left(\frac{d[A_2]}{dx}\right)_{x=0} \quad (6.38b)$$

The different cases are as follows:

$[A_2^*] \gg [A_1^*]$

Here, the transfer of A_2 may become gas film controlled, while the transfer of A_1 falls under pseudo-mth-order conditions. The specific rate of absorption of A_1 for a second-order reaction is given by

$$R_{A_1} = [A_1^*]\sqrt{D_{A_1}k_{A_1A_2}[A_2^*]} \quad (6.39)$$

and $[A_{2,o}] \simeq [A_2^*]$.

$[A_2^*] = [A_1^*]$ *and* $D_{A_1} = D_{A_2}$

Here, species A_1 and A_2 may be considered identical. The specific rate of absorption of A_1 for the case of a second-order reaction is given by

$$R_{A_1} = R_{A_2} = [A_1^*]\sqrt{\tfrac{2}{3}D_{A_1}k_{A_1A_2}[A_1^*]} \quad (6.40)$$

and $[A_{2,o}] = 0$.

Thus, for this case we see that the specific rate of absorption is given by an equation similar to that for the case of the absorption of a single gas accompanied by a (2, 0)-order reaction (see Eq. 2.44).

Intermediate Cases ($0 < [A_{2,o}] < [A_2^*]$)

Here, the problem is not amenable to analytical solution. Roper et al. (1962) have obtained a numerical solution to the problem for second-order reactions based on the penetration model for values of $\sqrt{M}$ ranging from 1 to 3. Ramachandran and Sharma (1971) have obtained an approximate analytical solution to the problem on the basis of linearized profiles for A_1 and A_2. The solution of this problem has attracted much attention, and a number of profiles for A_1 and A_2 have been suggested which allow an analytical solution (Chaudhari and Doraiswamy, 1974; Juvekar, 1974; Sada et al., 1976b; Bhargava, 1978). The values of $\sqrt{M}$ obtained from these solutions agree well with those obtained from numerical solution.

6.5.2. Gases Introduced Separately

When the two gases are introduced separately, they dissolve at separate sites and diffuse toward one another. The concentration profiles are shown in Figure 6.5. In practical cases we may not encounter such well-defined conditions. The reaction of two gases A_1 and A_2 may be "instantaneous" or may follow "fast" finite kinetics. A model for instantaneous reaction has been proposed by Balasubramanian et al. (1966) and Chua and Ratcliffe (1971). This model can be extended to the case of fast reactions also (Ramachandran and Sharma, 1971). The concentration profiles for the case of instantaneous reaction are shown in Figure 6.5*a*. The specific rate of absorption of A_1 is

$$R_{A_1} = k_L[A_1^*] + k_L \frac{D_{A_2}}{D_{A_1}} \frac{[A_{2,o}]}{Z} \qquad (6.41)$$

where $[A_{2,o}]$ is the concentration of dissolved species A_2 in the bulk liquid. The concentration of dissolved A_2 is obtained from the following equation.

$$R_{A_2} = k_L([A_2^*] - [A_{2,o}]) \qquad (6.42)$$

At steady state, $ZR_{A_1} = R_{A_2}$, and the unknown concentration term $[A_{2,o}]$ can be eliminated.

$$R_{A_1} = \frac{1}{1 + (D_{A_2}/D_{A_1})} k_L \left([A_1^*] + \frac{D_{A_2}}{D_{A_1}} \frac{[A_2^*]}{Z} \right) \qquad (6.43)$$

Some examples of the absorption of two gases that react with each other are discussed next.

6.5.3. Simultaneous Absorption of NH_3 and CO_2

The problem is encountered in the manufacture of urea. The reaction is

$$CO_2 + 2NH_3 \rightarrow NH_2COO^- + NH_4^+$$

The carbamate is decomposed to give urea. In the total recycle process, the unconverted carbamate is decomposed to NH_3 and CO_2, which must be recycled. Either NH_3 or CO_2 should be selectively absorbed so that NH_3 and CO_2 can be separately introduced into the reactor (compression of a mixture of NH_3 and CO_2 poses a number of practical problems). The simultaneous absorption of NH_3 and CO_2 is also relevant in the manufacture of soda ash by the Solvay process and some other industrial processes. Hatch and Pigford (1962) describe an experimental study in which NH_3 and CO_2 were simultaneously absorbed in water. The absorption of CO_2 was found to conform to a pseudo-first-order reaction mechanism. Pangarkar and Sharma (1974) have studied some aspects of the simultaneous absorption of NH_3 and CO_2 in a laboratory bubble column. The transfer of ammonia was found to be gas film controlled. The data pertaining to the rates of absorption of CO_2 could be satisfactorily correlated by Danckwerts' surface renewal theory (Eq. 2.68). A gaseous mixture of CO_2 and NH_3 was absorbed in deionized water in a 5-cm-i.d. bubble column. Rates of absorption of CO_2 were measured at various dissolved ammonia concentrations. The Danckwerts' plot of $(R_A a/[A^*]_{CO_2})^2$ against $k_{NH_3}[NH_3]$ was found to be a straight line. The values of k_L and a obtained from this Danckwerts' plot were found to be in good agreement with the values reported by Mashelkar (1969) under otherwise similar conditions. Alper and Danckwerts (1976) have also studied the simultaneous absorption of CO_2 and NH_3 in water in a countercurrently operated 10.2-cm-i.d. column packed with 1.27-cm ceramic Raschig rings up to a height of 158 cm. A model contactor made of a string of spheres (sphere diameter = 3.72 cm) was used with a view to predicting the performance of the packed tower (see Section 10.1.2). Because of the relatively high solubility of NH_3, most of the NH_3 is absorbed in a shallow zone near the bottom of the countercurrently operated packed column. In the remaining height of the column, the absorption of CO_2 is essentially one corresponding to physical absorption. The model contactor gave satisfactory predictions of the results in the packed column.

Teramoto (1973) has studied the simultaneous absorption of CO_2 and NH_3 in water in a laminar jet, a wetted-wall column, and a mechanically agitated contactor (operated continuously). Models were developed on the basis of the film and penetration models. The experimental results obtained in the laminar jet and in the CSTR agreed well with the predictions of the models. The wetted-wall column was used as a model for a spray column operated with NH_3 entering at the top close to the liquid inlet and CO_2 entering at the bottom. As mentioned earlier, the bulk of the NH_3 is absorbed in a short zone near its entry point. The liquid therefore builds up a significant NH_3 concentration before it contacts CO_2. The results of the wetted-wall column and the modified cocurrent spray column agree well. However, this type of arrangement is unlikely to be useful when the objective is the selective removal of NH_3. Nevertheless, for efficient removal of CO_2 the cocurrent mode of contacting is definitely more attractive than the countercurrent mode of contacting.

Hegner and Molzahn (1979) have also studied the simultaneous absorption of CO_2 and NH_3 in water. The model developed for predicting the rates of absorption takes into account both the material and enthalpy balances for each stage. A 5-cm-diameter bubble cap plate column was used, and the temperature profiles in the liquid phase and the mole fraction of CO_2 and NH_3 in the gas phase were measured. When compared with the predicted values, these results showed good agreement. Predictions were also made for a 50-cm-diameter packed column packed with 2.5-cm Pall rings.

Pangarkar and Sharma (1974) have also studied the simultaneous absorption of CO_2 and NH_3 in aqueous solutions of mono- and diethanolamine. Here the object was to achieve the selective absorption of CO_2. Since the second-order rate constant for monoethanolamine is much higher than that for diethanolamine, it is expected that the selectivity with respect to CO_2 will be correspondingly higher when monoethanolamine is used. Experimental data obtained from a 5-cm-i.d. bubble column agreed well with the theoretical predictions. (This matter was covered in Section 5.4.)

6.5.4. Chlorination of Acetylene

The reaction is generally carried out in the liquid phase in a medium of tetrachloroethane, which is also the product of the reaction. The reaction probably involves two steps:

$$C_2H_2 + Cl_2 \rightarrow C_2H_2Cl_2$$

$$C_2H_2Cl_2 + Cl_2 \rightarrow C_2H_2Cl_4$$

The reaction is carried out in the liquid phase at 70–80°C by bubbling both chlorine and acetylene separately into a batch of tetrachloroethane kept well agitated. Generally, iron filings, scrap iron, or ferric chloride is used as a catalyst. An important point in this process is the introduction of both gases separately so as to ensure against localized high concentrations of unreacted acetylene–chlorine mixtures, which may lead to violent explosion.

6.5.5. Manufacture of Trichloroethane

In the manufacture of trichloroethane, ethylene and chlorine are reacted in the liquid phase to form dichloroethane. The latter undergoes a slow reaction with dissolved chlorine in the bulk liquid. There will be some free chlorine in the bulk liquid, since the solubility of chlorine is much greater than that of ethylene. Chua and Ratcliffe (1970, 1971) have studied the problem in a bubble column reactor and in a mechanically agitated vessel. They have also proposed a reaction model for a sequence of consecutive reactions resulting in the formation of di-, tri-, tetra-, penta-, and hexachloroethane.

6.5.6. Simultaneous Absorption of SO_2 and Cl_2 in Water

In the Hargreaves process, lean mixtures of SO_2 and Cl_2 have to be removed from off-gases. The simultaneous absorption of SO_2 and Cl_2 in water appears to be attractive, since SO_2 will be converted to H_2SO_4 and Cl_2 to HCl. The overall reaction is as follows:

$$SO_2 + 2H_2O + Cl_2 \rightarrow H_2SO_4 + 2HCl$$

The solubility of SO_2 is very high as compared to that of Cl_2 in water (1.27×10^{-3} and 5.25×10^{-5} mol/cm^3 atm, respectively, at 30°C). Thus the controlling mechanism may be concerned with the absorption of chlorine.

Sadek et al. (1977) have studied the simultaneous absorption of SO_2 and Cl_2 in water in a 20-cm(8-in.)-diameter packed column, provided with 1.5-cm ($\frac{5}{8}$-in.) polypropylene Pall rings. The packed height was about 255 cm (10 ft.) and the inlet gas contained 0.23–0.63% SO_2. The absorbent consisted of 12–28.2% H_2SO_4 and 5–11.6% HCl.

A part of the dissolved Cl_2 exists as free dissolved Cl_2 and the rest as HOCl and $H^+ + Cl^-$:

$$Cl_2 + H_2O \rightleftharpoons HOCl + H^+ + Cl^-$$

A part of the dissolved SO_2 is converted to HSO_3^- and H^+:

$$SO_2 + H_2O \rightleftharpoons HSO_3^- + H^+$$

The reaction presumably occurs between dissolved SO_2 and HOCl.

It appears that the absorption of Cl_2 is accompanied by a fast pseudo-first-order reaction, and no free chlorine exists in the bulk; that is, Cl_2 reacts completely in the diffusion film.

6.5.7. Reaction between H_2S and Ethylene Oxide to Give Thiodiethylene Glycol (TDEG) in the Product as a Solvent

Thiodiethylene glycol is an industrially important solvent and is manufactured by the simultaneous absorption of H_2S and ethylene oxide in TDEG as a solvent at a temperature of 60–70°C:

$$H_2S + 2\underset{\diagdown\, O\, \diagup}{CH_2{-}CH_2} \rightarrow (HOCH_2CH_2)_2S$$

Attempts have been made to study the kinetics of this reaction, but there are controversies in the literature (Berbé, 1950; Repas et al., 1966). It appears, however, that in contactors where gas is dispersed in a liquid (e.g., a mechanically agitated contactor) diffusional factors are unimportant. Berbé found the reaction to be zero order in H_2S and first order in ethylene oxide. This system would in many respects be unique if the zero-order kinetics with respect to H_2S were taken to be representative.

6.5.8. Hydroformylation of Isobutylene with CO and H_2

The kinetics of the hydroformylation reaction (oxo reaction) of isobutylene with CO and H_2, in the presence of a dicobalt octacarbonyl catalyst dissolved in a solvent, has been studied by Polyakov et al. (1976). Experiments were carried out in a 500-cm³ magnetically stirred autoclave in the temperature range of 100–180°C and at pressures up to 300 atm. The main product was 3-methyl butanal, and by-products were 2,2-dimethyl propanal and isobutane. By working at higher speeds of agitation (the autoclave could be operated up to a speed of 2800 rev/min) diffusional factors could be eliminated and thus the reaction was kinetically controlled. The reaction was found to be first order in isobutylene concentration and catalyst concentration. The activation energies for the three reactions were quite different; the hydrogenation reaction showed the highest value of activation energy. Thus an increase in temperature from 115 to 173°C resulted in increasing the isobutane content in the product from 2.8 to 10%. (In current industrial practice homogeneous catalysts based on rhodium phosphine ligands are considered more attractive, since very much milder conditions can be employed and the selectivity with respect to the desired product is relatively high.)

Cornils (1980) has given an exhaustive account of various aspects of hydroformylation reactions of a variety of olefins.

6.6. SIMULTANEOUS EXTRACTION OF TWO SOLUTES: DISSOCIATION EXTRACTION

The separation of mixtures of isomeric or closely related organic compounds is frequently encountered in industry. Typical examples are isomeric cresols, chlorophenols, chlorobenzoic and trichlorobenzoic acids, and *N*-alkylanilines. The separation, in such cases, by the conventional methods of crystallization or distillation, may become quite impractical. When such mixtures consist of either acidic or basic compounds, a technique called *dissociation extraction* can sometimes be employed. This method exploits the difference in the values of the dissociation constants of the mixed compounds. Consider the case of a mixture of *p*-chlorophenol and 2,4-dichlorophenol. Their respective boiling points at 760 mm Hg are 218 and 210°C. If distillation is to be carried out at reduced pressure, their boiling points converge, making the separation very difficult. The acid dissociation constants of these compounds are 6.6×10^{-10} and 1.8×10^{-8} g ion/liter, respectively, at 25°C. If a solution of a mixture of these two compounds in an organic solvent (such as benzene) is contacted with an aqueous solution containing a stoichiometrically deficient quantity of an alkali, such as sodium hydroxide, the dichlorophenol, owing to its greater acidity, will react preferentially with the alkali and thus cause an enrichment of *p*-chlorophenol in the organic phase. The extraction process when carried out in a multistage contactor can lead to purer components at the two ends.

This problem can be analyzed in a way somewhat similar to that for binary distillation (Wise and Williams, 1964; Anwar et al., 1971a, 1973). Anwar et al. (1971a) have developed a theory for the separation of a mixture of two weak organic acids dissolved in an inert organic solvent that is immiscible with water. (An exactly similar analysis will hold for the separation of a mixture of two bases.) This organic phase is equilibrated with an aqueous solution of a strong alkali containing less than the stoichiometric amount of the alkali in relation to the total acids present.

The overall distribution coefficients of the two individual acids HA_1 and HA_2 are given by

$$X'_{A_1} = \frac{[HA_1]_s}{[HA_1]_a + [A_1^-]}$$

and

$$X'_{A_2} = \frac{[HA_2]_s}{[HA_2]_a + [A_2^-]} \quad (6.44)$$

This assumes that the salts of two acids are fully ionized.

Similarly, the distribution coefficients of the undissociated acids will be

$$X_{A_1} = \frac{[HA_1]_s}{[HA_1]_a} \quad \text{and} \quad X_{A_2} = \frac{[HA_2]_s}{[HA_2]_a} \quad (6.45)$$

The weak acids will partially dissociate in the aqueous phase and their dissociation constants will be given by

$$K_{A_1} = \frac{[A_1^-][H^+]}{[HA_1]_a} \quad \text{and} \quad K_{A_2} = \frac{[A_2^-][H^+]}{[HA_2]_a} \quad (6.46)$$

Equilibria established in the aqueous phase are

$$HA_1 \rightleftharpoons A_1^- + H^+$$

$$A_2^- + H^+ \rightleftharpoons HA_2$$

The relative strength of HA_1 and HA_2 will determine the equilibrium position of the following key exchange reaction, which is the sum of these two reactions:

$$HA_1 + A_2^- \rightleftharpoons HA_2 + A_1^- \quad (6.47)$$

The equilibrium constant for this reaction is given by

$$K_e = \frac{[HA_2]_a[A_1^-]}{[HA_1]_a[A_2^-]} \quad (6.48)$$

From Eq. 6.46 we get

$$K_e = \frac{K_{A_1}}{K_{A_2}} \quad (6.49)$$

From Eqs. 6.45 and 6.46, we get

$$\frac{[A_1^-]}{[A_2^-]} = \frac{K_{A_1}}{K_{A_2}} \frac{X_{A_2}}{X_{A_1}} \frac{[HA_1]_s}{[HA_2]_s} \quad (6.50)$$

With sodium hydroxide as the extracting reagent the general condition of the overall ionic balance in the aqueous phase is

$$[A_1^-] + [A_2^-] + [OH^-] = [H^+] + [Na^+] \quad (6.51)$$

Any practical dissociation extraction process must occur with stoichiometric deficiency of strong alkali in relation to the acids present, and therefore the pH of the aqueous solution would lie in the range of 4–10. Thus, the total concentration of the hydrogen and hydroxyl ions in the aqueous phase will be negligible compared to the concentration of other ions, and Eq. 6.51 can be written as

$$[A_1^-] + [A_2^-] \simeq [Na^+] = N \quad (6.52)$$

where N is the molar concentration of sodium hydroxide initially present.

The separation factor of the two acids is given by

$$\alpha_{A_1A_2} = \frac{X'_{A_1}}{X'_{A_2}} = \frac{[HA_1]_s}{[HA_1]_a + [A_1^-]} \; \frac{[HA_2]_a + [A_2^-]}{[HA_2]_s} \quad (6.53)$$

From Eqs. 6.45, 6.50, 6.52, and 6.53 we get

$$\alpha_{A_1A_2} = \frac{X_{A_1}}{X_{A_2}} \times \frac{X_{A_2}N + [HA_2]_s + \left(\frac{K_{A_1}}{K_{A_2}}\right)\left(\frac{X_{A_2}[HA_1]_s}{X_{A_1}}\right)}{X_{A_2}N\left(\frac{K_{A_1}}{K_{A_2}}\right) + [HA_2]_s + \left(\frac{K_{A_1}}{K_{A_2}}\right)\left(\frac{X_{A_2}[HA_1]_s}{X_{A_1}}\right)} \quad (6.54)$$

Equation 6.54 can be simplified further by substituting:

$$T = [HA_1]_s + [HA_2]_s \quad \text{and} \quad \delta' = \frac{[HA_1]_s}{[HA_2]_s}$$

so that

$$\alpha_{A_1A_2} = \frac{X_{A_1}}{X_{A_2}} \frac{K_{A_2}}{K_{A_1}} \times \left\{ \frac{N(\delta' + 1) + T\left[(1/X_{A_2}) + (K_{A_1}\delta')/(K_{A_2}X_{A_1})\right]}{N(\delta' + 1) + T\left[(K_{A_2}/(K_{A_1}X_{A_2}) + (\delta'/X_{A_1})\right]} \right\} \quad (6.55)$$

Thus the values of the separation factor $\alpha_{A_1A_2}$ can be calculated from the experimentally determined or predicted values of the distribution coefficients X_{A_1} and X_{A_2} and the known or predicted values of K_{A_1} and K_{A_2}.

Recently Kafarov et al. (1976) and Wadekar and Sharma (1981a) have extended the theory of dissociation extraction to multicomponent systems.

In the conventional dissociation extraction the consumption of reagent chemicals used as extracting and neutralizing agents make the process economically less attractive. However, in the regenerative process introduced by Anwar et al. (1971b, 1974, 1977) this shortcoming is overcome. The salient features of this regenerative process are as follows.

A weakly acidic or basic compound is used as an extracting agent, and dissociation extraction is carried out in, say, a multistage extractor. This gives an organic raffinate phase rich in the weaker component of the feed mixture and an aqueous extract rich in the stronger component, as a somewhat loosely bound salt with the extracting agent. This aqueous phase is contacted again in a multistage extractor with a secondary solvent that has a particularly high affinity for undissociated components. This contacting regenerates the weakly acidic or basic extracting agent in the aqueous phase and extracts the stronger component in the secondary solvent in undissociated form. Thus in a typical case a mixture of 3-picoline and 4-picoline (dissociation constants 4.59×10^{-9} and 10.62×10^{-9} g ion/liter, respectively; boiling points in the range 143–145°C at 760 mm Hg) in a primary solvent, benzene, can be contacted with an aqueous solution of a weakly acidic salt, sodium dihydrogen phosphate. 4-Picoline, being a stronger base, preferentially reacts with sodium dihydrogen phosphate. On subsequent contacting of the aqueous phase, rich in the salt of 4-picoline, with a secondary solvent, chloroform, which has a high affinity for undissociated picolines, sodium dihydrogen phosphate is regenerated. Thus we get enrichment of 3-picoline in the benzene stream and that of 4-picoline in the chloroform stream (Anwar et al., 1974).

Anwar et al. (1971b, 1974, 1977) have developed the theory for this case of dissociation extraction with a weakly acidic or basic extracting agent and verified it for different systems.

A limitation of regenerative processes that involve the use of weak extracting agents is that separation factors and amounts of solutes transferred to the aqueous phase may be low. Recently it was shown that it is possible to have a regenerative process, exactly like the one just described, even with use of a strong extracting agent (Pratt, 1979).

In these conventional regenerative processes two downstream operations, namely, secondary extraction and distillation, are required to recover the solutes and regenerate the extracting agent. Wadekar and Sharma (1981a) have introduced a thermally regenerative process that requires distillation as the only additional downstream operation to separate the solutes and the extracting agent.

It their state of the art review, Wadekar and Sharma (1981b) cover various aspects of dissociation extraction.

6.6.1. Separation of Water-Soluble Mixtures of Piperidine and *N*-Methyl Piperidine

Example

Piperidine and *N*-methyl piperidine have boiling points of 106.3° and 105.9°C at 760 mm Hg, respectively. A mixture of these two will be practically inseparable by ordinary distillation. However, their dissociation constants being 1.32×10^{-3} and 1.20×10^{-4}, respectively, separation by the technique of dissociation extraction can be attempted. Jagirdar and Sharma (1981) have reported the separation of this mixture by dissociation extraction.

Consider a 70 : 30 mol % mixture of these two compounds dissolved in 2-ethylhexanol at a total concentration of about 2×10^{-3} mol/cm³. Jagirdar and Sharma have reported the relevant data, and Eq. 6.55 can be used to predict the separation factor for this system:

$$K_{A_1} = 1.20 \times 10^{-4} \text{ g ion/liter},$$

$$K_{A_2} = 1.32 \times 10^{-3} \text{ g ion/liter}$$

$$X_{A_1} = 19 \qquad X_{A_2} = 6.5$$

$$N = 2.9\,N\ \text{HCl} \qquad T = 0.6 \text{ mol/liter} \qquad \delta' = 8$$

Therefore, from Eq. 6.55

$$\alpha_{A_1A_2} = \frac{19.0}{6.5} \times \frac{1.32 \times 10^{-3}}{1.20 \times 10^{-4}} \times \left[\frac{2.9 \times 9 + 0.6\left(\dfrac{1}{6.5} + \dfrac{1.20 \times 10^{-4}}{1.32 \times 10^{-3}} \times \dfrac{8}{19}\right)}{2.9 \times 9 + 0.6\left(\dfrac{1.32 \times 10^{-3}}{1.20 \times 10^{-4}} \times \dfrac{1}{6.5} + \dfrac{8}{19}\right)} \right]$$

$$= 32.15 \times \frac{26.26}{27.37}$$

$$= 30.79$$

The experimentally obtained separation factor was 29.5. Thus, the predicted separation factor value agrees well with the experimental value.

In view of the high value of α, this method deserves consideration for the separation of piperidine and *N*-methyl piperidine.

6.6.2. Separation of Cresols and Mixtures of 2,6-Xylenol with Cresols

Cresols

Ellis and Gibbon (1964) have investigated the separation of *m*- and *p*-cresols using benzene as the diluent and aqueous caustic soda solution as the extracting medium. They have reported separation factors for this system with an average value of 1.43. They carried out the experiments in batch as well as continuous extractors with total and partial reflux.

Anwar et al. (1971a) have also considered the problem of the separation of *m*- and *p*-cresols. They used a mixture of 80% hexane and 20% benzene as a diluent and aqueous trisodium phosphate as the extracting reagent. The main advantages of using a trisodium phosphate solution for extraction was that benzene could be used as a secondary solvent for regenerating the cresol from the extract phase after partial acidification using phosphoric acid, and that the cresol-free sodium phosphate solution could be reused for extraction.

Mixture of 2,6-Xylenol and Cresols

There are some situations in practice where mixtures of 2,6-xylenol and *m*-cresol and *p*-cresol are encountered. The boiling points of *m*-cresol and *p*-cresol and 2,6-xylenol are 202, 201.8, and 202°C at 760 mm Hg, respectively. There is a significant difference in the p*K* of *m*-cresol, *p*-cresol, and 2,6-xylenol (10.10, 10.28, and 10.62, respectively). Kiseleva et al. (1971) have found that benzene is a very good solvent for this system. Wadekar and Sharma (1981c) have shown that a 50 : 50% mixture of *m*-cresol and 2,6-xylenol in benzene as a solvent, when extracted with 1 *N* NaOH, resolves to give a separation factor of 22. When di-*n*-butyl ether was used as the solvent, a separation factor of nearly half this value was obtained.

Monomethylamine (bp at 760 mm Hg, −6.8°C; p*K* at 25°C, 10.6) dissolved in water can be used as a thermally regenerative extracting agent for these systems. Monomethylamine can be regenerated by distilling the aqueous extract containing salts of monomethylamine and the solutes (Wadekar and Sharma, 1981a).

6.6.3. Separation of Chlorophenols, Chlorocresols, and Chloroxylenols

Chlorophenols

2,4-Dichlorophenol (DCP), which is obtained by the controlled chlorination of phenol, is required for the manufacture of an important weedicide—2,4-dichlorophenoxy acetic acid. DCP may contain a significant amount of *p*-chlorophenol (PCP), which has practically the same boiling point as DCP (boiling points at 760 mm Hg; DCP = 209–10°C, PCP = 218°C; melting points: DCP = 45°C, PCP = 42°). DCP and PCP also cannot be separated by crystallization. However, there is a substantial difference in their dissociation constants (p*K* at 25°C: DCP = 7.75, PCP = 9.18). Laddha and Sharma (1978) have shown that the technique of dissociation extraction can be successfully employed to purify DCP from its mixture with PCP. With benzene as a solvent a separation factor of 3.5 was obtained. With di-*n*-butyl ether as a solvent the value of the separation factor was found to be 6.8 (Wadekar and Sharma, 1981c).

Recently, PCP and DCP have been separated by using ammonia (bp at 760 mm Hg, −33.4°C; p*K* at 25°C, 9.6) dissolved in water as a thermally regenerative extracting agent (Wadekar and Sharma, 1981a).

Milnes (1974) has reported that the mixtures of 2,4- and 2,5-dichlorophenols and 2,3- and 2,6-dichlorophenols obtained from the alkaline hydrolysis of polychlorobenzenes can be successfully separated by the technique of dissociation extraction. Bringing the mixture, dissolved in toluene, into contact with solutions of sodium hydroxide or sodium carbonate in a multistage extraction unit gives the desired separation. The use of reflux at either end of the contactor improved the overall separation. Anwar et al. (1977) have separated 2,3- and 2,6-dichlorophenol with monoethanolamine as a regenerative extractant, using toluene as a primary solvent and ethyl acetate as a secondary solvent.

Chlorocresols

4-Chloro-*o*-cresol is used as an intermediate in the manufacture of a weedicide. During the manufacture of this intermediate, some 6-chloro-*o*-cresol that has practically the same boiling point as *o*-cresol (bp of *o*-cresol = 191–192°C at 760 mm Hg; bp of 6-chloro-*o*-cresol = 191–192.3°C at 757 mm Hg) is also formed. Thus, the separation of 6-chloro-*o*-cresol and *o*-cresol is relevant. There is a good difference in their p*K* values (8.69 and 10.28, respectively) and hence dissociation extraction can probably be used for their separation. Wadekar and Sharma (1981c) have found that although practically no separation occurred between 6-chloro-*o*-cresol and *o*-cresol with benzene as a solvent, a separation factor as high as 3.15 was obtained with di-*n*-butyl ether as a solvent.

Chloroxylenols

p-Chloro-*m*-xylenol (PCMX) is an important germicide. In the manufacture of PCMX we encounter the problem of the separation of PCMX from 2,4-dichloro-*m*-xylenol (DCMX). The difference between their p*K*'s (9.70 and 8.28, respectively) is large and hence they can be separated by dissociation extraction. Wadekar and Sharma (1981c) have shown that a separation factor as high as about 5 can be obtained with the use of di-*n*-butyl ether as a solvent.

6.6.4. Separation of *N*-Alkylanilines and *N*-Alkyl Toluidines

Laddha and Sharma (1978) have studied the separation of *N*-diethylaniline from *N*-ethylaniline and of *N*-diethyl-*o*-toluidine from *N*-ethyl-*o*-toluidine by using stoichiometric deficiency of HCl in aqueous solutions. The p*K*'s of these amines at 25°C are 6.56, 5.11, 7.2, and 4.96, respectively. In the case of the first system, contrary to expectations, the use of a solvent immiscible with water resulted in practically no enrichment of *N*-ethylaniline in the organic phase. However, the use of a mixture of *N*-ethyl and *N*-diethyl derivative, in the absence of any solvent, gave good separations and the value of α ranged from 1.63 to 2. In the case of the *N*-diethyl-*o*-toluidine and *N*-ethyl-*o*-toluidine system very good separation was realized in both the presence and the absence of a solvent. The value of α ranged from 15.7 at 50 mol % to 19.0 at 90 mol % of *N*-ethyl-*o*-toluidine in the mixture.

6.6.5. Separation of Substituted Anilines: *m*-Chloroaniline and *o*-Anisidine

In the manufacture of *m*-nitrochlorobenzene, a mixture of *o*-nitrochlorobenzene and *m*-nitrochlorobenzene is obtained. One possible way of utilizing this by-product mixture is to subject it to methanolysis followed by reduction. This gives a close boiling mixture of *m*-chloroaniline and *o*-anisidine (bp at 760 mm Hg, 230.5° and 225°C, respectively), which show a significant difference in p*K* values. With monochlorobenzene as a solvent and aqueous hydrochloric acid as an extracting agent, separation factors as high as 12–14.5 have been realized for these substituted anilines (Wadekar and Sharma, 1981a).

Isomeric Xylidines

Nitration of mixed xylenes, followed by reduction, is an established method for preparing a mixture of different xylidines, which are used as intermediates for dyes and drugs. A fraction of these xylidines containing 2,4-, 2,5-, and 2,6-isomers (bp at 760 mm Hg: 216–217, 213–215, and 216°C, respectively) is not amenable to separation by distillation. This ternary mixture has been separated by Wadekar and Sharma (1981a). For example, in a typical run starting with an equimolar mixture of three xylidines, the following separation factors were realized with di-*n*-butyl ether as a solvent and 1 *N* HCl as an extracting agent:

$$\alpha_{2,6/2,4\text{-xylidine}} = 8.82, \qquad \alpha_{2,5/2,4\text{-xylidine}} = 4.5$$

$$\alpha_{2,6/2,5\text{-xylidine}} = 2.0$$

The separation factor values for the three constituent pairs of binary systems have also been reported.

6.6.6. Separation and Recovery of Low Molecular Weight Carboxylic Acids from Aqueous Streams

Jagirdar and Sharma (1980) have reported the separation and recovery of low molecular weight aliphatic carboxylic acids that appear in many industrial aqueous effluent streams. This method of separation differs slightly from the conventional form of dissociation extraction in the sense that the solute transfer occurs from the aqueous phase to the organic phase. For example, consider an aqueous mixture of acetic acid and monochloroacetic acid. This aqueous solution is contacted with a water-immiscible solvent like xylene containing a higher molecular weight amine like tri-*n*-octylamine. Monochloroacetic acid, being stronger than acetic acid, reacts preferentially with tri-*n*-octylamine, forming a salt that is highly soluble in the organic solvent. This results in the enrichment of monochloroacetic acid in the organic phase and that of acetic acid in the aqueous phase. By this method, using tri-*n*-octylamine as an extracting agent, Jagirdar and Sharma have separated mixtures of a variety of carboxylic acids, including acetic acid–formic acid, formic acid–oxalic acid, monochloroacetic acid–dichloroacetic acid, dichloroacetic acid–trichloroacetic acid, and glycolic acid–oxalic acid.

REFERENCES

Alper, E., and Danckwerts, P. V. (1976), *Chem. Eng. Sci.*, **31**, 599.

Anwar, M. M., Hanson, C., and Pratt, M. W. T. (1971a), *Trans. Inst. Chem. Eng.*, **49**, 95.

Anwar, M. M., Hanson, C., and Pratt, M. W. T. (1971b), *Proc. Int. Solvent Extraction Conf.*, p. 911.

Anwar, M. M., Hanson, C., Patel, A. N., and Pratt, M. W. T. (1973), *Trans. Inst. Chem. Eng.*, **71**, 151.

Anwar, M. M., Cook, T. M., Hanson, C., and Pratt, M. W. T. (1974), *Proc. Int. Solvent Extraction Conf.*, p. 895.

Anwar, M. M., Cook, S. T. M., Hanson, C., and Pratt, M. W. T. (1977), *Proc. Int. Solvent Extraction Conf.*, p. 671.

Astarita, G. (1967), *Mass Transfer with Chemical Reaction*, Elsevier, Amsterdam.

Astarita, G., and Gioia, F. (1965), *Ind. Eng. Chem. Fundam.*, **4**, 317.

Balasubramanian, S. N., Rihani, D. N., and Doraiswamy, L. K. (1966), *Ind. Eng. Chem. Fundam.*, **5**, 184.

Berbé, Fr. (1950), *Bull. Soc. Chim. Belges*, **59**, 449; *Chem. Abstr.*, (1951), **45**, 3696.

Bhargava, R. K. (1978), Kinetics of Heterogeneous Reactions, Ph.D. (Tech.) thesis, University of Bombay.

Chandalia, S. B. (1968), *Indian J. Technol.*, **6**, 88.

Chaudhari, R. V., and Doraiswamy, L. K. (1974), *Chem. Eng. Sci.*, **29**, 675.

Chem. Eng. News (1970), **48**(18), 68.

Chua, Y. H., and Ratcliffe, J. S. (1970), *Mech. Chem. Eng. Trans.*, **6**(2), 35.

Chua, Y. H., and Ratcliffe, J. S. (1971), *Mech. Chem. Eng. Trans.*, **7**, 6, 11, 17.

Cornils, B. (1980), in Falbe, J. (Ed.), *New Synthesis with Carbon Monoxide*; *Reactivity and Structure Concepts in Organic Chemistry*, Vol. 11, Springer-Verlag, Berlin, Heidelberg, New York.

Coughanowr, D. R., and Krause, F. E. (1965), *Ind. Eng. Chem. Fundam.*, **4**, 61.

Danckwerts, P. V., and Sharma, M. M. (1966), *Chem. Eng.*, *Inst. Chem. Eng.*, No. 202, CE244.

da Silva, A. T., and Danckwerts, P. V. (1973), *Chem. Eng. Sci.*, **28**, 847.

Davis, H. S., and Schuler, R. (1930), *J. Am. Chem. Soc.*, **52**, 721; 3757.

Dingman, J. C., and Moore, T. F. (1968), *Hydrocarbon Process. Petrol. Refiner*, **47**(7), 138.

Ellis, S. R. M., and Gibbon, J. D. (1964), in Pirie, J. M. (Ed.), *The Less Common Means of Separation*, Institution of Chemical Engineers, London, p. 119.

FIAT-843 (1947), Chlorinated Hydrocarbon from Acetylene.

Friend, L., Wender, L., and Yarze, J. C. (1968), *Adv. Chem. Ser.*, **70**, 168.

Garnell, F. H., Long, R., and Pennell, A. (1958), *J. Appl. Chem.* **8**, 325.

Gehlawat, J. K. (1969), Studies in Reactions of C_4-fraction, Ph.D. (Tech.) thesis, University of Bombay.

Gehlawat, J. K., and Sharma, M. M. (1968), *Chem. Eng. Sci.*, **23**, 1173.

Gioia, F. (1967), *La Chimica e L'Industria*, **49**, 1287.

Gioia, F., and Marrucci, G. (1970), *Chem. Eng. J.*, **1**, 91.

Goar, B. G. (1968), *Hydrocarbon Process. Petrol. Refiner*, **47**(9), 248.

Goettler, L. A., and Pigford, R. L. (1964), Paper presented at AIChE meeting, Boston.

Goettler, L. A., and Pigford, R. L. (1968), *Proc. Symp. Tripartite Chem. Eng. Conf.* (Montreal), p. 1.

Gunn, D. J., and Saleem, A. (1970), *Trans. Inst. Chem. Eng.*, **48**, T46.

Hahn, A. V. (1970), *The Petrochemical Industry—Market and Economics*, McGraw-Hill, New York.

Hanson, C., and Ismail, H. A. M. (1977), *Chem. Eng. Sci.*, **32**, 775.

Hanson, C., Marsland, J. G., and Wilson, G. (1971), *Chem. Eng. Sci.*, **26**, 1513.

Hatch, L. F. (1970), *Hydrocarbon Process. Petrol. Refiner*, **49**(3), 101.

Hatch, T. F., and Pigford, R. L. (1962), *Ind. Eng. Chem. Fundam.*, **1**, 209.

Hegner, B., and Molzahn, M. (1979), *Inst. Chem. Eng. (London) Symp. Ser.*, **56** (*Distillation*), 81.

Hikita, H., and Asai, S. (1964), *J. Chem. Eng. Japan*, **2**, 77.

Jagirdar, G. C., and Sharma, M. M. (1980), *J. Separ. Process Technol.*, **1**(2), 40.

Jagirdar, G. C., and Sharma, M. M. (1981), *J. Separ. Process Technol.*, **2**(3), 37.

Jordan, D. G. (1968), *Chemical Process Development*, Wiley-Interscience, New York.

Juvekar, V. A. (1974), *Chem. Eng. Sci.*, **29**, 1842.

Kafarov, V. V., Reutsii, V. A., and Zhuravleva, T. Yu. (1976), *J. Appl. Chem. USSR (Engl. Transl.)*, **49**(12), 2724.

Kiseleva, E. N., Belyaeva, V. A., and Gel'perin, N. I. (1971), *Khim. Prom.*, **47**, 178.

Laddha, S. S., and Sharma, M. M. (1978), *J. Appl. Chem. Biotechnol.*, **28**, 69.

La Force, R. C. (1966), *Trans. Faraday Soc.*, **62**, 1458.

Lites, I. L., Dilman, V. V., and Tagintaev, B. G. (1968), *Khim. Prom.*, **7**, 523.

Manogue, W. H., and Pigford, R. L. (1960), *AIChE J.*, **6**, 494.

Mashelkar, R. A. (1969), Studies in Mass Transfer, Ph.D. (Tech.) thesis, University of Bombay.

Milnes, M. H. (1974), *Proc. Int. Solvent Extraction Conf.*, p. 983.

Ninomiya, K., and Fuji, H. (1978), *Proc. Symp. on Multi-phase Concurrent Fixed Bed* (12th Fall Meeting, Soc. Chem. Eng. Japan, Okayama), p. G1-308.

Oloman, C., Murray, F. E., and Risk, J. B. (1969), *Pulp Paper Mag. Canada*, **70**(23), T499.

Onda, K., Sada, E., Kobayashi, T., and Fujine, M. (1970a), *Chem. Eng. Sci.*, **25**, 1023.

Onda, K., Sada, E., Kobayashi, T., and Fujine, M. (1970b), *Chem. Eng. Sci.*, **25**, 761.

Ouwerkerk, C. (1968), *Proc. Symp. Tripartite Chem. Eng. Conf.* (Montreal), p. 39.

Ouwerkerk, C. (1978), *Hydrocarbon Process. Petrol. Refiner*, **57**(4), 89.

Pangarkar, V. G., and Sharma, M. M. (1974), *Chem. Eng. Sci.*, **29**, 2297.

Polyakov, A. A., Gankin, V. Yu., Rybakov, V. A., and Fuks, I. S. (1976), *Int. Chem. Eng.*, **16**, 518.

Pratt, M. W. T. (1979), *Dissociation Extraction* (Lecture Notes), University of Bradford, England.

Ramachandran, P. A. (1971), *Chem. Eng. Sci.*, **26**, 349.

Ramachandran, P. A., and Sharma, M. M. (1968), Unpublished work.

Ramachandran, P. A., and Sharma, M. M. (1970), *Chem. Eng. Sci.*, **25**, 1743.

Ramachandran, P. A., and Sharma, M. M. (1971), *Trans. Inst. Chem. Eng.*, **49**, 253.

Repas, M., Macho, U., and Mistrik, E. J. (1966), *Chem. zvesti*, **20**, 501; *Chem. Abstr.* (1966), **65**, 15181.

Roper, G. H., Hatch, T. F., and Pigford, R. L. (1962), *Ind. Eng. Chem. Fundam.*, **1**, 144.

Sada, E., Kumazawa, H., and Butt, M. A. (1976a), *Can. J. Chem. Eng.*, **54**, 421.

Sada, E., Kumazawa, H., and Butt, M. A. (1976b), *Can. J. Chem. Eng.*, **54**, 97.

Sada, E., Kumazawa, H., Yamanaka, Y., Kudo, I., and Kondo, T. (1978), *J. Chem. Eng. Japan*, **11**(4), 276.

Sadek, S. E., Nawrocki, D. A., Sterbis, E. E., and Vivian, J. E. (1977), *Ind. Eng. Chem. Fundam.*, **16**, 36.

Sankholkar, D. S. (1974), Absorption of Olefins, Ph.D. (Tech.) thesis, University of Bombay.

Sankholkar, D. S., and Sharma, M. M. (1973), *Chem. Eng. Sci.*, **28**, 49.

Schmidt, A. (1970), *Chem. Ing.-Tech.*, **42**, 521.

Shah, Y. T., and Kenney, C. N. (1972), *Chem. Eng. Sci.*, **27**, 1.

Sherwood, T. K., and Pigford, R. L. (1952), *Absorption and Extraction*, McGraw-Hill, New York.

Takeuchi, H., and Yamanaka, Y. (1978), *Ind. Eng. Chem. Process Design Dev.*, **17**, 389.

Taylor, M. D. (1969), Paper presented at a Symposium on Gas–Liquid Reactions, Institution of Chemical Engineers, U.K.

Teramoto, M. (1973), *Mem. Fac. Ind. Arts, Kyoto Tech. Univ., Sci. Technol.*, **22**, 51.

Teramoto, M., Hashimoto, K., and Nagata, S. (1973), *J. Chem. Eng. Japan*, **6**, 522.

Treybal, R. E. (1968), *Mass Transfer Operations*, 2nd ed., McGraw-Hill, New York.

van Krevelen, D. W., and Baans, C. M. E. (1950), *J. Phys. Chem.*, **54**, 370.

Wadekar, V. V., and Sharma, M. M. (1981a), *J. Separ. Process. Technol.*, **2**(2), 28.

Wadekar, V. V., and Sharma, M. M. (1981b), *J. Separ. Process. Technol.*, **2**(1), 1.

Wadekar, V. V., and Sharma, M. M. (1981c), *J. Chem. Technol. Biotechnol.*, **31**, 279.

Wiewiorowski, T. K. (1969), U.S. 3, 447, 903.

Wise, W. S., and Williams, D. E. (1964), in Pirie, J. M. (Ed.), *The Less Common Means of Separation*, Institution of Chemical Engineers, London, p. 112.

CHAPTER SEVEN

Reaction in Both (Liquid) Phases

A number of industrially important reactions, such as the oximation of cyclohexanone, nitration, hydrolysis, alkylation, and the extraction of metals, involve two liquid phases where, in principle, the reaction can occur in both phases. Table 7.1 gives some examples of importance.

In the problems discussed in the previous chapters we assumed that the reaction occurs only in the B phase and that there is no solubility of B in the A phase. However, complications arise when B has a finite solubility in the A phase. Further, because of differences in the properties of the two phases, the values of the rate constants for the reaction between A and B may be substantially different in the two phases. The extent to which the reaction would occur in the A phase will depend on the solubility of B in the A phase and the value of the rate constant. The occurrence of reaction in the A phase may have a beneficial effect on the output of the reactor provided that no undesirable by-products are formed. It is conceivable that an undesirable reaction may occur in one of the phases. Thus the yield and the selectivity may differ significantly, depending on the phase in which the desired reaction and the side reaction occur. In certain circumstances it may be possible to change the operating conditions in such a way that the reaction is forced to take place in the desired phase (Scriven, 1961). We shall attempt to evolve procedures through which we can quantitatively account for the contribution of the reaction in the A phase. There is very little information in the literature on this subject, particularly for situations where the reaction between A and B occurs entirely in the films on either side of the interface.

In practical situations the mutual solubilities may change substantially with an increase in the conversion of A. Thus, for instance, in the nitration of benzene, toluene and the like, where the corresponding nitro compounds will essentially exist in the A phase (aromatic phase), the solubility of nitric acid in the A phase changes significantly with an increase in the concentration of nitro compounds. For the sake of simplicity, however, we will assume that the mutual solubilities remain constant. Further, it will be assumed that the reaction between A and B is irreversible in both phases and that the stoichiometric coefficient also has the same value in both phases. The following notation will be adopted:

Subscript o will denote the bulk quantities;
A will denote the quantities relating to the A-rich phase;
B will denote the quantities relating to the B-rich phase;
i will denote the quantities relating to the interface.

Thus $[A_{Bi}]$ will mean the concentration of A at the interface in the phase rich in B. Similarly, the quantity $k_{LA,B}$ will mean the physical mass transfer coefficient for the transport of A from the interface to the bulk of phase B. The term $k_{mn,A}$ represents the rate constant for the reaction in the A phase. The reaction under consideration is as follows:

$$A + ZB \rightarrow \text{products}$$

The following steps are involved:

1a. Transfer of A from the bulk of phase A to the interface.

1b. Reaction of A in the A phase with the other reactant, B, which may occur while B is diffusing from the interface to the bulk of phase A.

2. At the interface, equilibrium conditions prevail; that is,

$$[A_{Ai}] = m_A[A_{Bi}] \tag{7.1}$$

$$[B_{Ai}] = m_B[B_{Bi}] \tag{7.2}$$

TABLE 7.1. Examples of Reactions in Both (Liquid) Phases

System	Reference(s)
Oximation of cyclohexanone	Sharma and Nanda (1968); Rod (1976)
Nitration of aromatic compounds	Albright (1966a, 1967); Albright and Hanson (1969)
Sulfonation of aromatic compounds	Groggins (1958)
Alkylation of isobutane with isobutylene with liquid HF as a catalyst	Albright (1966b)
Hydrolysis of fats	Jeffreys et al. (1961)
Solvent extraction of metals	Bailes et al. (1976)
Interfacial polycondensation	Morgan (1965)
Reprocessing of irradiated fuel	Rozen et al. (1976)

It will be assumed that

$$m_A \gg 1, \qquad m_B \ll 1$$

3a. Diffusion of A from the interface to the bulk of phase B.

3b. Reaction of A and B in phase B, which may occur while A is diffusing from the interface to the bulk of the B phase.

It is convenient to discuss the problem with the following classification, which is based on the relative values of rates of diffusion and chemical reaction. (This classification is analogous to that adopted in Chapter 2.)

7.1. REACTIONS OCCUR IN THE BULK A AND B PHASES

Under certain conditions both phases may be saturated with respect to the relevant species and diffusional resistances to the transfer of A into the B phase and of B into the A phase are negligible. Figure 7.1 shows the typical concentration profiles for species A and B. The necessary conditions for the absence of diffusional resistances are as follows:

$$k_{LA,B}a[A_{Bi}] \gg lk_{mn,B}[A_{Bi}]^m[B_{Bo}]^n \quad (7.3)$$

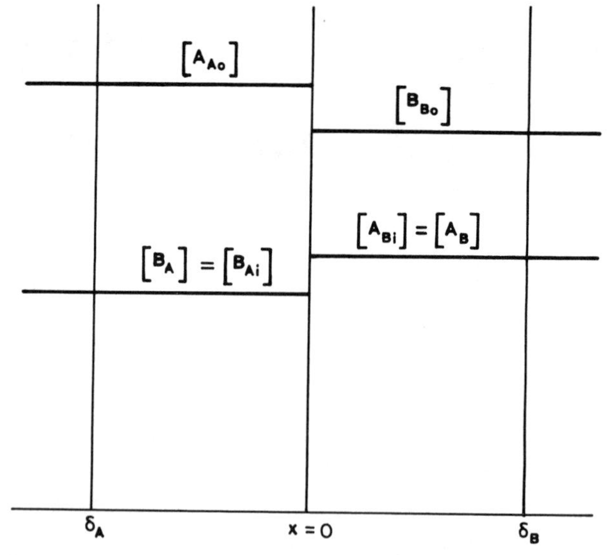

Figure 7.1. Concentration profiles of A and B when no reaction occurs in the films near the interface and the diffusional resistances for B in A phase and for A in the B phase are negligible.

and

$$k_{LB,A}a[B_{Ai}] \gg (1-l)k_{mn,A}[A_{Ao}]^m[B_{Ai}]^n \quad (7.4)$$

The specific rate of consumption of A, R_A, is given by

$$R_A = \frac{1-l}{a}k_{mn,A}[B_{Ai}]^n[A_{Ao}]^m + \frac{l}{a}k_{mn,B}[A_{Bi}]^m[B_{Bo}]^n \quad (7.5)$$

When the converse of the conditions given by expressions 7.3 and 7.4 is satisfied, the concentration of dissolved A in the bulk B phase and of dissolved B in the bulk A phase will be zero. The typical concentration profiles of species A and B are shown in Figure 7.2. The following expression gives the value of R_A:

$$R_A = k_{LA,B}[A_{Bi}] + \frac{k_{LB,A}[B_{Ai}]}{Z} \quad (7.6)$$

provided the following conditions are satisfied:

$$\frac{\sqrt{\frac{2}{m+1}D_{AB}k_{mn,B}[B_{Bo}]^n[A_{Bi}]^{m-1}}}{k_{LA,B}} \ll 1 \quad (7.7)$$

$$\frac{\sqrt{\frac{2}{n+1}D_{BA}k_{mn,A}[A_{Ao}]^m[B_{Ai}]^{n-1}}}{k_{LB,A}} \ll 1 \quad (7.8)$$

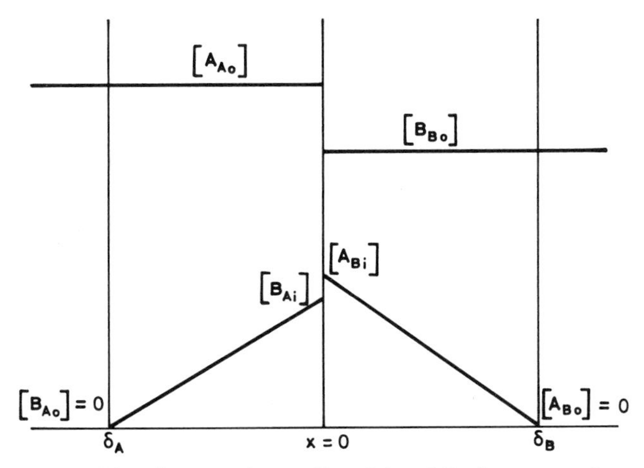

Figure 7.2. Concentration profiles of A and B when no reaction occurs in the films near the interface and reactions in the bulk are fast enough to keep the concentration of B in the A phase and of A in the B phase zero.

(These conditions ensure that no reaction occurs in the films.) When the two terms in expressions 7.3 and 7.4 are comparable, then an intermediate situation will arise in which there will be a finite concentration of A in the bulk B phase and of B in the bulk A phase, and the concentration of each of these species will be less than the respective saturation concentrations. This problem can be tackled in a way similar to that discussed in Section 2.3.

Example

Consider the following case.

$$D_{AB} = D_{BA} = 1 \times 10^{-5}\ \text{cm}^2/\text{sec}$$

$$k_{LA,B} = 1.2 \times 10^{-3}\ \text{cm}/\text{sec},$$

$$k_{LB,A} = 1.6 \times 10^{-3}\ \text{cm}/\text{sec}$$

$$[B_{Bo}] = 2 \times 10^{-3}\ \text{mol/cm}^3,$$

$$[A_{Ao}] = 1 \times 10^{-3}\ \text{mol/cm}^3$$

$$Z = 1, \quad m = 1, \quad n = 1,$$

$$l = 0.4, \quad a = 10\ \text{cm}^{-1}$$

$$k_{mn,A} = 10^3\ \text{cm}^3/\text{mol sec},$$

$$k_{mn,B} = 2 \times 10^3\ \text{cm}^3/\text{mol sec}$$

$$m_A = 400, \quad m_B = 0.001$$

Hence,

$$[A_{Bi}] = \frac{[A_{Ao}]}{m_A} = 0.25 \times 10^{-5}\ \text{mol/cm}^3$$

and

$$[B_{Ai}] = 0.20 \times 10^{-5}\ \text{mol/cm}^3$$

The reactions occur in the bulk of the phases, since the conditions given by expression 7.7 and 7.8 are satisfied.

$$\frac{D_{AB}k_{mn,B}[B_{Bo}][A_{Bi}]}{k_{LA,B}^2} = \frac{10^{-5} \times 2 \times 10^3 \times 2 \times 10^{-3} \times 0.25 \times 10^{-5}}{1.44 \times 10^{-6}}$$

$$= 0.695 \times 10^{-4}$$

$$\ll 1$$

$$\frac{D_{BA}k_{mn,A}[A_{Ao}][B_{Ai}]}{k_{LB,A}^2} = \frac{10^{-5} \times 10^3 \times 1 \times 10^{-3} \times 0.2 \times 10^{-5}}{2.56 \times 10^{-6}}$$

$$= 0.781 \times 10^{-5}$$

$$\ll 1$$

The reaction in both phases is controlled by diffusion of the relevant species since the converse of conditions given by expression 7.3 and 7.4 is satisfied.

$$k_{LA,B}a[A_{Bi}] = 1.2 \times 10^{-3} \times 10 \times 0.25 \times 10^{-5}$$

$$= 0.3 \times 10^{-7}$$

$$lk_{mn,B}[A_{Bi}][B_{Bo}] = 0.4 \times 2 \times 10^3 \times 0.25 \times 10^{-5} \times 2 \times 10^{-3}$$

$$= 0.4 \times 10^{-5}$$

$$k_{LB,A}a[B_{Ai}] = 1.6 \times 10^{-3} \times 10 \times 0.2 \times 10^{-5}$$

$$= 0.32 \times 10^{-7}$$

$$(1 - l)k_{mn,A}[A_{Ao}][B_{Ai}] = 0.6 \times 1 \times 10^3 \times 1 \times 10^{-3} \times 0.2 \times 10^{-5}$$

$$= 0.12 \times 10^{-5}$$

Hence the rate of consumption of A can be calculated by using Eq. 7.6.

$$R_A = (1.2 \times 10^{-3} \times 0.25 \times 10^{-5}) + (1.6 \times 10^{-3} \times 0.2 \times 10^{-5})$$

$$= 0.62 \times 10^{-8}\ \text{mol/cm}^2\ \text{sec}$$

The rates of reaction in each phase are as follows:

$$R_{A,B} = 0.3 \times 10^{-8}\ \text{mol/cm}^2\ \text{sec}$$

$$R_{A,A} = 0.32 \times 10^{-8}\ \text{mol/cm}^2\ \text{sec}$$

7.2. REACTION OCCURS ONLY IN THE B PHASE

The problem of reaction that occurs only in the B phase is analogous to that discussed in Chapter 2. However, there is some difference, which arises out of the finite flux of B at the interface toward the A phase (Figure 7.3). This type of problem has been discussed by Pangarkar (1972) for gas–liquid systems where B gets desorbed into the A phase (see Section 2.8). The conditions under which the interfacial concentration $[B_{Bi}]$ and the bulk concentration $[B_{Bo}]$ will be the same are given by the following expressions:

$$\frac{\sqrt{\frac{2}{m+1} D_{AB} k_{mn,B} [B_{Bo}]^n [A_{Bi}]^{m-1}}}{k_{LA,B}} \ll \frac{[B_{Bo}]}{Z[A_{Bi}]} \quad (7.9a)$$

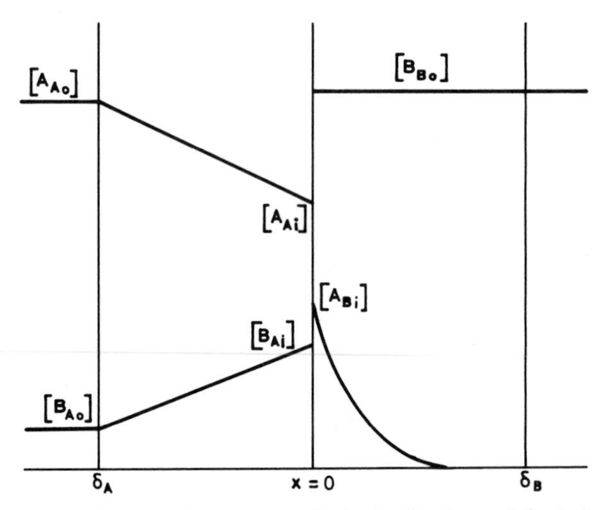

Figure 7.3. Reaction occurs only in the B phase while A is diffusing. The interface concentration $[B_{Bi}]$ is equal to $[B_{Bo}]$.

$$\gg 1 \quad (7.9b)$$

and

$$\frac{k_{LB,A} m_B}{k_{LB,B}} \ll 1 \quad (7.9c)$$

When the condition given by the expression 7.9a is not satisfied and the two terms are comparable, $[B_{Bi}]$ will be considerably different from $[B_{Bo}]$.

In general, the specific rate of transfer of A into the B phase is given by the following:

$$R_A = \phi_{AB} k_{LA,B} [A_{Bi}] \quad (7.10)$$

$$= k_{LA,A}([A_{Ao}] - [A_{Ai}]) \quad (7.11)$$

The value of ϕ_{AB} will depend on the relative rates of diffusion and chemical reaction of A in the B phase.

7.3. REACTION OCCURS IN BOTH PHASES IN THE FILMS ADJACENT TO THE INTERFACE

The transfer of A into the B phase and that of B into the A phase may be accompanied by fast pseudo-mth-order reactions. The situation differs from that given in Section 2.4 in that there is a finite flux of B into the A phase. The conditions for the validity of a fast pseudo-mth-order reaction are given by the following approximate expressions:

$$3 < \sqrt{M_{B,A}} = \frac{\sqrt{\frac{2}{n+1} D_{BA} k_{mn,A} [A_{Ao}]^m [B_{Ai}]^{n-1}}}{k_{LB,A}} \ll \frac{Z[A_{Ao}]}{[B_{Bo}] m_B} \quad (7.12a)$$

$$3 < \sqrt{M_{A,B}} = \frac{\sqrt{\frac{2}{m+1} D_{AB} k_{mn,B} [B_{Bo}]^n [A_{Bi}]^{m-1}}}{k_{LA,B}} \ll \frac{m_A [B_{Bo}]}{Z[A_{Ao}]} \quad (7.12b)$$

where

$$[A_{Bi}] = \frac{[A_{Ao}]}{m_A} \quad (7.13a)$$

$$[B_{Ai}] = [B_{Bo}] m_B \quad (7.13b)$$

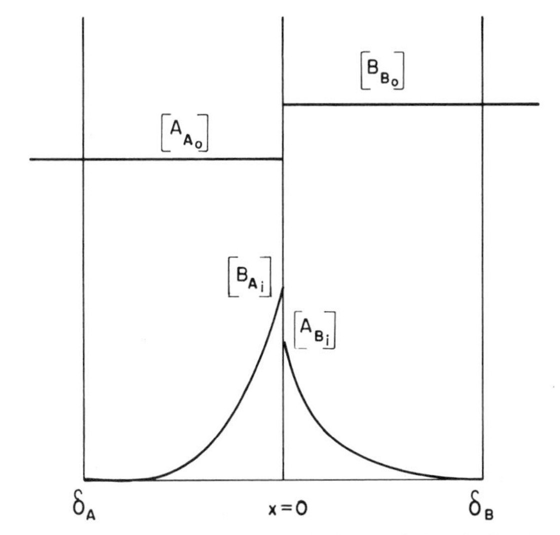

Figure 7.4. Reaction occurs in both phases while A is diffusing in B phase and B is diffusing in A phase.

Figure 7.4 indicates the concentration profiles for the species A and B. The specific rate of consumption of A is given by

$$R_A = m_B[B_{Bo}]\sqrt{\frac{2}{n+1}D_{BA}k_{mn,A}[A_{Ao}]^m[B_{Ai}]^{n-1}} + \frac{[A_{Ao}]}{m_A}\sqrt{\frac{2}{m+1}D_{AB}k_{mn,B}[B_{Bo}]^n[A_{Bi}]^{m-1}} \tag{7.14}$$

Example

Consider the following case:

$$k_{LA,B} = 1.2 \times 10^{-3}\ \text{cm/sec}$$

$$k_{LB,A} = 1.0 \times 10^{-3}\ \text{cm/sec}$$

$$[A_{Ao}] = 2 \times 10^{-3}\ \text{mol/cm}^3$$

$$[B_{Bo}] = 3 \times 10^{-3}\ \text{mol/cm}^3$$

$$k_{mn,A} = 4 \times 10^3\ \text{cm}^3/\text{mol sec}$$

$$k_{mn,B} = 8 \times 10^3\ \text{cm}^3/\text{mol sec}$$

$$m = n = 1, \qquad Z = 1$$

$$D_{BA} = 1.2 \times 10^{-5}\ \text{cm}^2/\text{sec}$$

$$D_{AB} = 1.4 \times 10^{-5}\ \text{cm}^2/\text{sec}$$

$$m_A = 200, \qquad m_B = 0.004$$

$$\sqrt{M_{B,A}} = \frac{\sqrt{D_{BA}k_{mn,A}[A_{Ao}]}}{k_{LB,A}} = \frac{\sqrt{1.2 \times 10^{-5} \times 4 \times 10^3 \times 2 \times 10^{-3}}}{1 \times 10^{-3}} = 9.8$$

$$\sqrt{M_{A,B}} = \frac{\sqrt{D_{AB}k_{mn,B}[B_{Bo}]}}{k_{LA,B}} = \frac{\sqrt{1.4 \times 10^{-5} \times 8 \times 10^3 \times 3 \times 10^{-3}}}{1.2 \times 10^{-3}} = 15.3$$

Hence the converse of the conditions given by expressions 7.7 and 7.8 is satisfied. The reaction occurs in the film adjacent to the interphase. The regime of the reaction can be determined from conditions 7.12a and 7.12b. We have

$$\frac{Z[A_{Ao}]}{[B_{Bo}]m_B} = \frac{2 \times 10^{-3}}{3 \times 10^{-3} \times 0.004} = 166.67$$

$$\frac{m_A[B_{Bo}]}{Z[A_{Ao}]} = \frac{200 \times 3 \times 10^{-3}}{2 \times 10^{-3}} = 300$$

Hence, conditions 7.12a and 7.12b are satisfied and Eq. 7.14 holds. The first and second terms on the right-hand side of Eq. 7.14 represent the specific rate of reaction in phase A and phase B ($R_{A,A}$ and $R_{A,B}$), respectively.

$$R_{A,A} = m_B[B_{Bo}]k_{LB,A}\sqrt{M_{B,A}} = 0.004 \times 3 \times 10^{-3} \times 1 \times 10^{-3} \times 9.8 = 11.76 \times 10^{-8}\ \text{mol/cm}^2\ \text{sec}$$

$$R_{A,B} = \frac{[A_{Ao}]}{m_A}k_{LA,B}\sqrt{M_{A,B}} = \frac{2 \times 10^{-3}}{200} \times 1.2 \times 10^{-3} \times 15.3 = 18.36 \times 10^{-8}\ \text{mol/cm}^2\ \text{sec}$$

Hence the total specific rate of consumption of A, R_A, is equal to 30.12×10^{-8} mol/cm² sec.

7.4. REACTION BETWEEN A AND B IS INSTANTANEOUS IN BOTH PHASES

Under certain conditions the reaction between A and B becomes so fast that it occurs at a plane close to the interface and the two species cannot coexist; hence the reaction can occur in only one phase. The rate is controlled by the diffusion of A and B to the reaction plane. Scriven (1961) has considered this problem on the basis of the penetration theory and obtained an analytic expression for R_A. The location of the reaction plane is dependent on the value of the dimensionless group, $([B_{Bo}]/Z[A_{Ao}])\sqrt{D_{BB}/D_{AA}}$. If the value of this group is less than unity, then the reaction plane moves into the B phase; if equal to unity, then it remains at the interface; and for a value greater than unity it moves into the A phase. A similar criterion can be derived in a much simpler way by using the film theory instead of the penetration theory (Mhaskar and Sharma, 1975). The typical concentration profiles for this case are given in Figure 7.5.

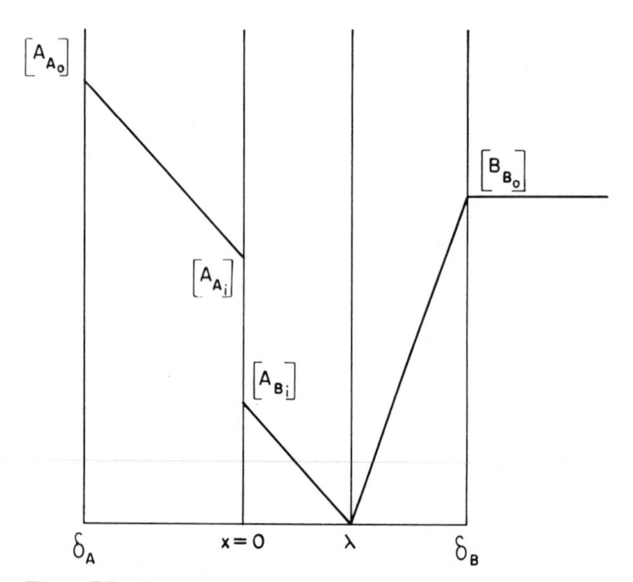

Figure 7.5. Instantaneous reaction, which can occur in only one phase, gives rise to a reaction plane where concentrations of both species are zero. Film theory is used to depict the profiles.

We have

$$\frac{D_{AA}}{\delta_A}([A_{Ao}] - m_A[A_{Bi}]) = \frac{D_{AB}[A_{Bi}]}{\lambda}$$

$$= \frac{D_{BB}[B_{Bo}]}{Z(\delta_B - \lambda)} \quad (7.15)$$

Hence

$$[A_{Bi}] = \frac{D_{AA}[A_{Ao}]/\delta_A}{m_A D_{AA}/\delta_A + D_{AB}/\lambda} \quad (7.16)$$

and

$$\lambda = \frac{ZD_{AB}D_{AA}[A_{Ao}]\delta_B - D_{BB}[B_{Bo}]D_{AB}\delta_A}{m_A D_{AA}D_{BB}[B_{Bo}] + D_{AB}D_{AA}[A_{Ao}]Z} \quad (7.17)$$

If we assume that $\delta_A = \delta_B$, then

$$\lambda \lesseqgtr 0$$

when

$$ZD_{AB}D_{AA}[A_{Ao}] - D_{BB}D_{AB}[B_{Bo}] \lesseqgtr 0 \quad (7.18)$$

as the terms in the denominator of Eq. 7.17 are positive. Hence we get

$$1 \lesseqgtr \frac{[B_{Bo}]}{Z[A_{Ao}]}\frac{D_{BB}}{D_{AA}} \quad (7.19)$$

The right-hand side of Eq. 7.19 is similar to that obtained on the basis of penetration theory except that the diffusivity ratio appears as a square root in the case of the penetration theory solution. Hence, by varying the bulk concentration $[B_{Bo}]$ or $[A_{Ao}]$ it should be possible to shift the reaction from the B phase into the A phase and vice versa (see the next example). The specific rate of consumption of A will be given by the following equation when the reaction occurs in the B phase:

$$R_A = k_{LA,B}[A_{Ao}] \times \frac{1 + q'}{(1 + q')m_A + (1 + q')(D_{AB}/D_{AA})} \quad (7.20)$$

where

$$q' = \frac{D_{BB}[B_{Bo}]}{ZD_{AA}[A_{Ao}]} \quad (7.21)$$

The following equations hold when the reaction occurs in the A phase:

$$q'' = \frac{ZD_{AA}[A_{Ao}]}{D_{BB}[B_{Bo}]} \tag{7.22}$$

$$R_A = \frac{k_{LB,A}[B_{Bo}]}{Z} \times \frac{1 + q''}{(1 - q'')/m_B + (1 + q'')(D_{BA}/D_{BB})} \tag{7.23}$$

Equation 7.20 differs from Eq. 2.83 derived for mass transfer accompanied by instantaneous reaction in the B phase. In Equation 7.21 the diffusivity terms refer to the diffusivity of species A in the A phase and species B in the B phase. By contrast, in Eq. 2.83 the diffusivity values of both species A and species B refer to that in the B phase.

It is also likely that the reaction may be reversible and can take place in both phases. This situation can be analyzed on the basis of the methods given by Olander (1960). Mhaskar and Sharma (1975) have analyzed the following instantaneous reversible reaction:

$$A + B \rightleftharpoons C$$

Example

Consider the following case of an instantaneous reaction:

$$m_B = 0.005$$

$$m_A = 250$$

$$[B_{Bo}] = 4 \times 10^{-3}\ \text{mol/cm}^3$$

$$[A_{Ao}] = 2 \times 10^{-3}\ \text{mol/cm}^3$$

$$D_{BB} = 1 \times 10^{-5}\ \text{cm}^2/\text{sec}$$

$$D_{AA} = 1.5 \times 10^{-5}\ \text{cm}^2/\text{sec}$$

$$D_{AB} = 1 \times 10^{-5}\ \text{cm}^2/\text{sec}$$

$$D_{BA} = 1.2 \times 10^{-5}\ \text{cm}^2/\text{sec}$$

$$Z = 1$$

$$k_{LA,B} = 1.2 \times 10^{-3}\ \text{cm/sec}$$

$$k_{LB,A} = 1.0 \times 10^{-3}\ \text{cm/sec}$$

The location of the reaction plane will be decided by the condition given by expression 7.19.

$$q' = \frac{[B_{Bo}]}{Z[A_{Ao}]}\frac{D_{BB}}{D_{AA}} = 1.33$$

This value is greater than unity and therefore the reaction occurs only in the *A phase*. The rate of consumption of B can be calculated from Eq. 7.23.

$$R_A = \frac{k_{LB,A}[B_{Bo}]}{Z} \times \frac{1 + q''}{(1 - q'')/m_B + (1 + q'')(D_{BA}/D_{BB})}$$

where

$$q'' = \frac{ZD_{AA}[A_{Ao}]}{D_{BB}[B_{Bo}]} = 0.75$$

Hence

$$R_A = 1 \times 10^{-3} \times 4 \times 10^{-3} \times \frac{1 + 0.75}{(1 - 0.75)/0.005 + 1.75 \times 1.2}$$

$$= 1.332 \times 10^{-7}\ \text{mol/cm}^2\ \text{sec}$$

Now consider a situation where the concentrations are

$$[B_{Bo}] = 2.5 \times 10^{-3}\ \text{mol/cm}^3$$

$$[A_{Ao}] = 4.0 \times 10^{-3}\ \text{mol/cm}^3$$

It is assumed that the other values of physicochemical properties remain unchanged. We have from Eq. 7.21,

$$q' = 0.416$$

This is less than unity and hence the reaction occurs in the *B phase*. The rate of consumption of A is obtained from Eq. 7.20:

$$R_A = 1.2 \times 10^{-3} \times 4 \times 10^{-3} \times \frac{1.416}{0.584 \times 250 + 1.416 \times (1/1.5)}$$

$$= 4.64 \times 10^{-8}\ \text{mol/cm}^2\ \text{sec}$$

7.5. REACTION IN BOTH PHASES IN THE DEPLETION REGIME

The situation becomes very complicated when the two terms in conditions 7.12a and 7.12b are comparable and we have depletion. Figure 7.6 shows the typical concentration profiles. Rod (1973) has attempted to analyze the situation on the basis of the film theory, using a collocation technique to get the values of the enhancement factor. Rod has actually solved the relevant equations for only one phase. However, the parameters of the equations involve interface concentrations, and these interface concentrations can be obtained only when the diffusion equations are solved simultaneously for both phases. Further, Rod has assumed the same rate constant value in both phases, which is unlikely to be the case in real systems. In a subsequent paper Rod (1974) has taken different values of the rate constant in the two phases. Mhaskar and Sharma (1975) have used the collocation technique to solve this problem by assuming a polynomial form of concentration profile. Recently Sada et al. (1977) have obtained an approximate analytical solution to this problem based on their earlier work on gas absorption with chemical reaction. These solutions compared fairly well with the numerical solutions obtained by using the quasilinearization technique proposed by Lee (1968). It should be noted, however, that all the methods just mentioned are approximate.

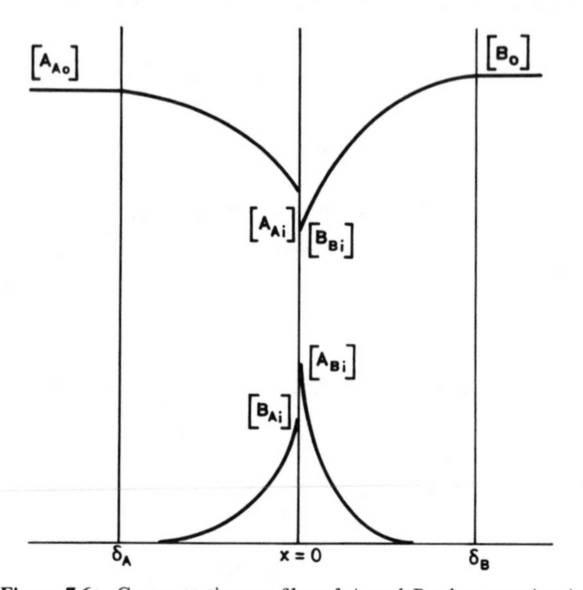

Figure 7.6. Concentration profiles of A and B when reaction is important in both phases and the interface concentration of the reactant in the phase in which it is rich, differs from the bulk concentration in that phase.

When the reaction is not instantaneous a reaction zone of finite width will exist. Scriven (1961) has given an approximate criterion for the case where the reaction proceeds in both phases. In this case if the quantity

$$\frac{k_{2,A}\left(m_A + \sqrt{\dfrac{D_{AB}}{D_{BA}} + \dfrac{D_{AB}}{D_{AA}}} - \sqrt{\dfrac{D_{AB}}{D_{BA}}}\right)}{k_{2,B}\left(m_B + \sqrt{\dfrac{D_{AB}}{D_{BA}}} + \sqrt{1 + \dfrac{D_{AB}}{D_{BB}}} - 1\right)}$$

is greater than unity, more reaction takes place in the A phase, and conversely. If the rate constant ratio is fairly temperature sensitive, then it may be possible to restrict the reaction only to one phase by changing the temperature.

7.6. EXAMPLES

7.6.1. Manufacture of Cyclohexanone Oxime from Cyclohexanone and Aqueous Hydroxylamine Sulfate

In one of the established processes for manufacturing caprolactam the first step involves the reaction between cyclohexanone and aqueous hydroxylamine sulfate containing ammonium sulfate. The liberated sulfuric acid is neutralized with aqueous ammonia.

$$2\ (\text{cyclohexanone, } C{=}O) + (NH_2OH)_2.H_2SO_4 \longrightarrow$$

$$2\ (\text{cyclohexanone oxime, } C{=}NOH) + 2H_2O + H_2SO_4$$

$$2NH_3 + H_2SO_4 \longrightarrow (NH_4)_2SO_4$$

The reaction is usually carried out at a temperature of about 83°C (so that the oxime exists as a melt) and a pH of about 5. For the subsequent processing it is necessary that the conversion of cyclohexanone to the oxime be better than 99.8% with a minimal excess of hydroxylamine sulfate. In order to achieve this objective it has been suggested that a countercurrent multistage extraction column reactor be used (Rod, 1974, 1976).

Sharma and Nanda (1968) have studied the kinetics of the reaction between pure cyclohexanone and aqueous hydroxylamine sulfate containing ammonium sulfate and have shown that extraction of cyclohexanone into the aqueous solution is accompanied by fast reaction. Rod has shown that when the level of conversion of cyclohexanone approaches high values the reaction also occurs in the organic phase. (This was proved on the basis of the reaction between a mixture of cyclohexanone and oxime containing a saturated amount of water and solid hydroxylamine sulfate.) The solubility of oxime in water is very small and almost all of this material is transferred to the organic phase. Thus under practical conditions the reaction occurs in both phases.

Rod carried out experiments in a 5-cm-i.d. 600-cm-high vibrating plate extractor provided with 35 perforated plates. Cyclohexanone (dispersed phase) was introduced at the bottom, and at the top 1.7 equivalent/liter hydroxylamine sulfate containing 7.4 equivalent/liter ammonium sulfate was introduced. It was possible to conduct experiments in such a way that the cyclohexanone content of the oxime was as low as 0.02%. An analysis of the data indicated very clearly that in the lower part of the column, where the concentration of cyclohexanone is high and that of hydroxylamine sulfate is low, the reaction occurs mainly in the water phase. In the upper part of the column, however, where the concentration of hydroxylamine sulfate is high and the concentration of cyclohexanone relatively low, the reaction occurs essentially in the organic phase.

7.6.2. Interfacial Polycondensation Reactions

The case of interfacial polycondensation reactions was discussed in Section 3.7.16. Here, depending on the nature of the reactants, the reaction can occur in the organic phase or the aqueous phase. Further, depending on the requirements of the process, the operating conditions can be adjusted to force the reaction to occur in the desired phase.

REFERENCES

Albright, L. F. (1966a), *Chem. Eng.*, **73**(9), 169.

Albright, L. F. (1966b), *Chem. Eng.*, **73**(18), 119.

Albright, L. F. (1967), in Kirk, R. E., and Othmer, D. F. (Eds.), *Encyclopedia of Chemical Technology*, 2nd ed., Wiley-Interscience, New York, Vol. 13, p. 784.

Albright, L. F., and Hanson, C. (1969), *Loss Prev.*, **3**, 26.

Bailes, P. J., Hanson, C., and Hughes, M. A. (1976), *Chem. Eng.*, **83**(18), 86.

Groggins, P. H. (Ed.) (1958), *Unit Processes in Organic Synthesis*, 5th ed., McGraw-Hill, New York, pp. 279, 282.

Jeffreys, G. V., Jenson, V. G., and Miles, F. R. (1961), *Trans. Inst. Chem. Eng.*, **39**, 389.

Lee, E. S. (1968), *AIChE J.*, **14**, 490.

Mhaskar, R. D., and Sharma, M. M. (1975), *Chem. Eng. Sci.*, **30**, 811.

Morgan, P. W. (1965), *Condensation Polymers: By Interfacial and Solution Methods*, Wiley-Interscience, New York, pp. 22, 66.

Olander, D. R. (1960), *AIChE J.*, **6**, 233.

Pangarkar, V. G. (1972), Mass Transfer with Chemical Reaction, Ph.D (Tech.) thesis, University of Bombay.

Rod, V. (1973), *Collect. Czech. Chem. Commun.*, **38**, 3228.

Rod, V. (1974), *Chem. Eng. J.*, **7**, 137.

Rod, V. (1976) *Proc. 6th European/4th Int. Symp. Chem. React. Eng.*, p. 271

Rozen, A. M., Zel'venskii, M. Ya., Koltunov, V. S., and Marchenko, V. I. (1976), *Teor. Osu. Khim. Tekhnol.*, **10**, 705.

Sada, E., Kumazawa, H., and Butt, M. A. (1977), *Can. J. Chem. Eng.*, **55**, 475.

Scriven, L. E. (1961), *AIChE J.*, **7**, 524.

Sharma, M. M., and Nanda, A. K. (1968), *Trans. Inst. Chem. Eng.*, **46**(2), T44.

CHAPTER EIGHT

Desorption with Chemical Reaction; Simultaneous Absorption–Desorption with Reaction

8.1. DESORPTION WITH REACTION

Desorption of volatile species from liquids with chemical reaction is fairly common in practice. Table 8.1 gives some examples of industrial importance. In this chapter we shall cover some more important aspects of this problem on the basis of the film theory. This subject has been discussed in a comprehensive way by Shah and Sharma (1976). Recently Savage et al. (1980) and Astarita and Savage (1980a, b) have also discussed this subject.

Desorption with reaction may be important in several contexts. For many absorption processes, the absorbent has to be regenerated and this is usually accomplished by stripping with steam (and sometimes with an inert gas) under boiling conditions. For instance, in the case of absorption processes for the removal of CO_2 and H_2S, using potash with and without catalysts or alkanolamine solutions, it is necessary to regenerate the solution. In many commercially important processes a volatile product that has to be removed in order to achieve certain results is formed. In the manufacture of polyesters and polyamides, for instance, ethylene glycol and water, respectively, are formed and must be removed to obtain the desired molecular weight of the polymers.

In the case of regenerative absorption processes of the CO_2–K_2CO_3 or CO_2–alkanolamine type, the desorption may occur (i) during flashing; (ii) in the main part of the column; and (iii) under boiling conditions in the reboiler. It is likely that the controlling mechanism during desorption in each of these situations is different. During the flashing operation desorption would occur into growing bubbles from a supersaturated solution. Further, in the reboiler, desorption also occurs into growing bubbles under boiling conditions. The mechanism under these conditions is very complex and has not yet been analyzed to the extent that it can be used for the design purposes. Desorption in the main part of the column, which accounts for most of the desorption of the volatile species, is usually amenable to an analytical treatment, and we shall consider some specific cases in this chapter.

Despite its great importance, desorption column design has received little attention. Utility requirements for such columns are quite high, and in many cases the investment necessary for desorption columns is substantially higher than that for the companion absorption columns.

Desorption systems can be broadly divided into two groups, depending on whether the liquid phase is polymeric or nonpolymeric. In the case of nonpolymeric systems, the diffusion coefficients of reactant B and the gaseous species A and A′ are of the same order of magnitude. Therefore, the diffusive fluxes of all the species have to be considered. In the case of polymeric systems the diffusivities of the polymeric species are lower by an order of magnitude than those for the volatile species, and hence the diffusive flux for the polymeric reactive species can be neglected. Thus the two cases of the CO_2–K_2CO_3-type system and polymeric systems will have to be treated differently.

In most cases the problem of physical desorption is akin to that of physical absorption. There are, however, certain basic differences. For instance, during the desorption of ammonia from aqueous solutions there is foaming, but no foaming occurs during absorption. Thus in types of contactors where a gas is dispersed in a pool of liquid the interfacial area of contact during the desorption in some cases will be significantly higher than that during the absorption process. This situation arises as a result of the Marangoni effect (Andrew, 1961).

8.2. PHYSICAL DESORPTION

Physical desorption has received considerable attention in the published literature (Perry and Chilton, 1973; Sherwood and Pigford, 1952; Turner, 1962; Treybal, 1968). The design procedure for a physical desorption tower is akin to that for an absorber in which physical mass transfer occurs. In this section we shall consider the desorption of a free dissolved gas A′ having bulk liquid and interfacial concentrations of $[A'_o]$ and $[A'^*]$, respectively. The specific rate of desorption in this case is

$$R_{A'} = k_L([A'_o] - [A'^*]) \tag{8.1}$$

A typical concentration profile of the desorbing gas is shown in Figure 8.1.

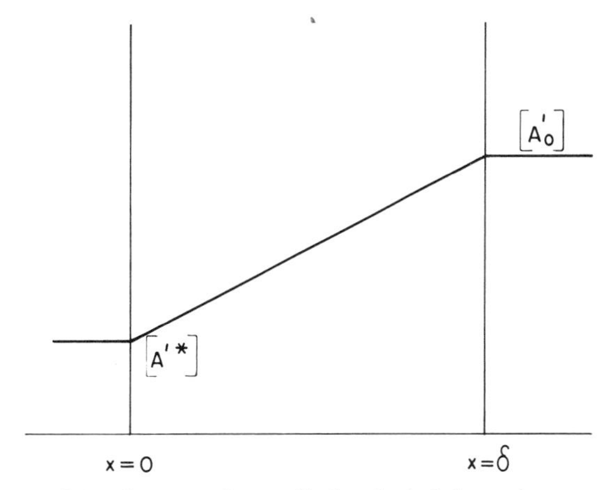

Figure 8.1. Concentration profile for physical desorption.

Equation 8.1 indicates that the rate of desorption is a function of k_L, which implies that it is a function of the hydrodynamics of the contactor used. Therefore, the choice of contactor can be made with a view to obtaining a high value of k_L.

Equation 8.1 also indicates that the rate of desorption is a function of the bulk liquid and interfacial concentrations of A′. Thus backmixing in both the gas and the liquid phase will decrease the rate of desorption.

8.3. DESORPTION PRECEDED BY A CHEMICAL REACTION IN NONPOLYMERIC SYSTEMS

There are many industrially important systems involving the desorption of a species preceded by a chemical reaction in a nonpolymeric liquid phase.

TABLE 8.1. Industrially Important Examples of Desorption Preceded by a Chemical Reaction

System	Reference(s)
Desorption of CO_2 and H_2S from carbonated solutions of potash, with or without catalysts, and carbonated solutions of alkanolamines	Danckwerts and Sharma (1966)
Desorption of CO from its complex with organometallic compounds	Haase and Waker (1974)
Desorption of SO_2 from solutions of sulfite–bisulfite buffer	Pangarkar (1972)
Desorption of HF from trinonylamine hydrofluoride	Hardwick and Wace (1965)
Desorption of ethylene glycol and water in the manufacture of polyesters and polyamides, respectively	Hoftyzer and van Krevelen (1968); Hoftyzer (1975)
Desorption of HCl in the manufacture of fatty alcohol sulfates by reaction between fatty alcohols and chlorosulfonic acid	Davidsohn and Midwilsky (1972)
Extraction of isoamylene from "fat" sulfuric acid solutions with *n*-heptane	Foster et al. (1960); Sanholkar and Sharma (1975)
Extraction of *m*-xylene from *m*-xylene complex with HF–BF_3	*Hydrocarbon Process. Petrol. Refiner* (1971)
Desorption in hydrometallurgical field	Rosenbaum et al. (1971); Habashi (1969); Hughes (1975); Bailes et al. (1976)

(Table 8.1 gives some relevant examples.) These systems can be treated much like that for gas absorption accompanied by a chemical reaction (Chapter 2). Thus, for instance, the general classification in the four regimes given in Chapter 2 can be applied here.

Astarita and Savage (1980a) have discussed the general theory of chemical desorption on the basis of the film model. These authors have shown that chemical desorption is analogous to chemical absorption, in particular where the reaction regimes are 3 and 4. However, whereas the absorption case can be considered truly irreversible ($[A_o] \to 0$), the same is not true for the desorption analogue. The transport of the desorbing species to the gas phase requires a finite interfacial concentration, and hence the driving force expressed as a ratio ($[A'_o]/[A'^*]$) has to be finite. It is common to find $[A_o]$ equal to 0 in absorption processes and the analogous driving force ratio $[A^*]/[A_o]$ tends to infinity, which corresponds to truly irreversible behavior. In the case of regime 4 for desorption, the physical picture involving a reaction plane leads to paradoxes and therefore is obviously untenable. The reversible characteristics of the reaction leading to desorption must inevitably be considered in the development of the theory.

A problem we shall consider here is as follows: A liquid-phase reactant B reacts reversibly to give the volatile species A′ according to the reaction:

$$B \underset{k'}{\overset{k}{\rightleftharpoons}} A'(g) \tag{8.2}$$

The reaction denoted by Eq. 8.2 can occur in the four regimes indicated in Chapter 2. The rate of desorption of A′ will vary, depending on the regime prevailing for the reaction given by Eq. 8.2. Thus, following the classification of Chapter 2 we will consider each regime separately and obtain analytical expressions for the rate of desorption. In the case of the very slow reaction regime (regime 1) diffusional factors will not be important.

8.3.1. Slow Reaction Regime

When the reaction denoted by Eq. 8.2 is sufficiently slow, then for all practical purposes the reversible nature of the reaction can be neglected without causing any significant error. The reaction in this case will occur in the bulk liquid phase, and consequently the same concentration profiles in the diffusion film will be maintained as in the case of physical desorption (Figure 8.1). The rate of desorption can thus be approximated by Eq. 8.1. The condition to be satisfied is

$$\frac{\sqrt{D_{A'}k}}{k_L} \ll 1 \tag{8.3}$$

In this case backmixing in both the gas and liquid phases will significantly alter the rate of desorption and these factors should be considered while designing the desorbers.

8.3.2. Fast Reaction Regime

In the fast reaction regime the reaction occurs predominantly in the film. The concentration gradients in the film are thus affected and as a consequence the rate of desorption increases over that given by Eq. 8.1. Figure 8.2 shows the typical concentration profiles.

The film model equations for the diffusing species with the reaction occurring simultaneously are

$$-D_{A'}\frac{d^2[A']}{dx^2} = D_B\frac{d^2[B]}{dx^2} = k[B] - k'[A'] \tag{8.4}$$

The boundary conditions for Eq. 8.4 are

$$x = 0, \quad \frac{d[B]}{dx} = 0, \quad [A'] = [A'^*] \tag{8.5}$$

$$x = \delta, \quad [B] = [B_o], \quad [A'] = [A'_o] \tag{8.6}$$

The boundary condition 8.5 for the reactant B is derived from the fact that species B is considered to be nonvolatile. Therefore, the transfer of species B across the interface into the gas phase cannot occur, and hence the flux of B at the interface must be zero.

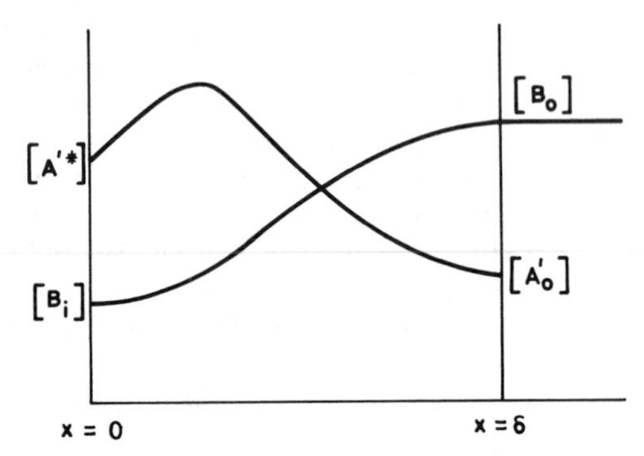

Figure 8.2. Concentration profile for desorption accompanied by fast reaction in the liquid phase.

The rate of desorption of A′ is obtained by solving Eq. 8.4 (assuming $D_{A'} = D_B$) and subsequently obtaining the flux of A′ at the interface (Shah and Sharma, 1976):

$$R_{A'} = k_L\{[A'_o](K_1\cosh\sqrt{M'} + K_2) - [A'^*](K_1^2\cosh\sqrt{M'} + K_2\cosh\sqrt{M'} + K_1K_2\cosh\sqrt{M'}) + [B_o](K_1\cosh\sqrt{M'} - K_1)\}\Big/\left[\cosh\sqrt{M'}\,(K_1^2 + K_1K_2) + K_2\frac{\sinh\sqrt{M}}{\sqrt{M'}}\right] \quad (8.7)$$

where

$$K_1 = \frac{k}{k+k'}, \qquad K_2 = \frac{k'}{k+k'},$$

$$\sqrt{M'} = \sqrt{\frac{k+k'}{D_{A'}}}\cdot\delta \quad (8.7a)$$

Example

The point rate of desorption of A′ in a contactor is to be evaluated for the following conditions:

$$D_{A'} = D_B = 2\times10^{-5}\ \text{cm}^2/\text{sec}$$

$$k_L = 2\times10^{-2}\ \text{cm/sec}$$

$$[A'_o] = 3\times10^{-4}\ \text{mol/cm}^3$$

$$[A'^*] = 2.2\times10^{-4}\ \text{mol/cm}^3$$

$$[B_o] = 1\times10^{-4}\ \text{mol/cm}^3$$

$$k = 100\ \text{sec}^{-1}$$

$$k' = 60\ \text{sec}^{-1}$$

$$a = 1.6\ \text{cm}^2/\text{cm}^3$$

For substitution in Eq. 8.7, the values of K_1, K_2, and $\sqrt{M'}$ are needed:

$$K_1 = 0.625, \qquad K_2 = 0.375, \qquad \sqrt{M'} = 2.825$$

Substitution in Eq. 8.7 gives

$$R_{A'} = 0.943\times10^{-6}\ \text{mol/cm}^2\ \text{sec}$$

$$R_{A'}a = 0.943\times10^{-6}\times1.6$$

$$= 1.5\times10^{-6}\ \text{mol/cm}^3\ \text{sec}$$

8.3.3. Instantaneously Reversible "Equilibrium" Reaction

In the case when both the forward and reverse reactions in Eq. 8.2 are very fast, equilibrium will be attained instantaneously. An instantaneously reversible reaction can be visualized as that reaction in which both the forward and reverse reaction constants are very large. This statement can be quantified as follows:

$$\text{(i)}\qquad \frac{[B_o]}{[A'^*]} \ll \frac{\sqrt{D_{A'}k[B_o]}}{k_L} > 3 \quad (8.8)$$

$$\text{(ii)}\qquad \frac{[A'_o]}{[B_i]} \ll \frac{\sqrt{D_Bk'[A'_o]}}{k_L} > 3 \quad (8.9)$$

Olander (1960) has considered this case. The film model gives the following equation:

$$D_{A'}\frac{d^2[A']}{dx^2} + D_B\frac{d^2[B]}{dx^2} = 0 \quad (8.10)$$

(The flux of A′ is negative according to convention, since A′ is generated by the reaction given by Eq. 8.2.)

The boundary conditions and the equilibrium condition are

$$x = 0, \quad [A'] = [A'^*] \quad (8.11)$$

$$x = \delta, \quad [A'] = [A'_o] \quad (8.12)$$

and

$$x = x, \quad \frac{[A']}{[B]} = K \quad (8.13)$$

where $K = k/k'$ is the equilibrium constant for the reaction given by Eq. 8.2.

The rate of desorption is given by the following

equation:

$$R_{A'} = D_{A'}\frac{d[A']}{dx} + D_B\frac{d[B]}{dx} \qquad (8.14)$$

On integrating Eq. 8.10 twice, the following equation is obtained:

$$D_{A'}[A'] + D_B[B] = C_1x + C_2 \qquad (8.15)$$

The conditions given by Eqs. 8.11–8.13 are then used to evaluate C_1 and C_2. The rate of desorption can be readily obtained by using Eq. 8.14 as

$$R_{A'} = k_L([A'_o] - [A'^*])\left(1 + \frac{D_B}{KD_{A'}}\right) \qquad (8.16)$$

where $k_L = D_{A'}/\delta$.
Comparing Eqs. 8.16 and 8.1, we can see that the enhancement factor for desorption is

$$\phi_d = 1 + \frac{D_B}{KD_{A'}} \qquad (8.17)$$

In this case also, backmixing in the gas and liquid phases significantly affects the rate of desorption. In Eq. 8.16 [B] does not enter directly, but since [A′] and [B] are related by the condition of equilibrium, any change in [A′] causes a corresponding change in [B] and vice versa.

Example

Calculate the rate of desorption for the system outlined in Section 8.3.3 under the following conditions:

$$D_{A'} = 1 \times 10^{-5}\ \text{cm}^2/\text{sec}$$

$$D_B = 4 \times 10^{-6}\ \text{cm}^2/\text{sec}$$

$$[A'_o] = 1 \times 10^{-3}\ \text{mol/cm}^3$$

$$[A'^*] = 5 \times 10^{-4}\ \text{mol/cm}^3$$

$$k_L = 1 \times 10^{-2}\ \text{cm/sec}$$

$$K = 0.5$$

Substitution of these data in Eq. 8.16 gives

$$R_{A'} = 9 \times 10^{-6}\ \text{mol/cm}^2\ \text{sec}$$

The enhancement factor for the desorption process can be obtained from Eq. 8.17:

$$\phi_d = 1.8$$

Astarita and Savage (1980b) have treated the case of gas absorption and desorption with a reversible instantaneous reaction of the type $A' + ZB \rightleftharpoons$ Products on the basis of the film model. The generalized equations can be reduced to three asymptotes defined by the driving force ratio $\psi = [A'^*]/[A'_o]$. For the case where $\psi \simeq 1$ (regions in which the driving force is very small) the asymptote obtained shows that the gas-film resistance to the process becomes important. The authors applied the results of the analysis to the regenerative cycle for removal of H_2S by DIPA. The use of the model assuming the reaction to be reversible gives a deviation of between 10 and 225% for the top and bottom sections, respectively, of an absorption column. The same deviation for the desorber is expected to be much higher on the basis of the analysis and is indeed found to be between 400 and 180,000% for the top and bottom sections, respectively.

8.4. DESORPTION PRECEDED BY A CHEMICAL REACTION IN POLYMERIC SYSTEMS

In the manufacture of a number of polymeric substances, a volatile species is generated along with the desired polymer. The rate of such polycondensation reactions has been shown to depend on the rate of desorption of this volatile species (Hoftyzer and van Krevelen, 1968; Hoftyzer, 1975). For instance, in the manufacture of polyamides, water is one of the products and has a high vapor pressure under conditions employed in practice. Similarly, in the process for the manufacture of polyesters, the corresponding glycol is the volatile species. At high degrees of conversion, the reversible reaction may become important and the net rate of formation of the product will consequently decrease. However, if one of the products of the forward reaction is continuously removed from the system, the equilibrium is favorably displaced and high conversions can be achieved. The equation representing such reactions can be written as

$$B + C \underset{k_2'}{\overset{k_2}{\rightleftharpoons}} A' + D \tag{8.18}$$

Species B and C are the liquid-phase reactive species, species D is the desired product, and A′ is the volatile product that is desorbed.

The diffusion coefficients of polymeric species are very low as compared with those of the desorbing component A′ mainly because of their very large molecular weight and size. Also, entanglements of polymeric chains cause considerable reduction in their diffusion rates (Secor, 1969). Therefore, the diffusive fluxes of the species B, C, and D are negligible in comparison to that of A′. Thus, in the differential mass balances, only the accumulation terms for the polymeric species are considered. Because of this the resulting differential equations describe an unsteady-state process.

Secor (1969) has solved the unsteady-state differential equations by employing the assumptions mentioned above. The results of the numerical solution are presented as plots of the enhancement factor for the desorption of A′, ϕ_d, against the dimensionless time $k_2'[D_o]t$ (Figure 8.3). The model proposed by Secor is valid for the final stages of the polymerization reaction. Under these conditions the reactivity of every functional group can be assumed to be independent of the molecular weight of the polymer molecule of which it is a part. The rate of reaction for this case can be written in terms of the concentrations of the functional groups.

8.5. SIMULTANEOUS ABSORPTION–DESORPTION WITH REACTION

The absorption of a solute gas A accompanied by chemical reaction can result in a volatile species A′, which desorbs into the A phase. Such cases are common in practice. For instance, acid gases like NO_x, sulfur dioxide, and phosgene are absorbed in aqueous solutions of sodium carbonate and sodium bicarbonate (Zhavoronkov and Martynov, 1959). These gases react with the alkaline absorbent to liberate carbon dioxide, which desorbs into the gas phase. In the pulp and paper industry the spent bisulfide solution is treated for the recovery of hydrogen sulfide by stripping with carbon dioxide. Table 8.2 lists some typical cases of industrial importance.

Gas A dissolves into a liquid phase containing a nonvolatile reactant B and undergoes a reaction given by

$$A + Z_1B \xrightarrow{k_A} Z_2A' \tag{8.19}$$

The product species A′ is a volatile component and thus part of it desorbs into the gas phase. A′ can also react with B according to the reaction

$$A' + Z_3B \xrightarrow{k_{A'}} \text{products} \tag{8.20}$$

We shall assume that the reaction given by Eq. 8.20 is

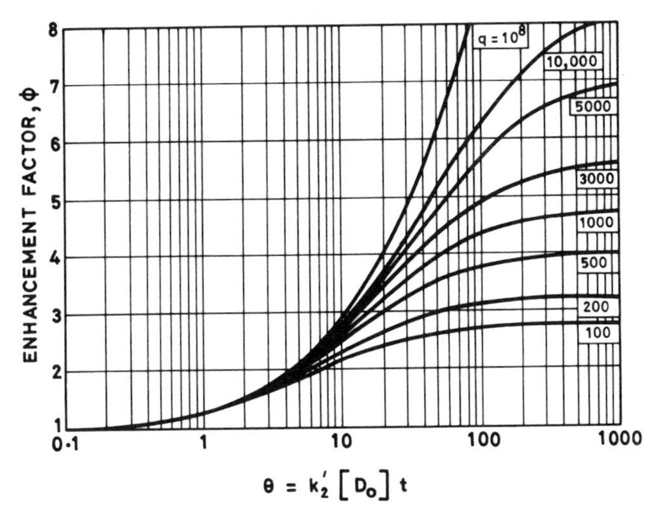

Figure 8.3. Enhancement factor for the desorption process as a function of $\theta = k'_2[D_o]t$ for $K = 1$, $[A'^*] = 0$, and various values of $q = [D_o]/[A'_o]$.

TABLE 8.2. Industrially Important Examples of Simultaneous Absorption–Desorption with Chemical Reaction

System	Reference(s)
Absorption of SO_2, HCl, HF, etc. in aqueous solutions of carbonate (desorption of CO_2)	Ramachandran and Sharma (1971); Pangarkar (1972)
Absorption of phosgene in water (desorption of CO_2)	Ramachandran and Sharma (1970)
Substitution chlorination of organic compounds (desorption of HCl)	Kosorotov et al. (1971)
Absorption of Cl_2 in aqueous solutions of sodium carbonate or sodium hydroxide (desorption of HClO)	Lahiri et al. (1983)
Absorption of Cl_2 in aqueous solution of NaBr (desorption of BrCl)	Stasinevich (1979)
Absorption of nitrous gases ($NO_2 + N_2O_4$) in water (desorption of NO); absorption of NO in aqueous solutions of NaClO (desorption of NO_2)	Andrew and Hanson (1961); Baveja (1979)
Absorption of nitrosyl chloride in cyclohexane (desorption of HCl)	Hulme and Turner (1967)
Conversion of HCl to chlorine via the Kel-Chlor process; absorption of HCl in nitrosyl sulfuric acid (desorption of NOCl)	van Dijk and Schreiner (1973)
Oxidation of organic compounds like toluene, paraffins, and cyclohexane/cyclododecane (desorption of water)	Chandalia (1970); Alagy et al. (1974)
Absorption of CO_2 in an aqueous solution of barium sulfide (desorption of H_2S)	Gupta and Sharma (1967)
Reaction between HCl and alcohols in the presence of $ZnCl_2$ as catalyst (desorption of H_2O)	Kingsley and Bliss (1952)
Bromination with BrCl (desorption of HCl)	Mills and Schneider (1973)
Reactions in pyrometallurgical operations [e.g., absorption of O_2 and/or CO_2 in decarburization of iron (desorption of CO)]	Richardson (1975)
Absorption of acetylene in aqueous solutions of cuprous chloride, ammonium chloride, and hydrogen chloride (desorption of vinyl acetylene); absorption of monovinyl acetylene and HCl in aqueous solutions of cuprous chloride containing hydrochloric acid (desorption of chloroprene)	Goldstein and Waddams (1967)
Absorption of O_3 in unsaturated fatty acid esters (desorption of O_2)	Throckmorton et al. (1968); Throckmorton and Pryde (1972)

slow, as indicated by the following inequality (assuming that the reaction is first order in A′ as well as B):

$$\frac{\sqrt{D_{A'}k_{A'}[B_o]}}{k_L} \ll 1 \qquad (8.21)$$

Thus A′ cannot react in the film and any consumption of B that occurs in the film is due to the reaction given by Eq. 8.19, which can occur in any of the four regimes of chemical absorption.

For the sake of simplicity the solutions based on the film model will be considered and the reaction will be assumed to be first order with respect to A as well as B. Further we shall assume that k_L for A and A′ are the same.

8.5.1. Slow Reaction Regime

In this case, as discussed in Section 2.2, the transfer of A across the film occurs without any significant reaction. The condition to be satisfied is as follows:

$$\frac{\sqrt{D_A k_A [B_o]}}{k_L} \ll 1 \qquad (8.22)$$

The rate of generation of A′ in the bulk liquid phase is

$$R_{A'}a = Z_2 R_A a \qquad (8.23)$$

Desorption of A′ can occur when A′ exists in the liquid phase in the free state, that is, the reaction given by Eq. 8.20 cannot completely consume the total amount of A′ generated by reaction 8.19. Thus the rate of homogeneous reaction between A′ and B must be less than the rate of generation of A′. The rate of the reaction given by Eq. 8.20 is given as $lk_{A'}[A'_o][B_o]$. The condition for finite desorption of A′ is therefore given by

$$lk_{A'}[A'_o][B_o] < Z_2 R_A a \qquad (8.24)$$

The absorption rate of A, R_A, will be different for the two situations that can occur in this regime: (i) kinetically controlled or very slow reaction regime; (ii) diffusion-controlled or slow reaction regime. We will consider these cases separately.

Kinetically Controlled or Very Slow Reaction Regime

The kinetically controlled or very slow reaction regime is valid when the following inequality holds (Section 2.1).

$$k_L a \gg lk_A[B_o] \qquad (8.25)$$

Typical concentration profiles are shown in Figure 8.4.

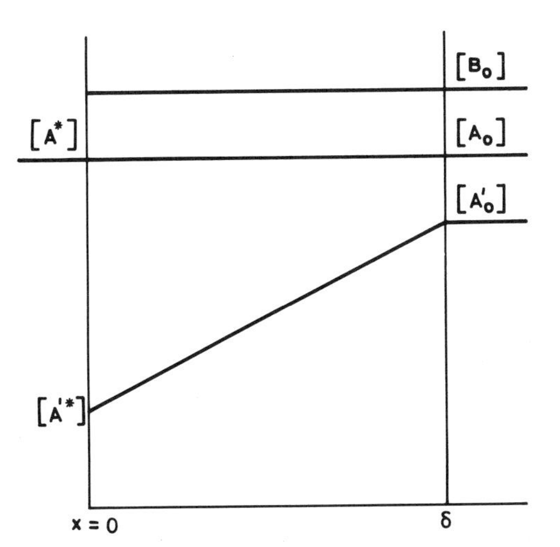

Figure 8.4. Concentration profiles for simultaneous absorption–desorption with reaction: kinetically controlled slow reaction.

The volumetric absorption rate is then given by

$$R_A a = lk_A[A^*][B_o] \qquad (8.26)$$

Substituting for $R_A a$ in expression 8.24, we get the condition for finite desorption of A′:

$$k_{A'}[A'_o] < Z_2 k_A[A^*] \qquad (8.27)$$

Since A′ is incapable of reacting in the film, the concentration profile of A′ is unaltered and the rate of desorption of A′ is given by

$$R_{A'}a = k_L a([A'_o] - [A'^*]) \qquad (8.28)$$

In the case when $[A'_o] \gg [A'^*]$, a mass balance for A′ gives

$$[A'_o] = \frac{Z_2 lk_A[B_o]}{k_L a + lk_{A'}[B_o]}[A^*] \qquad (8.29)$$

Substituting for $[A'_o]$ in Eq. 8.28, we get the rate of desorption of A′ for the case when $[A'_o] \gg [A'^*]$:

$$R_{A'}a = Z_2 k_L a\left(\frac{lk_A[B_o]}{k_L a + lk_{A'}[B_o]}\right)[A^*] \qquad (8.30)$$

Equation 8.30 reduces to the appropriate expression for the two limiting situations that can occur: For $k_L a \ll lk_{A'}[B_o]$,

$$R_{A'}a \simeq 0 \qquad (8.31)$$

and for $k_L a \gg lk_{A'}[B_o]$,

$$R_{A'}a \simeq Z_2 lk_A[B_o][A^*] \simeq Z_2 R_A a \qquad (8.32)$$

In the first limiting case the homogeneous reaction between A′ and B is very rapid as compared with the rate of diffusion of A′ through the film, and therefore before A′ can diffuse into the film it is consumed by the reaction. Since the concentration of free dissolved A′ in the film is negligible, the desorption rate also is very insignificant. In the second limiting case the converse of the first situation holds. The homogeneous reaction is very slow as compared with the rate of diffusion in the film. Thus, practically all the A′ liberated by the reaction given by Eq. 8.19 is available for desorption and the rate of desorption is approximately equal to the rate of generation of A′.

Diffusion-Controlled or Slow Reaction Regime

The diffusion-controlled or slow reaction regime occurs when the converse of expression 8.25 holds. The rate of absorption of A is given by

$$R_A a = k_L a[A^*] \qquad (8.33)$$

Substituting for $R_A a$ in expression 8.24, we get the condition for finite desorption of A′:

$$lk_{A'}[B_o][A'_o] < Z_2 k_L a[A^*] \qquad (8.34)$$

The rate of desorption of A′ is given by Eq. 8.28. As in the previous case we shall consider the limiting case of $[A'_o] \gg [A'^*]$. The mass balance for A′ gives the following equation for $[A'_o]$:

$$[A'_o] = \frac{Z_2 k_L a[A^*]}{k_L a + lk_{A'}[B_o]} \qquad (8.35)$$

On substitution of $[A'_o]$ in Eq. 8.28 we get the rate of desorption of A′:

$$R_{A'} a = \left(\frac{Z_2 (k_L a)^2}{k_L a + lk_{A'}[B_o]}\right)[A^*] \qquad (8.36)$$

The two limiting cases for Eq. 8.36 and the corresponding expressions for $R_{A'}a$ are, for $k_L a \ll lk_{A'}[B_o]$,

$$R_{A'} a \simeq 0 \qquad (8.37)$$

and for $k_L a \gg lk_{A'}[B_o]$,

$$R_{A'} a \simeq Z_2 k_L a[A^*] \simeq Z_2 R_A a \qquad (8.38)$$

Typical concentration profiles for this case are shown in Figure 8.5.

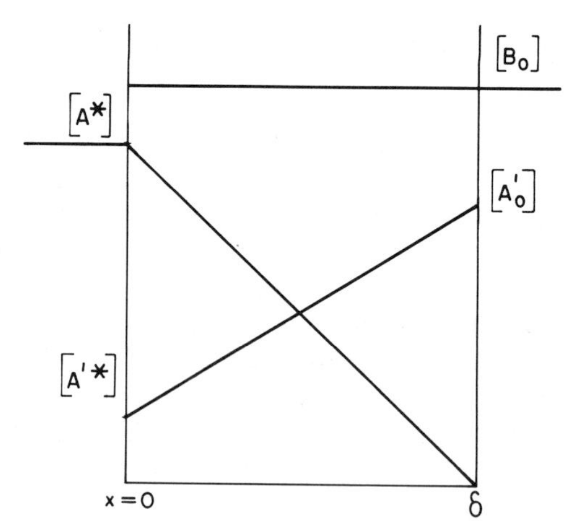

Figure 8.5. Concentration profiles for simultaneous absorption–desorption with reaction: diffusion-controlled slow reaction.

8.5.2. Fast Reaction Regime

The condition to be satisfied in the fast reaction regime is (see Section 2.4)

$$\frac{\sqrt{D_A k_A [B_o]}}{k_L} > 3 \qquad (8.39)$$

The reaction between A and B occurs predominantly in the film. Consequently, A′ is generated in the film according to the reaction given by Eq. 8.19. Since the generating reaction significantly increases the concentration of A′ in the film, there is also a corresponding increase in $R_{A'}$.

For the sake of simplicity the bulk liquid concentration of A′, $[A'_o]$, will be considered to be zero. This will be true when the following condition holds:

$$k_L a \ll lk_{A'}[B_o] \qquad (8.40)$$

The film model equations for the diffusion of A and A′ are as follows:

$$D_A \frac{d^2[A]}{dx^2} = k_A[A][B] \qquad (8.41)$$

$$-D_{A'} \frac{d^2[A']}{dx^2} = Z_2 k_A[A][B] \qquad (8.42)$$

Equation 8.42 does not include any term for the reaction between A′ and B since this reaction is considered to occur only in the bulk liquid phase (the condition given by expression 8.21 is satisfied). The boundary conditions for the foregoing equations are

$$x = 0, \qquad [A] = [A^*], \qquad [B] = [B_i],$$

$$[A'] = [A'^*] \qquad \frac{d[B]}{dx} = 0,$$

$$D_{A'} \frac{d[A']}{dx} = \frac{k_{G_{A'}}}{H_{A'}}([A'^*] - [A'_G]) \qquad (8.43)$$

$$x = \delta, \qquad [A] = [A'] = 0, \quad [B] = [B_o] \qquad (8.44)$$

Pangarkar (1972) has given the following solutions to Eqs. 8.43 and 8.44 based on the method of van

Krevelen and Hoftyzer (1948):

$$[A] = [A^*]\frac{\sinh\left[\sqrt{\dfrac{k_A[B_i]}{D_A}}(\delta - x)\right]}{\sinh\left(\sqrt{\dfrac{k_A[B_i]}{D_A}}\,\delta\right)} \tag{8.45}$$

$$[A'] = -Z_2[A^*]\frac{\sinh\left[\sqrt{\dfrac{k_A[B_i]}{D_A}}(\delta - x)\right]}{\sinh\left(\sqrt{\dfrac{k_A[B_i]}{D_A}}\,\delta\right)} + Z_2\sqrt{M_{A,i}}[A^*]\left(1 - \frac{x}{\delta}\right) - \frac{k_{G_{A'}}}{H_{A'}k_L} \times([A'^*] - [A'_G])\left(1 - \frac{x}{\delta}\right) \tag{8.46}$$

$$\frac{[B_i]}{[B_o]} = \frac{\phi_a - \sqrt{M_{A,o}}\sqrt{[B_i]/[B_o]}}{\phi_a - 1} \tag{8.47}$$

where

$$\sqrt{M_{A,i}} = \frac{\sqrt{D_A k_A [B_i]}}{k_L}, \qquad \sqrt{M_{A,o}} = \frac{\sqrt{D_A k_A [B_o]}}{k_L}$$

The specific rate of desorption of A′ is obtained by the following equation (flux of A′ at the interface):

$$R_{A'} = \frac{k_{G_{A'}}}{H_{A'}}([A'^*] - [A'_G]) \tag{8.48}$$

$[A'^*]$ can be evaluated from Eq. 8.46 and used in Eq. 8.48 with the proper value of $[A'_G]$ to get the rate of desorption.

This treatment is valid for the general case of comparable gas-film and liquid-film resistances for the desorption process. This point is reflected in the boundary condition for the flux of A′ at the interface in Eq. 8.43. This boundary condition has to be replaced appropriately when the desorption process is liquid-film-controlled. Typical concentration profiles for gas-film-controlled desorption are shown in Figure 8.6.

The procedure for obtaining the point rate of desorption is outlined in the following example.

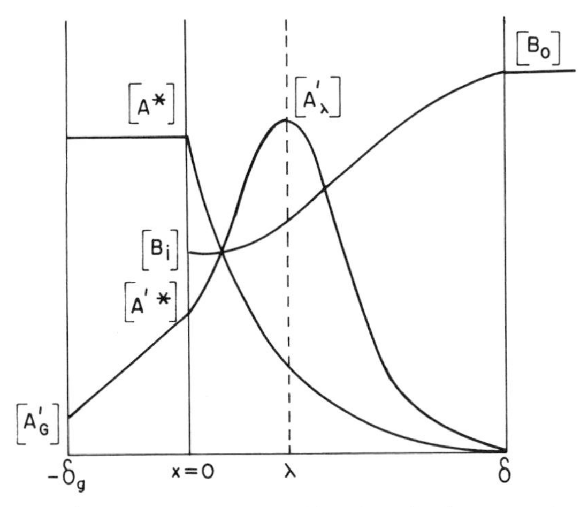

Figure 8.6. Concentration profiles for simultaneous absorption–desorption with reaction: gas-film-controlled desorption, fast reaction.

Example

For the scheme outlined in Section 8.5.2, calculate the rate of desorption of species A′ for the following conditions:

$$[A^*] = 8 \times 10^{-4}\ \text{mol/cm}^3$$

$$D_A = D_{A'} = 1 \times 10^{-5}\ \text{cm}^2/\text{sec}$$

$$k_L = 1 \times 10^{-2}\ \text{cm/sec}$$

$$[A'_G] = 2 \times 10^{-5}\ \text{mol/cm}^3$$

$$\sqrt{M_{A,i}} = 12$$

$$\frac{k_{G_{A'}}}{H_{A'}k_L} = 2$$

$$Z_1 = Z_2 = 1$$

From Eq. 8.46 $[A'^*]$ can be obtained:

$$[A'^*] = 2.94 \times 10^{-3}\ \text{mol/cm}^3$$

Substituting for $[A'^*]$ in Eq. 8.48 we get the point rate of desorption of A′ as

$$R_{A'} = 5.8 \times 10^{-5}\ \text{mol/cm}^2\ \text{sec}$$

The backmixing in both phases affects the rate of absorption of A when the order of reaction with respect to both A and B is not zero. Since the rate of desorption is directly affected by the rate of absorption, the same is true for the desorption process also.

8.5.3. Liquid-Phase-Controlled Desorption of A′

As mentioned in the previous section, when the desorption of A′ is liquid film controlled, the boundary condition for the flux of A′ at the interface in Eq. 8.43 should be appropriately replaced.

The concentration profile for A′ is related to the concentration profile of A and is expected to be nonlinear (i.e., hyperbolic terms would be present). Figure 8.7 shows the concentration profiles. Pangarkar (1972) has shown that for large values of $\sqrt{M_{A,i}}$ a linear approximation for the profile of A′ gives satisfactory results. The assumed and the actual expected concentration profiles are shown in Figure 8.7. It can be seen that there are two distinct zones of concentration gradients of opposite signs for the species A′ in the diffusion film. There is a maximum value of [A′], $[A'_\lambda]$, at the plane where these two zones meet. On the left side of this plane the driving force is for the desorption of A′. The boundary condition for the flux of A′ at the interface is as follows:

$$R_{A'} = D_{A'}\frac{d[A']}{dx} = \frac{D_{A'}}{\lambda}([A'_\lambda] - [A'^*]) \quad (8.49)$$

Equations 8.41 and 8.42 can now be solved in a straightforward manner by using the boundary conditions given by Eqs. 8.43, 8.44, and 8.49.

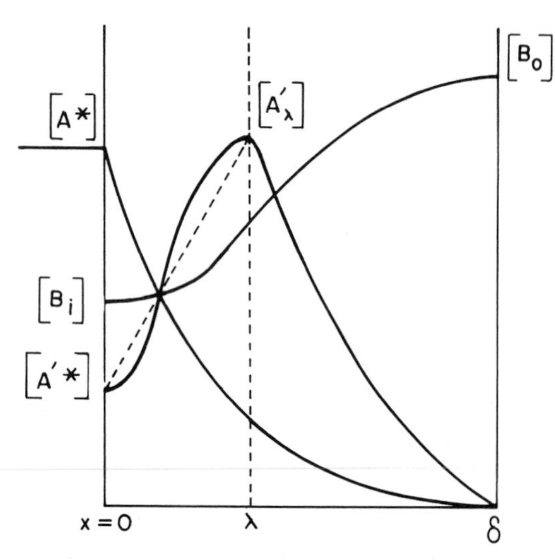

Figure 8.7. Concentration profiles (———, actual; - - -, assumed) for simultaneous absorption–desorption with reaction: liquid-film-controlled desorption, fast reaction.

$$[A'] = -Z_2[A^*]\frac{\sinh\left[\sqrt{\dfrac{k_A[B_i]}{D_A}}(\delta - x)\right]}{\sinh\left(\sqrt{\dfrac{k_A[B_i]}{D_A}}\,\delta\right)} - \frac{D_{A'}([A'_\lambda] - [A'^*])}{k_L\lambda}\left(1 - \frac{x}{\delta}\right) + \sqrt{M_{A,i}}\,[A^*]\left(1 - \frac{x}{\delta}\right) \quad (8.50)$$

The rate of desorption is given by Eq. 8.49 and can be calculated if λ and $[A'_\lambda]$ are known. The maxima in [A′] occurs when the first derivative of Eq. 8.50 is zero. Differentiating Eq. 8.50 and then equating the derivative to zero with [A′] replaced by $[A'_\lambda]$ and x by λ gives another equation between $[A'_\lambda]$ and λ. Using this equation in conjunction with Eq. 8.50, we can evaluate $[A'_\lambda]$ and λ.

8.5.4. Instantaneous Reaction Regime

For the instantaneous reaction regime the following inequality is valid:

$$\frac{\sqrt{D_A k_A[B_o]}}{k_L} \gg \frac{[B_o]}{Z_1[A^*]} \quad (8.51)$$

Ramachandran and Sharma (1970) have considered this case. The rate of absorption of A is given by

$$R_A = k_L[A^*]\left(1 + \frac{[B_o]}{Z_1[A^*]}\right) \quad (8.52)$$

The location of the plane at which the reaction occurs is given by

$$\lambda = \frac{Z_1[A^*]\delta}{[B_o] + Z_1[A^*]} \quad (8.53)$$

Typical concentration profiles are shown in Figure 8.8. It can be seen that the maxima in [A′], $[A'_\lambda]$, occurs at $x = \lambda$. The value of $[A'_\lambda]$ can be obtained

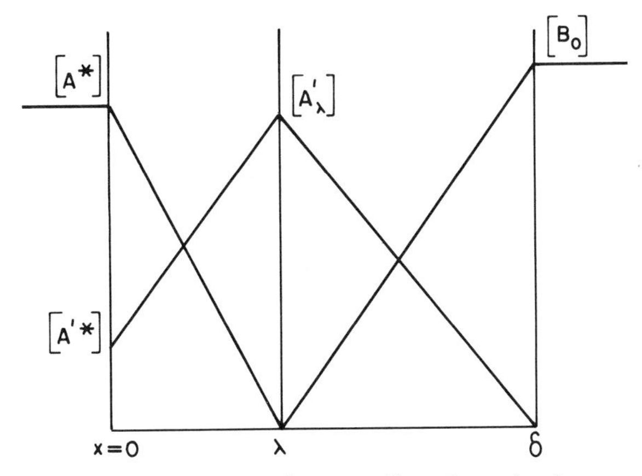

Figure 8.8. Concentration profiles for simultaneous absorption–desorption: desorption accompanied by instantaneous reaction.

by a mass balance for A′ at $x = \lambda$:

$$[A'_\lambda] = \frac{Z_2 R_A \lambda(\delta - \lambda) + D_{A'}[A'^*](\delta - \lambda)}{D_{A'}\delta} \tag{8.54}$$

Substituting for λ in Eq. 8.54 and using the value of $[A'_\lambda]$ thus obtained in Eq. 8.49 the rate of desorption can be calculated.

8.6. SUPERSATURATION DURING SIMULTANEOUS ABSORPTION–DESORPTION WITH REACTION

In the case of simultaneous absorption–desorption systems a new situation connected with the phenomenon of supersaturation in the close proximity of the interface can arise. In order to illustrate this point we shall first consider the simple case of a simultaneous physical absorption–desorption system.

8.6.1. Physical Absorption–Desorption

Brian et al. (1967) have considered the problem of physical absorption–desorption. By definition, supersaturation occurs when the total pressure profile of the dissolved gases A and A′ in the liquid film exhibits a maxima (Figure 8.9). It is evident that if the total pressure profile is linear, no point of inflection can be obtained. Thus the film model, which gives linear profiles for [A] and [A′] (and consequently for $[A_p]$ and $[A'_p]$ where the subscript "p" denotes concentrations in pressure units), cannot show a maximum. By contrast, the penetration model profiles are nonlinear, and therefore under certain conditions, the total pressure profile for this model can exhibit a maximum.

We shall consider a case in which the gases A and A′ are simultaneously absorbed and desorbed. The directions of transfer of A and A′ are opposite and are given by

$$[A_p^*] - [A_{po}] > 0 \tag{8.55}$$

$$[A'_{po}] - [A'^*_p] > 0 \tag{8.56}$$

The dissolved concentration function, $f(\pi)$, is now defined as

$$f(\pi) = \frac{[A_p] + [A'_p] - [A_p^*] - [A'^*_p]}{[A_p^*] - [A_{po}]} \tag{8.57}$$

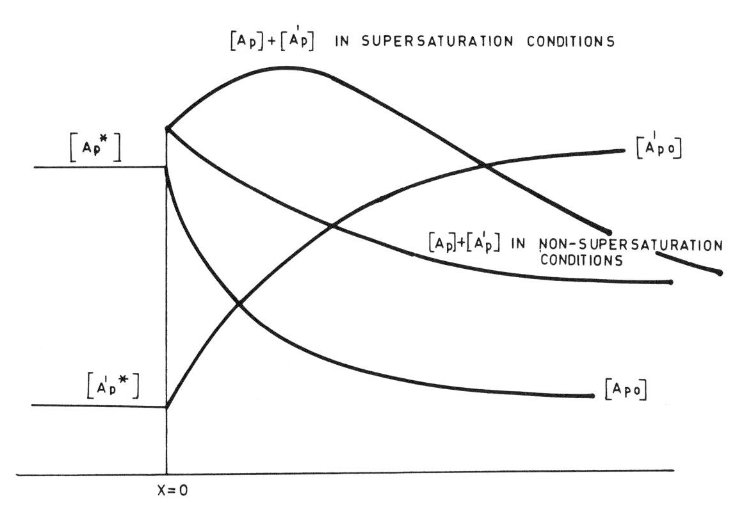

Figure 8.9. Typical pressure distributions of A, A′, and A + A′ during simultaneous absorption–desorption process.

The individual equations for $[A_p]$ and $[A'_p]$ are those given by the penetration model for physical absorption and physical desorption, respectively (Brian et al., 1967). Substituting these equations in Eq. 8.57 and simplifying, we get

$$f(\pi) = \operatorname{erf}(\pi) - (1 - [\bar{c}]) - [\bar{c}]\operatorname{erf}\left(\pi/\sqrt{r_{A'}}\right) \tag{8.58}$$

where

$$\pi = \frac{x}{2\sqrt{D_A t_E}} \tag{8.58a}$$

$$r_{A'} = \frac{D_{A'}}{D_A} \tag{8.58b}$$

$$[\bar{c}] = \frac{[A'_{po}] - [A'^*_p]}{[A^*_p] - [A_{po}]} \tag{8.58c}$$

Supersaturation would occur when Eq. 8.58 shows a maximum, that is, when

$$\frac{df(\pi)}{d\pi} = 0, \quad \text{and} \quad \frac{d^2 f(\pi)}{d\pi^2} < 0$$

Applying these conditions, it can be seen that supersaturation is possible when the following conditions are satisfied:

$$\frac{D_{A'}}{D_A} < 1 \tag{8.59}$$

$$\frac{[A^*_p] - [A_{po}]}{[A'_{po}] - [A'^*_p]}\sqrt{\frac{D_{A'}}{D_A}} < 1 \tag{8.60}$$

Effect of Supersaturation on the Rates of Mass Transfer

In the case of a supersaturated system, the concentration of the desorbing species in the liquid film is not in equilibrium with the gas phase. The gas–liquid-phase equilibrium is thus metastable. The system may continue in this state of metastable equilibrium if the degree of supersaturation is low. On the other hand, at relatively higher degrees of supersaturation, the system will tend to reach the stable equilibrium state spontaneously. Thus spontaneous desorption will occur, which will be preceded by nucleation of bubbles rich in species A′ at various sites in the liquid film. Under favorable conditions, these bubbles will tend to grow. This process of nucleation and growth in the liquid film will increase the degree of turbulence within the film and will hence increase the mass transfer rates significantly. There is some evidence in the literature that the desorption process increases the rates of mass transfer in a packed column when conditions for the existence of supersaturation are satisfied (Brian et al., 1967). Bhargava (1978) has studied absorption of HCl gas in chlorobenzene containing dissolved CO_2 so that k_L for CO_2 desorption can be measured. Here the conditions given by expressions 8.59 and 8.60 are satisfied. The k_L values for CO_2 obtained with HCl gas were about 2–2.5 times higher than those obtained with air as the stripping gas where the necessary conditions for supersaturation to occur are not satisfied. A continuously operated stirred cell and a packed column were employed.

8.6.2. Supersaturation during Simultaneous Absorption–Desorption with Reaction

Shah et al. (1974) have considered the problem of supersaturation during simultaneous absorption and desorption with reaction. We shall discuss an illustrative case. For mass transfer accompanied by, say, a fast pseudo-first-order reaction the film model also gives a nonlinear concentration profile. Thus, the film model can also be used for obtaining the criteria for supersaturation.

We shall consider the following reaction:

$$A \xrightarrow{k} A' \tag{8.61}$$

The reaction given by Eq. 8.61 is a fast first-order reaction that occurs predominantly in the liquid film. There is no gas-phase resistance to the transfer of either A or A′. The dimensionless concentration profiles for A and A′ obtained by solving the relevant film model equations are given by the following equations (Shah et al., 1974):

$$\frac{[A]}{[A^*]} = \frac{\sinh\left[\sqrt{M}(1 - x/\delta)\right]}{\sinh\sqrt{M}} \tag{8.62}$$

and

$$\frac{[A'_p]}{[A^*_p]} = \left(\frac{[A'_{po}] - [A'_p{}^*]}{[A^*_p]} - \frac{1}{r_{A'}}\right)\left(\frac{x}{\delta}\right) + \left(\frac{[A'_p{}^*]}{[A^*_p]} + \frac{1}{r_{A'}}\right) - \frac{1}{r_{A'}}\left\{\frac{\sinh[\sqrt{M}(1 - x/\delta)]}{\sinh\sqrt{M}}\right\}$$

$$\sqrt{M} = \sqrt{\frac{k}{D_A}}\,\delta \quad \text{and} \quad r_{A'} = \frac{D_{A'}H_{A'}}{D_A H_A} \qquad (8.63)$$

On the basis of an analysis similar to that discussed under physical absorption–desorption (i.e., Eqs. 8.57–8.60) the following criteria for the occurrence of supersaturation are obtained:

$$\left\{\cosh\left[\sqrt{M}\left(1 - \frac{x}{\delta}\right)\right]\right\}\left(1 - \frac{1}{r_{A'}}\right) - \frac{\sinh\sqrt{M}}{\sqrt{M}}\left(\frac{[A'_{po}] - [A'_p{}^*]}{[A^*_p]} - \frac{1}{r_{A'}}\right) = 0$$

$$\text{for} \quad 1 > \frac{x}{\delta} > 0 \qquad (8.64)$$

and

$$\frac{M}{\sinh\sqrt{M}}\sinh\left[\sqrt{M}\left(1 - \frac{x}{\delta}\right)\right]\left(1 - \frac{1}{r_{A'}}\right) < 0$$

$$\text{for} \quad 1 > \frac{x}{\delta} > 0 \qquad (8.65)$$

From Eq. 8.65 it is evident that the total concentration $\bar{c}$ [or $f(\pi)$ for the penetration model] defined by Eq. 8.58c will show a maximum in the liquid film when $r_{A'} < 1$. Also, from Eq. 8.64 it can be seen that for $r_{A'} < 1$,

$$\frac{[A'_{po}] - [A'_p{}^*]}{[A^*_p]} < \frac{1}{r_{A'}} \qquad (8.66)$$

The limiting case of Eq. 8.64 is obtained when $\sqrt{M} \to 0$. In this case both hyperbolic terms in Eq. 8.64 approach unity, and therefore $([A'_{po}] - [A'_p{}^*])/[A^*_p]$

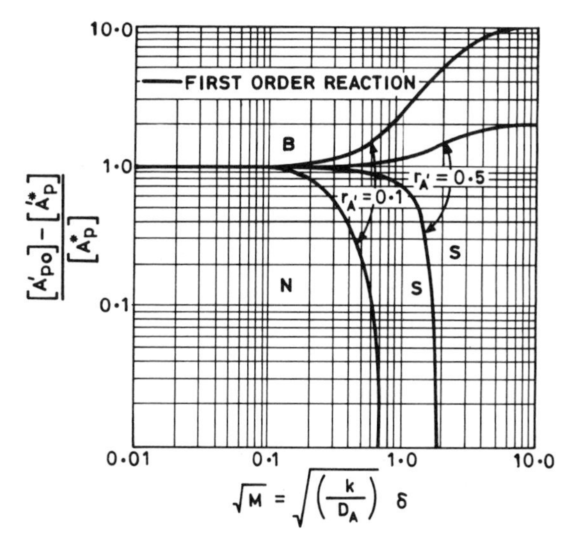

Figure 8.10. Typical critical supersaturation curves predicted by film theory.

must also approach unity. For this situation the reaction given by Eq. 8.61 is slow and occurs in the bulk liquid phase. For $r_{A'} < 1$, the occurrence of supersaturation would depend on the relative values of $\sqrt{M}$ and $([A'_{po}] - [A'_p{}^*])/[A^*_p]$. Shah et al. have solved Eq. 8.64 numerically and presented the results as plots of the variables $\sqrt{M}$ and $([A'_{po}] - [A'_p{}^*])/[A^*_p]$ for two typical values of $r_{A'} = 0.5$ and 0.1. These plots (Figure 8.10) indicate the regions in which supersaturation can occur (region S) and those in which supersaturation cannot occur (region N) for the case $0 < x/\delta < 1$. The region above the upper branches (region B) of the supersaturation curves are the regions where supersaturation would occur only in the bulk and not in the reaction film.

8.7. EXAMPLES OF INDUSTRIAL IMPORTANCE

Tables 8.1 and 8.2 list some examples of industrial importance. A few of these will be discussed further.

8.7.1. Very Slow Reaction

Desorption of Carbon Dioxide from Hot Potassium Bicarbonate–Potassium Carbonate Solutions in an Agitated Contactor

An agitated contactor provides very high $k_L a$ values. Thus, a reaction that falls in the diffusion-controlled slow reaction regime in a packed column may shift to the very slow reaction regime when an agitated contactor is used. Langley and Haselden (1968) have studied the desorption of CO_2 from a hot potash solution in a laboratory agitated desorber. It was found that the desorption in this case was completely controlled by the rate of homogeneous reaction at high speeds of agitation. In industrial practice an agitated desorber involving high power inputs would not be desirable. Langley and Haselden have suggested the use of a plate column with high liquid holdup per plate.

8.7.2. Slow Reaction

Desorption of Carbon Dioxide from Hot Potassium Bicarbonate–Potassium Carbonate Solutions in a Bubble Cap Plate Column

This system has been studied by McLachlan and Danckwerts (1972) in a laboratory column containing a single plate and a single bubble cap in the temperature range of 50–80°C. The bicarbonate to carbonate ratio was 0.65 and the total potassium concentration was 3.39 g atom/liter. The following condition (Eq. 8.3) for diffusion-controlled desorption was satisfied:

$$\frac{\sqrt{D_{A'}k}}{k_L} < 1 \qquad (8.3)$$

Thus, for instance, at 80°C,

$$D_{A'} = 3.17 \times 10^{-5}\ \text{cm}^2/\text{sec}$$

$$k_L = 7.8 \times 10^{-2}\ \text{cm/sec}$$

$$k \simeq 20\ \text{sec}^{-1}$$

From these data the left-hand side of the inequality given by expression 8.3 is calculated as 0.33, indicating the validity of expression 8.3.

The other condition needed for the validity of the slow reaction regime is

$$k_L a \ll lk$$

The following data are representative of the conditions in a bubble cap plate column and can be used to test this condition:

$$a = 2\ \text{cm}^2/\text{cm}^3, \qquad l = 0.8$$

Therefore

$$k_L a \simeq 16 \times 10^{-2}\ \text{sec}^{-1} \ll lk \simeq 16\ \text{sec}^{-1}$$

Thus, since both conditions are satisfied, the relevant expression for the specific rate of desorption in the slow reaction regime case can be used. If a packed column were to be used in place of a plate column, the k_L value would go down by approximately a factor of 10. Inequality 8.3 would therefore not be satisfied and the system would conform to the fast reaction regime (discussed next).

8.7.3. Fast Reaction

Desorption of Carbon Dioxide from Potassium Bicarbonate–Potassium Carbonate Solutions Containing Potassium Arsenite as Catalyst

McLachlan and Danckwerts (1972) have compared the rate of desorption of this system with and without a catalyst under similar conditions. It was found that at lower catalyst loadings the system lies in between the slow and fast reaction regimes (regime between 2 and 3). However, at higher temperatures and higher concentrations of the catalyst it was shown that the system falls in the fast reaction regime (regime 3). Thus, for example, at 80°C, the pseudo-first-order rate constant is approximately 2000 sec^{-1}. Using a k_L value of 8×10^{-2} cm/sec and $D_{A'} = 3.17 \times 10^{-5}$ cm^2/sec, we see that

$$\frac{\sqrt{D_{A'}k}}{k_L} = 3.14$$

indicating the validity of the fast reaction regime. Here, too, if a packed column were to be employed, the system would fall in the fast reaction regime even at low concentrations of the catalyst.

Manufacture of Poly(ethylene) Terephthalate: Desorption of Ethylene Glycol

Polyethylene terephthalate (PET) is manufactured by the polycondensation of diglycol terephthalate:

$$(\text{—COO}(C_6H_4)\text{COOCH}_2\text{CH}_2\text{OH})$$
$$+ (-\text{CH}_2\text{CH}_2\text{COO}(C_6H_4)\text{COOCH}_2\text{CH}_2\text{OH})$$
$$\rightleftharpoons (\text{—CH}_2\text{CH}_2\text{COO}(C_6H_4)\text{COO—})_2$$
$$+ \text{HOCH}_2\text{CH}_2\text{OH}$$

Hoftyzer (1975) has discussed the role of mass transfer in this process. The products of this reaction are the polymer PET and ethylene glycol. The kinetics of the reaction is complicated by some side reactions that degrade the polymer. For instance, the following degradation reaction occurs:

$$—OCO(CH_2)_2OCO— \rightarrow —COOH + \text{other products}$$

This side reaction can be followed by the esterification reaction

$$—OCO(CH_2)_2OH + —OCOH \rightleftharpoons —OCO(CH_2)_3OCO— + H_2O$$

It has been shown that in the later stages of the main polycondensation reaction the reversible nature of the reaction plays a dominant role, as a result of which the removal of the product glycol determines the net rate. The importance of the desorption of ethylene glycol is also evident from a number of patents that describe modifications in the design of the reactor. For instance, film reactors have been suggested (Widmer, 1973; see Section 14.1.1).

Hoftyzer and van Krevelen (1968) have shown that the polycondensation process can be treated in the same manner as gas absorption with chemical reaction. These authors have used some typical values of the rate constant and other relevant variables to prove that in the final stages the polycondensation process is analogous to gas absorption accompanied by a fast pseudo-first-order reaction. This conclusion is supported by the experimental observation of the dependence of the volumetric reaction rate on physicochemical parameters and on effective interfacial area, a characteristic of regime 3 that was discussed in Section 2.4. However, because of a lack of information about the kinetic parameters, the actual process cannot be fully explained. For a rational reactor design more information on these parameters and on the effective interfacial area per unit volume is needed. There are no published data on the effective interfacial area in such a system.

Yokoyama and Sano (1979) have also discussed some aspects of the kinetics of this reaction and the importance of the desorption of ethylene glycol has been brought out. These authors have also suggested the use of a disk reactor for polycondensation reactions.

Shima et al. (1973) have shown that at an advanced stage of polycondensation, the overall rate of reaction can be markedly increased by the addition of a small amount of acid derivatives such as cyclic organoboronic anhydride, diphenyl dicarboxylate, or diphenyl carbonate. It is likely that with these substances the reaction rate constant would be substantially higher than in the conventional system, and hence higher rates are realized.

Manufacture of Isoamylene

Isoamylene can be recovered for industrial use from the C_5 fraction of naphtha crackers by selective extraction into 60–70% w/w aqueous sulfuric acid. The temperature is usually in the range of 10–30°C. Foster et al. (1960) have reported that isoamylene in this "fat" acid can be recovered by extraction into a solvent like *n*-heptane. The kinetics of desorption of isoamylene from fat acid into *n*-heptane has been studied by Sankholkar and Sharma (1975) in a stirred cell as well as in an agitated contactor. These authors have shown that the specific rate of desorption is independent of the speed of stirring in the stirred cell and the holdup of the acid phase. The specific rate was proportional to the concentration of isoamylene in the acid phase. From these findings it is apparent that the desorption is preceded by a fast pseudo-first-order reaction.

8.7.4. Simultaneous Absorption–Desorption with Reaction

Slow Reaction: Oxidation of Cyclohexane / Cyclododecane: Desorption of Water

Steeman et al. (1961) and Alagy et al. (1974) have studied the absorption of oxygen in cyclohexane and cyclododecane with and without boric acid. These reactions are employed in the manufacture of cyclohexanone and cyclohexanol, and cyclododecanone and cyclododecanol, respectively, and are therefore of considerable industrial importance in the manufacture of monomers for nylons. Alagy et al. have shown that under conditions of practical importance the reaction does not occur in the film and therefore may conform to the slow reaction regime (regime 2) or to the regime between the very slow and slow reaction regimes (regime between 1 and 2). In this reaction water is formed. In bubble columns the superficial gas velocity was found to have an effect on the selectivity. Alagy et al. have attributed this observation to the effect of gas velocity on the rate of stripping of water. At higher gas velocities the rate of stripping of water will be correspondingly high. This will facilitate the esterification of cyclohexanol (a product of oxidation of cyclohexane) with boric acid and thereby improve the selectivity.

Fast Reaction: Absorption of Phosgene ($COCl_2$) in Water and Aqueous Sodium Carbonate–Sodium Bicarbonate Buffer Solutions: Desorption of CO_2

The absorption of phosgene in water and aqueous sodium carbonate and sodium bicarbonate buffer solutions with the subsequent desorption of CO_2 was discussed in Section 6.4.2.

Instantaneous Reaction: Absorption of Sulfur Dioxide in an Aqueous Sodium Carbonate–Sodium Bicarbonate Solution: Desorption of CO_2

When SO_2 is absorbed in aqueous sodium carbonate–sodium bicarbonate solutions the following reactions occur, resulting in the generation and subsequent desorption of CO_2:

$$SO_2 + CO_3^{2-} + H_2O \rightarrow HCO_3^- + HSO_3^-$$

$$SO_2 + HCO_3^- \rightarrow CO_2 + HSO_3^-$$

Both these reactions are instantaneous. HSO_3^- formed in the above reactions diffuses from the reaction plane toward both the interface and the bulk liquid. In the bulk liquid phase the following reaction occurs:

$$HSO_3^- + CO_3^{2-} \rightarrow HCO_3^- + SO_3^{2-}$$

SO_2 is also capable of reacting with SO_3^{2-} according to

$$SO_2 + SO_3^{2-} + H_2O \rightarrow 2HSO_3^-$$

According to this scheme the predominant ion at the interface is HSO_3^-. The hydration reaction of CO_2 is catalyzed by SO_3^{2-} but the rate constant is very small. Pangarkar (1972) has studied this system in a laminar jet apparatus under conditions such that the bulk liquid concentration of CO_2 is zero (i.e., the condition given by expression 8.40 holds). The agreement between the experimental results and those predicted by Eq. 8.52 was found to be good. For this system the ratio of diffusivities of A′ and A, $r_{A'}$, is greater than 1. The results showed no increase in the mass transfer and this can be attributed to the absence of supersaturation as indicated by the criteria for supersaturation given by Shah et al. (1974) (see Section 8.6.2).

Two-step instantaneous reaction: Absorption of chlorine in aqueous sodium hydroxide or carbonate: Desorption of hypochlorous acid

Hypochlorous acid is manufactured by effecting the absorption of Cl_2 in 40–70% aqueous alkali metal hydroxide at or below atmospheric pressure in a sweep reactor and the recovery of the hypochlorous acid vapors in a water scrubber (Brennan et al., 1979; Wojtowicz and Klanica, 1979).

The two-step instantaneous and reversible reaction of Cl_2 with OH^- ions is

$$Cl_2 + OH^- \rightleftharpoons HClO + Cl^- \quad \text{(i)}$$

$$HClO + OH^- \rightleftharpoons ClO^- + H_2O \quad \text{(ii)}$$

The equilibrium constants of both these steps have very high values and the ratio of the equilibrium constant of step (i) to that of step (ii) is of the order of 10^4. As a consequence, Cl_2 and OH^- ions cannot coexist in the liquid film. Therefore, two reaction planes are formed within the liquid film where the following reactions take place irreversibly:

$$Cl_2 + ClO^- + H_2O \rightarrow 2HClO + Cl^- \quad \text{(iii)}$$

$$HClO + OH^- \rightarrow OCl^- + H_2O \quad \text{(iv)}$$

Lahiri et al. (1983) have studied some aspects of this reaction and shown that HClO can be desorbed under certain conditions. It is most interesting to find that HClO can be desorbed despite a large excess of hydroxyl ions in the bulk liquid phase. On desorption HClO gives Cl_2O and H_2O in the gas phase and this further improves the driving force for the desorption of HClO. Lahiri et al. have given a theoretical model for this case and the agreement between the predicted and experimental rates of desorption can be rated as fair. A low value of k_L and a high value of k_G are conducive for higher rates of desorption of HClO.

Manufacture of Bromine Chloride

Bromine chloride has acquired some industrial importance as an effective brominating agent (Mills and Schneider, 1973). Bromine is manufactured by aqueous-phase chlorination of dissolved bromides. However, this is a two-step reaction:

$$Cl_2 + Br^- \rightleftharpoons BrCl + Cl^-$$

$$BrCl + Br^- \rightleftharpoons Br_2 + Cl^-$$

The equilibrium constant of the first reaction is greater than that of the second by two orders of magnitude, and therefore the former determines the equilibrium of the whole process. The Br^- concentration is many times lower than the Cl^- concentration in brines used for the manufacture of Br_2, and this results in a situation whereby the concentrations of Br_2, BrCl, and Br^- become comparable. Since BrCl is also volatile, we can manipulate conditions to ensure its desorption to a considerable extent. Stasinevich (1979) has studied some aspects of this problem.

REFERENCES

Alagy, J., Trambouze, P., and van Landeghem, H. (1974), *Ind. Eng. Chem. Process Design Dev.*, **13**, 317.

Andrew, S. P. S. (1961), *Alta Technol. Chim.*, p. 153.

Andrew, S. P. S., and Hanson, D. (1961), *Chem. Eng. Sci.*, **14**, 105.

Astarita, G., and Savage, D. W. (1980a), *Chem. Eng. Sci.*, **35**, 649.

Astarita, G., and Savage, D. W. (1980b), *Chem. Eng. Sci.*, **35**, 1755.

Bailes, P. J., Hanson, C., and Hughes, M. A. (1976), *Chem. Eng.*, **83**(18), 86.

Baveja, K. K. (1979), Studies in Gas–Liquid Reactions, Ph.D. thesis, I.I.T., Delhi, India.

Bhargava, R. K. (1978), Kinetics of Heterogeneous Reactions, Ph.D. (Tech.) thesis, University of Bombay.

Brennan, J. P., Wojtowicz, J. A., and Campbell, P. H. (1979), U.S. Pat. 4, 146, 578; *Chem. Abstr.* (1979), **90**, 189244.

Brian, P. L. T., Vivian, J. E., and Matiatos, D. C. (1967), *Chem. Eng. Sci.*, **22**, 7.

Chandalia, S. B. (1970), *Chem. Process. Eng. (Bombay)*, **4**(4), 19.

Danckwerts, P. V., and Sharma, M. M. (1966), *Chem. Eng., Inst. Chem. Eng.* No. 202 CE244.

Davidsohn, A., and Midwilsky, B. M. (1972), *Synthetic Detergents*, 5th ed., Leonard Hill, London, p. 138.

Foster, R. L., Wunderlich, D. K., Patinkin, S. H., and Sanford, R. A. (1960), *Petrol. Refiner* **39**(11), 229.

Goldstein, R. F., and Waddams, A. L. (1967), *The Petroleum Chemicals Industry*, 3rd ed., Spon, London, pp. 321, 237.

Gupta, R. K., and Sharma, M. M. (1967), *Indian Chem. Eng. (Trans.)*, **9**(13), 100.

Haase, D. J., and Waker, D. G. (1974), *Chem. Eng. Prog.*, **70**(5), 74.

Habashi, F. (1969), *Principles of Extractive Metallurgy*, Vol. 1, *General Principles*, Gordon & Breach, New York.

Hardwick, W. H., and Wace, P. F. (1965), *Chem. Process. Eng.*, **46**, 283.

Hoftyzer, P. J. (1975), in Platzer, N. A. J. (Ed.), *Polymerization and Polycondensation Processes* (Appl. Polymer Symp. No. 26), Wiley, New York, p. 349.

Hoftyzer, P. J., and van Krevelen, D. W. (1968), *Proc. 4th European Symp. Chem. React. Eng.* (Suppl. to *Chem. Eng. Sci.*), p. 139.

Hughes, M. A. (1975), *Chem. Ind. (London)*, No. 24, 1042.

Hulme, P., and Turner, P. E. (1967), *Chem. Process. Eng.*, **48**(11), 96.

Hydrocarbon Process. Petrol. Refiner (1971), **50**(11), 226.

Kingsley, H. A., and Bliss, H. (1952), *Ind. Eng. Chem.*, **44**, 2479.

Kosorotov, V. I., Dzhagatspanyan, R. V., Stul', B.Ya., and Luzyanin, B. P. (1971), *Theoret. Found. Chem. Eng. USSR (Engl. Transl.)*, **5**, 211.

Lahiri, R. N., Yadav, G. D., and Sharma, M. M. (1983), *Chem. Eng. Sci.* **38**, 1119.

Langley, P. E., and Haselden, G. G. (1968), *Proc. Symp. Tripartite Chem. Eng. Conf.* (Montreal), p. 57.

McLachlan, C. N. S., and Danckwerts, P. V. (1972), *Trans. Inst. Chem. Eng.*, **50**, 300.

Mills, J. F., and Schneider, J. A. (1973), *Ind. Eng. Chem. Prod. Res. Dev.*, **12**, 160.

Olander, D. R. (1960), *AIChE J.*, **6**, 233.

Pangarkar, V. G. (1972), Mass Transfer with Chemical Reaction, Ph.D. (Tech.) thesis, University of Bombay.

Perry, R. H., and Chilton, C. H. (Ed.) (1973), *Chemical Engineers' Handbook*, 5th ed., McGraw-Hill, New York.

Ramachandran, P. A., and Sharma, M. M. (1970), *Chem. Eng. Sci.*, **25**, 1743.

Ramachandran, P. A., and Sharma, M. M. (1971), *Trans. Inst. Chem. Eng.*, **49**, 253.

Richardson, F. D. (1975), in Dahl, W., Lange, K. W., and Papamantellos, D. (Eds.), *Kinetics of Metallurgical Processes in Steel Making*, Verlag Stahleisen M. B. H., Dusseldorf, W. Germany, p. 279.

Rosenbaum, J. B., George, D. R., and May, J. T. (1971), Metallurgical Application of Solvent Extraction 2: Practice and Trends, U.S. Department of the Interior, Bureau of Mines Information Circular 8502.

Sankholkar, D. S., and Sharma, M. M. (1975), *Chem. Eng. Sci.*, **30**, 729.

Savage, D. W., Astarita, G., and Joshi, S. (1980), *Chem. Eng. Sci.*, **35**, 1513.

Secor, R. M. (1969), *AIChE J.*, **15**, 861.

Shah, Y. T., and Sharma, M. M. (1976), *Trans. Inst. Chem. Eng.*, **54**, 1.

Shah, Y. T., Pangarkar, V. G., and Sharma, M. M. (1974), *Chem. Eng. Sci.*, **29**, 1601.

Sherwood, T. K., and Pigford, R. L. (1952), *Absorption and Extraction*, McGraw-Hill, New York.

Shima, T., Urasaki, T., and Oka, I. (1973), *Adv. Chem. Ser.* **128**, 183.

Stasinevich, D. S. (1979), *J. Appl. Chem. USSR (Engl. Transl.)*, **52**, 960.

Steeman, J. W. M., Kaarsemaker, S., and Hoftyzer, P. J. (1961), *Chem. Eng. Sci.*, **14**, 139.

Throckmorton, P. E., and Pryde, E. H. (1972), *J. Am. Oil Chem. Soc.*, **49**, 643.

Throckmorton, P. E., Hansen, L. I., Christenson, R. C., and Pryde, E. H. (1968), *J. Am. Oil Chem. Soc.*, **45**, 59.

Treybal, R. E. (1968), *Mass Transfer Operations*, 2nd ed., McGraw-Hill, New York.

Turner, J. C. R. (1962), *Brit. Chem. Eng.*, **7**, 576.

van Dijk, C. P., and Schreiner, W. C. (1973), *Chem. Eng. Prog.*, **69**(4), 57.

van Krevelen, D. W., and Hoftyzer, P. J. (1948), *Chim. Ind. XXI Int. Chim. Ind.*, p. 163.

Widmer, F. (1973), *Adv. Chem. Ser.*, **128**, 51.

Wojtowicz, J. A., and Klanica, A. J. (1979), U.S. Pat., 4, 147, 761; *Chem. Abstr.*, (1979), **90**, 189245.

Yokoyama, H., and Sano, T. (1979), *Chem. Economy Eng. Review*, **11**(132), 31.

Zhavoronkov, N. M., and Martynov, Yu. M. (1959), *Khim. Prom.*, **2**, 150.

CHAPTER NINE

Complex Reactions

9.1. GAS ABSORPTION WITH AUTOCATALYTIC REACTION

Gas absorption with autocatalytic reaction is likely to be encountered in the air oxidation and chlorination of organic compounds. Some of these systems involve chain reactions, and the radicals formed in the first step may have an autocatalytic effect. The reaction can be represented as follows:

$$\mathrm{A}(g) \to \mathrm{A}(l); \qquad \mathrm{A}(l) + \dot{\mathrm{R}}(l) \xrightarrow{k_2} \dot{\mathrm{R}}(l) + \dot{\mathrm{R}}(l) \tag{9.1}$$

where $\dot{\mathrm{R}}$ stands for the radical that is already present in the liquid phase. We shall assume that the reaction is first order with respect to species A as well as to radicals $\dot{\mathrm{R}}$. It is also assumed that the $\dot{\mathrm{R}}$ are nonvolatile.

Sim and Mann (1975) have considered this problem and have shown that the enhancement factor with autocatalytic effect can be substantially greater than that for the "equivalent" first-order reaction.

The following differential equations hold:

$$D_{\mathrm{A}} \frac{d^2[\mathrm{A}]}{dx^2} = k_2[\mathrm{A}][\dot{\mathrm{R}}] \tag{9.2}$$

$$D_{\dot{\mathrm{R}}} \frac{d^2[\dot{\mathrm{R}}]}{dx^2} = -k_2[\mathrm{A}][\dot{\mathrm{R}}] \tag{9.3}$$

The relevant boundary conditions are, at

$$x = 0, \quad [\mathrm{A}] = [\mathrm{A}^*], \quad \frac{d[\dot{\mathrm{R}}]}{dx} = 0 \tag{9.4}$$

and at

$$x = \delta, \quad [\mathrm{A}] = 0, \quad [\mathrm{R}] = [\dot{\mathrm{R}}_{\mathrm{o}}] \tag{9.5}$$

Sim and Mann have solved Eqs. 9.2 and 9.3 numerically, but their procedure is rather complicated. Juvekar (1976) has used the collocation technique, which is simpler than the procedure adopted by Sim and Mann, to solve these differential equations. We shall cover the method suggested by Juvekar.

The following concentration profile for A is assumed:

$$\frac{[\mathrm{A}]}{[\mathrm{A}^*]} = \frac{\sinh[m_{\mathrm{c}}(1 - x/\delta)]}{\sinh(m_{\mathrm{c}})} \tag{9.6}$$

where m_{c} is a collocation parameter.

Equations 9.2 and 9.3 can be solved simultaneously to obtain

$$\frac{[\dot{\mathrm{R}}]}{[\dot{\mathrm{R}}_{\mathrm{o}}]} = \frac{1}{q_{\dot{\mathrm{R}}}}\left[\frac{m_{\mathrm{c}}(1 - x/\delta)}{\tanh(m_{\mathrm{c}})} + q_{\dot{\mathrm{R}}} - \frac{\sinh[m_{\mathrm{c}}(1 - x/\delta)]}{\sinh(m_{\mathrm{c}})}\right] \tag{9.7}$$

where

$$q_{\dot{\mathrm{R}}} = \frac{[\dot{\mathrm{R}}_{\mathrm{o}}]}{[\mathrm{A}^*]} \frac{D_{\dot{\mathrm{R}}}}{D_{\mathrm{A}}} \tag{9.8}$$

The concentration profile for A and $\dot{\mathrm{R}}$ obtained from Eqs. 9.6 and 9.7 can now be substituted into the right-hand side of Eq. 9.2. The resulting equation on first integration with respect to x gives

$$\frac{d[A]}{dx} = \frac{[A^*]}{\delta}\frac{M_{\dot{R}}}{q_{\dot{R}}}\left[-q_{\dot{R}}\frac{\cosh[m_c(1-x/\delta)]}{m_c\sinh(m_c)} - \frac{(1-x/\delta)\cosh[m_c(1-x/\delta)]}{\sinh(m_c)\tanh(m_c)} + \frac{\sinh[m_c(1-x/\delta)]}{m_c\sinh(m_c)\tanh(m_c)} + \frac{\sinh[m_c(1-x/\delta)]\cosh[m_c(1-x/\delta)]}{2m_c\sinh^2(m_c)} + \frac{x/\delta}{2\sinh^2(m_c)}\right] + C_1 \qquad (9.9)$$

where

$$M_{\dot{R}} = \frac{D_A k_2[\dot{R}_o]}{k_L^2} \qquad (9.10)$$

(here $k_L = D_A/\delta$) and C_1 is the constant of integration.

Equation 9.6 on differentiation with respect to x gives

$$\frac{d[A]}{dx} = -\frac{[A^*]}{\delta}\frac{m_c\cosh[m_c(1-x/\delta)]}{\sinh(m_c)} \qquad (9.11)$$

Equations 9.9 and 9.11 are matched at the points $x = 0$ and $x = \delta$. As a result, the following equation in m_c is obtained:

$$M_{\dot{R}} = q_{\dot{R}}\left[\frac{m_c}{\tanh(m_c)} - \frac{m_c}{\sinh(m_c)}\right] \Big/ \left[\frac{1}{2\sinh^2(m_c)} + \frac{q_{\dot{R}} - 1.5}{m_c\tanh(m_c)} + \frac{1}{\tanh^2(m_c)} - \frac{q_{\dot{R}}}{m_c\sinh(m_c)}\right] \qquad (9.12)$$

The enhancement factor ϕ for A can be obtained from the following equation:

$$\phi = \frac{m_c}{\tanh(m_c)} \qquad (9.13)$$

The values of $M_{\dot{R}}$ and ϕ for different values of m_c and $q_{\dot{R}}$ can be calculated from Eqs. 9.12 and 9.13, respectively. A few values of $\sqrt{M_{\dot{R}}}$ and ϕ are reported in Table 9.1. These values agree very well with the numerical solution of Sim and Mann (1975). It may be noted that for very high values of $q_{\dot{R}}$ (approaching ∞) ϕ is equal to $\sqrt{M_{\dot{R}}}$.

TABLE 9.1. Gas Absorption with Autocatalytic Reaction: Typical Values of $\sqrt{M_{\dot{R}}}$ and ϕ

	$\sqrt{M_{\dot{R}}}$			
ϕ	$q_{\dot{R}} = 10^{-3}$	$q_{\dot{R}} = 0.1$	$q_{\dot{R}} = 10$	$q_{\dot{R}} = \infty$
2.078	0.0674	0.638	1.910	2
4.000	0.0785	0.770	3.560	4
10.000	0.1080	1.080	7.350	10
100.000	0.318	3.180	30.400	100

Zero-order reactions ($m = 0$)

There are some oxidation reactions (and probably some photochemical chlorination reactions) that are zero order with respect to species A (Hobbs et al., 1972). In such cases the concentration profile and the enhancement factor can be analytically calculated. The relevant differential equations are

$$D_A\frac{d^2[A]}{dx^2} = k_1[\dot{R}] \quad \text{for} \quad 0 \leqslant x \leqslant \lambda_o \qquad (9.14)$$

$$D_{\dot{R}}\frac{d^2[\dot{R}]}{dx^2} = -k_1[\dot{R}] \quad \text{for} \quad 0 \leqslant x \leqslant \lambda_o \qquad (9.15)$$

λ_o is the distance from the interface at which concentration of A falls to zero. For $x \geqslant \lambda_o$, where there is no finite concentration of A, we have

$$[A] = 0, \quad \frac{d[A]}{dx} = 0 \qquad (9.16)$$

and

$$\frac{d^2[\dot{R}]}{dx^2} = 0 \qquad (9.17)$$

The boundary conditions are, at

$$x = 0, \quad [A] = [A^*], \quad \frac{d[\dot{R}]}{dx} = 0 \qquad (9.18)$$

at

$$x = \lambda_o, \quad [A] = 0, \quad \frac{d[A]}{dx} = 0 \qquad (9.19)$$

$$[\dot{R}]\big|_{\lambda_o^+} = [\dot{R}]\big|_{\lambda_o^-}, \quad \left.\frac{d[\dot{R}]}{dx}\right|_{\lambda_o^+} = \left.\frac{d[\dot{R}]}{dx}\right|_{\lambda_o^-} \qquad (9.20)$$

and at

$$x = \delta, \quad [\dot{R}] = [\dot{R}_o] \qquad (9.21)$$

The solutions to these equations give the following concentration profile for A for $0 \leqslant x \leqslant \lambda_o$:

$$\frac{[\mathrm{A}]}{[\mathrm{A}^*]} = \left(1 - \frac{x}{\lambda_o}\right)$$

$$+ \frac{q_{\dot{R}}\left\{\left[1 - \cos\left(x\sqrt{\frac{k_1}{D_{\dot{R}}}}\right)\right] - \frac{x}{\lambda_o}\left[1 - \cos\left(\lambda_o\sqrt{\frac{k_1}{D_{\dot{R}}}}\right)\right]\right\}}{\left[\cos\left(\lambda_o\sqrt{\frac{k_1}{D_{\dot{R}}}}\right) - \sqrt{\frac{k_1}{D_{\dot{R}}}}(\delta - \lambda_o)\sin\left(\lambda_o\sqrt{\frac{k_1}{D_{\dot{R}}}}\right)\right]} \tag{9.22}$$

The value of λ_o can be obtained from boundary condition 9.16, that is, $d[\mathrm{A}]/dx = 0$ at $x = \lambda_o$. The following equation for λ_o is obtained:

$$\sqrt{\frac{k_1}{D_{\dot{R}}}}\left[\delta + \lambda_o(q_{\dot{R}} - 1)\right]\sin\left(\lambda_o\sqrt{\frac{k_1}{D_{\dot{R}}}}\right) + (q_{\dot{R}} - 1)\cos\left(\lambda_o\sqrt{\frac{k_1}{D_{\dot{R}}}}\right) = q_{\dot{R}} \tag{9.23}$$

Equation 9.23 should be solved by trial and error to obtain λ_o. The specific rate of reaction of A is

$$R_{\mathrm{A}} = -D_{\mathrm{A}}\left(\frac{d[\mathrm{A}]}{dx}\right)_{x=0}$$

$$= \frac{D_{\mathrm{A}}[\mathrm{A}^*]}{\lambda_o} \times \left\{\frac{1 + q_{\dot{R}}\left[1 - \cos\left(\lambda_o\sqrt{\frac{k_1}{D_{\dot{R}}}}\right)\right]}{\cos\left(\lambda_o\sqrt{\frac{k_1}{D_{\dot{R}}}}\right) - \sqrt{\frac{k_1}{D_{\dot{R}}}}(\delta - \lambda_o)\sin\left(\lambda_o\sqrt{\frac{k_1}{D_{\dot{R}}}}\right)}\right\} \tag{9.24}$$

Worked Example

An air oxidation reaction is autocatalytic with a second-order rate constant of 1×10^8 cm^3/mol sec (first order in A). Find the enhancement factor for the absorption of oxygen under the following conditions:

$$[\mathrm{A}^*] = 2 \times 10^{-6}\ \mathrm{mol/cm^3}$$

$$[\dot{\mathrm{R}}_o] = 2 \times 10^{-6}\ \mathrm{mol/cm^3}$$

$$D_{\mathrm{A}} = D_{\dot{R}} = 2 \times 10^{-5}\ \mathrm{cm^2/sec}$$

$$k_{\mathrm{L}} = 2.0 \times 10^{-2}\ \mathrm{cm/sec}$$

Compare the enhancement factor above with that for an "equivalent" first-order reaction with no autocatalytic effect.

Solution. Here

$$M_{\dot{R}} = \frac{D_{\mathrm{A}}k_2[\dot{\mathrm{R}}_o]}{k_{\mathrm{L}}^2} = \frac{2 \times 10^{-5} \times 1 \times 10^8 \times 2 \times 10^{-6}}{(2 \times 10^{-2})^2} = 10$$

$$q_{\dot{R}} = \frac{[\dot{\mathrm{R}}_o]D_{\dot{R}}}{[\mathrm{A}^*]D_{\mathrm{A}}} = \frac{2 \times 10^{-6} \times 2 \times 10^{-5}}{2 \times 10^{-6} \times 2 \times 10^{-5}} = 1$$

The value of m_c can now be obtained from Eq. 9.12 and is found to be 9.47.

$$\phi = \frac{m_c}{\tanh(m_c)} = 9.47$$

Consider an equivalent first-order reaction:

$$\mathrm{A}(l) + \dot{\mathrm{R}}(l) \xrightarrow{k_2} \text{products} \tag{9.25}$$

where the products do not have any catalytic effect on the rate of the reaction. The corresponding film theory equations are

$$D_{\mathrm{A}}\frac{d^2[\mathrm{A}]}{dx^2} = k_2[\mathrm{A}][\dot{\mathrm{R}}] \tag{9.26}$$

and

$$D_{\dot{R}}\frac{d^2[\dot{\mathrm{R}}]}{dx^2} = k_2[\mathrm{A}][\dot{\mathrm{R}}] \tag{9.27}$$

The boundary conditions are the same as those given by Eqs. 9.4 and 9.5. The equations above can be solved by the method described in Section 2.7 for the case of depletion of B in the film to give

$$\phi = \sqrt{M}_{\dot{R}}\left(\frac{1 + q_{\dot{R}} - \phi}{q_{\dot{R}}}\right)^{1/2} \tag{9.28}$$

Solutions of Eq. 9.28 gives an enhancement factor ϕ of 1.71. It is clear that there is a considerable enhancement in the rate of absorption of oxygen as a result of the autocatalytic effect.

9.1.1. Autocatalytic Effect of a Volatile Intermediate; Chlorination of Cyclohexanone; Autocatalytic Effect of Volatile HCl

Joosten et al. (1980) have considered an autocatalytic reaction where the product (or one of the products) that catalyzes the reaction is volatile and can therefore get stripped into the gas phase. Consider the chlorination of ketones such as acetone, methyl ethyl ketone, cyclohexanone and cyclopentanone:

$$Cl_2 + R_1COCH_2R_2 \rightarrow R_1COCHClR_2 + HCl \tag{9.29}$$

In this case, HCl, which is one of the products of the reaction and is volatile, catalyzes the main chlorination reaction. The main chlorination reaction appears to be fast and zero order in chlorine. Joosten et al. (1980) have considered this problem on the basis of the penetration and film theories and compared the predicted values of the specific rates of absorption with those measured experimentally in a stirred cell for the absorption of chlorine in cyclohexanone dissolved in carbon tetrachloride. The reaction was found to be zero order in chlorine, first order in cyclohexanone, and 1.2 order in HCl. Measurements of k_L were made under conditions of gas absorption with reaction by noting the rate of desorption of dissolved propane. The measured values of the enhancement factor agreed with the predicted values. A step-by-step procedure has been reported for the calculation of the enhancement factor.

9.1.2. Gas Absorption with a Radical-Multiplying Chain-Type Reaction

Flores-Fernandez and Mann (1978) have made a theoretical analysis of gas absorption accompanied by a fast reaction involving a radical-multiplying chain-type reaction:

$$A(g) \rightarrow A(l);\ A(l) + R(l) \rightarrow (n+1)\dot{R}(l), \quad n \geqslant 1 \tag{9.30}$$

Both film and penetration theories were employed. Under conditions close to pseudo-first-order ones, the two theories give practically the same answer. As radical accumulation close to the interface becomes important, however, the two theoretical approaches begin to diverge appreciably.

9.2. GAS ABSORPTION WITH PHOTOCHEMICAL REACTION

Gas absorption with chemical reaction activated by high-energy radiation (photons) has a considerable practical value, particularly in the synthesis of organic compounds and wastewater treatment. Some typical photochemical reactions are chlorination of *n*-alkanes and alkylaromatics, sulfochlorination and sulfoxidation of *n*-alkanes, and nitrosation of cycloalkanes (Fisher, 1978; Prengle et al., 1975). In the ozonolysis of wastewater containing deleterious organic substances, a considerable enhancement in the rate of absorption of ozone can be realized in the presence of photochemical activation or irradiation (Schorr et al., 1971).

Mahajani and Sharma (1981) have theoretically analyzed the problem of gas absorption accompanied by a fast pseudo-first-order reaction in the presence of photons, where the photochemical activation of the liquid-phase reactant B as well as the dissolved solute gas A is considered.

We shall consider an irreversible reaction between the solute gas A and liquid-phase reactant B on a wetted-wall column made of glass; the source of the photons is located inside the tube. The reaction conforms to the fast pseudo-first-order reaction regime (regime 3). The analysis is based on the film theory with the following assumptions:

1. A monochromatic beam of radiation is used.
2. The rectilinear coordinate system for mass and photon transfer is valid.
3. The Beer–Lambert law holds for photon transfer.
4. The activation step is first order with respect to the light absorbed.

We shall consider two typical cases of this problem where only one of the two reactive species is photochemically activated.

9.2.1. Photochemical Activation of Liquid-Phase Reactant B

When only species B is activated as a result of the photons, the following reactions will take place:

$$\mathrm{A + B} \xrightarrow{k_2} \text{products} \tag{9.31}$$

$$\mathrm{B} + h\nu \xrightarrow{\bar{k}_B} \bar{\mathrm{B}} \tag{9.32}$$

$$\mathrm{A} + \bar{\mathrm{B}} \xrightarrow{\bar{k}_2} \text{products} \tag{9.33}$$

where $\bar{k}_B$ is the first-order rate constant for the activation of species B; k_2 and $\bar{k}_2$ are the second-order rate constants for the reaction of A with the unactivated and activated B, respectively. Typical concentration profiles are shown in Figure 9.1. The following differential equations hold:

$$D_A \frac{d^2[\mathrm{A}]}{dx^2} = k_2[\mathrm{A}][\mathrm{B}] + \bar{k}_2[\mathrm{A}][\bar{\mathrm{B}}] \tag{9.34}$$

The relevant boundary conditions are, at

$$x = 0, \quad [\mathrm{A}] = [\mathrm{A}^*], \quad [\mathrm{B}] = [\mathrm{B_o}], \quad \frac{d[\mathrm{B}]}{dx} = 0 \tag{9.35}$$

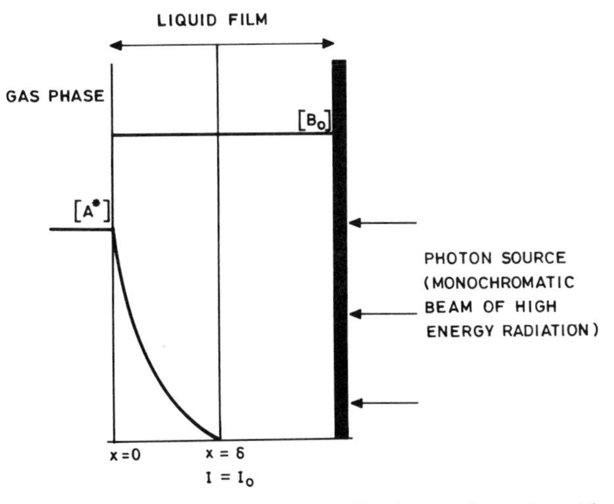

Figure 9.1. Typical concentration profiles for gas absorption with fast pseudo-first-order photochemical reaction.

and at

$$x = \delta, \quad [\mathrm{A}] = 0, \quad [\mathrm{B}] = [\mathrm{B_o}] \tag{9.36}$$

By applying the steady-state principle to $\bar{\mathrm{B}}$, we get

$$\bar{k}_B I_a = \bar{k}_2[\mathrm{A}][\bar{\mathrm{B}}] \tag{9.37}$$

Hence,

$$[\bar{\mathrm{B}}] = \frac{\bar{k}_B I_a}{\bar{k}_2[\mathrm{A}]} \tag{9.38}$$

where I_a, the light absorbed per unit volume, is given by

$$\begin{aligned} I_a &= I\mu_\lambda \\ &= \alpha_\lambda[\mathrm{B}] \cdot I_o \exp\{-\alpha_\lambda[\mathrm{B}](\delta - x)\} \end{aligned} \tag{9.39}$$

where α_λ is the molal absorptivity and μ_λ is the attenuation coefficient.

Substituting for $[\bar{\mathrm{B}}]$ and I_a from Eqs. 9.38 and 9.39 in Eq. 9.34, we get

$$D_A \frac{d^2[\mathrm{A}]}{dx^2} = k_2[\mathrm{A}][\mathrm{B}] + \bar{k}_B I_o \alpha_\lambda [\mathrm{B}] \exp\{-\alpha_\lambda[\mathrm{B}](\delta - x)\} \tag{9.40}$$

Since there is no depletion of B at the gas–liquid interface, [B] is reckoned to be constant over the film thickness δ. As a consequence, the following quantities are constant:

$$k = k_2[\mathrm{B}], \quad \bar{k} = \bar{k}_B I_o \alpha_\lambda [\mathrm{B}], \quad \bar{Z} = -\alpha_\lambda[\mathrm{B}] \tag{9.41}$$

Equation 9.40 can now be solved with the help of boundary conditions 9.35 and 9.36 to get the concentration profile of A as

$$[\mathrm{A}] = \frac{\{[\mathrm{A}^*] - \beta \exp(-\bar{Z}\delta)\}\sinh\left[\sqrt{\alpha}\,(\delta - x)\right]}{\sinh(\sqrt{\alpha}\,\delta)} - \frac{\beta \sinh(\sqrt{\alpha}\,x)}{\sinh(\sqrt{\alpha}\,\delta)} + \beta \exp\left[-\bar{Z}(\delta - x)\right] \tag{9.42}$$

The specific rate of absorption of A is given by

$$R_A = -D_A\left(\frac{d[A]}{dx}\right)_{x=0}$$

$$= \frac{\{[A^*] - \beta\exp(-\bar{Z}\delta)\}\sqrt{D_A k}}{\tanh(\sqrt{\alpha}\,\delta)} + \frac{\sqrt{\alpha}\,D_A\beta}{\sinh(\sqrt{\alpha}\,\delta)}$$

$$-D_A\beta\bar{Z}\exp(-\bar{Z}\delta) \tag{9.43}$$

where

$$\alpha = \frac{k}{D_A}, \quad \beta = \frac{\xi}{\bar{Z}^2 - \alpha}, \quad \xi = \frac{\bar{k}}{D_A} \tag{9.44}$$

If $\sqrt{\alpha}\,\delta > 10$, $\tanh\sqrt{\alpha}\,\delta \to 1$ and $\sinh\sqrt{\alpha}\,\delta \to (\exp\sqrt{\alpha}\,\delta)/2$. Under these conditions,

$$R_A = \sqrt{D_A k}\{[A^*] - \beta\exp(-\bar{Z}\delta)\}$$

$$+2\beta\sqrt{D_A k}\exp(\sqrt{\alpha}\,\delta)$$

$$-D_A\beta\bar{Z}\exp(-\bar{Z}\delta) \tag{9.45}$$

In the absence of photochemical activation, that is, when $\beta = 0$, Eq. 9.45 reduces to

$$R_A = [A^*]\sqrt{D_A k} \tag{9.46}$$

which is the same as Eq. 2.67, for gas absorption accompanied by fast pseudo-first-order reaction. Thus, it is obvious from Eq. 9.45 that the specific rate of absorption is *not* directly proportional to the interfacial concentration of the solute gas for a fast pseudo-first-order reaction when activation of B is taken into consideration.

9.2.2. Photochemical Activation of Dissolved Gas A

We can have, in principle, photochemical activation of the dissolved gas A (e.g., Cl_2, NOCl, O_3). In addition to reaction 9.31, the following reactions will occur in the liquid phase. Typical concentration profiles are the same as shown in Figure 9.1.

$$A + h\nu \xrightarrow{\bar{k}_A} \bar{A} \tag{9.47}$$

$$\bar{A} + B \xrightarrow{\bar{k}_2} \text{products} \tag{9.48}$$

The relevant differential equation is

$$D_A\frac{d^2[A]}{dx^2} = k_2[A][B] + \bar{k}_2[\bar{A}][B]$$

$$= k_2[A][B] + \bar{k}_A I_a \tag{9.49}$$

and the boundary conditions are, at

$$x = 0, \quad [A] = [A^*], \quad [B] = [B_o],$$

$$\frac{d[B]}{dx} = 0 \tag{9.50}$$

and at

$$x = \delta, \quad [A] = 0, \quad [B] = [B_o] \tag{9.51}$$

$$I_a = I\mu_\lambda$$

$$= I_o\alpha_\lambda[A]\exp\{-\alpha_\lambda[A](\delta - x)\} \tag{9.52}$$

Substituting Eq. 9.52 in 9.49, we get

$$D_A\frac{d^2[A]}{dx^2} = k_2[A][B]$$

$$+\bar{k}_A I_o\alpha_\lambda[A]\exp\{-\alpha_\lambda[A](\delta - x)\} \tag{9.53}$$

If we assume constant light intensity throughout the film, the terms containing $\alpha_\lambda[A](\delta - x)$ in the expansion of the exponential term in Eq. 9.53 can be neglected. Therefore, we get

$$D_A\frac{d^2[A]}{dx^2} = k_2[A][B] + \bar{k}_A I_o\alpha_\lambda[A]$$

$$= \{k_2[B] + \bar{k}_A I_o\alpha_\lambda\}[A]$$

$$= \bar{k}_1[A] \tag{9.54}$$

where

$$\bar{k}_1 = k_2[\text{B}] + \bar{k}_\text{A} I_\text{o} \alpha_\lambda$$
$$= \text{a constant} \qquad (9.55)$$

Equation 9.54, on integration with boundary conditions 9.50 and 9.51, gives the concentration profile for A as

$$[\text{A}] = \frac{[\text{A}^*]\sinh\left[\sqrt{\bar{k}_1/D_\text{A}}\,(\delta - x)\right]}{\sinh\left(\sqrt{\bar{k}_1/D_\text{A}}\,\delta\right)} \qquad (9.56)$$

Therefore, the specific rate of absorption of A is given by

$$R_\text{A} = -D_\text{A}\left(\frac{d[\text{A}]}{dx}\right)_{x=0}$$
$$= [\text{A}^*]\sqrt{D_\text{A}\bar{k}_1}$$
$$= [\text{A}^*]\sqrt{D_\text{A}(k_2[\text{B}_\text{o}] + \bar{k}_\text{A} I_\text{o} \alpha_\lambda)} \qquad (9.57)$$

9.3. GLOSSARY OF REACTION SCHEMES CONSIDERED

Table 9.2 presents a glossary of the reaction schemes considered in Chapters 2–9.

9.4. GLOSSARY OF COMPLEX REACTIONS: LITERATURE REVIEW

Table 9.3 gives a glossary of various cases of complex reactions considered in the literature that are not discussed in this volume.

TABLE 9.2. Tabulation of Reaction Schemes Considered in Chapters 2–9

Reaction Scheme	Theory Used	Section(s)
Irreversible reactions		
General-order (m, n)th irreversible chemical reaction $\text{A} + Z\text{B} \rightarrow \text{products}$	Film, penetration, and surface renewal theories	2.2–2.7
Pseudo-first-order reaction $(m = 1, n = 1)$; reactant B is volatile $\text{A} + Z\text{B} \rightarrow \text{products}$	Film theory	2.8
Reversible reactions		
Reversible pseudo-first-order reaction $\text{A} \underset{k_2}{\overset{k_1}{\rightleftharpoons}} \text{C}$	Film and surface renewal theories	2.10
Reversible pseudo-first-order reaction $\text{A} + \text{B} \underset{k_2'}{\overset{k_2}{\rightleftharpoons}} \text{C} + \text{E}$	Film and surface renewal theories	2.10
Reversible reaction with generalized kinetics $Z_\text{A}\text{A} + Z_\text{B}\text{B} \rightleftharpoons Z_\text{C}\text{C} + Z_\text{E}\text{E}$	Film and penetration theories	2.10
Reversible instantaneous reactions $\text{A} \rightleftharpoons \text{C}$ $\text{A} \rightleftharpoons 2\text{C}$ $\text{A} + \text{B} \rightleftharpoons \text{C}$ $\text{A} + \text{B} \rightleftharpoons \text{C} + \text{D}$	Surface renewal theory	2.10
Reversible instantaneous reaction: generalized case $\text{A} \rightleftharpoons \Sigma Z_\text{E}\text{E}$	Surface renewal theory	2.10

TABLE 9.2. (*Continued*)

Reaction Scheme	Theory Used	Section(s)
Consecutive reactions		
A + B → C A + C → D	Film theory	4.1
i. Both reactions in slow or very slow reaction regime		
ii. First reaction in fast pseudo-first-order and second reaction in slow reaction regime		
iii. Both reactions fast pseudo first order		
iv. Fast reactions accompanied by depletion of B and C in the film		
v. First reaction instantaneous		
Two-step chemical reactions		
A + B → C C + B → product	Film and penetration theories	4.2
i. Fast reaction		
ii. Depletion of the reactant in the film		
iii. Instantaneous reaction		
One gas–two reactants		
$A + Z_1B_1 \rightarrow$ products $A + Z_2B_2 \rightarrow$ products		
i. Pseudo-first-order and instantaneous reactions	Film theory	5.3 and 5.4
ii. One reaction instantaneous; depletion reactions	Film theory	5.5 and 5.6
Simultaneous absorption of two gases		
$A_1 + Z_{A_1}B \rightarrow$ products $A_2 + Z_{A_2}B \rightarrow$ products		
i. Pseudo-mth-order reaction	Film and penetration theories	6.2
ii. One gas reacts instantaneously	Film and penetration theories	6.2
iii. Two gases react instantaneously	Film and penetration theories	6.2
Reaction product of the first gas acting as a reactant for the second gas		
$A_1 + B \rightarrow C +$ product $A_2 + C \rightarrow B$	Film theory	6.4
i. Irreversible reaction		
ii. Reversible reaction		
Reaction of gas A_1 resulting in the formation of A_2		
$A_1 + B \rightarrow A_2 + C$	Film theory	6.4
Simultaneous absorption with reversible reactions		
$A_1 + B \rightleftharpoons C_1 + C_2$ $A_2 + B \rightleftharpoons E_1 + E_2$	Film theory	6.4

TABLE 9.2. (*Continued*)

Reaction Scheme	Theory Used	Section(s)
Simultaneous absorption of two gases that react with each other		
$A_1 + ZA_2 \rightarrow$ products		
i. instantaneous reaction	Film theory	6.5
ii. fast reaction	Film theory	6.5
Extraction with chemical reaction in both phases		
$A + ZB \rightarrow$ products		
Reaction occurs without depletion in both phases in the films adjacent to the either side of interface	Film and penetration theories	7.3
Reaction is instantaneous in both the phases	Film and penetration theories	7.4
Reaction occurs with depletion in both the phases in the films	Film theory	7.5
Desorption of the product		
Nonpolymeric systems		
$B \rightleftharpoons A'$	Film theory	8.3
i. Fast reaction regime		
ii. Instantaneous reversible (equilibrium reaction)		
Polymeric systems		
$B + C \rightleftharpoons A' + D$	Film and penetration theories	8.4
Simultaneous absorption–desorption with reaction (including aspects of supersaturation)		
$A + Z_1B \rightarrow Z_2A'$ $A' + Z_3B \rightarrow$ products $A \rightarrow A'$	Film and penetration theories	8.5 and 8.6
Autocatalytic reaction		
First- and zero-order reactions		
$A(g) \rightarrow A(l)$; $A(l) + \dot{R}(l) \rightarrow \dot{R}(l) + \dot{R}(l)$	Film theory	9.1
Absorption with radical multiplying chain type reaction		9.1
$A(l) + \dot{R}(l) \rightarrow (n+1)\dot{R}(l), \quad n \geqslant 1$	Penetration theory	
Photochemical reaction		
$A + B \xrightarrow{h\nu}$ product	Film theory	9.2
(activation of B or A)		

TABLE 9.3. Mass Transfer Accompanied by Complex Chemical Reaction

No.	Reaction Scheme	Theory Used	Reference(s)
1.	Irreversible reaction in a liquid of finite depth $A + ZB \rightarrow$ products $A + ZB \rightarrow$ products (Michaelis–Menton equation)	 Film–Penetration theory Film theory	 Sada and Ameno (1973) Tsao (1972)
2.	Reversible reaction $A + ZB(l) \rightleftharpoons Z_E E + Z_F F$	Penetration and surface renewal theories	Onda (1972)
3.	Reversible reaction $A + B \rightleftharpoons E$	Penetration theory	Hikita et al. (1977)
4.	Consecutive reactions $Z_A A + Z_B B(l) \rightarrow Z_C C(l)$ $Z_A A + Z_C C(l) \rightarrow$ products	Penetration and surface renewal theories	Onda et al. (1972)
5.	$A + B \rightarrow C$ $A + E \rightarrow F$, $A + E \rightarrow G$ $A + C \rightarrow D$, $A + C \rightarrow E$	Very slow reactions	Chua and Ratcliffe (1971); Mann et al. (1977)
6.	Consecutive/parallel irreversible reaction $A + B \rightarrow C_{11}$, C_{12}; $C_{11}, C_{12} \rightarrow D_1$ $A + B \rightarrow C_{21}$, C_{22}; $C_{21}, C_{22} \rightarrow D_2$	Film theory	Sheth (1977)
7.	$A + B \rightarrow C(l) + A'$ $A' + C \rightarrow D(l)$ $A + C \rightarrow E(l)$ $A' + B \rightarrow F(l)$	Film theory	Bhargava (1978)
8.	$A + ZB \rightarrow ZI(l)$ $A + I \rightarrow I'(l)$ $I(l) + B \rightarrow P(l)$ $I'(l) + B \rightarrow X(l)$	Film theory	Beenackers and van Swaaij (1978)
9.	Two-step reversible reactions (instantaneous and fast) $A + B \rightleftharpoons C$ $C + B \rightleftharpoons E$	Penetration theory	Hikita et al. (1972)
10.	Two-step reversible reactions $A + B \rightleftharpoons C + C'$ $C + B \rightleftharpoons F$	Film and penetration theories	Hikita et al. (1973)
11.	$A_1 + Z_{A_1} B \rightarrow A_2 + P_1$ $A_2 + Z_{A_2} B \rightarrow P_2$ $A_2 \rightarrow P_3$	Film theory	Sada et al. (1979)
12.	Consecutive/parallel reversible reactions $A + B \rightleftharpoons E \rightleftharpoons P$ $A \xrightarrow{+B_1} Q_1$, $A \xrightarrow{+B_2} Q_2$, …, $A \xrightarrow{+B_m} Q_m$ $P \rightarrow P_1, P_2, \ldots, P_m$	Film and penetration theories	Kuo and Huang (1970, 1973)
13.	Network of reversible reactions $A_1 \rightleftharpoons A_2$, $A_1 \rightleftharpoons A_3$, $A_3 \rightleftharpoons A_2$	Film and surface renewal theories	Chu (1971)

TABLE 9.3. (*Continued*)

No.	Reaction Scheme	Theory Used	Reference(s)
14.	Simultaneous absorption with reaction of two gases $A_1 + A_1 \rightarrow$ product $A_1 + A_2 \rightarrow$ product $A_2 + A_2 \rightarrow$ product	Film theory	Mhaskar (1975)
15.	Simultaneous absorption with reaction of two gases and parallel reaction $A_1 + ZA_2 \rightarrow P_1$ $A_1 + ZE \rightarrow P_2$	Film theory	Sada et al. (1976)
16.	Complex reversible/irreversible reactions $2A \rightleftharpoons A^+ + A$ $A^+ + B \rightarrow P$	Film theory	Sada and Kumazawa (1974)
17.	Parallel reversible first-order reactions $A \rightleftharpoons B$ $\searrow\!\!\nwarrow C$	Film theory	Li et al. (1974)
18.	Parallel reversible reactions $A + B \rightleftharpoons C$ $\searrow\!\!\nwarrow D$	Film theory	Li et al. (1974)
19.	Complex reaction scheme $Z_A A + Z_B B \rightarrow Z_X X$ $Z_B B + Z_C C \underset{k_3}{\overset{k_2}{\rightleftharpoons}} Z_E E + Z_F F$ $Z_A A + Z_E E \rightarrow Z_Y Y$	Film theory	Chaudhari et al. (1975)
20.	Complex reversible reaction scheme $Z_A A + Z_{B_1} B \rightleftharpoons Z_C C + Z_{D_1} D$ $Z_{D_2} D + Z_E E(g) \rightleftharpoons Z_{B_2} B$	Film and penetration theories	Shah and Kenney
21.	Autocatalytic reaction: volatile species $A + B \rightarrow A' + D$ (A' = volatile intermediate product that exercises an autocatalytic effect)	Film and penetration theories	Joosten et al. (1980)
22.	Simultaneous reaction in the gas phase $A_1(g) + ZA_2(g) \rightarrow A_3(g)$	Penetration theory	Lefers et al. (1980)
23.	Reactions in both gas and liquid phases $A + ZB \rightarrow$ products	Film theory	Rod (1973)

REFERENCES

Beenackers, A. A. C. M., and van Swaaij, W. P. M. (1978), *Chem. Eng. J.*, **15**, 25.

Bhargava, R. K. (1978), Kinetics of Heterogeneous Reactions, Ph.D. (Tech.) thesis, University of Bombay.

Chaudhari, R. V., Kulkarni, B. D., Doraiswamy, L. K., and Juvekar, V. A. (1975), *Chem. Eng. Sci.*, **30**, 945.

Chu, C. (1971), *Chem. Eng. Sci.*, **26**, 305.

Chua, Y. H., and Ratcliffe, J. S. (1971), *Mech. Chem. Eng. Trans.*, **7**, 6, 11, 17.

Fisher, M. (1978), *Angew. Chem. Int. Ed. Engl.*, **17**, 16.

Flores-Fernandez, G., and Mann, R. (1978), *Chem. Eng. Sci.*, **33**, 1545.

Hikita, H., Asai, S., and Takatsuka, T. (1972), *Chem. Eng. J.*, **4**, 31.

Hikita, H., Asai, S., Himukashi, Y., and Takatsuka, T. (1973), *Chem. Eng. J.*, **5**, 77.

Hikita, H., Asai, S., Ishikawa, H., and Hirano, S. (1977), *J. Chem. Eng. Japan*, **10**, 120.

Hobbs, C. C., Drew, E. G., van't Hof, H. A., Mesich, F. G., and Onore, M. J. (1972), *Ind. Eng. Chem. Prod. Res. Dev.*, **11**, 220.

Joosten, G. E. H., Maatman, H., Prins, W., and Stamhuis, E. J. (1980), *Chem. Eng. Sci.*, **35**, 223.

Juvekar, V. A. (1976), *Chem. Eng. Sci.*, **31**, 91.

Kuo, C. H., and Huang, C. J. (1970), *AIChE J.*, **16**, 493.

Kuo, C. H., and Huang, C. J. (1973), *Chem. Eng. J.*, **5**, 43.

Lefers, J. B., de Boks, F. C., van den Bleek, C. M., and van den Berg, P. J. (1980), *Chem. Eng. Sci.*, **35**, 145.

Li, K. Y., Kuo, C. H., and Weeks, J. L. Jr. (1974), *Can. J. Chem. Eng.*, **52**, 569.

Mahajani, V. V., and Sharma, M. M. (1981), *Chem. Eng. Sci.*, **36**, 595.

Mann, R., Middleton, J. C., and Parker, I. B. (1977), *Proc. 2nd European Conference on Mixing*, Cambridge, England, p. F3.

Mhaskar, R. D. (1975), *Chem. Eng. Sci.*, **30**, 1441.

Onda, K. (1972), *Mem. Fac. Eng. Nagoya Univ.*, **24**(2), 165.

Onda, K., Sada, E., Kobayashi, T., and Fujine, M. (1972), *Chem. Eng. Sci.*, **27**, 247.

Prengle, H. W., Mauk, C. E., Legan, R. W., and Hewes, C. G. (1975), *Hydrocarbon Process. Petrol. Refiner*, **54**(10), 82.

Rod, V. (1973), *Collect. Czech. Chem. Commun.*, **38**, 3228.

Sada, E., and Ameno, T. (1973), *J. Chem. Eng. Japan*, **6**, 247.

Sada, E., and Kumazawa, H. (1974), *Chem. Eng. Sci.*, **29**, 335.

Sada, E., Kumazawa, H., and Butt, M. A. (1976), *Can. J. Chem. Eng.*, **54**, 97.

Sada, E., Kumazawa, H., Kudo, I., and Kondo, T. (1979), *Ind. Eng. Chem. Process Design Dev.*, **18**, 275.

Schorr, V., Boval, B., Hancil, V., and Smith, J. M. (1971), *Ind. Eng. Chem. Process Design Dev.*, **10**, 509.

Shah, Y. T., and Kenney, C. N. (1972), *Chem. Eng. Sci.*, **27**, 1.

Sheth, M. N. (1977), Kinetics of Heterogeneous Reactions, M. Chem. Eng. thesis, University of Bombay.

Sim, M. -T., and Mann, R. (1975), *Chem. Eng. Sci.*, **30**, 1215.

Tsao, G. T. (1972), *Chem. Eng. Sci.*, **27**, 1593.

CHAPTER TEN

Use of Models in the Simulation and Design of Fluid–Fluid Reactors

10.1. GAS–LIQUID SYSTEMS

If the physicochemical data for the system are available, then, as discussed in Chapters 2 and 3, it is possible to predict the effect of chemical reaction on the rate of mass transfer in any industrial equipment. It would be necessary to know the values of k_L and a separately in the industrial equipment to be used. In many cases, however, the physicochemical data may not be available. Danckwerts and Sharma (1966), Danckwerts (1970), Charpentier and Laurent (1974), Danckwerts and Alper (1975), Alper and Danckwerts (1976), Charpentier (1978), and Laurent et al. (1980) have considered some aspects of the use of small-scale apparatus to predict the rate of absorption in industrial equipment.

10.1.1. Modeling by the *Point Method*

We shall first consider modeling those systems where all the reaction occurs in the film and therefore no free A exists in the bulk liquid (no reaction occurs in the bulk of the liquid). The method of modeling considered here is referred to as *point modeling* (Danckwerts and Alper, 1975).

Transient Rates of Absorption

All forms of surface renewal theories lead to practically the same result in so far as the effect of chemical reaction is concerned, provided that D_A and D_B are almost equal. It is convenient to adopt Higbie's penetration theory for the purpose of design. The contact time t_E of elements of the liquid surface is equal to $4D_A/\pi k_L^2$. If we know the value of k_L for a nonreacting solution, then the time of contact t_E can be calculated. The following procedure for obtaining the rates of absorption should be followed. The partial pressure of the gas in the model apparatus should be the same as in the industrial equipment.

1. Experimentally determine the value of $R_A(t_E)$, the amount of gas absorbed per unit of interfacial area of the reacting solution during the time of contact t_E, under conditions in which the liquid can be regarded as stagnant and infinitely deep. The specific rate of absorption R_A is then given by $R_A(t_E)/t_E$.
2. Repeat the foregoing procedure for other combinations of the concentrations of A and B.

It can be seen that the design of the equipment can be attempted without knowledge of the physicochemical properties of the system and the kinetic nature of the reactions.

There is very little information in the literature that describes the experimental verification of the foregoing procedure. Danckwerts et al. (1963) have compared the rates of absorption of CO_2 in a packed column with predictions made on the basis of transient rates of absorption measured in a wetted-wall column. The reacting solutions were aqueous carbonate–bicarbonate buffer and sodium hydroxide. Aqueous solutions of sodium sulfate that had the same viscosity as the reacting solutions were taken as inert solutions. There was good agreement between the measured and the predicted values of the rates of absorption. It is, however, necessary to obtain more extensive information on this procedure before it can be accepted for design purposes.

Two types of model apparatus, which cover almost the entire range of k_L values encountered in practice, are particularly useful—the wetted-wall column ($k_L = 6–15 \times 10^{-3}$ cm/sec) and the jet apparatus ($k_L = 15–60 \times 10^{-3}$ cm/sec). It is relatively easy to discern the mechanism of absorption in these apparatuses (see Section 2.11).

Absorption in Model Apparatus

An alternative approach would be to measure the rate of absorption in an apparatus that simulates the essential features of the industrial equipment. It appears that any apparatus that can provide a value of k_L equal to that expected in the industrial equipment can be used as a satisfactory model apparatus (see Table 14.1 for common values of k_L and a provided by a variety of industrial equipment). Typical k_L values in laboratory equipment, where the hydrodynamics of the system is properly understood, as well as in other model contactors where the interfacial area is accurately known, are listed in Table 10.1 along with other relevant details of these apparatuses.

A variety of apparatuses can be employed as a model unit. Danckwerts and Gillham (1966) have suggested that the stirred cell can be advantageously used. Here, standard beakers of 500- to 1000-cm^3 capacity can be employed, and the depth of the liquid is maintained at 2–3 cm. It can be modified to have a continuous flow of liquid at a predetermined rate. Only the surface of the liquid is stirred. The stirrer is of cruciform type. It is usually possible to operate these stirred cells at stirring speeds of from 20 to 150 rev/min without any significant vortex formation. For fluids like water and common gases like O_2, CO_2, and C_2H_4, typical k_L values would lie in the range of $2\text{–}15 \times 10^{-3}$ cm/sec. A variety of industrial equipment (particularly packed columns) offer values of k_L in this range. It should then be possible to use the stirred cell as a model apparatus. The procedure should be as follows:

1. Operate the stirred cell at a stirring speed that will give a value of k_L equal to that in the industrial apparatus. A nonreacting solution that otherwise simulates the properties of the reacting solution can be employed to obtain k_L values in the stirred cell.
2. The nonreacting solution is substituted by the reacting solution and the value of the mass transfer coefficient with reaction, k_{LR}, is found experimentally in the stirred cell. The enhancement factor obtained in the stirred cell should be the same as that which would be realized in industrial equipment. Since the enhancement factor is a function of k_L and the ratio of the concentration of the reactive species B and the dissolved A, it will be necessary to use the same respective values of B and A as would be encountered in industrial practice.

In many industrial operations the partial pressure of the solute gas varies from a very small value to a few atmospheres. Further, depending on circumstances, there may be a significant gas-side resistance. In order to avoid any gas-side resistance in the stirred cell, it is imperative to use pure solute gas. The stirred cell can be operated satisfactorily at a pressure ranging from, say, 0.2 to about 2–3 atm. Thus da Silva and Danckwerts (1968), for instance, designed a stirred cell that could be satisfactorily operated at reduced pressures.

When it becomes necessary to use dilute gas, then the stirred contactor should be employed, since it can satisfactorily simulate the gas-side mass transfer coefficient values actually encountered in industrial contactors (e.g., packed columns).

Danckwerts and Gillham (1966), da Silva and Danckwerts (1968), and Charpentier (1978) have reported experimental data that indicate clearly that the stirred cell can be used as a satisfactory model apparatus for predicting the performance of packed columns. Jhaveri and Sharma (1968) worked with the system O_2–dithionite, which is zero order in O_2 and second order in dithionite, and also showed that a stirred cell can be used as a satisfactory model for packed columns. Here, the conditions for testing the utility of the stirred cell were more stringent than in the case of CO_2 absorption in aqueous alkaline solutions, where the order with respect to the reactive species is one.

Danckwerts and Alper (1975) have shown that the stirred contactor can be used as a model contactor to predict the performance of packed columns where gas-side resistance is also important. Their experimental work was concerned with the absorption of CO_2 diluted with air in aqueous solutions of sodium hydroxide containing some sodium carbonate. A 10.2-cm-i.d. column provided with 1.27-cm ceramic Raschig rings was used. Charpentier (1978) has reported that for this system satisfactory simulation for a 30-cm-i.d. column packed with 20-mm glass Raschig rings up to a height of 192 cm could be done with a 10-cm-i.d. stirred contactor.

Andrew (1961) has described the use of a disk column for the study of absorption of CO_2 in ammoniacal and carbonated ammoniacal solutions. If the column is operated under conditions of complete wetting, this apparatus can also be used, under some conditions, as a model apparatus. The k_L values in a

TABLE 10.1. Salient Features of Model Gas–Liquid Contactors[a]

Apparatus	Liquid Residence Time (sec)	Contact Time (sec)	Interfacial Area (cm^2)	Area/Liquid Volume (cm^2/cm^3)	$k_G \times 10^5$ (mol/cm^2 sec atm)	$k_L \times 10^3$ (cm/sec)	Suitable as Simulator for
Known hydrodynamics							
Rotating drum	0.002–0.25	0.002–0.25	150–350 (high precision)	100–1250	—	10–115	Plate column; spray column; bubble column; mechanically agitated contactor
Cylindrical wetted wall	0.1–2	0.1–2	10–100 (high precision)	25–60	1–9	3.5–16	Plate column; packed column
Spherical wetted wall	0.05–5	0.05–5	10–40 (high precision)	20–60	1–9	2.5–22.5	Plate column; packed column
Conical wetted wall	0.2–1	0.2–1	80 (high precision)	40–70	1–9	5–11.5	Packed column
Laminar jet	0.04–0.006	0.001–0.1	0.3–5 (high precision)	20–80	10–40	16–160	Plate column; bubble column; mechanically agitated contactor; spray column; venturi jet scrubber
Uncertain Hydrodynamics							
Stirred cell	Very wide range	0.1–2	80 (good precision)	0.15–0.30	1–5 (limited control over k_G)	3.5–16	Packed column; spray column
Stirred contactor	Very wide range	0.2–1	80 (good precision)	0.08–0.15	1–30 (independent control over k_G and k_L)	5–11.5	Packed column; mechanically agitated contactor
String of multiple spheres (with depression in top of each sphere)	Very wide range	0.05–0.5	30–360 cm^2 (moderate precision)	20–60	1–25	2.5–22.5	Packed column

[a]Absorbent, water; liquid-phase diffusivity of solute gas, $D_A = 2 \times 10^{-5}$ cm^2/sec; gas-phase diffusivity of solute gas, $D_G = 0.12$ cm^2/sec; temperature = 25°C.

disk column for water and common gases lie in the range of 8–20 × 10^{-3} cm/sec, which are practically the same as those provided by industrial packed columns.

Use of a Small-Scale Contactor

The maximal value of k_L for fluids like water that can be obtained in the stirred cell is about 15–20 × 10^{-3} cm/sec. However, in the case of practically all contactors where gas is dispersed in the liquid (e.g., bubble cap or sieve-plate column, bubble column) the k_L value might be in the range of 30–60 × 10^{-3} cm/sec. It then becomes impractical to use the stirred cell as a model apparatus. It would be preferable to use a small bubble cap rather than a sieve plate as a model contactor, since in the case of the former the physical properties like viscosity, surface tension, and ionic strength do not significantly affect the hydrodynamics of the system (Sharma et al., 1969). It is known that in the case of a sieve-plate column these properties affect the quality of the dispersion significantly. It should be possible to obtain values of k_L as high as 60 × 10^{-3} cm/sec in bubble cap plate columns.

Complications Due to Additional Slow Reactions in the Bulk-Liquid

There are some cases where a slow chemical reaction may occur in the bulk phase. This reaction in the bulk phase might change the concentration of B significantly. In these cases the value of the specific interfacial area per unit volume of liquid becomes important. It is evident from Eq. 2.15 that if the system falls in the regime between 1 and 2, the value of $lk_2[B_o]$ (for a second-order reaction) becomes important. The value of l in the model and industrial apparatus may be quite different. Thus, for instance, in the case of the stirred cell, the value of the volume of liquid per unit of interfacial area (cm^3/cm^2) may be 2, but in the case of a packed column it may be 0.1. It becomes necessary to give careful consideration to the use of a model apparatus for the purpose of scale-up.

It is important to carefully consider the chemistry of the overall reaction. Thus, in the case of absorption of CO_2 in aqueous solutions of amines the following reactions occur:

$$RNH_2 + CO_2 \rightleftharpoons RNHCOO^- + H^+ \quad \text{(a)}$$

$$RNH_2 + H^+ \rightleftharpoons RNH_3^+ \quad \text{(b)}$$

$$2RNH_2 + CO_2 \rightleftharpoons RNHCOO^- + RNH_3^+$$

The first reaction (a) is rate controlling; the second step (b) is instantaneous. At low levels of the carbonation of amine (say less than 0.3 mol of CO_2 per mol of amine) and temperatures up to 30–50°C, the reaction can be considered essentially irreversible. At higher levels of carbonation, however, particularly when the amount of CO_2 corresponds to about 0.5 mol of CO_2 per mol of amine, the reaction becomes reversible. Since the amine solutions are alkaline, the free CO_2 can undergo the following reactions, which are essentially slow:

$$2RNH_2 + CO_2 \xrightarrow{H_2O} HCO_3^- + RNH_3^+ + RNH_2 \quad \text{(c)}$$

$$2RNH_2 + CO_2 \xrightarrow{OH^-} HCO_3^- + 2RNH_2 \quad \text{(d)}$$

(These reactions are classified as secondary reactions.)

The secondary reactions (c) and (d) are relatively slow and do not occur in the film in all types of industrial contactors. However, these reactions occur in the bulk liquid, and the extent of the reactions will depend on the residence time of the liquid. The net effect of the secondary reactions is that the free amine concentration increases (and hence the pH increases) and the equilibrium partial pressure of CO_2 decreases. The reaction between CO_2 and H_2O can be catalyzed by anions such as arsenite.

Equilibrium data reported for CO_2–amines in the literature refer to the overall equilibrium, including secondary reactions. Thus the value of the equilibrium partial pressure of CO_2 read from these data would be lower than in the case when only the primary equilibrium has been set up. At low levels of carbonation the difference is insignificant, but it can become marked at higher levels of carbonation. In a model contactor it is quite likely that only the primary equilibrium has been established.

Andrew (1969) has given an interesting example of absorption of CO_2 in aqueous solutions of ammonia. He has plotted the partial pressure of CO_2 against the carbonation ratio for the two limiting cases, namely, when only the primary equilibrium is set up and when the secondary equilibrium has also been set up. The difference between the two partial pressure values is marked when the carbonation ratio exceeds 0.4. Further, the free ammonia concentration in the two cases will also be different. If the laboratory experiments were now done in such a way that sufficient time was allowed for complete equilibrium to be established, then the rate of the absorption in a solution of specific CO_2 loading would be relatively high, because of the low equilibrium partial pressure of CO_2 and higher amine concentration than in industrial absorbers, where the residence time of the liquid to allow complete equilibrium to be established may be short. Actually a situation can arise where a considerable amount of absorption might occur in the laboratory absorber but none might occur under industrial conditions. The converse of this situation can also occur—when the residence time of the liquid in the industrial contactor is long and that in the laboratory contactor is short.

It is necessary to take the foregoing factors into consideration for the purpose of scale-up. It may be possible to use the integral method of modeling in order to overcome the problems just mentioned.

10.1.2. Modeling by the *Integral Method*

So far we have considered the point modeling method for the design of contactors. In some complicated cases that are encountered in practice, however, such as the case of slow reactions in the bulk liquid (considered above), the absorption of one gas into a medium containing two reactants (Chapter 5), and the simultaneous absorption of two gases (Chapter 6), it becomes difficult to employ the point modeling method. In such cases the so-called *integral modeling* method may prove attractive.

Packed Columns

Consider the case of a countercurrently operated packed column. In the proposed model contactor, feeds of gas and liquid at the right composition, pressure, and temperature are introduced countercurrently in the right ratio of feed rates. Further, the composition of the outlet gas and liquid streams should be the same as expected from the industrial equipment that is being modeled. Danckwerts and Alper (1975) and Alper and Danckwerts (1976) have considered this matter and suggested a new model contactor design.

The height of the industrial packed column for a reacting system is given by the following equation

$$\frac{aH_1}{V_L} = \int_{[B_o]_f}^{[B_o]_i} \frac{d[B]}{R_A} \tag{10.1}$$

and for the model contactor by

$$\frac{AH_2}{L} = \int_{[B_o]_f}^{[B_o]_i} \frac{d[B]}{R_A} \tag{10.2}$$

where A is the wetted area per unit height of the model contactor, and L is the liquid flow rate. (H_1 and H_2 are the heights of the industrial and model equipment, respectively.) We will use the same value of k_G and k_L in the model contactor as would be exhibited by the industrial equipment. In order to get the same value of $[B_o]_i$ and $[B_o]_f$ the integrals on the right-hand side of Eqs. 10.1 and 10.2 must be equal. Thus

$$\frac{aH_1}{V_L} = \frac{AH_2}{L} \tag{10.3}$$

and hence

$$\frac{H_1}{H_2} = \frac{V_L/a}{L/A} \tag{10.4}$$

(V_L/a and L/A represent flow per unit of wetted perimeter.) We would naturally be interested in having the height of the model contactor to be about 10–20% of the industrial equipment. Further, if some reactions occur in the bulk liquid, then the mean residence time of the liquid must be the same in the model contactor as in the industrial column. In other words, we should have the same volume of liquid per unit of effective area in both the model and the industrial contactor.

The foregoing requirements are quite stringent and cannot be easily satisfied in a small packed column or simple or modified wetted-wall column. Alper and Danckwerts (1976) have shown that a string of spheres column can meet the requirements. The value of liquid holdup can also be matched by making a depression in the top of each sphere. The depression in the top of each sphere also helps in providing practically the same value of k_L on all spheres, since the amplitude of ripples is probably the same on each sphere. The values of k_L and k_G can be varied by suitably changing the sphere diameter and the column diameter (k_G can be varied by changing the clearance between the sphere and wall).

Packed columns have been successfully modeled with packing sizes up to 12.5 mm ($\frac{1}{2}$ in.) where the scale-up factor was about 3. The following systems were studied:

1. Absorption of CO_2 into an MEA solution containing arsenite. (Here the arsenite catalyzes the secondary reaction, $RNHCOO^- + H_2O \rightarrow RNH_2 + HCO_3^-$, which occurs in the bulk.)
2. Absorption of CO_2 from air into 2,6-dimethyl morpholine solution, (There is substantial gas-side resistance in this case.)
3. Absorption of CO_2 into a solution containing two amines (see Chapter 5).
4. Simultaneous absorption of NH_3 and CO_2 into water (see Chapter 6).
5. Simultaneous absorption of CO_2 and SO_2 into amine solutions (see Chapter 6).

The following procedure has been recommended by Alper and Danckwerts (1976):

1. Select the flow rate L so that the k_L value in the sphere column is the same as in the proposed packed column.
2. The gas flow rate in the sphere column should be $L \times V_G/V_L$.
3. Select the diameter of the tube in which the sphere column is confined in such a way that it reproduces the value of k_G as expected in the packed column.
4. Select the dimensions of the pool in the top of

the sphere so as to reproduce the ratio of liquid holdup to surface area as expected in the packed column.

5. Calculate the number of spheres N that will make the ratio of the heights of the columns the same as the ratio of the wetting rates.
6. In case the height of the model sphere column is found to be inconvenient, this procedure should be repeated for a different sphere size.

Use of Laminar Jet Apparatus as an Integral Simulator for Venturi Jet Scrubber

Laurent et al. (1980) have successfully used a laminar jet apparatus (0.5-mm-diameter and 15-mm-long jet) as an integral model for simulating a pilot-scale turbulent Venturi jet scrubber (50 mm in diameter, 700 cm long, and having a 33-mm throat diameter of the Venturi diffuser; the ejector diameters were 3, 4, and 5 mm). The integral simulation was restricted to operating conditions where the influence of one or many of the variables of the simulation criteria—k_L, k_G, ratio of total interfacial area in the scrubber to the volumetric holdup in the scrubber, ratio of the volumetric liquid flow rate to the total interfacial area, and ratio of the volumetric gas flow rate to the total interfacial area—can be neglected. The influence of the liquid holdup in the scrubber was eliminated by employing the theory of absorption of a lean gas accompanied by an instantaneous reaction and the simulation was done for k_G and ratio of the volumetric gas flow rate to the interfacial area. Lean H_2S (0.5–4%) from air was absorbed in 1.2×10^{-3} mol/cm^3 DEA to simulate the k_G values to within 1–7%.

10.2. LIQUID–LIQUID SYSTEMS

In principle, an approach similar to that used for the gas–liquid system can be employed here, provided that the resistance to mass transfer is confined to the B phase. Thus, Sharma and Nanda (1968) have shown that a stirred cell can be satisfactorily used as a model for a spray column when extraction is accompanied by a fast second-order reaction (extraction of fast-reacting esters into an aqueous NaOH solution—this system falls in the regime between 3 and 4). However, complications are expected to arise if the resistance to mass transfer exists in both phases. Stirred cells have been used in the study of problems of extraction with reaction and it is possible to stir both phases without significantly distorting the interface. (See Table 14.2 for common values of the mass transfer coefficient and a provided by a variety of liquid–liquid contactors.)

10.3. USE OF SMALL-SCALE APPARATUS

Sharma and Mashelkar (1968) have shown that in the case of bubble columns, a small bubble column of, say, 6- to 8-cm i.d. can be satisfactorily used provided the superficial velocity of the gas is kept at the same value as in the larger columns (Figure 10.1). Similarly, in the case of packed bubble columns a smaller column can be used with the same packing as desired in the large-scale operation (Sahay and Sharma, 1973; see Figure 10.2).

In the case of mechanically agitated liquid–liquid and gas–liquid contactors, experiments can be carried out in a small-scale unit (say, 20-cm-i.d. reactor) and data so obtained can be used for scale-up. The available evidence in the literature suggests that the tip speed of the impeller is by far the most important factor (Fernandes and Sharma, 1967; Mehta and Sharma, 1971; Juvekar, 1976; see Figure 10.3).

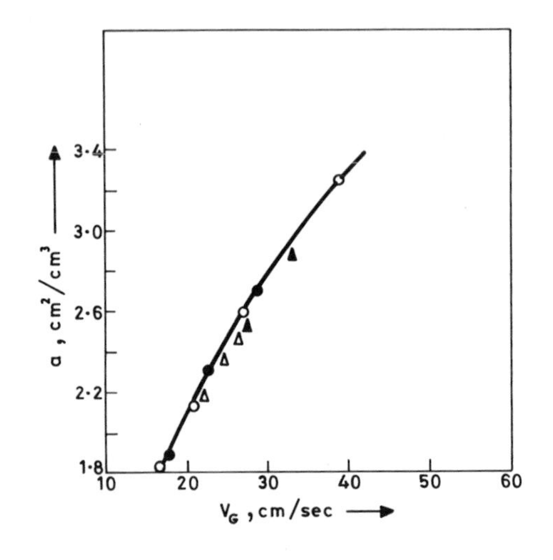

Figure 10.1. Scale-up criterion for bubble columns: plot of effective interfacial area versus superficial gas velocity.

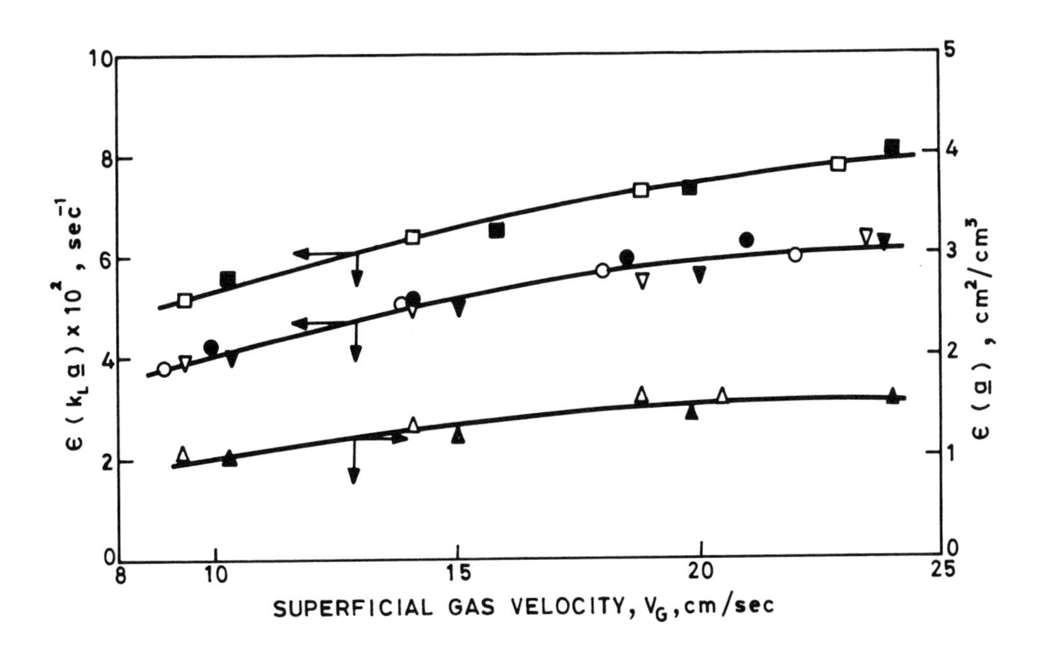

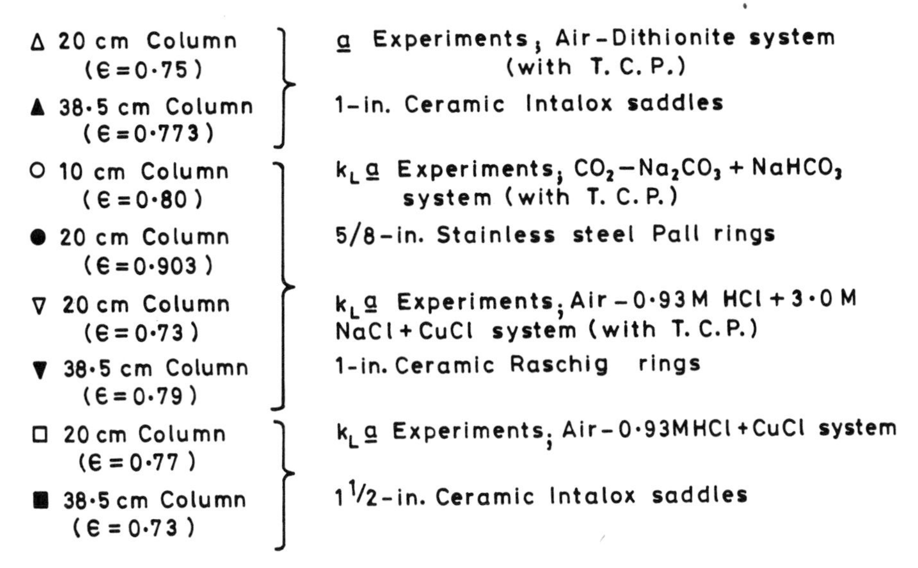

Figure 10.2. Scale-up of packed bubble columns.

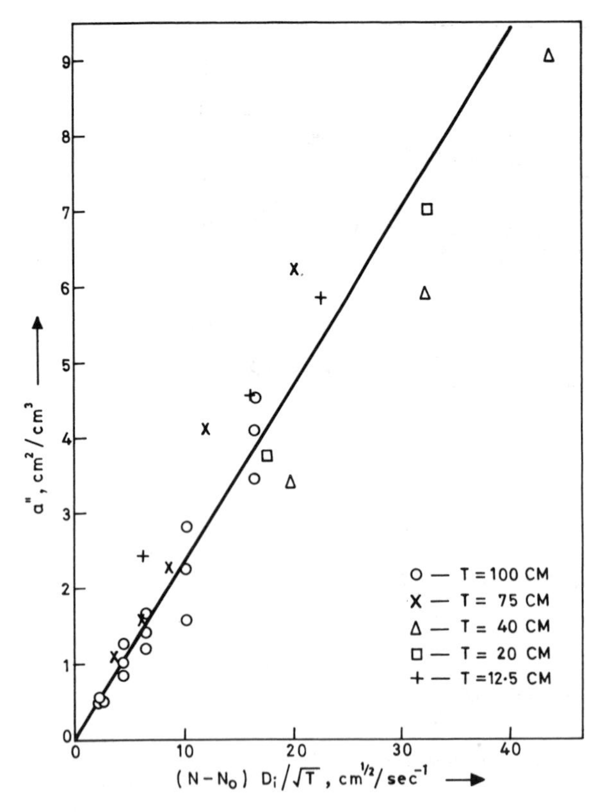

Figure 10.3. Scale-up criterion for a mechanically agitated contactor: plot of a'' versus $(N - N_0)D_i/\sqrt{T}$ (impeller: six-straight-blade disk turbine).

REFERENCES

Alper, E., and Danckwerts, P. V. (1976), *Chem. Eng. Sci.*, **31**, 599.

Andrew, S. P. S. (1961), *Alta Technol. Chim.*, p. 153.

Andrew, S. P. S. (1969), Paper presented at the "Dropping the Pilot" Symposium, Inst. Chem. Eng., London, p. 15.

Charpentier, J. C. (1978), *Adv. Chem. Ser.* **72**, 223.

Charpentier, J. C., and Laurent, A. (1974), *AIChE J.*, **20**, 1029.

Danckwerts, P. V. (1970), *Gas–Liquid Reactions*, McGraw-Hill, New York.

Danckwerts, P. V., and Alper, E. (1975), *Trans. Inst. Chem. Eng.*, **53**, 34.

Danckwerts, P. V., and Gillham, A. J. (1966), *Trans. Inst. Chem. Eng.*, **44** T42.

Danckwerts, P. V., Kennedy, A. M., and Roberts, D. (1963), *Chem. Eng. Sci.*, **18**, 63.

Danckwerts, P. V., and Sharma, M. M. (1966), *Chem. Eng., Inst. Chem. Eng.*, No. 202, CE244.

da Silva, A. T., and Danckwerts, P. V. (1968), *Proc. Symp. Tripartite Chem. Eng. Conf.* (Montreal), p. 48.

Fernandes, J. B., and Sharma, M. M. (1967), *Chem. Eng. Sci.*, **22**, 1267.

Jhaveri, A. S., and Sharma, M. M. (1968), *Chem. Eng. Sci.*, **23**, 1.

Juvekar, V. A. (1976), Studies in Mass Transfer in Gas–Liquid and Gas–Liquid–Solid Systems, Ph.D. (Tech) thesis, University of Bombay.

Laurent, A., Fonteix, C., and Charpentier, J. C. (1980), *AIChE J.*, **26**, 282.

Mehta, V. D., and Sharma, M. M. (1971), *Chem. Eng. Sci.*, **26**, 461.

Sahay, B. N., and Sharma, M. M. (1973), *Chem. Eng. Sci.*, **28**, 2245.

Sharma, M. M., and Mashelkar, R. A. (1968), *Proc. Symp. Tripartite Chem. Eng. Conf.* (Montreal), p. 10.

Sharma, M. M., and Nanda, A. K. (1968), *Trans. Inst. Chem. Eng.*, **46**, T44.

Sharma, M. M., Mashelkar, R. A., and Mehta, V. D. (1969), *Brit. Chem. Eng.*, **14**, 70.

CHAPTER ELEVEN

Solid–Liquid Reactions

A variety of solid–liquid reactions are encountered in practice. Tables 1.3 and 1.4 give examples of industrial importance for slightly soluble and insoluble solids, respectively. Some special cases, such as reactions involving ion-exchange resins as catalyst, will also be considered. There may be some distinct advantages in carrying out some homogeneous reactions with insoluble polymeric and nonpolymeric supports. Consider a case where the removal of the desired product from the reaction mixture is very difficult. If the chemical reagent were to be covalently linked to an insoluble polymeric support, then the product of the reaction would remain attached to the insoluble support and could simply be filtered from the reaction mixture; the product could then be recovered from the polymeric support and the support could be recycled. Leznoff (1974) has given a number of examples of practical importance (e.g., epoxidation, acetylation, and condensation). McKillop and Young (1979) have given a state-of-the art review on organic synthesis using supported reagents. An inorganic support, such as celite, silica, alumina, molecular sieves, or kieselguhr, will provide an increase in the effective surface area for reaction, and the presence of pores may constrain both substrate and reactant and thus lower the entropy of activation. It appears that many reactions, such as oxidation or condensation, can be carried out cleanly in relatively high yields at fairly good reaction rates using supported reagents; attempts to carry out the same reactions without any support have often failed or given poor yields. There is very limited information in the literature on the kinetics of such reactions. We shall first discuss some aspects of mass transfer associated with the liquid film on the solid surface.

There are situations in which the rates of liquid–liquid reactions are not attractive for industrial purposes because the maximal interfacial area that can be created is not high enough to give acceptable rates. It can be highly advantageous if the system happens to be of a type that can be converted to a solid–liquid reaction system, since a relatively high interfacial area can then be ensured. Consider the case of the reaction between molten phosphorus and water (in a phosphoric acid medium) to give phosphine and phosphoric acid. In processes patented by Albright and Wilson and Hooker chemicals, liquid phosphorus is emulsified in phosphoric acid and first converted into very fine particles of solid red phosphorus, which then react in a subsequent step to give phosphine and phosphoric acid (Harnisch, 1980).

Ion-exchange resins have also proved their utility as carriers of ions that can react with substances in solution. Martinola (1980) has briefly reviewed this subject and pointed out that hydrosulfite ion can be bound to anion exchangers, and this is capable of reacting with O_2. Another example that has been cited refers to the use of copper ions for reduction reaction.

11.1. MASS TRANSFER IN SOLID–LIQUID SYSTEMS

Mass transfer associated with the liquid film adjacent to solid particles is important in the areas of dissolution of solids with or without chemical reaction, reactions between insoluble solids and liquid, crystal growth, slurry and trickle-bed reactors, polymerization in the presence of solid particles as catalyst or reactant, liquid phase containing ion-exchange resins, electrochemical processes, aerobic fermentation, and so on. In fluid–fluid dispersions, whenever the size of the dispersed-phase bubbles or droplets is small (say, less than 2 mm), they tend to behave like rigid spheres. Thus data obtained from solid–liquid systems are also likely to be applicable to some cases of fluid–fluid systems.

There is a considerable amount of information in the published literature on the mass transfer coefficient in solid–liquid systems, with or without chemical reaction, in mechanically agitated contactors (Juvekar, 1971; Levins and Glastonbury, 1972a, b; Nienow, 1975; Nienow and Miles, 1978). The major difficulty in the interpretation of results arises out of our poor understanding of the hydrodynamics in mechanically agitated or gas-sparged contactors (see Sections 11.1.6 and 11.1.7). Some important aspects of mass transfer in solid–liquid systems will be discussed in this section.

When solid particles are used as catalysts, the problem of the change in particle size does not generally arise except in the case of slurry polymerization. However, when solid particles act as one of the reactants, then the size of the particles changes and this aspect should be taken into consideration.

11.1.1. Methods of Measuring the Solid–Liquid Mass Transfer Coefficient, k_{SL}

The following methods have been employed to measure values of k_{SL}: (1) solid dissolution; (2) ion exchange, (3) solid particles as catalysts; (4) electrochemical; (5) chemical; (6) moment analysis of dynamic data.

From Solids Dissolution

The solids dissolution method (Barker and Treybal, 1960; Harriott, 1962; Nienow, 1969; Brown and Coulson, 1971; Miller, 1971; Levins and Glastonbury, 1972a, b) is an obvious, and probably the simplest, method of obtaining k_{SL}. A range of particle sizes and densities can be employed, and the particles may be kept suspended by mechanical agitation or by sparging of the gas through the system. It would be preferable to use particles that are sparingly soluble in the solvent so that rapid changes in the particle size can be avoided. If solids are highly soluble and the viscosity and the density of the solution are significantly altered by the dissolved solids, then complications will arise as a result of the change in system properties.

Lemay et al. (1975) have suggested a modified method where a fluorescent dye is dissolved in the solute. This method offers two advantages: (1) The outlet concentration can be recorded continuously with a fluorometer. (2) Since the dye can be measured at concentrations as low as 10^{-11} g/cm^3, the accuracy of the analytical method becomes very high. These authors used 1 wt. % Rhodamine B in benzoic acid. Since the solubility of the dye in water is much greater than that of benzoic acid, the rate of release of the dye into the solution will be controlled by the rate of dissolution of benzoic acid.

Sometimes the extraction of a partially miscible liquid from porous particles into another liquid flowing through the system has also been employed for the measurement of k_{SL}.

In turbulent systems the value of k_{SL} becomes independent of the particle size (Harriott, 1962) and here the technique suggested by Nienow (1969), where the time required for the disappearance of the spherical particles is noted, might prove to be simple and valuable. The following relationship holds between k_{SL} and the time required for the complete dissolution of solids, t_d:

$$k_{SL} = \frac{3}{t_d \, \Delta[A] S_i} \tag{11.1}$$

(where S_i is the initial surface area per unit mass of particles and $\Delta[A]$ is the dimensionless concentration driving force $= (\omega_i - \omega_o)/(\omega_t - \omega_i)$). (Note that only in Eq. 11.1 are the units of k_{SL} g/cm^{2}sec; throughout Chapters 11, 12, and 13 units of k_{SL} will be cm/sec).

In principle, the method of the growth of solid particles suspended in supersaturated solution can also be adopted for obtaining k_{SL}. However, this method would be relatively complicated, since the temperature has to be maintained very precisely; besides, the solid–liquid film is not the only source of resistance—the surface reaction can also be the controlling factor. This method should not be considered for obtaining k_{SL}.

Use of Ion-Exchange

The technique of ion exchange (Selke et al., 1956; Calderbank and Jones, 1961; Harriott, 1962), where ions of the same charge (but of different species and having the same or a different valency) are exchanged between two phases can sometimes be conveniently employed to obtain k_{SL}. Under certain conditions the mass transfer resistance is essentially confined to the solid–liquid film (see Section 11.4). The typical ion-exchange resin size is in the range of 10–1000 μm. While conducting the experiments it should be ensured that the resistance to the transfer is confined almost entirely to the solid–liquid film. Further, if the two exchanging ions have markedly different diffusion coefficients, then an electric field will be set up in each phase and these fields will affect the diffusion process. It is necessary to account for this factor, since it can have a substantial effect on the accuracy of results (Turner et al., 1966; Turner and Snowdon, 1968).

Use of Solid Particles as Catalyst

In slurry reactors, under certain conditions, the controlling resistance may be confined to the solid–liquid film (see Section 13.1). Thus a gas may be absorbed in a medium containing suspended solid particles and the k_{SL} value may be obtained from the reaction rate data. The particle size must be based on actual measurement of a sample taken from the slurry and not on the original particle size of the catalyst. However, this method is involved and it is necessary to ensure, by doing carefully selected experiments, that no resistance other than that due to the solid–liquid film is important. This method is not recommended for obtaining k_{SL}.

Electrochemical Method

The electrochemical technique (Hubbard and Lightfoot, 1966) involves the transfer of electrically charged ions from a liquid electrolyte to the surface of a solid electrode, followed by an oxidation reaction (transfer of electrons from charged ions to the electrode) or a reduction reaction (transfer of electrons from the electrode to charged ions). This method is relatively simple and offers a number of advantages. Thus, for instance, point values of k_{SL} can be obtained even in awkward locations and the system properties can be conveniently changed over a wide range. The most common system employed in practice is that of potassium ferrocyanide–potassium ferricyanide.

Chemical Method

This method is based on the reaction between solid particles and reactive species in the liquid. Sykes and Gomezplata (1967) suspended copper particles electroplated with cadmium in an aqueous potassium iodide solution containing iodine. Iodine readily combines with iodide ions to give tri-iodide ions, which react with cadmium to form cadmium iodide. Three resistances in series are involved: (1) migration of the tri-iodide ions to the particle; (2) reaction between tri-iodide ions and cadmium; and (3) migration of the product away from the solid surface. It is possible to select experimental conditions under which the migration of tri-iodide ions to the particle becomes the controlling factor and hence k_{SL} can be obtained.

The dissolution of copper in aqueous sulfuric acid containing potassium dichromate can also be employed (Hirose et al., 1974). At sufficiently high acidity of the solution (say, in 1 M H_2SO_4) the rate of transport of dichromate ion to the copper surface becomes the controlling factor. The method appears to be fairly simple and is likely to be useful.

The dissolution of a solid accompanied by instantaneous chemical reaction can also be employed to obtain values of k_{SL}. Here it is desirable to ensure that the solubility of the solid particles in the solvent is fairly low. The theoretical aspects of this problem will be discussed in Section 11.2.

Moment Analysis of Dynamic Data

In some specific cases it is possible to obtain the value of k_{SL} by a dynamic method. Here a pulse of adsorbable tracer is introduced in a mechanically agitated slurry (slurry adsorber), containing a specified adsorbent, and the response curve of the effluent is analyzed (Furusawa and Smith, 1973). In well-mixed two-phase systems three resistances are important: (1) mass transfer from the bulk fluid to the particle surface; (2) intraparticle diffusion; and (3) adsorption at an interior site in the porous adsorbent. It is necessary that these steps be linear processes, a requirement that can be readily satisfied at low concentrations of adsorbate. A range of mean residence times and particle sizes should be covered, and these provide adequate data for the evaluation of k_{SL}. Furusawa and Smith (1973) have successfully employed this method with activated carbon particles suspended in water; benzaldehyde was used as a tracer.

Niiyama and Smith (1976) have extended the foregoing method to three-phase slurry adsorbers. Nitric oxide was adsorbed in a mechanically agitated aqueous slurry of activated carbon particles. As in the foregoing case the method is restricted to first-order processes. Niiyama and Smith (1977) have shown that an analysis of breakthrough curves from three-phase reactors can provide data on k_La and k_{SL}. Experiments were made with adsorption of O_2 in aqueous slurries of activated carbon. Ramachandran and Smith (1977) have considered the dynamic behavior of three-phase slurry reactors in terms of response characteristics of the reaction to a pulse or step input. Such an analysis can provide mass transfer data.

11.1.2. Mass Transfer in Stagnant Media

The solution of the steady-state diffusion equation in an infinite stagnant medium for a spherical particle, in the absence of free convection, shows that the Sherwood number, $k_{SL}d_p/D_A$, becomes equal to 2 (Sherwood et al., 1975). Thus, the mass transfer coefficient is inversely proportional to the particle size and directly proportional to the diffusivity of the solute. In practical situations a stagnant medium is rarely encountered, but the Reynolds number may tend to be very small and the conditions may very nearly approach that of a stagnant infinite medium. For instance, when the particle size is relatively small (say, less than 10 μm), then the value of the particle Reynolds number will be very low and approach 0. In actual practice when solid particles are used as catalysts, their size is usually greater than 50 μm and therefore the value of the Sherwood number may not be equal to 2. However, in those cases where solid particles constitute one of the reactants and fairly complete utilization of solid particles is desired, then the final particle size tends to zero.

11.1.3. Film Flow (Trickle-Bed) Reactors

The various flow regimes encountered in fixed-bed reactors will be covered in Section 13.2. Here we will consider only aspects of mass transfer associated with the solid–liquid film for the various flow regimes.

In some situations we may be concerned with mass transfer in solid–liquid systems where the solid particles, which act as reactant or catalyst, are packed in a tower (here gas is *not* passed through the column). Examples are some leaching reactions and insolubilized enzyme particles as catalyst. We also have a number of examples of practical importance where gas is passed through the column and reaction occurs between dissolved gas and liquid with solid particles acting as catalyst (e.g., hydrodesulfurization). In some cases in these three-phase systems the solid particles may also act as a reactant (e.g., the leaching of Cu with H_2SO_4 in the presence of air; reaction between dissolved SO_2 and $CaCO_3$ particles).

There is a considerable amount of information in the literature on mass transfer associated with solid–liquid film in trickle-bed reactors in the absence of gas flow. Mass transfer coefficient data have been obtained by a variety of methods. A very wide range of Reynolds numbers (based on particle diameter) has been covered. This field has been exhaustively reviewed by Upadhyay and Tripathi (1975a), Kumar et al. (1977) and Goto et al. (1977).

There is limited information in the literature on mass transfer associated with solid–liquid films in trickle-bed reactors where the gas velocity varies over a wide range. Typical values of k_{SL} range from 2×10^{-3} to 1.5×10^{-2} cm/sec for substances having a diffusivity of about 1×10^{-5} cm^2/sec and fluids like water. The published data were obtained from the dissolution of solid particles that were used as packings. The $Cu–H_2SO_4–K_2Cr_2O_7$ system has also been employed. Only a limited range of liquid and gas flow rates has been studied. There is scant information on k_{SL} in organic solvents.

Goto and Smith (1975) have studied mass transfer associated with the dissolution of β-naphthol particles (0.0541–0.241 cm in diameter) in water in a 2.58-cm-i.d. column. The range of superficial gas velocity covered by the authors was very limited (< 0.8 cm/sec). These authors found that the superficial gas velocity had an insignificant effect on the value of $k_{SL}a$. Hirose et al. (1976) have also reported k_{SL} data obtained with three different sizes of spheres in the range of 2.8–12.7 mm. Dissolution of benzoic acid as well as the $Cu–H_2SO_4–K_2Cr_2O_7$ systems were employed. These authors have also shown that the superficial gas velocity has practically no effect on k_{SL} as long as the film flow regime exists (i.e., the gas phase is the continuous phase). In some cases their superficial gas velocity was as high as about 50 cm/sec. In this regime the Sherwood number varies as the 0.5 power of the particle Reynolds number for the liquid. Satterfield et al. (1978) have used 3 mm $\times$ 3 mm and 6 mm $\times$ 6 mm cylindrical pellets of benzoic acid in a 6.96-cm-diameter column. A wide range of gas flow rate (0–1.6 kg/m^2 sec) and liquid flow rate (0.8–25 kg/m^2 sec) was covered. Further, a tenfold variation in gas density was realized by using helium, argon, and nitrogen. In the trickle flow regime the effect of the gas flow rate on k_{SL} was found to be insignificant. The recent work of Ruether et al. (1980), with 6.35-mm ($\frac{1}{4}$-in.) Berl saddles coated with a molten mixture of benzoic acid and a fluorescent dye, in a 7.6-cm-diameter column, also indicates that the effect of the gas flow rate on the k_{SL} value in the trickle flow regime is small.

There is need for further work in order to arrive at rational correlations, particularly with catalyst pellets of the sizes generally used in trickle-bed reactors and for the relevant ranges of gas and liquid flow rates for the types of fluids that are commonly encountered in practice. It would be useful to have data for the temperatures that are normally employed in practice.

It would also be desirable to ascertain the effect of a second liquid phase, immiscible with the main liquid phase, on the mass transfer characteristics.

In the case of spherical packing, the k_{SL} value can be calculated, since the hydrodynamics of the liquid flow can be characterized. In fact, as in the case of gas–liquid and liquid–liquid systems, the flow of the liquid over a solid sphere can be utilized for the measurement of diffusivity (Mashelkar and Chavan, 1973; Hirose et al., 1974).

11.1.4. Pulsing Flow Reactors

Lemay et al. (1975) have obtained values of k_{SL} in the pulsing flow regime by the modified solid dissolution procedure, which makes use of a fluorescent dye (see Section 11.1.1). Experiments were made in a 7.6-cm-i.d. column and cocurrent downward flow was adopted. For the benzoic acid–water system the k_{SL} value was found to range from 7×10^{-3} to 1.1×10^{-2} cm/sec. The value of k_{SL} increases with the 0.25 power of the power dissipation parameter. Hirose et al. (1976) have also covered this regime and have reported k_{SL} values that are higher than those obtained in the film flow regime. Here the value of k_{SL} depends on the superficial gas velocity. A major part of the improvement in $k_{SL}a_p$ over the film flow regime value appears to be due to a higher effective solid–liquid interfacial area. The increase in the k_{SL} value over that in the single-phase flow regime is approximately equal to the reciprocal of the liquid holdup.

The pulsing flow regime has also been covered by Satterfield et al. (1978). Their results indicate that a transition from a trickle to a pulse flow regime results in increasing the value of k_{SL} by a factor as high as 2.6, and that k_{SL} is dependent on the gas flow rate. Ruether et al. (1980) have also found that the gas flow rate affects the k_{SL} value. However, the k_{SL} value does not depend on the gas density explicitly if correlated in terms of an energy dissipation function.

Ruether et al. (1980) have correlated k_{SL} data for different flow regimes in terms of a modified Reynolds number and a modified Sherwood number, utilizing an average actual liquid velocity and actual effective interfacial area. The characteristic dimension of the packing was assessed to be that of a sphere having the same surface area; the effect of the gas velocity was assessed on the basis of the variation in the liquid holdup.

Recently Chou et al. (1979) have measured the local particle–liquid mass transfer coefficient in the pulsing flow regime by the electrochemical method involving potassium ferricyanide-ferrocyanide solutions. Experiments were made in a 15.2-cm-i.d. column provided with 7.8-mm-diameter alumina spheres. Their results show that complete wetting of the packings occurs upon transition to the pulsed flow regime. Further, the time-averaged local coefficients are comparable to the volume-averaged results of other investigators. The fluctuations in the value of the mass transfer rate are not very high. (The root mean square of the fluctuation was around 38% of the average.)

11.1.5. Packed Bubble Column Reactors

Mochizuki and Matsui (1974) have reported some data on the k_{SL} in a packed bubble column. Experiments were carried out in an 8.7-cm-i.d. column provided with 5 mm × 5 mm cylinders (fractional voidage = 0.335) and the k_{SL} was obtained by the electrochemical method (one active platinum cylinder 5 mm × 5 mm was used). The column was operated cocurrently with upward flow. The following observations were made:

1. At zero gas flow rate the Sherwood number (Sh) is proportional to the square root of the particle Reynolds number (Re based on liquid properties) at higher values of Re. At zero liquid flow rate the limiting value of the Sh was found to be 2.7.
2. At lower values of the liquid Re the Sh was primarily a function of the gas flow rate ($Sh \propto Re_G^{0.25}$) and the liquid flow rate had practically no effect. It is therefore clear that the gas flow rate affects the k_{SL} value significantly.

Hirose et al. (1976) have also covered this regime; they found the enhancement in the k_{SL} value over the single-phase flow to be approximately equal to the reciprocal of the liquid holdup. Hofmann (1978, 1982), has reviewed the subject of mass transfer in packed bubble column reactors.

11.1.6. Liquid Fluidized-Bed and Spouted-Bed Reactors

Liquid Fluidized-Bed Reactors

We may encounter situations where the mass transfer in liquid fluidized beds is important (e.g., fluidized-bed ion exchange). There is limited information in the literature on this subject. Damronglerd et al.

(1975) have studied the dissolution of benzoic acid pellets in water in a 94-mm-i.d. contactor. The particle size was varied from 4.61 to 8.19 mm and the particle Reynolds number from about 200 to 1300. These authors have reviewed the previous work. Upadhyay and Tripathi (1975a) have also reviewed the previous work in this area.

The work of Damronglerd et al. clearly establishes that the trend of the variations of $\mathrm{Sh\,Sc}^{-1/3}$ versus ϵ (void fraction) changes completely for a particular value of the bed void fraction ($\epsilon \simeq 0.815$; $\mathrm{Re\,Ga}^{-1/2} = 0.405$)

$$\mathrm{Sh} = 0.763\epsilon^{-1.20}\mathrm{Re}^{0.556}\mathrm{Sc}^{1/3} \qquad (\epsilon < 0.815) \tag{11.2}$$

$$= 0.268\epsilon^{-2.40}\mathrm{Re}^{0.669}\mathrm{Sc}^{1/3} \qquad (\epsilon > 0.815) \tag{11.3}$$

Their data can also be successfully correlated with Ga (the Galileo number) as a parameter:

$$\mathrm{Sh} = 0.301\mathrm{Re}^{0.038}\mathrm{Ga}^{0.305}\mathrm{Sc}^{1/3} \qquad (\mathrm{Re\,Ga}^{-1/2} < 0.405) \tag{11.4}$$

$$= 0.138\mathrm{Re}^{-0.086}\mathrm{Ga}^{0.412}\mathrm{Sc}^{1/3} \qquad (\mathrm{Re\,Ga}^{-1/2} > 0.405) \tag{11.5}$$

The reasons for the fairly sharp change at an ϵ of 0.815 (or $\mathrm{Re\,Ga}^{-1/2}$ of 0.405) are not clear but are likely to be connected with the bed behavior, as is evident from the fact that the variations of ϵ with Re also show similar trends.

Equations 11.4 and 11.5 show that for a given system and a specified particle size, the influence of Re on Sh is very weak, and this may well have some important implications from a practical point of view. Upadhyay and Tripathi (1975b) have also found that the mass transfer coefficient for a specified particle size is practically independent of the Reynolds number. Recent work of Tournie et al. (1979) shows that Sh is practically independent of Re. These authors have also exhaustively reviewed the previous work on this subject. An important conclusion emerges from this study, namely, that k_{SL} is practically independent of d_p and the superficial liquid velocity.

The region of low particle Reynolds numbers (Re < 10), which is not uncommon in practice, has not been adequately covered (Rowe, 1975).

Spouted-Bed Reactors

Spouted beds can handle mixed sizes of particles and even large particles can be satisfactorily suspended. In spouted beds the particles undergo frequent accelerations and decelerations as they circulate within the contactor, and the relative velocity within the contactor between the particles and liquids is very large. Consequently we can expect high k_{SL} values in spouted beds. Thus it may be advantageous to employ spouted beds in some reaction systems involving liquid–solid and gas–liquid–solid reactions. Nishikawa et al. (1976) have studied mass transfer in a 15-cm-i.d. spouted bed that was provided with a nozzle having a diameter of 1.3 cm; the cone angle was 60°. The benzoic acid–water and $Cu–K_2Cr_2O_7–H_2SO_4$ systems were employed to obtain the k_{SL}.

The k_{SL} value was independent of the particle size over a wide range. (The overall range was about 200–2000 μm.) Further, the k_{SL} varied as the square root of the superficial liquid velocity in the range of 0.4–3 cm/sec. In the range of variables covered by these authors the k_{SL} value varied from approximately 0.008 to 0.02 cm/sec. The effect of aeration on the k_{SL} value was also studied. This effect is rather complex, and the k_{SL} value may initially increase with an increase in the superficial gas velocity and then decrease. In the range covered by these authors the maximum k_{SL} value was about 20% higher than that obtained in the absence of the gas flow.

It appears that relatively high k_{SL} values are obtained in the spouted bed and at the same Reynolds number the values of k_{SL} provided by a single sphere, fluidized bed, fixed bed, and spouted bed are in the ratio of 1 : 1.5 : 3 : 7.5. In the case of the $Cu–K_2Cr_2O_7–H_2SO_4$ system, where copper particles are suspended, considerably higher power will be required to provide the same k_{SL} value in a mechanically agitated contactor than that required in the spouted-bed reactor. It appears that on the basis of minimum power consumption, spouted beds are very attractive as compared with fluidized beds and mechanically agitated contactors, particularly for systems where the difference between the density of the solid particles and the liquids is large.

11.1.7. Bubble Column Reactors

Gas-sparged solid–liquid contactors are sometimes employed in practice. Here the gas agitates the liquid phase and thus keeps the solid particles in uniform

TABLE 11.1. Mass Transfer in Solid–Liquid Systems: Bubble Column Reactors

Systems Studied	Technique	$\frac{h_t}{T}$	Characteristics of Sparger: Hole Dia. (mm)	Characteristics of Sparger: Hole Area (%)	Superficial Gas Velocity (cm/sec)	Characteristics of Solid Particles: d_p (μm)	Characteristics of Solid Particles: $(\rho_p - \rho_L)$ (g/cm^3)	Correlations	Reference
Benzoic acid–water	Solid dissolution	0.7–2.7	0.5–4.0	0.03–1.48	0.1–37	2000–7500	0.27	[a]	Yoshitome et al. (1964)
α-Naphthol–water, β-naphthol–water, H-type resin–water, Na-type resin–water	Solid dissolution, ion exchange	2–9	—	—	0.2–10	100–10000	0.18–0.52	$\frac{k_{SL} d_p}{D_A} = 2.0 + 0.212 \times \left(\frac{d_p^3 \Delta\rho g}{\mu_L D_A}\right)^{1/3} \times \left(\frac{d_p V_G \rho_L}{\mu_L}\right)^{0.112} \left(\frac{V_G}{V_L}\right)^{0.33}$	Kobayashi and Saito (1965)
Benzoic acid–water, calcium carbonate–water, barium carbonate–water, lead iodide–water	Solid dissolution	—	0.5–2	0.024–0.156	—	5–60	0.27–5.16	$\frac{k_{SL} d_p}{D_A} = 0.72 \times \left[\frac{(P/V)^{5/12} \rho_L^{5/6} d_p^{5/3}}{\mu_L^{5/4}}\right]^{1/2} \times \left(\frac{\mu_L}{\rho_L D_A}\right)^{1/3}$ [a]	Kawamura et al. (1966)
Copper–acidic solution of potassium dichromate	Dissolution controlled by mass transfer of dichromate ion to the solid surface	2.4–8.2	[a]	[a]	1.0–15	—	—		Patil and Sharma (1983)

[a] Original reference may be consulted.

suspension. There is little information in the literature on solid–liquid mass transfer in bubble column contactors. Table 11.1 lists some of the important investigations. The following conclusions can be drawn in light of the available information: (1) The size of the particles that are usually employed in bubble columns is small (10–15 μm). For such small particles the Sherwood number approaches a value of 2. (2) For coarser particles the most important variable deciding the solid–liquid mass transfer coefficient is the gas velocity. It is generally observed that k_{SL} is a function of the gas velocity up to a certain critical value of that velocity, after which it remains essentially constant. (3) The characteristics of the gas distributor seem to have a significant effect on the k_{SL} at low gas velocities, but the exact nature of this effect has not yet been investigated. At higher gas velocities (say, greater than about 5 cm/sec) the design of the gas distributor appears to be unimportant.

In some cases the amount of fine solid particles may be relatively high and we may have a three-phase fluidized bed with slug flow of the gas. Such a situation is encountered in the carbonation of a slurry of lime in a bubble column (Juvekar and Sharma, 1973). There is practically no information on the mass transfer coefficient in such systems.

11.1.8. Mechanically Agitated Reactors

Two types of theories have been advanced to correlate the data on mass transfer for solid–liquid systems in mechanically agitated contactors (Juvekar, 1971; Levins and Glastonbury, 1972a, b; Nienow, 1975; Nienow and Miles, 1978): slip velocity theories and Kolmogoroff's theory of local isotropic turbulence. Table 11.2 lists the important correlations that have been proposed.

TABLE 11.2. Mass Transfer in Solid–Liquid Systems: Mechanically Agitated Reactors

		Characteristics of the Contactor			
Systems Studied	Technique	T (cm)	Type of Impeller	Impeller Speed Range (rev/min)	Baffled or Unbaffled
Phthalic anhydride–water, benzoic anhydride–water	Solid dissolution	10	Four blade paddle	150–1000	Unbaffled, baffled
Benzoic acid–water, benzoic acid–sucrose solution, sodium chloride–brine, boric acid–water, boric acid–sucrose solution	Solid dissolution	15,30 15,75	Six-flat-blade turbine	200–1000	Unbaffled, baffled
Ion-exchange resin (Zeocarb 266)–sodium hydroxide solution	Ion exchange	—	—	100–700	Baffled
Benzoic acid–water, benzoic acid–aqueous glycerol, o-salicyclic acid–water	Solid dissolution	15	Six-flat-blade turbine	—	Baffled

Slip Velocity Theories

The slip velocity is defined as the bulk fluid velocity relative to the particle. In a practical situation the bulk fluid velocity varies from point to point and is a function of the design of the agitator. Thus it is difficult to estimate the average fluid velocity. Calderbank and Jones (1961) have suggested that the terminal velocity of a particle in a still fluid may be taken as the slip velocity. On the basis of this observation a recommendation has been made for estimating k_{SL} (see Table 11.2). This equation would be expected to hold near the point of particle suspension, where gravity forces are predominant. (The agitator speed at which particle suspension occurs can be estimated by the method of Zwietering, 1958.) However, the equation suggested by Calderbank and Jones is unlikely to hold at speeds much above the value at which the particles suspension occurs. Harriott (1962), Schwartzberg and Treybal (1968), and Nienow (1969) have suggested other methods to estimate the slip velocity.

Nienow and Miles (1978) have made measurements of the k_{SL} over a very wide range of operating conditions with six-blade disk turbines, two-blade flat paddles, and four-blade 45°-pitch turbines in 14- and 28-cm-diameter closed vessels. Their extensive data clearly indicate that under conditions when particles are just fully suspended, the k_{SL} values are practically the same. However, to achieve just full suspension with these types of agitators a 30-fold variation in the specific power consumption was observed. Thus it is clear that the mass transfer coefficient under conditions of just fully suspended particles is definitely independent of power consumption.

In general it is desirable to use larger impellers with a small clearance from the bottom of the vessel, since these designs consume less power than other

Characteristics of Solid Particles				
d_p (μm)	ρ_p (g/cm^3)	$(\rho_p - \rho_L)$ (g/cm^3)	Correlation	Reference
10–1590	—	0.46	$\frac{k_{SL} D_i}{D_A} \propto \left(\frac{D_i^2 N \rho_L}{\mu_L}\right)^{p} \left(\frac{\mu_L}{\rho_L D_A}\right)^{q}$ [a] $p = 0.36\left(\frac{\rho_p - \rho_L}{\rho_L}\right)^{0.22} \times \left(\frac{d_p}{D_i}\right)^{-0.23}$ $q = 0.48\{\log\left[\left(\frac{\rho_p - \rho_L}{\rho_L}\right) + 0.043\right] + 1.35\}10^{-13.5 d_p/D_i}$	Nagata et al. (1959)
—	—	0.06–0.99	$\ln(10 k_{SL}) = (I_1 \text{ or } I_2) + 0.85 V^{0.02875}$ [a, b] $\times \ln\left(\frac{\pi D_i^2 N \rho_L}{\mu_L} \times 10^{-4}\right)$ $I_1 = 0.676 - 1.266 V^{1/3}$ $(T < 15 \text{ or } T > 75 \text{ cm})$ $I_2 = 0.8235 - 1.544 V^{1/3} + 0.115 V^{2/3}$ $(15 < T < 75 \text{ cm})$	Barker and Treybal (1960)
900	—	0.174–0.184	$k_{SL}\left(\frac{\mu_L}{D_A \rho_L}\right)^{2/3} = 0.31\left[\frac{(\rho_p - \rho_L)\mu_L g}{\rho_L^2}\right]^{1/3}$	Calderbank and Jones (1961)
—	—	—	$\frac{k_{SL} T}{D_A} = 0.332\left(\frac{\mu_L}{D_A \rho_L}\right)^{1/3}\left(\frac{N D_i^2 \rho_L}{\mu_L}\right)^{1/2}$	Marangozis and Johnson (1961)

TABLE 11.2. ***(Continued)***

Systems Studied	Technique	Characteristics of the Contactor: T (cm)	Type of Impeller	Impeller Speed Range (rev/min)	Baffled or Unbaffled
Ion-exchange resin–Sodium hydroxide, benzoic acid–water, boric acid–water, lead sulfate–water, zinc–dilute hydrochloric acid	Ion-exchange, solid dissolution	10	Six-flat-blade turbine	150–600	Baffled
Cadmium–polyiodide solution	Reaction of tri-iodide ion and cadmium on plated particles	14	Fan-disk turbine, propeller,	200–600	Baffled
Ice–brine	Simultaneous heat and mass transfer	—	Three-blade marine impeller	300	Baffled
Pivalic acid–water	Solid dissolution	12.2	Turbine, marine propeller	100–400	Unbaffled, baffled
Potassium sulfate–water, ammonium chloride–water, ammonium alum–water, sodium chloride–water, potassium chloride–water	Solid dissolution	14	Four- and six-blade turbines	200–2000	Baffled
Ion-exchange resins–aqueous acids and bases, copper–polyiodide solution, aluminum nitrate–ethanol, stearic acid–ethanol, naphthalene–methanol	Solid dissolution, ion exchange, reaction of tri-iodine ion and copper on plated particles	12.6–25.0	Flat-blade turbine, Curved-blade turbine, 45°-pitch-blade turbine, marine propeller	—	Baffled, unbaffled
Sodium chloride–water	Solid dissolution	14.3–28.6	Disk turbine, two-blade flat paddle, four-blade 45°-pitch turbine	180–1500	Baffled
Benzoic acid–water	Solid dissolution	9,19, 29,40 63.4	Six-bladed disk turbine	—	Baffled
Copper–acidic solution of potassium dichromate	Dissolution controlled by mass transfer of dichromate ion to the solid surface	30.5,100	Six-bladed disk turbine, pitch blade turbine, curved blade turbine, propeller	40–1200	Baffled

Characteristics of Solid Particles				
d_p (μm)	ρ_p (g/cm^3)	$(\rho_p - \rho_L)$ (g/cm^3)	Correlation	Reference
10–1000	—	0.006–6.14	[a]	Harriott (1962)
3000	1–1.25	0.05–0.3	$\frac{k_{SL} d_p}{D_A} = 2 + 0.109\left(\frac{N D_i^2 \rho_L f}{\mu_L}\right)^{0.38} \times \left(\frac{\mu_L}{D_A \rho_L}\right)^{0.5}$ [c]	Sykes and Gomezplata (1967)
700–2500	—	(−0.05)–(−0.09)	[a]	Brian and Hales (1969)
700–2500	0.8–1.25	—	[a]	Brian et al. (1969)
200–8000	1.99–2.66	0.53–1.59	[a]	Nienow (1969)
30.8–1953	0.8–8.43	0.01–7.13	$\frac{k_{SL} d_p}{D_A} = 2.0 + 0.47 \times \left(\frac{d_p^{4/3} \epsilon_p^{1/3} \rho_L}{\mu_L}\right)^{0.62} \times \left(\frac{D_i}{T}\right)^{0.17} \left(\frac{\mu_L}{\rho_L D_A}\right)^{0.36}$ (for low $\rho_p - \rho_L$) $\frac{k_{SL} d_p}{D_A} = 2.0 + 0.44 \times \left(\frac{d_p u_R \rho_L}{\mu_L}\right)^{1/2} \left(\frac{\mu_L}{\rho_L D_A}\right)^{0.38}$ (for high $\rho_p - \rho_L$) [a]	Levins and Glastonbury (1972a, b)
2230	1.198	—	[a]	Nienow and Miles (1978)
—	—	—	$\mathrm{Sh} = 0.046\,\mathrm{Re}^{0.283}\mathrm{Ga}^{0.173} \times u^{-0.011} (T/d_p)^{0.019} \times \mathrm{Sc}^{0.461}$	Boon-Long et al. (1978)
—	—	—	[a]	Patil (1982)

[a] Original references may be consulted.
[b] Here k_{SL} (ft/hr) and V (ft^3) are in FPS units.
[c] $f = (N_p / N_{p_{FDT}})^{1/3}$, where $N_{p_{FDT}}$ is the power number for fan–disk turbine.

configurations. A proper selection of impeller type and dimensions should be made to achieve the desired k_{SL} values at the lowest power consumption.

Boon-Long et al. (1978) have also studied the k_{SL} in 9- to 63.4-cm-diameter mechanically agitated contactors provided with six-blade disk turbines whose diameter is one-third that of the contactor. These authors have given a correlation based on the Reynolds number, Galileo number, Schmidt number, and so on.

The presence of gas can make considerable difference to the choice of operating conditions to achieve full suspension of particles (Subba Rao and Taneja, 1979). There is need for further work in this area when three phases are encountered.

Kolmogoroff's Theory of Local Isotropic Turbulence

We are concerned with a situation where the gravity effect is negligible, that is, the speed of agitation is substantially greater than that required to ensure particle suspension.

Turbulent flow produces primary eddies that have a scale similar in magnitude to the dimensions of the main flow stream. These primary eddies are unstable and disintegrate into smaller eddies until all their energy is dissipated by the viscous flow. In the process of the disintegration of the eddies the directional nature of primary eddies is gradually lost. Thus, if a volume of fluid is considered whose dimensions are small compared to the scale of the main flow, then there exists isotropic turbulence, that is, the fluctuating components of the fluid velocity in all directions are equal. Kolmogoroff concluded that all eddies that are much smaller than the primary eddies are statistically independent of them, and that the properties of these small eddies are determined solely by the local energy dissipation per unit mass of fluid. The mean square fluctuating velocity over a distance d_p in the turbulent fluid field where $L_e \gg d_p \gg r_e$ (L_e is the scale of primary eddies and r_e that of the smallest eddies) is given by the following equation:

$$\bar{u}^2_{(d_p)} \propto \left(\frac{P}{V}\right)^{2/3} \left(\frac{d_p}{\rho}\right)^{2/3} \qquad (11.6)$$

where P/V represents power input per unit volume of the fluid. Calderbank and Moo-Young (1961) have suggested the use of $\sqrt{\bar{u}^2_{(d_p)}}$ as a slip velocity for a particle of diameter d_p.

The key factor in making use of this approach lies in having an accurate knowledge of the power input per unit volume of the system (P/V). In general, for the common types of agitators and liquids the value of P/V can be estimated with reasonable accuracy. When the concentration of solids is fairly high the effect of the presence of solids on the value of P/V should be taken into consideration.

Some doubts have been expressed about the application of Kolmogoroff's theory. Cutter (1966) has suggested, on the basis of indirect measurements, that the local rate of energy dissipation varies by several orders of magnitude throughout the stirred tank and thus the use of an average P/V does not appear to be completely rational. Further, Kolmogoroff postulated that the energy dissipation in the main stream is negligible, which implies that practically no mass transfer occurs in the region close to the impeller, where the primary eddies are created. However, it appears that significant mass transfer occurs in the region of primary eddies. Nienow (1975) has pointed out that plots based on the dimensionless groupings obtained from this theory are unsatisfactory because of the swamping effects that arise as a result of the very wide range of particle size as compared to the limited range of the other variables. There are also reasons to believe that equal power input does not yield equal values of k_{SL}. It was pointed out earlier that Nienow and Miles (1978) have clearly established that under conditions when particles are just fully suspended, the value of k_{SL} does not change over a 30-fold variation in the specific power consumption.

When the impeller speed is between the two regions (close to the particle suspension and far from the speed required for particle suspension, so that isotropic turbulence exists), then the correlation of mass transfer data becomes difficult. Such cases are likely to be common in practice. Further, the presence of a gas is also likely to result in a different correlation.

Shrinking and Transpiration

Shrinking and transpiration effects are observed in a solid–liquid system where the solid is highly soluble in the liquid (or is continuously consumed by the reaction with the liquid) and the density of the solid is significantly different from that of the liquid.

The effect of shrinking is observed when the dissolving particle shrinks at a very fast rate so that the rate of transport is a strong function of time. Because of the density difference between the diffusing solute and the liquid, there will be bulk flow of liquid to the particle surface or away from the particle surface in a radial direction; this is called transpiration. Brian and Hales (1969) have theoretically evaluated the effect of particle shrinking and transpiration.

Effect of Operating Variables. The following are some of the important conclusions that can be inferred from the available data:

1. It is desirable to use impellers the ratio of whose diameter to that of the tank ranges from 0.5 to 0.6 rather than from 0.3 to 0.4. Further, the clearance of the impeller from the bottom of the tank should be kept small. (It should be less than 20% of the height of the liquid and less than the impeller diameter.) The 45°-pitch turbine impeller or propeller are attractive types of agitators.
2. At impeller speeds at which particle suspension just occurs, the k_{SL} value is approximately constant for any particular system and is independent of the geometry of the vessel, the design of the impeller, and the specific power consumption. (Here the equation based on slip velocity theory can be used.)
3. The functional dependence between k_{SL} and the speed of agitation depends on the regime of agitation.
4. In the turbulent regime the k_{SL} value is independent of particle size.
5. When the impeller speed is close to the speed required for the suspension of particles, k_{SL} will be a fairly strong function of the difference between the density of the solid particles and that of the fluid. In the turbulent regime, however, k_{SL} would be practically independent of this factor.
6. The relationship between k_{SL} and the diffusivity of the dissolved solute can give us some meaningful information about the applicability of various theories. However, the range of diffusivities covered by the various authors for any specified solvent is very limited. In most cases the diffusivity was varied by increasing the viscosity of the solvents by the addition of some highly viscous materials. However, this change affects the hydrodynamic conditions. Further, when the viscosity is greater than 4 cP the estimation of the diffusivity becomes somewhat unreliable. (In most cases the value of the diffusivity was estimated on the assumption that $D\mu_L/T'$ = constant.) Further work is desirable in this area.
7. The terminal velocity–slip velocity approach seems to be more satisfactory except for situations where the difference between the density of the particle and that of the liquid medium approaches zero. In the disk turbine type of impeller, both the Kolmogoroff and terminal-velocity–slip-velocity theories predict practically the same k_{SL} value. The correlation proposed by Levins and Glastonbury is recommended (Nienow, 1975).

Example 1

An aqueous slurry containing 5×10^{-2} g/cm^3 of solid-free liquid of 324 μm potassium sulfate particles and rest water is agitated in a 60-cm-i.d. mechanically agitated contactor at a temperature of 25°C. A six-blade disk turbine 20 cm in diameter is used for this purpose. The height of the liquid in the tank is 60 cm and the clearance of the impeller from the bottom of the vessel is 20 cm. Calculate the

(a) minimum impeller speed required for the complete suspension of solids;
(b) solid–liquid mass transfer coefficient at this impeller speed;
(c) rate of dissolution of the solids at this impeller speed.

Data

D_A, diffusivity of K_2SO_4 in water,

$$= 9.9 \times 10^{-6} \text{ cm}^2/\text{sec}$$

μ_L, viscosity of the solution, = 1.01 cP

ρ_L, density of the solution, = 1.08 g/cm^3

ρ_p, density of K_2SO_4, = 2.66 g/cm^3

Solubility of K_2SO_4 in water = 0.12 g/g of solution

Bulk concentration of K_2SO_4 in water

$$= 0.09 \text{ g/g of solution}$$

Solution

(a) The minimum impeller speed, N_m, required for the complete suspension of solids is given by the following equation (Zwietering, 1958):

$$N_m = \frac{s\nu^{0.1} d_p^{0.2} (g\,\Delta\rho/\rho_L)^{0.45} (X)^{0.13}}{D_i^{0.85}} \quad (11.7)$$

where s is a constant given by the following equation (Nienow, 1968):

$$s = 2\left(\frac{T}{D_i}\right)^{1.33} \quad \text{for } \frac{D_i}{T} = \frac{h_c}{h_t} = \frac{1}{3}$$

$$= 2\left(\frac{60}{20}\right)^{1.33} = 8.62 \quad (11.8)$$

and X is the weight percentage of solids:

$$X = \frac{50 \times 100}{(1000 \times 1.08) + (50)}$$

$$= 4.425$$

Thus

$$N_m = \frac{8.62\left(\dfrac{1.01 \times 10^{-2}}{1.08}\right)^{0.1} (3.24 \times 10^{-2})^{0.2}}{(20)^{0.85}}$$

$$\times \left(\frac{981 \times 1.58}{1.08}\right)^{0.45} (4.425)^{0.13}$$

$$= 6.850 \text{ rev/sec} \quad (411 \text{ rev/min})$$

(b) The Sherwood number at the point when complete suspension of particles occurs is given by the following equation (Nienow, 1969):

$$\text{Sh} = 2 + 0.72\,\text{Re}^{1/2}\text{Sc}^{1/3} \quad (11.9)$$

where

$$\text{Re} = \frac{d_p u_t \rho_L}{u_L} \quad (11.10)$$

The terminal settling velocity for particles less than 500 μm in size is given by the following equation (Perry, 1950):

$$u_t = \frac{0.153 g^{0.71} d_p^{1.14} (\Delta\rho)^{0.71}}{\rho_L^{0.29} \mu_L^{0.43}}$$

$$= \frac{0.153(981)^{0.71}(3.24 \times 10^{-2})^{1.14}(1.58)^{0.71}}{(1.08)^{0.29}(1.01 \times 10^{-2})^{0.43}}$$

$$= 3.98 \text{ cm/sec} \quad (11.11)$$

Therefore,

$$\text{Re} = \frac{3.24 \times 10^{-2} \times 3.98 \times 1.08}{1.01 \times 10^{-2}}$$

$$= 13.8$$

$$\text{Sc} = \frac{\mu_L}{\rho_L D_A} = \frac{1.01 \times 10^{-2}}{1.08 \times 9.9 \times 10^{-6}}$$

$$= 945$$

Therefore,

$$\text{Sh} = 2 + 0.72(13.8)^{1/2}(945)^{1/3}$$

$$= 28.3$$

$$k'_{SL} = \frac{\text{Sh}\, D_A}{d_p} = \frac{28.3 \times 9.9 \times 10^{-6}}{3.24 \times 10^{-2}}$$

$$= 8.65 \times 10^{-3} \text{ cm/sec}$$

This value is to be corrected for the effect of turbulence in the liquid. The correction factor is obtained from Figure 7 (p. 255) of Nienow's paper (Nienow, 1969) and is

$$\frac{k_{SL}}{k'_{SL}} = 1.15$$

$$k_{SL} = 1.15 \times 8.65 \times 10^{-3}$$

$$= 9.95 \times 10^{-3} \text{ cm/sec}$$

(c) The rate of dissolution of K_2SO_4 is obtained from the following equation:

$$R_A^+ = k_{SL}([A_s]^+ - [A_o]^+)$$

$$= 9.95 \times 10^{-3}(0.12 - 0.09) \times 1.08$$

[Note that 1.08 (the density of the solution) is the conversion factor for the concentration of A from g/g of solution to g/cm³ of solution. Further, the units of R_A^+ are g/cm² sec.]

$$= 3.22 \times 10^{-4} \text{ g/cm}^2 \text{ sec}$$

$$a_p = \frac{6w}{\rho_p d_p} = \frac{6 \times 0.05}{2.66 \times 3.24 \times 10^{-2}}$$

$$= 3.48 \text{ cm}^2/\text{cm}^3 \text{ of solid-free liquid}$$

Therefore, the total rate of dissolution is

$$R_A^+ a_p V = 3.22 \times 10^{-4} \times 3.48 \times \left[\frac{\pi}{4}(60)^3\left(\frac{1000}{1000 + 50/2.66}\right)\right]$$

$$= 1.87 \text{ g/sec}$$

Example 2

Calculate the solid–liquid mass transfer coefficient (k_{SL}) in a mechanically agitated contactor for catalyst particles (d_p = 100 μm, ρ_p = 1.08 g/cm³) suspended in an aqueous solution (ρ_L = 1.0 g/cm³) under the following conditions:

Impeller speed = 200 rev/min
Vessel diameter = 60 cm
Impeller diameter = 20 cm
Impeller type: six-straight-blade disk turbine
Viscosity of solution = 1 cP
Diffusivity of solute in solution, $D_A = 2 \times 10^{-5}$ cm²/sec

Solution. Since the density of the catalyst particles is nearly equal to the density of aqueous phase ($\Delta\rho$ = 0.08 g/cm³), the method of calculation based on the slip velocity theory is not recommended and the method proposed by Levins and Glastonbury will be used (1972a, b):

$$\frac{k_{SL} d_p}{D_A} = 2 + 0.47\left(\frac{d_p^{4/3}\epsilon_p^{1/3}}{\nu}\right)^{0.62}\left(\frac{D_i}{T}\right)^{0.17}\left(\frac{\mu_L}{\rho_L D_A}\right)^{0.36} \quad (11.12)$$

The power input

$$P = N_p \rho_L N^3 D_i^5 \quad (11.13)$$

where

$$N = \frac{200}{60} = 3.33 \text{ rev/sec}$$

$$N_p = \text{power number}$$

$$= 6 \quad \text{(Rushton et al., 1950)}$$

Hence,

$$P = 6 \times 1 \times (3.33)^3 \times (20)^5$$

$$= 7.09 \times 10^8 \text{ erg/sec}$$

The power input per unit mass of liquid

$$\epsilon_p = \frac{7.09 \times 10^8}{(\pi/4)(60)^2 \times 60 \times 1} = 4.18 \times 10^3 \text{ erg/g sec}$$

$$d_p = 1 \times 10^{-2} \text{ cm}$$

$$\nu = 1 \times 10^{-2} \text{ cm}^2/\text{sec}$$

$$D_i = 20 \text{ cm}$$

$$T = 60 \text{ cm}$$

Therefore,

$$k_{SL} = \frac{2 \times 10^{-5}}{10^{-2}} \times \left\{2 + 0.47\left[\frac{(1 \times 10^{-2})^{4/3}(4.18 \times 10^3)^{1/3}}{1 \times 10^{-2}}\right]^{0.62} \times \left(\frac{20}{60}\right)^{0.17}\left(\frac{1 \times 10^{-2}}{2 \times 10^{-5}}\right)^{0.36}\right\}$$

$$= 1.98 \times 10^{-2} \text{ cm/sec}$$

(The slip velocity theory predicts a k_{SL} value of 8.91×10^{-3} cm/sec. It is clear that this value is very different from the one predicted by the method proposed by Levins and Glastonbury (1972a, b). As pointed out at the outset, the value obtained from the method proposed by Levins and Glastonbury should be considered representative.)

11.1.9. Horizontal Pipeline Reactors

In some situations we may be concerned with solid–liquid mass transfer in horizontal pipeline contactors. Further, we may also have three-phase systems. For instance, aerobic treatment of wastewater and sewage in pipeline contactors is under consideration. Pipeline reactors have been suggested for the manufacture of zinc dithionite, which involves the reaction between SO_2 and suspended zinc particles in water (Szabo and Kaldi, 1976), and of aluminum trialkyl, which involves reaction between aluminum particles suspended in a suitable solvent (Lobo, 1961). Pipeline reactors have also been suggested for the leaching of low-grade ores. There is a dearth of data in the literature on solid–liquid mass transfer in such systems.

11.1.10. Non-Newtonian Systems

The problem of solid–liquid mass transfer in non-Newtonian liquids is of some practical importance. A number of liquid effluents from industry exhibit non-Newtonian characteristics. Sometimes these effluents are treated in trickling filters that are microbially coated. The transport of oxygen through the film is coupled with an effective microbial reaction at the solid surface, and when this reaction is particularly rapid the overall transport rates may be governed by mass transport at the solid–non-Newtonian liquid surface. In recent years attention has been given to the hydrogenation of polymeric particles, suspended/dissolved in suitable solvents, in the presence of Raney nickel or Pd/C catalysts (Falk, 1976). Here resistance associated with the solid–liquid film (non-Newtonian liquid) may be encountered. There is very limited information on this subject, particularly experimental, where the influence of rheology on solid–liquid mass transfer processes has been examined. Mashelkar and Chavan (1973) have examined the problem of solid–liquid mass transfer from a falling film of a non-Newtonian liquid. Their work indicated that pseudo-plastic fluids yield higher mass transfer rates than the Newtonian fluids. These effects, however, are marginal and it is unlikely that rheology will significantly influence the solid–liquid mass transfer rates in the range of practical interest. Kumar et al. (1978) have reviewed some aspects of mass transfer in such systems.

11.2. SOLID–LIQUID REACTIONS: SOLIDS SPARINGLY SOLUBLE

Solid dissolution accompanied by chemical reaction is of some industrial importance. There are cases of sulfonation and nitration where some solid aromatic substances, which are slightly soluble in the medium, are involved. Table 1.3 lists some examples. The literature provides considerable information on the dissolution of sparingly soluble acids in aqueous alkaline solutions, primarily as a part of the study of mass transfer in solid–liquid systems.

Consider the reaction

$$\mathrm{A}(s) + Z\mathrm{B}(l) \rightarrow \text{products}$$

The analysis of this problem can be made in the same way as in the case of fluid–fluid reactions (Chapter 2; see also Nagata et al., 1959; Marangozis et al., 1963). Thus the four regimes will also be encountered here. However, complications arise when we are in the regime where part of the reaction occurs in the liquid film adjacent to the solid–liquid interface and part in the bulk liquid phase (i.e., the regime between 2 and 3). Further, in the case of instantaneous reactions, neither the film theory nor the penetration theory may hold and the situation can probably be better described by the boundary layer theory. Insofar as the fast reaction regime (regime 3) is concerned, there is no difference between the predictions based on various theories. In the case of the regime between 3 and 4, where the concentration of the reactive species B at the interface is substantially lower than that in the bulk, the calculations for the enhancement factor can be made in the same way as outlined in Section 2.7, but the value of ϕ_a should be calculated from the following equation rather than from Eq. 2.112:

$$\phi_a = 1 + \frac{[\mathrm{B_o}]}{Z[\mathrm{A}^*]}\left(\frac{D_\mathrm{B}}{D_\mathrm{A}}\right)^{2/3} \qquad (11.14)$$

In this section we shall also consider a special case where we have a solid–liquid reacting system but the solid is insoluble and there is diffusion of B accompanied by chemical reaction (dyeing with reactive dyes; see Section 11.2.3).

11.2.1. Solid Dissolution Accompanied by Reaction: Only Part of the Reaction Occurs Very Near the Interface

Vieth et al. (1963) have considered this problem on the basis of the turbulent boundary layer theory. The predicted values of the enhancement factor were found to be in close agreement with those obtained from the film and penetration theories. This is to be expected, since even in the case of gas–liquid and liquid–liquid systems, the differences between the predictions based on the film, Higbie's penetration, and Danckwerts' surface renewal theories are insignificant (see Section 2.4). Further, as pointed out earlier, for $\sqrt{M}$ greater than 3, all theories give the same answer (namely, $\phi = \sqrt{M}$).

11.2.2. Solid Dissolution Accompanied by Instantaneous Reaction

This problem has been considered by a number of authors primarily for the purpose of testing the applicability of the boundary layer theory (Sherwood and Ryan, 1959; Marangozis et al., 1963; Meyerink and Friedlander, 1962). Marangozis and Johnson (1961) made a study in a diaphragm cell as well as in a mechanically agitated contactor. Their results agree with the predictions based on the boundary layer theory corrected for ion-diffusion effects. Baldi and Specchia (1976) have also considered some aspects of solid dissolution accompanied by an instantaneous reaction.

In most cases the rate of dissolution was found to vary as the 2/3 power of D_B/D_A (provided that $[B_o] \gg [A^*]$). However, the range of D_A covered in the literature is rather narrow (only about a factor of 2–3 in any specified medium), and hence there is a need to cover a much wider range of D_B before firm conclusions can be drawn regarding the relationship between the rate of dissolution and D_B/D_A.

Sadasivan et al. (1968) have studied the dissolution of acid particles in a packed bed under the conditions of turbulent flow of aqueous caustic alkali solutions.

11.2.3. Examples

Very Slow Reaction (Regime 1)

Reaction Between Terephthalic Acid* (TPA) *and Ethylene Oxide. In the established process for making polyethylene terephthalate, the monomer bis(2-hydroxyethyl) terephthalate (BHET) is usually made by the reaction between dimethyl terephthalate and ethylene glycol. However, with the availability of fiber-grade TPA, attention has been given to the manufacture of BHET by reaction between TPA and ethylene oxide in the presence of various types of catalysts. This process is potentially attractive. Bhatia et al. (1976) have studied the kinetics of the reaction between suspended TPA particles and ethylene oxide dissolved in *n*-butanol in the presence of triethylamine as a catalyst in the temperature range of 60–100°C. A 2-liter Parr autoclave was used. It was found that varying the stirring speed from 600 to 1000 rev/min and particle size from 0.127 to 0.280 mm had no effect on the rate under otherwise similar conditions. This implies that mass transfer factors associated with the dissolution of TPA were unimportant. The reaction was controlled by the homogeneous reaction between dissolved TPA and ethylene oxide. The value of the activation energy was found to be between 19.3 and 21.6 kcal/mol.

Kobayashi and Ichikawa (1975) have also studied the kinetics of this esterification reaction batchwise in an autoclave, in a solvent catalyzed by an amine. These authors have also found that for this heterogeneous reaction, the chemical reaction is rate controlling in the temperature range of 120–200°C.

Hydrolysis of Phthalic Anhydride / Maleic Anhydride. Nagata et al. (1959) have studied the hydrolysis of phthalic anhydride particles in a 10-cm-i.d. agitated vessel provided with a 5-cm four-blade paddle agitator. Agitation speeds in the range of 250–650 rev/min had practically no effect on the rate of reaction. The calculated average value of the first-order rate constant at 25°C of 0.01 sec^{-1} was the same as the previously published value. In view of this very low rate constant value, it can easily be shown that diffusional factors will be unimportant in the foregoing experiments. (Even with the very conservative value of $k_{SL}a_p$ of 0.2 sec^{-1} the necessary condition for the validity of the very slow reaction regime, regime 1, will be satisfied.)

Specchia and Baldi (1975) have also studied the hydrolysis of phthalic anhydride and maleic anhydride at temperatures of 20–40°C in a CSTR. A 10.3-cm-i.d. contactor was used; on the reactor wall a cavity 2 mm deep and 5 cm high was provided for keeping the solid reactant. Mass transfer factors were found to be unimportant. Their first-order rate constant values agree with previously published values

(Bunton et al., 1963).

Solid–Liquid Phase Transfer Catalysis **(S–L PTC).** Benzyl esters are manufactured by reaction between benzyl chloride and suspended solid particles of sodium carboxylate in the presence of triethylamine as a catalyst.

$$RCOONa(s) + C_6H_5CH_2Cl(l)$$
$$\rightarrow RCOOCH_2C_6H_5(l) + NaCl(s)$$

It appears that instead of triethylamine, the use of phase transfer catalysts like quaternary ammonium or phosphonium salts, crown ethers, cryptates, diamines, or polyamines may be far more beneficial (Weber and Gokel, 1977; Starks and Liotta, 1979). Such catalysts bound to insoluble resins such as cross-linked polystyrene, known as triphase catalysts, are also likely to be attractive (Regen, 1979).

Recently, Yadav and Sharma (1981) have studied the kinetics of the solid–liquid phase-transfer-catalyzed reaction of benzyl chloride with solid sodium acetate and/or benzoate in the presence of a variety of tertiary amines and quaternary ammonium salts at 101°C in a 10-cm-i.d. mechanically agitated contactor. The kinetics of this solid–liquid reaction has certain unique features. The diffusional factors were found to be unimportant beyond a speed of 1000 rev/min, as could be seen from the effect of the speed of agitation (1000–2500 rev/min) and particle loading (7–33% w/w; particle size of 5 μm) on the rate of reaction per unit volume of the liquid phase. The rate of reaction was found to vary linearly over a 20-fold range of the catalyst concentration (the maximum catalyst concentration was 5 mol % of the substrate concentration). The locale of the reaction was the organic phase, and the reaction was found to be first order in benzyl chloride as well as the catalyst.

In the case of tertiary amines, the catalysis was due to the generation of a quaternary ammonium salt (Q^+X^-) *in situ*. The quaternization reaction as well as the reaction of the quaternary salt (Q^+X^-) with the dissolved solid reactant (M^+Y^-) to generate a reactive ion pair (Q^+Y^-) of the quaternary cation and the nucleophile were found to be very fast as compared with the reaction of benzyl chloride with (Q^+Y^-). The following mechanism was found to hold in this system, which is amenable to phase transfer catalysis (see Section 3.1.16):

$$NR'_3 + RX \rightarrow (R'_3RN^+X^-)$$
$$(\equiv Q^+X^-)$$
$$(Q^+X^-) + (M^+Y^-) \rightleftharpoons (Q^+Y^-) + (M^+X^-)$$
$$RX + (Q^+Y^-) \rightarrow RY + (Q^+X^-)$$
$$\text{(product)}$$

(The parentheses denote the "loose" ion pairs; MY is the solid reactant.)

The rate of reaction was found to increase with an increase in the polarity of the medium. The kinetic studies were made in the temperature ranges of 90–110°C and 101–140°C, for toluene and benzyl acetate as solvents, respectively. The apparent energy of activation for the reaction of benzyl chloride with solid sodium acetate in the presence of cetyldimethylbenzylammonium chloride (CDMBAC), the most efficient catalyst found among those studied, including triethylamine, was estimated as 14.5 kcal/mol. The value of the second-order rate constant for this reaction at a CDMBAC concentration of 5.9×10^{-5} mol/cm^3 at 101°C was found to be 8.1 cm^3/mol sec.

Reduction of Solid Aromatic Nitro Compounds with Aqueous Solutions of Sodium Sulfides. In Section 3.1.14 we considered the example of the reduction of aromatic nitro compounds with Na_2S_x in a liquid–liquid system. In some cases solid aromatic nitro compounds are encountered (e.g., *m*-dinitrobenzene). Bhave and Sharma (1981) have studied the reduction of solid *m*-dinitrobenzene particles to *m*-nitroaniline by aqueous solutions of sodium sulfide in a 10-cm-i.d. mechanically agitated contactor at 60°C. The product *m*-nitroaniline is also a solid. The particle size of *m*-dinitrobenzene was varied in the range from 40 to 60 μm. There was no effect of speed of agitation on the rate of reduction per unit volume of aqueous phase in the range of 600–1200 rev/min. The average sodium sulfide concentration was about 0.2 *M* and the average loading of solids about 7% w/w of total charge. Further, there was no effect of dispersed-phase fraction on the rate of reduction per unit volume of aqueous phase in the range of 0.05–0.25 (w/w of total charge). Here the speed of agitation was 1200 rev/min and the average sodium sulfide concentration 0.2 *M*. These results indicate that diffusional resistance was absent and that the reduction reaction was limited by the kinetics. The second-order rate constant value was found to be about 1000 cm^3/mol sec.

For this system, it is conceivable that at higher temperatures and/or higher sulfide concentrations the controlling regime would shift from regime 1 to regime 2 and then to regime 3. Thus, at higher temperatures the value of the second-order rate constant may be such that the mass transfer is accompanied by a fast pseudo-first-order reaction (regime 3).

Reaction of Solid Phosphorus Pentoxide with Alcohols. Hugo and Schaper (1980) have reported a study of the kinetics of the reaction between solid P_2O_5 particles and alcohols such as *n*-butanol and *n*-octanol in solvents like carbon tetrachloride, ethylene dichloride, and trixylenyl phosphate.

$$P_2O_5 + 3ROH \rightarrow PO(OH)_2OR + PO(OH)(OR)_2$$

They have shown that at temperatures higher than −50°C the reaction is mass transfer controlled.

Fast Reactions (Regime 3)

Dissolution of Sparingly Soluble Esters and Acetals Accompanied by Hydrolysis in an Alkaline Medium. The dissolution of sparingly soluble solid esters and acetals accompanied by hydrolysis in an alkaline medium has been studied under such conditions that a fast reaction occurred and the value of $\sqrt{M}$ was greater than 3 (Sharma, 1969; Sharma and Sharma, 1970a, b). Thus, knowing the solubility of the ester and its diffusivity, we can calculate the value of the second-order rate constant in the same manner as for the liquid esters (see Section 3.4.13). The following materials were studied: di-β-chloroethyl oxalate, dicyclohexyl oxalate, dimethyl fumarate, methyl *p*-nitrobenzoate, ethyl *p*-nitrobenzoate, and benzylidene diacetate.

Experiments were carried out in a 2.5-cm-i.d. glass bubble column where a single pellet of the ester with an area of about 3.7 cm^2 was kept in a fixed position. The pellet was kept submerged in the liquid and agitation was provided by sparging nitrogen. The superficial gas velocity was varied from 6.25 to 25 cm/sec and it was found that the rate of dissolution at a specified concentration of NaOH was independent of the superficial gas velocity. This indicates that the hydrodynamic factors were unimportant. Since the value of $\sqrt{M}$ was greater than 3 and the reactions are first order in A as well as B, the specific rate of mass transfer is given by

$$R_A = [A^*]\sqrt{D_A k_2 [OH^-]} \qquad (11.15)$$

The calculated values of the rate constant agreed reasonably well with those reported in the literature or assessed on the basis of the available information.

In the case of benzylidene diacetate (m.p. 45°C) and ethyl *p*-nitrobenzoate (m.p. 57°C) experiments were made at temperatures higher than their melting point in a liquid–liquid stirred cell. The values of the rate constant obtained by the foregoing method when extrapolated to the temperature at which solid dissolution experiments were carried out gave very good agreement between the two sets of values.

In the case of slower-reacting esters no reaction might occur in the film and the system may conform to regime 2 or 1.

Nitration of Solid Aromatic Compounds. Nitration of acetylated *p*-toluidine is carried out industrially to give the *m*-nitro compound. Here dissolution of the solid particles is accompanied by chemical reaction. There is no information in the literature on the rate constant for this specific compound. However, on the basis of the published information on the rate constant for a variety of substances (see Section 3.17) it can be shown that under industrial conditions the dissolution of the acetylated product is likely to be accompanied by a fast reaction. This mechanism is also likely to hold for the nitration of naphthalene and acetylated *p*-anisidine.

Dissolution of Phthalic Anhydride in Aqueous Carbonate Buffer Solutions and Aqueous Solutions of Sodium Hydroxide. We have already discussed, under the very slow reaction category, the dissolution of phthalic anhydride in water. Specchia and Baldi (1975) have studied the reaction of solid phthalic anhydride in aqueous potassium carbonate–bicarbonate buffered solutions. The first step in this reaction, resulting in the formation of $HOOCC_6H_4COO^-$, is the rate-controlling one and follows pseudo-first-order kinetics. (The second step, for the conversion of $HOOCC_6H_4COO^-$ to $^-OOCC_6H_4COO^-$, is instantaneous, being basically a neutralization reaction involving ions.) Under conditions employed by these workers the reaction conformed to regime 3 and enhancement factors up to 15 were found.

Specchia and Baldi (1975) have also made measurements of the dissolution of phthalic anhydride in aqueous solutions of sodium hydroxide under conditions such that the system conformed to the depletion regime (regime between 3 and 4).

Manufacture of Isocyanates. Isocyanates based on amines (such as toluene diamines and 4,4′-diaminodiphenyl methane) are manufactured on a large scale as intermediates for urethanes. Here a heterogeneous system, with the reaction between solid particles and a liquid-phase reactant, is involved. The solid particles may be in the form of the amine hydrochloride or carbomyl chloride (Twitchett, 1974; Tsigin and Konstantinov, 1979). (Attempts have also been made to make isocyanates via reaction between solid particles of sodium cyanate and RCl.) There is little information in the literature on the kinetics of such reactions. Tsigin and Konstantinov (1979) have made a study with aniline and *p*-chloroaniline hydrochlorides in a toluene medium containing dissolved phosgene. It is clear from their work, where the temperature was varied from 55 to 90°C, that the particle size has a profound effect on the rate of phosgenation under otherwise comparable conditions. Thus it is clear that diffusional factors are important. Values of rate constants are apparently not available, and therefore, it is not possible to give a clear indication of the controlling regime.

Special Cases

Separation of Isomeric Chlorobenzoic Acids and Chloroxylenols by Reaction with a Stoichiometric Deficiency of Aqueous NaOH

Chlorobenzoic acids. *o*-Chloro- and *p*-chlorobenzoic acids (CBA) have practically the same boiling points, and hence their separation by distillation may not be practicable. However, there is a substantial difference in the ionization constant of these two acids (*o*-CBA = 1.2×10^{-3}, *p*-CBA = 1.04×10^{-4} g ion/liter at 25°C) and the technique of dissociation extraction (discussed in Section 6.6) may be employed to separate these isomers. Laddha and Sharma (1978) have worked with this system and have shown that a mixture containing 61% *p*-CBA and 39% *o*-CBA when contacted with a stoichiometric deficiency of aqueous 0.2 *N* NaOH at 27°C can enrich it to 87% *p*-CBA in a single stage. Further, at a higher temperature of 60°C still better enrichment can be obtained, and in fact in one stage almost pure *p*-CBA can be obtained. The higher selectivity at 60°C can be attributed to the relatively higher solubility of *o*-CBA, which also happens to be the stronger acid.

p-Chloro-m-xylenol and 2,4-dichloro-m-xylenol. The separation of *p*-chloro-*m*-xylenol (PCMX) and 2,4-dichloro-*m*-xylenol (DCMX) provides yet another instance where dissociation extraction can be employed. Here also the separation can be attempted in a solid–liquid as well as a liquid–liquid system. (The latter system was considered in Section 6.6.) A separation factor of 10 was obtained at 27°C with a 60% PCMX and 40% DCMX mixture with a stoichiometric deficiency of 1 *N* NaOH. In the case of a liquid–liquid system with di-*n*-butyl ether as a solvent and a stoichiometric deficiency of 1 *N* NaOH, a separation factor of about 5 was obtained by Wadekar and Sharma (1981) (see Section 6.6.3).

Dissolution with Reaction of Silver Halides in Aqueous Systems. In the photographic industry the dissolution of undeveloped silver halide in aqueous solutions of sodium thiosulfate is very important and has received much attention. However, it is not known unambiguously whether the process is controlled by the formation of the silver thiosulfate complex or by the diffusion of thiosulfate. Shiao et al. (1975) have studied the dissolution rates of a liquid–silver halide dispersion in an agitated system. The dissolution rate of AgX was measured by directly monitoring the rate of formation of the soluble Ag^+–ligand complex. Aqueous alkaline gelatin solutions containing excess ligands such as ethanolamines, glycine, and thiosulfate were used. The initial dissolution rates were found to be independent of the crystal habit of AgX but increased in direct proportion to the effective surface area and its apparent solubility product. The activation energy for a AgBr–sodium thiosulfate system was found to be 6.4 kcal/mol. From the foregoing it is clear that diffusional factors are important and it appears that the diffusion of complexed Ag^+ at the surface into the bulk of the solution is the controlling step.

Dyeing of Cellulosic Fabrics with Reactive Dyes. Reactive dyes are now widely employed for the dyeing of a variety of cellulosic fibers. Here a reactive group in the dye reacts with cellulose O^- (cellulosate ions) and thus the dye becomes an integral part of the cellulose. This is an interesting example of great practical interest since here instead of solid dissolution accompanied by chemical reaction we have the uptake of reactive species B on cellulose accompanied by chemical reaction. It will be shown that diffusion of the dye into the cellulosic material is accompanied by a chemical reaction with the cellulosate ion in parallel and we have interaction between diffusion and chemical reaction in a way somewhat similar to the case of the dissolution of A accompanied by a fast chemical reaction (regime between 2 and 3) (see Sections 2.4 and 3.5).

It is assumed that the primary hydroxyl group in each anhydroglucose unit of cellulose reacts with the reactive dye in preference to the other two secondary hydroxyl groups.

Preston and Fern (1961), Sumner and Weston (1963), Rattee and Breuer (1974), and Peters (1975) have discussed this subject. Experiments have been made in a flow system with a viscose film where freshly mixed dye and alkali flowed past the film. The rate of uptake of dye by the film as a function of the time of reaction was measured by the optical density method.

A typical reactive dye, Procion Brilliant Red 2B, has the following structure:

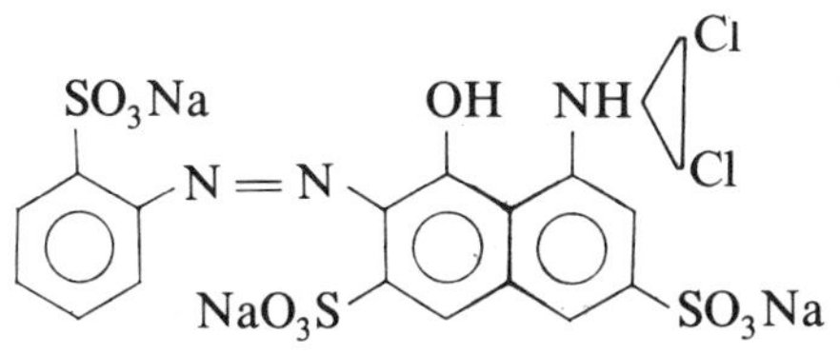

SO_3Na OH NH–(Cl, Cl)

N=N

NaO_3S SO_3Na

where

{ (Cl, Cl) stands for triazine ring $-C$ with N–C(Cl), N=C(Cl) }

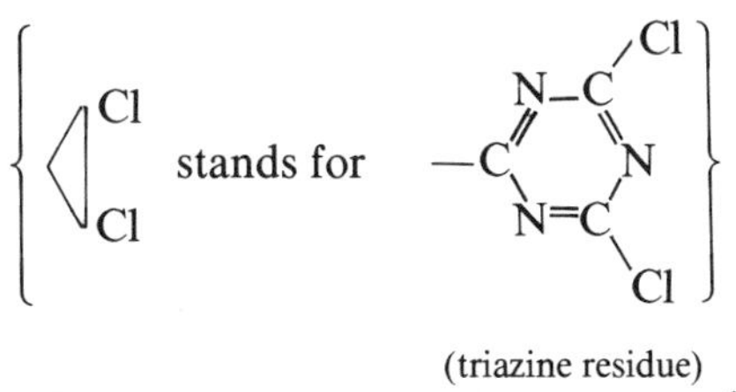

(triazine residue)

In the dyeing process usually one —Cl or (Cl, Cl) reacts with cellulose O^-. This —Cl is also capable of hydrolyzing and reacting with OH^-.

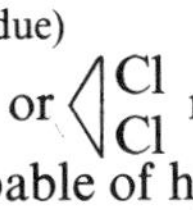

It is most interesting that Eq. 2.65, which holds for the regime between 2 and 3 (i.e., a part of the reaction occurs while A is diffusing and the rest occurs in the bulk), was applied. This equation, written in the form of the amount reacted per unit area as a function of time, is as follows:

$$Q = [B^*]\sqrt{D_B k_1}\left(t + \frac{1}{2k_1}\right) \qquad (11.16)$$

(Here [B*] is the equilibrium surface concentration of the dye.) Linear plots of Q against t were obtained. These linear plots show clearly that the fixed dye (i.e., reacted dye) is wholly responsible for the measured rates, since normal diffusion of the dye would have given the hyperbolic curve.

Equation 11.16 holds under somewhat simplifying conditions which imply that the dye bath is maintained at a constant dye concentration and there is a uniform concentration of OH^- in the fiber prior to the entry of the dye.

The value of the equilibrium surface concentration was assessed by making measurements with two *inactive* forms of the dye under a range of alkaline conditions. (Since the reactive dye undergoes reaction under alkaline conditions, the value of the equilibrium surface concentration of this dye cannot be experimentally measured.) The value of the diffusion coefficient of the dye, D_B, was also measured experimentally.

Under alkaline conditions the extent of side reaction with OH^- will be quite small because the equilibrium surface concentration of dye would be expected to be about 20–100 times greater than in the water. Further, the pK of cellulose is lower than that of water, which will further reduce the extent of the reaction with OH^-. The importance of diffusion coupled with chemical reaction can also be seen from the fact that in its absence the surface saturation would limit the amount of dye that can be fixed. A typical value of $k_{\text{cellulose O}^-}$ is in the range of $3\text{–}12 \times 10^{-3}\ \text{sec}^{-1}$. Typical diffusivity values of reactive dyes at 30°C lie in the range of $1.5\text{–}25 \times 10^{-8}\ \text{cm}^2/\text{sec}$. Motomura and Morita (1977) have recently suggested a method of estimating D_B and k_1 from the diffusion profiles of both immobilized and active species of reactive dyes obtained by using a cylindrical cellophane film.

The rate of dyeing as well as the extent of the reaction of the dye with OH^- are of practical importance because the former will decide whether dyeing can be completed in an economic time and the latter will be a direct reflection on the efficiency of the dyeing. The value of k_1 varies from dye to dye (perhaps by as much as a factor of 10) and D_B is also a function of $[B^*]/[B_o]$ (where $[B_o]$ is the concentration of the dye in the solution). (In the field of dyeing the ratio of [B*] to $[B_o]$ is also referred to as the substantivity ratio.) Thus high values of k_1 and $[B^*]/[B_o]$ and low values of the rate constant of the dye with OH^- are conducive to faster and more efficient dyeing. The value of $[B^*]/[B_o]$ is by far the most important parameter. Thus, for instance, by using neutral salts the value of $[B^*]/[B_0]$ can be increased and this should have a favorable effect on the rate of dyeing.

11.3. SOLID–LIQUID REACTIONS: SOLIDS INSOLUBLE IN THE MEDIUM

Solid–liquid reactions where the solids are not soluble in the medium will be considered in Section 12.2, the only difference being that the resistance associated with the transfer of A does not exist. Some examples pertaining to this category will be covered in Section 12.2.3.

11.4. SYSTEMS INVOLVING ION-EXCHANGE RESINS

Ion-exchange operation is used in industry for water softening, the recovery of metals from industrial wastes, the separation of rare earths, and the like. Ion-exchange resins are also used as catalysts for a variety of organic reactions catalyzed by H^+ or OH^- ions. Since these catalysts are in the form of solids, they can be readily separated from the reaction mixture. Further, continuous operation in columns is possible. It is also likely that the purity of the product is superior to that obtained with homogeneous catalysts. Typical examples where ion-exchange resins can be used as catalysts are the hydration of olefins, conversion of epoxides to the corresponding glycols, alkylation of phenols and substituted phenols with isobutylene, aldol-type reactions, inversion of sugar, oligomerization of isobutylene, esterification reactions, and reactions between butenes and acetic acid (Martinola, 1980). The recent availability of resins based on perfluorosulfonic acid (e.g., Nafions of Du Pont in the United States) has had considerable impact, since these resins can withstand higher temperatures.

Helfferich (1962) has discussed various aspects of the foregoing problems. We shall cover this subject very briefly, confining our attention to the role of diffusional factors in the use of ion-exchange resins.

In an ion-exchange process, ions of the same charge, but of different species, are exchanged between two phases. Usually ion-exchange substances are polymerized resins in the form of solids. The ion-exchange process is inherently a stoichiometric one. Because of the electroneutrality requirement, any ions that leave the ion exchanger should be replaced by an equivalent amount of other counterions. In most of the cases that have been studied so far the rate-determining step was established to be the diffusion of the counterions. The resistance to mass transfer may be confined to both phases, although in many practical cases one or the other may be dominant. Thus the rate-controlling steps are

1. Interdiffusion of counterions within the ion-exchange particles (particle diffusion);
2. Interdiffusion of counterions in the liquid film adjacent to solid particles (film diffusion);
3. Surface reaction (chemical reaction at the particle surface).

The following procedure may be adopted in order to determine the controlling mechanism in the absence of a second fluid phase:

1. In a mechanically agitated contactor, a film-diffusion-controlled process will be considerably affected by the agitation. A particle-diffusion-controlled process will be essentially independent of the speed of the agitator beyond a certain minimum speed required to keep a uniform concentration of ions in the liquid phase. It should, however, be established by independent experiments, or it should be known unambiguously, that in the range of the speed of the agitator covered, the value of the mass transfer coefficient increases with an increase in the speed of agitation (see Section 11.1.8).
2. The rate of a film-diffusion-controlled process will be inversely proportional to the particle diameter (it is usually assumed that resin particles are spherical in shape) under otherwise uniform conditions. By contrast, the rate of a particle-diffusion-controlled process will be inversely proportional to the square of the particle diameter. This point is applicable only under those conditions in which the value of the liquid-film mass transfer coefficient becomes independent of the particle size. In any case, it is clear that for particle-diffusion-controlled processes the particle diameter will have a marked effect on the rate of reaction.
3. The concentration of the solution will have a direct effect on the rate of a film-diffusion-controlled process. On the other hand, par-

ticle-diffusion-controlled processes will be independent of the solution concentration.

4. A convenient and good method for discerning the controlling mechanism, referred to as the *interruption test*, was suggested by Helfferich (1962). In this test the resin particles are removed from the solution for a brief period and are then reimmersed. In the brief period of interruption the concentration gradients in the resin particles disappear. Thus it would be expected that with a particle-diffusion-controlled process the rate soon after the reimmersion would be greater than that just prior to the interruption. In the case of a film-diffusion-controlled process, there are no concentration gradients in the resin particles; hence interruption and reimmersion of particles will have practically no influence on the rate of the process.
5. At low particle Reynolds numbers, the k_{SL} value will be inversely proportional to the particle size, and hence the rate will vary inversely as the square of the particle size for a film-diffusion-controlled system. The surface-reaction-controlled system will show the rate of reaction to be inversely proportional to the particle size.
6. The controlling mechanism can be unambiguously established by varying the catalyst ion concentration (e.g., by partial replacement of the catalytically active counterion by an inactive one). The surface-reaction-controlled system will show a direct dependence of the rate on the catalyst ion concentration, but in the case of a film-diffusion-controlled system the rate will be independent of the catalyst ion concentration.

Presence of a Second Fluid Phase

When a heterogeneous (gas–liquid or liquid–liquid) reaction is catalyzed by an ion-exchange resin, an additional resistance associated with the transfer of the solute may become important. Such cases can be treated like slurry or trickle-bed reactors (see Chapter 13).

Nernst–Planck Model

It is possible for the two exchanging ions to have substantially different diffusion coefficients. In such cases an electric field that will affect the diffusion processes will be set up in each phase. The Nernst–Planck model can account for these effects. An important implication of this effect will be that the rate of reaction will become markedly composition dependent. Further details can be obtained from the book by Helfferich (1962) and papers by Turner et al. (1966) and Turner and Snowdon (1968).

Examples

Esterification Reactions

There are distinct advantages of employing ion-exchange resins (rather than mineral acids, such as sulfuric acid) as catalysts for esterification reactions: The construction material problem is less severe and —more important—there is no need to wash the product in the reactor to get rid of the acid catalyst. A number of investigations have been made, and two examples will be discussed.

Bochner et al. (1965) have studied the esterification of salicylic acid with methanol in 3- and 5-liter reactors using the acid form of a sulfonated polystyrene–divinyl benzene ion-exchange resin [Dowex 50-W (X-8) in H^+ form]. There was no effect of the stirring speed on the rate of reaction, and therefore external mass transfer (transfer of reactants to the catalyst surface) resistance is unimportant. Further, a change in the particle size from 200–400 mesh to 50–100 mesh had no effect, which clearly indicates that intraparticle diffusion is also not rate controlling. (This observation regarding the effect of particle size provides additional support for the absence of external mass transfer resistance.) Thus the rate is controlled by kinetic factors.

Kekre and Gopalrao (1969) have studied the esterification of acetic acid with *n*-butanol in a 1-liter reactor using Dowex 50-W (in H^+ form) as the catalyst. These authors also found, on the basis of the insignificant effect of the stirring speed on the rate, that the external mass transfer resistance is unimportant. It was observed that the rate increased with a decrease in the particle diameter from 0.768 mm to 0.410 mm. Additional experiments were carried out with different resin cross-linkages. These experiments indicated that with nearly the same catalyst concentration and particle size, the rate increased substantially with a decrease in the resin cross-linkage. Thus the surface reaction kinetics as the controlling step can be ruled out. Therefore, intraparticle resistance (pore diffusion) appears to be the rate-controlling factor.

Triphase Catalysis

Phase transfer catalysis in two-phase systems was discussed in Section 3.1.16. Triphase catalysis (TC) has recently been introduced as a separate class of heterogeneous catalysis in which the solid catalyst and each of a pair of liquid-phase reactants are located in separate phases (Regen, 1979). Cross-linked polystyrene resins and silica gel are used for insolubilizing synthetically important catalysts and reagents, and the catalysts are categorized on the basis of the nature of the active sites, namely, ion-exchange groups, crown ethers and cryptands, and cosolvents. Therefore, this technique is also called immobilized solid-phase transfer catalysis. All the polymers that have proven active as triphase catalysts reside at the liquid–liquid interface. A variety of synthetic applications have been listed by Regen (1979) with 42 references. The catalyst activity is demonstrated by the reaction of the cyanide ion with 1-bromo- and 1-chlorooctane in water–benzene systems, using a cross-linked polystyrene resin-based catalyst. Some ephedrinium-based chiral triphase catalysts are used for making asymmetric compounds.

REFERENCES

Baldi, G., and Specchia, V. (1976), *Chem. Eng. J.*, **11**, 81.

Barker, J. J., and Treybal, R. E. (1960), *AIChE J.*, **6**, 289.

Bhatia, S., Gopala Rao, M., and Rao, M. S. (1976), *Chem. Eng. Sci.*, **31**, 427.

Bhave, R. R., and Sharma, M. M. (1981), *J. Chem. Tech. Biotechnol.*, **31**, 93.

Bochner, M. B., Gerber, S. M., Vieth, W. R., and Rodger, A. J. (1965), *Ind. Eng. Chem. Fundam.*, **4**, 314.

Boon-Long, S., Laguerie, C., and Couderc, J. P. (1978), *Chem. Eng. Sci.*, **33**, 813.

Brian, P. L. T., and Hales, H. B. (1969), *AIChE J.*, **15**, 419.

Brian, P. L. T., Hales, H. B., and Sherwood, T. K. (1969), *AIChE J.*, **15**, 727.

Brown, D. E., and Coulson, J. M. (1971), in Sherwood, J. N., Chadwick, A. V., Muir, W. M., and Swimton, F. L. (Eds.), *Diffusion Processes*, Vol. 2, Gordon & Breach, New York.

Bunton, C. A., Fuller, N. A., Perry, S. G., and Shiner, V. J. (1963), *J. Am. Chem. Soc.*, **85**, 2918.

Calderbank, P. H., and Jones, S. J. R. (1961), *Trans. Inst. Chem. Eng.*, **39**, 363.

Calderbank, P. H., and Moo-Young, M. B. (1961), *Chem. Eng. Sci.*, **16**, 39.

Chou, T. S., Worley, F. L., and Luss, D. (1979), *Ind. Eng. Chem. Fundam.*, **18**, 279.

Cutter, L. A. (1966), *AIChE J.*, **12**, 35.

Damronglerd, S., Couderc, J. P., and Angelino, H. (1975), *Trans. Inst. Chem. Eng.*, **53**, 175.

Falk, J. C. (1976), in Rylander, P. N., and Greenfield, H. (Eds.), *Catalysis in Organic Syntheses*, Academic Press, New York.

Furusawa, T., and Smith, J. M. (1973), *Ind. Eng. Chem. Fundam.*, **12**, 360.

Goto, S., and Smith, J. M. (1975), *AIChE J.*, **21**, 706; 714.

Goto, S., Levec, J., and Smith, J. M. (1977), *Catal. Rev. Sci. Eng.*, **15**(2), 187.

Harnisch, H. (1980), *Pure Appl. Chem.*, **52**, 809.

Harriott, P. (1962), *AIChE J.*, **8**, 93.

Helfferich, F. (1962), *Ion Exchange*, McGraw-Hill, New York.

Hirose, T., Mori, Y., and Sato, Y. (1974), *J. Chem. Eng. Japan*, **7**, 19.

Hirose, T., Mori, Y., and Sato, Y. (1976), *J. Chem. Eng. Japan*, **9**, 220.

Hofmann, H. (1978), *Catal. Rev. Sci. Eng.*, **17**(1), 71.

Hofmann, H. (1982), *Chem. Ing. Tech.*, **54**, 865.

Hubbard, W. D., and Lightfoot, E. N. (1966), *Ind. Eng. Chem. Fundam.*, **5**, 370.

Hugo, P., and Schaper, W. (1980), *Ger. Chem. Eng.*, **3**, 103.

Juvekar, V. A. (1971), *Chem. Process. Eng.* (India), **5**, 25.

Juvekar, V. A., and Sharma, M. M. (1973), *Chem. Eng. Sci.*, **28**, 825.

Kawamura, K., Sasano, T., and Mifune, A. (1966), *Kagaku Kogaku*, **4**, 83.

Kekre, S. Y., and Gopalrao, M. (1969), *Indian Chem Eng.* (*Trans.*), **11**, T115.

Kobayashi, O., and Ichikawa, Y. (1975), *Kagaku Kogaku, Ronbunshu*, **1**, 510.

Kobayashi, T., and Saito, H. (1965), *Kagaku Kogaku*, **3**, 210.

Kumar, S., Upadhyay, S. N., and Mathur, V. K. J. (1977), *Ind. Eng. Chem. Process Des. Dev.*, **16**, 1.

Kumar, S., Upadhyay, S. N., and Mathur, V. K. J. (1978), *J. Chem. Eng. Data*, **23**, 139.

Laddha, S. S., and Sharma, M. M. (1978), *J. Appl. Chem. Biotechnol.*, **28**, 69.

Lemay, Y., Pineault, G., and Ruether, J. A. (1975), *Ind. Eng. Chem. Process Des. Dev.*, **14**, 280.

Levins, D. M., and Glastonbury, J. R. (1972a), *Trans. Inst. Chem. Eng.*, **50**, 32.

Levins, D. M., and Glastonbury, J. R. (1972b), *Trans. Inst. Chem. Eng.*, **50**, 132.

Leznoff, C. C. (1974), *Chem. Soc. Rev.*, **3**, 65.

Lobo, P. A. (1961), U.S. 2,971,696; *Chem. Abstr.* (1961), **55**, 10961.

McKillop, A., and Young, D. W. (1979), *Synthesis*, **6**, 401; **7**, 481.

Marangozis, J., and Johnson, A. I. (1961), *Can. J. Chem. Eng.*, **39**, 152.

Marangozis, J., Trass, O., and Johnson, A. I. (1963), *Can. J. Chem. Eng.*, **41**, 195.

Martinola, F. (1980), *Ger. Chem. Eng.*, **3**, 79.

Mashelkar, R. A., and Chavan, V. V. (1973), *J. Chem. Eng. Japan*, **6**, 160.

Meyerink, E. S., and Friedlander, S. K. (1962), *Chem. Eng. Sci.*, **17**, 121.

Miller, D. N. (1971), *Ind. Eng. Chem. Process Design Dev.*, **10**, 365.

Mochizuki, S., and Matsui, T. (1974), *Chem. Eng. Sci.*, **29**, 1328.

Motomura, H., and Morita, Z. (1977), *J. Appl. Polymer Sci.*, **21**, 487.

Nagata, S., Yamaguchi, I., and Harada, M. (1959), *Mem. Fac. Eng. Kyoto Univ.*, **21**, 275.

Nienow, A. W. (1968), *Chem. Eng. Sci.*, **23**, 1453.

Nienow, A. W. (1969), *Can. J. Chem. Eng.*, **47**, 248.

Nienow, A. W. (1975), *Chem. Eng. J.*, **9**, 153.

Nienow, A. W., and Miles, D. (1978), *Chem. Eng. J.*, **15**, 13.

Niiyama, H., and Smith, J. M. (1976), *AIChE J.*, **22**, 961.

Niiyama, H., and Smith, J. M. (1977), *AIChE J.*, **23**, 592.

Nishikawa, M., Inui, K., Yonezawa, Y., and Nagata, S. (1976), *Int. Chem. Eng.*, **16**, 714.

Patil, V. K., and Sharma, M. M. (1983), *Chem. Eng. Res. Des.*, **61**, 21.

Patil, V. K. (1982), Mass Transfer Characteristics of Fluid–Fluid Contactors, Ph.D (Tech.) thesis, University of Bombay.

Perry, J. H. (Ed.), (1950), *Chemical Engineers' Handbook*, 1st ed., McGraw-Hill, New York.

Peters, R. H. (1975), *Textile Chemistry*, Vol. 3, *The Physical Chemistry of Dyeing*, p. 598, Elsevier, Amsterdam.

Preston, C., and Fern, A. S. (1961), *Chimia (Aarau)*, **15**, 177.

Ramachandran, P. A., and Smith, J. M. (1977), *Chem. Eng. Sci.*, **32**, 873.

Rattee, I. D., and Breuer, M. M. (1974), *The Physical Chemistry of Dye Adsorption*, Academic Press, London, p. 244.

Regen, S. L. (1979), *Angew. Chem. Int. Ed. Engl.*, **18**, 421.

Rowe, P. N. (1975), *Chem. Eng. Sci.*, **30**, 7.

Ruether, J. A., Yang, C-S., and Hayduk, W. (1980), *Ind. Eng. Chem. Process Design Dev.*, **19**, 103.

Rushton, J. H., Costich, E. W., and Everett, H. J., (1950), *Chem. Eng. Prog.*, **46**, 395.

Sadasivan, K., Krishnaswamy, C. S., and Laddha, G. S. (1968), *Indian Chem. Eng. (Trans.)*, **10**, 114.

Satterfield, C. N., Vaneek, M. W., and Bliss, G. S. (1978), *AIChE J.*, **24**, 709.

Schwartzberg, H. G., and Treybal, R. E. (1968), *Ind. Eng. Chem. Fundam.*, **7**, 1, 6.

Selke, W. A., Bard, Y., Pasternak, A. D., and Aditya, S. K. (1956), *AIChE J.*, **2**, 468.

Sharma, R. C. (1969), Kinetics of Alkaline Hydrolysis of Esters, Ph.D. thesis, University of Bombay.

Sharma, R. C., and Sharma, M. M. (1970a), *Bull. Chem. Soc. Japan*, **43**, 642.

Sharma, R. C., and Sharma, M. M. (1970b), *Bull. Chem. Soc. Japan*, **43**, 1282.

Sherwood, T. K., and Ryan, J. M. (1959), *Chem. Eng. Sci.*, **11**, 81.

Sherwood, T. K., Pigford, R. L., and Wilke, C. R. (1975), *Mass Transfer*, McGraw-Hill, New York.

Shiao, D. D. F., Fortmiller, L. J., and Herz, A. H. (1975), *J. Phys. Chem.*, **79**, 816.

Specchia, V., and Baldi, G. (1975), *Ing. Chim. Ital.*, **11**, 111.

Starks, C. M., and Liotta, C. (1979), *Phase Transfer Catalysis, Principles and Techniques*, 1st ed., Academic Press, New York.

Subba Rao, D., and Taneja, V. K. (1979), Paper D-3 presented at the 3rd European Conf. on Mixing, April, York, England (organized by BHRA Fluid Engineering in Conjunction with the Inst. Chem. Eng., U.K.), p. 229.

Sumner, H. H., and Weston, C. D. (1963), *Am. Dyestuff Reporter*, **52**, 442.

Sykes, P., and Gomezplata, A. (1967), *Can. J. Chem. Eng.*, **45**, 189.

Szabo, M., and Kaldi, P. (1976), *Hungarian J. Ind. Chem.* (in English), **4**, 39.

Tournie', P., Laguerie, C., and Couderc, J. P. (1979), *Chem. Eng. Sci.*, **34**, 1247.

Tsigin, B. M., and Konstantinov, I. I. (1979), *J. Appl. Chem. USSR (Engl. Transl.)*, **52**, 2181.

Turner, J. C. R., and Snowdon, C. B. (1968), *Chem. Eng. Sci.*, **23**, 221.

Turner, J. C. R., Church, M. R., Johnson, A. S. W., and Snowdon, C. B. (1966), *Chem. Eng. Sci.*, **21**, 317.

Twitchett, H. J. (1974), *Chem. Soc. Rev.*, **3**(2), 209.

Upadhyay, S. N., and Tripathi, G. (1975a), *J. Sci. Ind. Res.*, **34**, 10.

Upadhyay, S. N., and Tripathi, G. (1975b), *J. Chem. Eng. Data*, **20**, 20.

Vieth, W. R., Porter, J. H., and Sherwood, T. K. (1963), *Ind. Eng. Chem. Fundam.*, **2**, 1.

Wadekar, V. V., and Sharma, M. M. (1981), *J. Chem. Tech. Biotechnol.*, **31**, 279.

Weber, W. P., and Gokel, G. W. (1977), *Phase Transfer Catalysis in Organic Synthesis*, 1st ed., Springer-Verlag, New York.

Yadav, G. D., and Sharma, M. M. (1981), *Ind. Eng. Chem. Process Design Dev.*, **20**, 385.

Yoshitome, H., Makihara, M., and Tsuchiya, Y. (1964), *Kagaku Kogaku*, **28**, 228.

Zwietering, T. N. (1958), *Chem. Eng. Sci.*, **8**, 244.

CHAPTER TWELVE

Mass Transfer With Reaction in Fluid–Fluid–Solid Systems

12.1. SOLIDS SLIGHTLY SOLUBLE

In this section we shall consider the problem of the absorption of a gas into a liquid containing suspended solids. The solids are sparingly soluble in the medium, and the reaction considered is between the dissolved gas and dissolved species. This problem is of considerable industrial importance. Thus, for instance, carbon dioxide is absorbed in an aqueous slurry of lime for the manufacture of precipitated calcium carbonate, which is required in large quantities as a rubber filler, a pigment, and so forth. Here the lime is slightly soluble in water and the reaction occurs between the dissolved carbon dioxide and OH^- ions. Similarly, lean mixtures of SO_2 are absorbed in slurries of lime and limestone. Table 1.5 gives some examples of industrial importance.

The treatment that follows is concerned with gas–liquid–solid systems, but it can be easily extended to liquid–liquid–solid systems. The problem can be represented by the following scheme:

$$A(g) \rightarrow A(l) \tag{12.1}$$

$$B(s) \rightarrow B(l) \tag{12.2}$$

$$A(l) + ZB(l) \rightarrow \text{products} \tag{12.3}$$

It will be assumed that the reaction between A and B is first order with respect to both A and B. The problem can be subdivided into two main classes (Ramachandran and Sharma, 1969):

1. *Solid dissolution in the liquid film next to the gas–liquid interface is negligible.* The solid dissolution in the liquid film next to the gas–liquid interface is negligible when the concentration of the solids is relatively small or when the particle size of the solids is relatively large as compared to the thickness of the liquid film. (By liquid film thickness is meant the diffusion film thickness within which the resistance to mass transfer is confined for mass transfer in the absence of chemical reaction.) Under these conditions, the extent of solid dissolution while species B is diffusing in the film can be neglected and the solid dissolution and chemical reaction can be assumed to be processes in series. The condition under which this assumption would be valid is as follows:

$$\frac{k_{SL} a_p}{4k_L^2} \frac{D_A^2}{D_B} \ll 1 \tag{12.4}$$

The rationale for the condition given by expression 12.4 will be brought out later in this section.

The k_{SL} values encountered in practice range from 5 to 40×10^{-3} cm/sec and can be as high as 0.4 cm/sec. In general, condition 12.4 will be valid if the average diameter of the particles is greater than five times the liquid film thickness.

2. *Solid dissolution in the liquid film is significant.* When the average diameter of the particles is considerably less than the thickness of the liquid film ($d_p < \delta/5$), the solid dissolution in the film becomes significant. For this case, the solid dissolution and chemical reaction become parallel steps. The converse of the condition given by expression 12.4 holds:

$$\frac{k_{SL} a_p}{4k_L^2} \frac{D_A^2}{D_B} \gg 1 \tag{12.5}$$

12.1.1. Solid Dissolution in the Liquid Film Next to the Gas–Liquid Interface is Negligible

The following steps are involved:

1. Diffusion of the gaseous species A through the gas film;

2. Dissolution of the solid species B;
3. Diffusion and simultaneous chemical reaction of the dissolved gas in the liquid film near the gas–liquid interface.

The rates of the various steps are assumed to be the same under steady-state conditions. The rates of steps (1) and (2) are

$$R'_A = k_{G_A} a''(p_A - p_{A,i}) \tag{12.6}$$

for diffusion through the gas film and

$$R'_A = \frac{k_{SL} a_p}{Z}([B_s] - [B_o]) \tag{12.7}$$

for solid dissolution.

The rate of step (3) will depend on the mechanism under which the gas is being absorbed. The concentration profiles for the various cases are shown in Figure 12.1.

Pseudo-First-Order Reaction

In pseudo-first-order reactions the concentration of the dissolved species at the interface is practically the same as in the bulk liquid. The rate of absorption is given by

$$R'_A = \frac{a'' H_A p_A \sqrt{D_A k_2 [B_o]}}{1 + \dfrac{H_A \sqrt{D_A k_2 [B_o]}}{k_{G_A}}} \tag{12.8}$$

where

$$[B_o] = [B_s] - \frac{Z R'_A}{k_{SL} a_p} \tag{12.9}$$

For large values of $k_{SL} a_p$, the resistance associated with the dissolution of the solid particles becomes unimportant and the rate of absorption is the same as that for a solution saturated with B, since in these circumstances $[B_o]$ is equal to $[B_s]$.

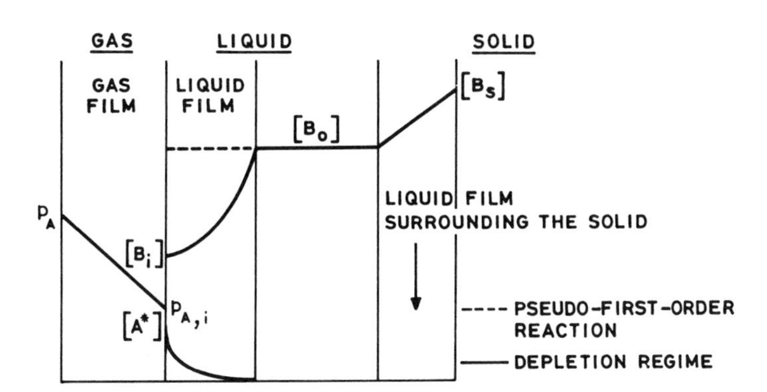

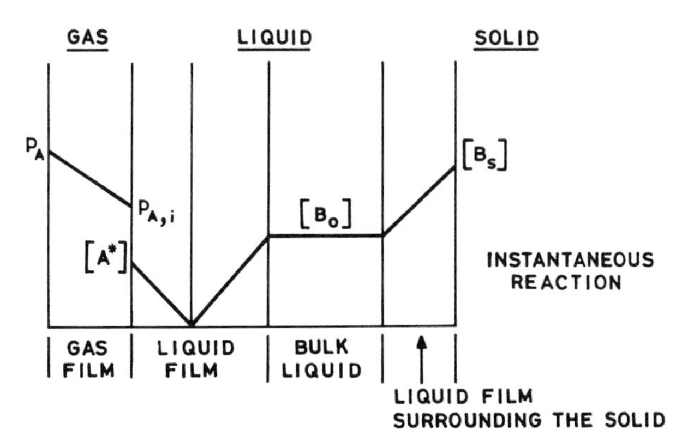

Figure 12.1. Concentration profiles based on the film theory for gas–liquid–solid systems when the solid dissolution in the film is negligible.

Depletion Regime

In the depletion regime the concentration of B at the interface, $[B_i]$, is significantly lower than that in the bulk. By the method of Hikita and Asai (1964), the rate of absorption can be calculated if the interfacial concentration of B is known. Thus we have

$$R'_A = \frac{a'' H_A p_A \sqrt{D_A k_2 [B_i]}}{1 + \dfrac{H_A \sqrt{D_A k_2 [B_i]}}{k_{G_A}}} \tag{12.10}$$

The value of $[B_i]$ is obtained by a material balance:

$$[B_i] = [B_s] + \frac{Z D_A}{D_B} H_A p_A - Z R'_A \left[\left(\frac{H_A}{k_{G_A} a''} + \frac{1}{k_L a''} \right) \frac{D_A}{D_B} + \frac{1}{k_{SL} a_p} \right] \tag{12.11}$$

(See Section 2.7 for the method to be used for the calculation of $[B_i]$.)

Instantaneous Reaction

The rate expression when the reaction between the dissolved gas and dissolved species is instantaneous can be shown to be (the classification of a reaction as instantaneous was discussed in Section 2.6):

$$R'_A = \frac{H_A p_A + \dfrac{D_B}{D_A} \dfrac{[B_s]}{Z}}{\dfrac{H_A}{k_{G_A} a''} + \dfrac{1}{k_L a''} + \dfrac{D_B}{D_A} \dfrac{1}{k_{SL} a_p}} \tag{12.12}$$

From Equations (12.6) and (12.7) we have

$$p_{A,i} = p_A - \frac{R'_A}{k_{G_A} a''}$$

and

$$[B_o] = [B_s] - \frac{Z R'_A}{k_{SL} a_p}$$

Equation 12.12 is valid only if $p_{A,i} \geqslant 0$ and $[B_o] \geqslant 0$.

If $p_{A,i} = 0$ while $[B_o] > 0$, then the rate is given by $R'_A = k_{G_A} a'' p_A$ and the operation is gas-film-controlled.

If $p_{A,i} > 0$ while $[B_o] = 0$, then the rate is given by $R'_A = k_{SL} a_p [B_s]/Z$ and the operation is controlled by solid dissolution.

12.1.2. Solid Dissolution in the Liquid Film is Significant

Here, the diffusion of B and solid dissolution become parallel steps. When absorption is accompanied by a fast pseudo-first-order reaction (i.e., it conforms to regime 3 according to the classification given in Chapter 2) then the interfacial and bulk concentrations of B are the same. The simultaneous dissolution of solid particles in the film will therefore not make any contribution to the specific rate of absorption. The effect of the dissolution of solid particles in the film will be most marked in the case of an instantaneous reaction, which is discussed next.

Instantaneous Reaction

The concentration profiles for an instantaneous reaction are shown in Figure 12.2. The necessary condition for the reaction to be treated as instantaneous is

$$\frac{\sqrt{D_A k_2 [B_s]}}{k_L} \gg \frac{[B_s]}{Z[A^*]} \left(1 + \frac{k_{SL} a_p}{4 k_L^2} \frac{D_A^2}{D_B} \right) \tag{12.13}$$

The effect of the solid dissolution in the film is to shift the reaction plane closer to the interface and thereby enhance the rate of absorption.

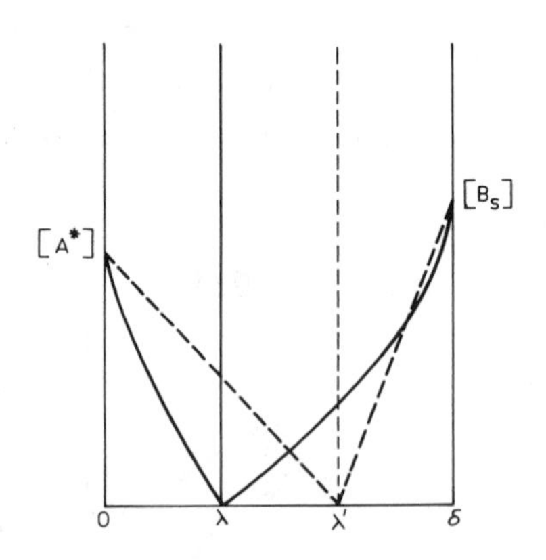

Figure 12.2. Concentration profiles for an instantaneous reaction when solid dissolution in the film is significant.

The differential equations for this case are

$$D_A \frac{d^2[A]}{dx^2} - k_{SL} a_p \frac{[B_s]}{Z} = 0, \qquad 0 < x < \lambda \qquad (12.14)$$

$$D_B \frac{d^2[B]}{dx^2} + k_{SL} a_p([B_s] - [B]) = 0, \qquad \lambda < x < \delta \qquad (12.15)$$

(The term $k_{SL} a_p[B_s]$ in Eq. 12.14 accounts for the solid dissolution in the region from 0 to λ.)

The boundary conditions are, at

$$x = 0, \qquad [A] = [A^*] \qquad (12.16)$$

$$x = \lambda, \qquad [A] = [B] = 0$$

$$-D_A\left(\frac{d[A]}{dx}\right)_{x=\lambda} = \frac{D_B}{Z}\left(\frac{d[B]}{dx}\right)_{x=\lambda} \qquad (12.17)$$

$$x = \delta, \qquad [B] = [B_s] \qquad (12.18)$$

The required specific rate of absorption is given by

$$R_A = -D_A\left(\frac{d[A]}{dx}\right)_{x=0} \qquad (12.19)$$

The solution of the foregoing differential equations under the specified boundary conditions, when it is noted that R_A is given by Eq. 12.19 and that Eq. 12.17 should be satisfied, gives the following equations for the specific rate of absorption:

$$R_A = \frac{D_A[A^*]}{\lambda} + k_{SL} a_p [B_s] \frac{\lambda}{2Z} \qquad (12.20)$$

$$R_A = \frac{[B_s]}{Z}\sqrt{D_B k_{SL} a_p}\coth\left[(\delta - \lambda)\sqrt{\frac{k_{SL} a_p}{D_B}}\right] + k_{SL} a_p [B_s]\frac{\lambda}{Z} \qquad (12.21)$$

The value of R_A is obtained by a trial-and-error procedure. Assume a value of λ ($< \delta$) and see if it satisfies both Eqs. 12.20 and 12.21. Repeat this procedure until both Eqs. 12.20 and 12.21 are satisfied (see the solved example at the end of this section).

It can be seen that Eq. 12.20 reduces to the familiar expression for gas absorption accompanied by instantaneous reaction when $k_{SL} a_p = 0$.

When $k_{SL} a_p$ is large, the solid dissolution becomes extremely rapid and the reaction plane probably shifts to the gas–liquid interface ($\lambda \to 0$). The specific rate of absorption is then given by

$$R_A = \frac{[B_s]}{Z}\sqrt{D_A k_{SL} a_p} \qquad (12.22)$$

provided that

$$\sqrt{\frac{k_{SL} a_p}{D_B}}\,\delta > 5 \qquad (12.23)$$

and

$$\frac{[B_s]}{Z} \gg [A^*] \qquad (12.24)$$

Under these conditions, the rate of absorption becomes proportional to the square root of particle loading, $w(R_A \propto \sqrt{a_p} \propto \sqrt{w})$.

Equation 12.22 can also be derived independently. For the case when $[B_s]$ is very much greater than $[A^*]$ the reaction plane shifts to the interface, and for practical purposes λ can be taken as 0. In such cases we need consider only Eq. 12.15, which describes the transport of B with the boundary conditions changed to $0 < x < \delta$; Eq. 12.14 can be ignored. The integration of Eq. 12.15 is straightforward, and noting that

$$R_A = \frac{D_B}{Z}\left(\frac{d[B]}{dx}\right)_{x=0}$$

we get

$$R_A = \frac{[B_s]}{Z}\sqrt{D_B k_{SL} a_p}\coth\left(\sqrt{\frac{k_{SL} a_p}{D_B}}\,\delta\right) \qquad (12.25)$$

For $\sqrt{k_{SL} a_p / D_B}\,\delta > 5$ Eq. 12.25 reduces to Eq. 12.22.

***Absorption into a Finite Slurry.** In the foregoing analysis we assumed that the concentration of dissolved B in the bulk liquid corresponds to the saturation concentration, since the particle size is small. However, we can conceive a situation where as a result of the relatively low concentration of solid particles, the bulk liquid phase is not saturated with respect to B. It is also conceivable that the solid-liquid-film mass transfer coefficient, k_{SL}, is different in the film and in the bulk. Sada et al. (1979a) have analyzed this problem and have analyzed data on the absorption of dilute SO_2 in a $Mg(OH)_2$ slurry in a self-induced spray scrubber.

Enhancement in the Dissolution Rate of Solid Particles in the Film. It is possible to conceive of a situation where the concentration of the dissolved gas is higher than $[B_s]$, and in such cases there will be an enhancement in the rate of dissolution of B if the reaction between dissolved A and B is instantaneous (e.g., absorption of a very dilute SO_2–air mixture in a slurry of limestone). Uchida et al. (1975) have considered this case. The enhancement factor for the dissolution of particles accompanied by instantaneous reaction was calculated on the basis of the film theory. Figure 12.3 shows the modified concentration profiles.

Equation 12.14 for $0 < x < \lambda$ now becomes

$$D_A \frac{d^2[A]}{dx^2} - \frac{k_{SL}a_p}{Z}[B_s]\left(1 + \frac{Z[A]}{[B_s]}\frac{D_A}{D_B}\right) = 0 \tag{12.26}$$

(Eqs. 12.15–12.19 hold).

Following the procedure outlined earlier in this section, we get

$$R_A = \phi_D D_A[A^*]\coth(\phi_D\lambda) + \frac{\phi_D D_B[B_s]}{Z} \times \left[\coth(\phi_D\lambda) - \frac{1}{\sinh(\phi_D\lambda)}\right] \tag{12.27}$$

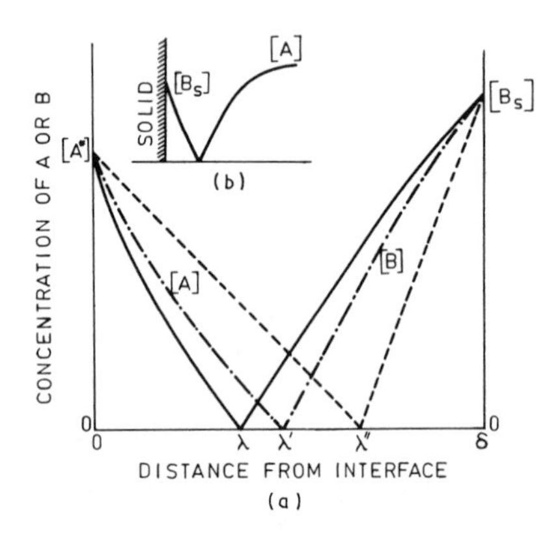

Figure 12.3. Concentration profiles for A and B (λ, λ', and λ'' are the main reaction planes for the three models) (*a*) in the liquid film near the gas–liquid interface; (*b*) in the neighborhood of solid particles present in the region from $x = 0$ to $x = \lambda$.

$$= \frac{\phi_D D_B[B_s]}{Z}\coth[\phi_D(\delta - \lambda)] + \phi_D\left(D_A[A^*] + \frac{2D_B[B_s]}{Z}\right) \times \left[\coth(\phi_D\lambda) - \frac{1}{\sinh(\phi_D\lambda)}\right] \tag{12.28}$$

where

$$\phi_D = \sqrt{\frac{k_{SL}a_p}{D_B}} \tag{12.29}$$

The value of λ can be obtained by a trial-and-error procedure or by the following equation, which is also derived from boundary condition 12.17:

$$\frac{\phi_D D_B[B_s]}{Z}\left[\coth(\phi_D\lambda) - \frac{1}{\sinh(\phi_D\lambda)}\right] + \phi_D\frac{[B_s]D_B}{Z}\coth[\phi_D(\delta - \lambda)] - \frac{D_A[A^*]\phi_D}{\sinh(\phi_D\lambda)} = 0 \tag{12.30}$$

Example

Consider the following case of gas absorption in a slurry of sparingly soluble fine particles.

Data

Solubility of the solids,

$$[B_s] = 5 \times 10^{-5}\ \text{mol/cm}^3$$

Interfacial concentration of the gas for the specified conditions,

$$[A^*] = 1 \times 10^{-5}\ \text{mol/cm}^3$$

$$D_A = D_B = 1 \times 10^{-5}\ \text{cm}^2/\text{sec}$$

$$k_L = 1 \times 10^{-2}\ \text{cm/sec}$$

$$k_{SL} = 0.1\ \text{cm/sec}$$

$$\rho_p = 1\ \text{g/cm}^3$$

$$Z = 1$$

Calculate the specific rate of absorption in a saturated solution and in a solid suspension containing 0.1 g of solids per cubic centimeter of clear liquid; the average diameter of the solids is 2×10^{-4} cm. Assume the reaction to be instantaneous.

Solution. (i) Thickness of the liquid film

$$\delta = \frac{D_A}{k_L} = \frac{1 \times 10^{-5}}{1 \times 10^{-2}} = 1 \times 10^{-3} \text{ cm}$$

(ii) Absorption in the saturated solution containing no suspended solids is calculated from Eq. 2.83.

$$R_A = k_L[A^*]\left(1 + \frac{[B_s]}{Z[A^*]}\right)$$

$$= 6 \times 10^{-7} \text{ mol/cm}^2 \text{ sec}$$

(iii) Absorption in a solid suspension:
surface area of the solids

$$a_p = \frac{6w}{\rho_p d_p} = \frac{6 \times 0.1}{1 \times 2 \times 10^{-4}}$$

$$= 3 \times 10^3 \text{ cm}^2/\text{cm}^3 \text{ of clear liquid}$$

$$\frac{k_{SL} a_p}{4k_L^2} \frac{D_A^2}{D_B} = \frac{0.1 \times 3 \times 10^3 \times (1 \times 10^{-5})^2}{4 \times (1 \times 10^{-2})^2 \times 1 \times 10^{-5}}$$

$$= 7.5$$

Since this quantity is very much greater than unity, it is evident that there will be an appreciable contribution by the simultaneous solid dissolution in the film (see the condition given by expression 12.5). Now

$$\delta\sqrt{\frac{k_{SL}a_p}{D_B}} = 1 \times 10^{-3}\sqrt{\frac{0.1 \times 3 \times 10^3}{1 \times 10^{-5}}}$$

$$= 5.48 > 5$$

The condition given by expression 12.23 is therefore satisfied. However, the condition given by expression 12.24 is not satisfied because $[B_s]$ (5×10^{-5} mol/cm^3) is not very much greater than $[A^*]$ (1×10^{-5} mol/cm^3).

If $\delta \gg \lambda$, Eq. 12.21 reduces to

$$R_A = \frac{[B_s]}{Z}\sqrt{k_{SL}a_p D_B} + k_{SL}a_p[B_s]\frac{\lambda}{Z} \tag{12.31}$$

Solving Eqs. 12.20 and 12.31 we get

$$\lambda = \frac{-[B_s]\sqrt{\dfrac{k_{SL}a_p D_B}{Z}}}{k_{SL}a_p\dfrac{[B_s]}{Z}} + \frac{\sqrt{k_{SL}a_p\dfrac{[B_s]}{Z}\left(D_B\dfrac{[B_s]}{Z} + 2D_A[A^*]\right)}}{k_{SL}a_p\dfrac{[B_s]}{Z}} \tag{12.32}$$

The specific rate of absorption is given by

$$R_A = \sqrt{k_{SL}a_p\frac{[B_s]}{Z}\left(\frac{D_B[B_s]}{Z} + 2D_A[A^*]\right)} \tag{12.33}$$

Substituting the relevant values we get

$$\lambda = 3.34 \times 10^{-5} \text{ cm} \ll \delta(1 \times 10^{-3} \text{ cm})$$

and

$$R_A = 3.24 \times 10^{-6} \text{ mol/cm}^2 \text{ sec}$$

Hence the specific rate of absorption in a solid suspension containing fine particles is higher by a factor of 5.4 than in the case of a saturated solution in the absence of solid particles.

(iv) Uchida's modification. Here the value of λ can be obtained from Eq. 12.30. For $\lambda \ll \delta$, Eq. 12.30 on simplification gives

$$\frac{\phi_D D_B[B_s]}{Z}\left[\coth(\phi_D\lambda) - \frac{1}{\sinh(\phi_D\lambda)}\right] + \frac{\phi_D[B_s]D_B}{Z} = \frac{D_A[A^*]\phi_D}{\sinh(\phi_D\lambda)} \tag{12.34}$$

Equation 12.34 on simplification gives

$$\exp(\phi_D\lambda) = 1 + \frac{ZD_A[A^*]}{D_B[B_s]} \tag{12.35}$$

Now

$$\phi_D = \sqrt{\frac{k_{SL}a_p}{D_B}} = 5.48 \times 10^3$$

The solution of Eq. 12.35 gives λ equal to 3.32×10^{-5} cm. The substitution of relevant values in Eq. 12.27 gives R_A equal to 3.29×10^{-6} mol/cm² sec. It is clear that in this case the increase in the specific rate of absorption due to the enhancement in the rate of dissolution of solid particles is insignificant (< 2%). This situation arises because the value of $[B_s]$ is five times the value of $[A^*]$.

Depletion Regime (Second-Order Reactions)

The pertinent film theory equations for second-order reactions are:

$$D_A \frac{d^2[A]}{dx^2} = k_2[A][B] \tag{12.36}$$

and

$$D_B \frac{d^2[B]}{dx^2} + k_{SL}a_p([B_s] - [B]) = Zk_2[A][B] \tag{12.37}$$

The boundary conditions are, at

$$x = 0, \quad [A] = [A^*], \quad \frac{d[B]}{dx} = 0, \quad [B] = [B_i] \tag{12.38}$$

and at

$$x = \delta, \quad [A] = 0, \quad [B] = [B_s] \tag{12.39}$$

Equations 12.36 and 12.37 cannot be solved analytically. However, an approximate solution can be obtained by assuming an average driving force of $([B_s] - [B_i])/2$ for solid dissolution (Ramachandran and Sharma, 1969). The interfacial concentration of species B is then given by the following equation:

$$\frac{[B_i]}{[B_s]} + \frac{\sqrt{D_A k_2 [B_s]}}{k_L} \frac{[A^*]}{[B_s]} \frac{ZD_A}{D_B} \times \left(1 + \frac{k_{SL}a_p}{4k_L^2} \frac{D_A^2}{D_B}\right)^{-1} \sqrt{\frac{[B_i]}{[B_s]}} - \left[1 + \frac{[A^*]}{[B_s]} \frac{ZD_A}{D_B} \left(1 + \frac{k_{SL}a_p}{4k_L^2} \frac{D_A^2}{D_B}\right)^{-1}\right] = 0 \tag{12.40}$$

A knowledge of $[B_i]$ enables the specific rate of absorption of gas A (which is approximately equal to $[A^*]\sqrt{D_A k_2 [B_i]}$) to be calculated.

From Eq. 12.40 it can be deduced that the term $(k_{SL}a_p/4k_L^2)(D_A^2/D_B)$ represents the extent to which the solid dissolution in the film is capable of increasing the rate of transfer, and this explains the rationale of the conditions given by expressions 12.4 and 12.5.

Equation 12.37 can be modified to take into account the enhancement in the rate of dissolution due to the reaction in the solid–liquid film. The modified form of Eq. 12.37 is (Sada et al., 1977a)

$$D_B \frac{d^2[B]}{dx^2} + k_{SL}a_p\phi_s[A]([B_s] - [B]) = Zk_2[A][B] \tag{12.41}$$

where ϕ_s is the enhancement factor for solid dissolution and is given by the following equation:

$$\phi_s = \frac{\sqrt{\left(\frac{Zk_2[A]D_B}{k_{SL}^2}\right)\frac{\phi_{sa} - \phi_s}{\phi_{sa} - 1}}}{\tanh\left[\sqrt{\left(\frac{Zk_2[A]D_B}{k_{SL}^2}\right)\frac{\phi_{sa} - \phi_s}{\phi_{sa} - 1}}\right]} \tag{12.42}$$

where ϕ_{sa} is the enhancement factor for an instantaneous reaction between dissolved B and A.

$$\phi_{sa} = 1 + \frac{D_A}{D_B} \frac{Z[A^*]}{[B_s]} \tag{12.43}$$

Sada et al. (1977a) have presented a numerical solution of Eqs. 12.36, 12.37, and 12.41. There is satisfactory agreement between the numerical solution and their experimental results with the absorption of CO_2 into a slurry containing fine particles of $Ca(OH)_2$. For common situations the simplified solution of Ramachandran and Sharma gives satisfactory results.

Under certain conditions the simultaneous dissolution of solid particles in the film may result in a situation where the interfacial concentration of B, $[B_i]$, becomes equal to $[B_s]$.

Instantaneous Reactions: Two Steps

We may encounter a situation where two steps, both instantaneous, are involved in reactions. Consider the absorption of Cl_2 in an aqueous slurry of lime. Here we get OCl^- in the first step and HClO in the second step and both steps are instantaneous. Yadav (1980) has considered this case, as well as a situation where the final product, HClO, is volatile and gets desorbed into the gas phase. The base case of a two-step instantaneous reaction with dissolved B (i.e., in the absence of solid particles) was referred to in Section 8.7.4. Sada et al. (1980) have also considered this type of situation and have cited the example of the absorption of SO_2 in aqueous slurries of $Mg(OH)_2/CaCO_3$, where SO_3^{2-} is capable of reacting further to give HSO_3^-.

12.1.3. Simultaneous Absorption of Two Gases into a Slurry Containing Soluble Fine Particles (One or Two Solid Reactants)

We may encounter a situation in practice where two gases, such as H_2S–CO_2, H_2S–SO_2, or CO_2–SO_2, are absorbed in a slurry of fine soluble particles, such as $Ca(OH)_2$. We may also have situations where two solid reactants are involved that are sparingly soluble. Mahajani (1976) has extended the treatment given in Sections 12.1.1 and 12.1.2 to these cases. Sada et al. (1977b) have also considered this problem and have given a solution for the case of absorption accompanied by fast reaction resulting in the depletion of species B in the film.

12.1.4. Examples

Absorption of CO_2 in a Suspension of Lime (Solid Dissolution in the Film Negligible)

The absorption of CO_2 in a suspension of lime is industrially important for the manufacture of precipitated calcium carbonate. Juvekar and Sharma (1973) have studied the mechanism of absorption of lean CO_2 in an aqueous suspension of lime containing 2–40% w/w of $Ca(OH)_2$ in a small mechanically agitated contactor and a bubble column. It was found that the solid dissolution in the film was negligible, that is, the condition given by expression 12.4 is satisfied.

A plot of the rate of carbonation versus the total calcium hydroxide concentration in a semibatch reactor (i.e., the gas is passed continuously through a batch of slurry) shows two distinct regions: a constant-rate period during which the rate of absorption of CO_2 is practically constant, and a falling-rate period where the rate of absorption of CO_2 decreases continuously with time.

During the constant-rate period the aqueous phase is almost saturated with OH^- ions ($[B_o] \approx [B_s]$). The following condition is satisfied:

$$\frac{k_{SL} a_p [B_s]}{Z} \gg \frac{a'' H_A p_A \sqrt{D_A k_2 [B_s] + k_L^2}}{1 + \dfrac{H_A \sqrt{D_A k_2 [B_s] + k_L^2}}{k_{G_A}}} \tag{12.44}$$

The rate of absorption of CO_2 during the constant-rate period is given by the following equation:

$$R'_A = \frac{a'' H_A p_A \sqrt{D_A k_2 [B_s] + k_L^2}}{1 + \dfrac{H_A \sqrt{D_A k_2 [B_s] + k_L^2}}{k_{G_A}}} \tag{12.45}$$

During the falling-rate period there is a gradual fall in the concentration of OH^- ions in the liquid with time. The total surface area of particles available for dissolution diminishes to such an extent that the resistance associated with the dissolution of solid particles becomes important. The following condition is satisfied during the falling-rate period:

$$\frac{k_{SL} a_p [B_s]}{Z} \approx k_L a'' [A^*] \phi_A \tag{12.46}$$

where ϕ_A is the enhancement factor based on $[B_o]$. The rate of absorption during the falling-rate period is given by the following equation:

$$R'_A = \frac{a'' H_A p_A \sqrt{D_A k_2 [B_i] + k_L^2}}{1 + \dfrac{H_A \sqrt{D_A k_2 [B_i] + k_L^2}}{k_{G_A}}} \tag{12.47}$$

where $[B_i]$ can be obtained from Eq. 12.11.

Absorption of CO_2 and SO_2 in Slurries of $Ca(OH)_2$ and $Mg(OH)_2$ (Dissolution of Solid Particles in the Film Significant; Instantaneous as well as Depletion Reaction Regime)

Sada et al. (1977a) have studied the absorption of pure CO_2 and SO_2 in a stirred contactor having an effective contact area of 50 cm^2. The volume of the slurry taken in the contactor was 250 cm^3. The values of the physical mass transfer coefficient in the slurries used for the foregoing experiments were measured independently by the absorption of a nonreacting gas (N_2O). At a stirring speed of 150 rev/min in the liquid phase the k_L value was found to be 1.6×10^{-3} cm/sec. The k_L values for CO_2 and SO_2 were obtained from this value by assuming that k_L varies as $D_A^{2/3}$. The value of k_L was apparently unaffected by the variation in the slurry concentration.

In the case of the SO_2–$Ca(OH)_2$ system the reaction between the dissolved SO_2 and OH^- is instantaneous and hence the model proposed by Ramachandran and Sharma (1969; see Section 12.1.4) should apply. The product of the reaction, $CaSO_3$, is insoluble in the medium. If the rate of dissolution of the solid particles is enhanced, then the modification proposed by Uchida et al. (1975) should be applied. It is clear from the data reported by Sada et al. that the specific rate of absorption increases with an increase in the concentration of solids. Experimental data confirm theoretical predictions.

Sada et al. (1977c) have studied the absorption of lean SO_2 in slurries of $Mg(OH)_2$ in a 10-cm-i.d. stirred contactor (the gas phase was independently stirred). Here an additional complication arises because $MgSO_3$ is quite soluble in water and hence the dissolved SO_2 also reacts instantaneously with SO_3^{2-} to give HSO_3^-, which in turn further enhances the specific rate of absorption. Sada et al. (1979a) have also studied the absorption of lean SO_2 in a finite slurry of $Mg(OH)_2$ in a self-induced spray absorber.

Sada et al. (1977b) have studied the simultaneous absorption of SO_2 and CO_2 in slurries of lime in a stirred contactor where a plane interface could be maintained, and gas and liquid phases were independently stirred. The volume of the slurry was kept at 250 cm³. SO_2 reacts instantaneously with OH^- and its specific rate of absorption agreed with predicted values. For all practical purposes, CO_2 can be considered an inert gas when SO_2 is absorbed.

Absorption of Lean NO in Aqueous Slurries of Lime Containing Dissolved Sodium Chlorite (Solid Dissolution in the Film Negligible)

In Section 3.4.5 we covered the absorption of lean NO in a variety of aqueous solutions. The specific rate of absorption of lean NO in aqueous alkaline solutions of sodium chlorite is a function of the pH; a decrease in OH^- concentration results in an increase in the specific rate of absorption. Sada et al. (1979b) therefore made measurements of the specific rate of absorption of lean NO_2 in aqueous slurries of $Ca(OH)_2$ (and $Mg(OH)_2$) containing dissolved $NaClO_2$. The solids concentration had no effect on the specific rate of absorption, since the system conformed to the fast pseudo-mth-order reaction regime (regime 3).

Absorption of Acetylene in an Aqueous Slurry of Cuprous Chloride (Solid Dissolution in the Film Negligible)

Tamhankar and Chaudhari (1979) have studied the absorption of pure acetylene in aqueous slurries of CuCl. Under the conditions employed by these authors the reaction between C_2H_2 and dissolved CuCl was found to be instantaneous. However, the criterion given by Equation 12.4 indicated that simultaneous dissolution in the gas–liquid film was negligible.

12.2. SOLID PARTICLES INSOLUBLE IN THE MEDIUM

In this section we shall consider some aspects of mass transfer in fluid–fluid systems containing suspended solid particles. The solids are assumed to undergo a chemical reaction and are essentially insoluble in the fluid phase. This situation is fairly common in industrial practice. For instance, the leaching of a variety of ores falls in this category. The chlorination of wood pulp suspended in water is another example. Table 1.6 gives some examples of industrial importance. In some cases it may be desirable to carry out the reaction between gaseous and solid reactants in an inert medium. For instance, Phadtare and Doraiswamy (1965, 1966) have studied the carbonation of the sodium salt of β-naphthol suspended in a kerosene medium. (In some uncommon cases the coarse solid reactant particles may be placed in a tower and the reaction conducted with liquid trickling down and gas flowing countercurrently. Copper sulfate is manufactured in towers packed with copper shot, and dilute sulfuric acid trickles down the tower in the presence of air. This situation has to be considered somewhat differently.)

The problem can be schematically represented as

$$\text{A}(\textit{phase}\ \text{A}) \rightarrow \text{A}(\textit{phase}\ \text{B})$$

$$\text{A}(\textit{phase}\ \text{B}) + \text{B}(\textit{solid}) \rightarrow \text{soluble products}$$
$$\xrightarrow{\text{or}} \text{insoluble products}$$
$$\xrightarrow{\text{or}} \text{soluble and insoluble products} \qquad (12.48)$$

Here A is the species present in phase A, and it diffuses into phase B. Phase B contains some suspended solids which react with the dissolved A. The treatment of the problem is in many respects similar to that for gas–solid reactions (see Volume 1).

12.2.1. Rate of Reaction for Spherical Particles of Constant Size

When the product formed is a solid that adheres to the reacting solid, we have constant-size spherical particles. Here the initial reaction occurs on the outermost surface of the solid particles. The zone of the reaction then moves into the interior of the solid, leaving behind a completely converted material through which the reactants have to diffuse.

The reaction scheme for this case consists of the following steps (it is assumed that gas-side resistance is absent):

1. Diffusion of species A from phase A to phase B;
2. Diffusion of the dissolved species A through the liquid film adjoining the solid particles to the reactant surface;
3. Diffusion of species A through the layer of reacted solids to the reaction surface;
4. Chemical reaction of the dissolved reactant A with the solid species B.

The concentration profiles for this case are shown in Figure 12.4.

The rates of the various steps can be easily formulated. At steady state, the rate of each of the foregoing steps is the same.

$$R'_A = k_L a''([A^*] - [A_o]) \tag{12.49}$$

for diffusion of A from phase A to phase B;

$$= k_{SL} a_p([A_o] - [A_s]) \tag{12.50}$$

for transport of A to the solid surface;

$$= \frac{D_S a_p}{r - r_c}([A_s] - [A_{r_c}]) \tag{12.51}$$

for diffusion through the layer of the reacted solid;

$$= k_R 4\pi r_c^2 n_p [A_{r_c}] \tag{12.52}$$

for a first-order chemical reaction at the solid surface;

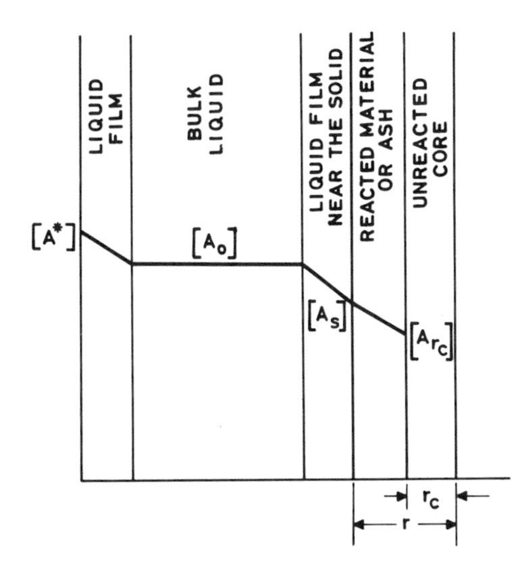

Figure 12.4. Concentration profiles for gas–liquid–solid systems where solids are reacting but insoluble in the liquid; the solids are of constant size.

where n_p is the number of particles per unit liquid volume $= \dfrac{3w}{4\pi r^3 \rho_p}$ cm^{-3}

Equations 12.49–12.52 can be combined to yield overall expression for the rate of reaction. The latter can also be expressed in terms of the rate at which the reacting core moves inward in the solids. Thus we have

R'_A = rate of A reacting per unit volume (cm^3) of clear liquid per second

= rate of B reacting per unit volume (cm^3) of clear liquid per second

$$= n_p \frac{d}{dt}\left(\frac{4\pi}{3}\frac{r_c^3 \rho_p}{M_B}\right) \tag{12.53}$$

where M_B is the molecular weight of B.

Equations 12.49–12.53 give

$$\frac{[A^*]M_B}{4\pi\rho_p n_p}\frac{1}{r_c^2}\left(\frac{dt}{dr_c}\right) = \frac{1}{k_L a''} + \frac{1}{4\pi r^2 n_p}\left(\frac{1}{k_{SL}} + \frac{r - r_c}{D_S} + \frac{1}{k_R}\frac{r^2}{r_c^2}\right) \tag{12.54}$$

TABLE 12.1. Controlling Mechanisms for Constant-Size Particles

Controlling Mechanism	Controlling Rate Term	Relation between Time and Fractional Conversion	Remarks
1. Mass transfer from phase A to phase B	$k_L a''$	$X_B \propto t$	Hydrodynamic factors are very important.
2. Solid–liquid mass transfer	k_{SL}	$X_B \propto t$	Hydrodynamic factors have some effect in the turbulent regime.
3. Diffusion through solid product layer	D_S	$t \propto [(1 - X_B)^{2/3} + (1 - X_B)]$	Hydrodynamic factors are likely to be unimportant; effect of temperature should be insignificant.
4. Chemical reaction	k_R	$X_B \propto t^3$	Effect of temperature is very significant; no effect of hydrodynamic factors.

Integration of Eq. 12.54 gives a relation between time and r_c. The latter can be related to the fractional conversion X_B as follows:

$$X_B = 1 - \left(\frac{r_c}{r}\right)^3 \tag{12.55}$$

The various controlling mechanisms are summarized in Table 12.1.

12.2.2. Rate of Reaction for Particles with Changing Size

When the product formed is soluble in the liquid, the reacting solid shrinks during the course of the reaction and ultimately disappears. The reaction scheme for this case consists of following steps (see Figure 12.5; it is assumed that the gas-side resistance is absent):

1. Diffusion of species A from phase A to phase B;
2. Diffusion of the dissolved species A through the liquid film adjoining the solid particle to the solid surface;
3. Chemical reaction at the solid surface.

The rate expressions for steps 1 and 2 are given by Eqs. 12.49 and 12.50. The rate of the surface reaction (step 3) is given by

$$R'_A = k_R 4\pi r^2 n_p [A_s] \tag{12.56}$$

(for a first-order reaction).

Also, the rate of reaction can be related to the rate of shrinkage of the solid particles by the following equation:

$$R'_A = n_p \frac{d}{dt}\left(\frac{4\pi}{3} r^3 \frac{\rho_p}{M_B}\right) \tag{12.57}$$

Combining the rate expressions for the various steps,

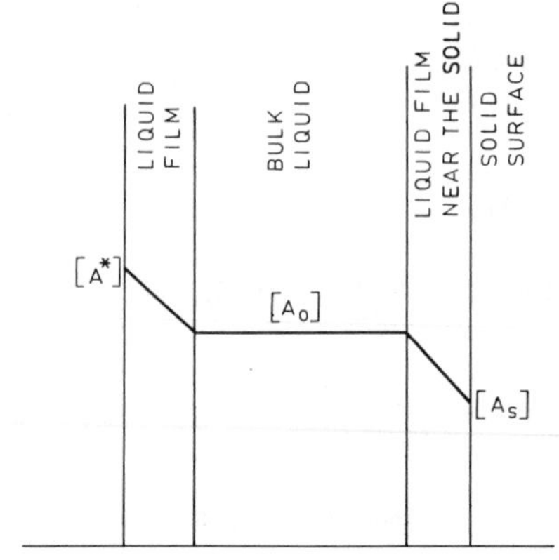

Figure 12.5. Concentration profiles for gas–liquid–solid systems where solids are reacting but insoluble in the liquid; the solids are of changing size.

TABLE 12.2. Controlling Mechanisms for Shrinking Particles

Controlling Mechanism	Controlling Rate Term	Relation between Time and Fractional Conversion	Remarks
1. Mass transfer from phase A to phase B	$k_L a''$	$X_B \propto t$	Hydrodynamic factors are very important.
2. Mass transfer to solid particles	k_{SL}	$X_B \propto t$	Hydrodynamic factors have some effect in the turbulent regime.
3. Chemical reaction at the surface	k_R	$X_B \propto t^3$	Effect of temperature is significant; no effect of hydrodynamic factors.

we have

$$\frac{[A^*]M_B}{4\pi\rho_p n_p}\left(\frac{1}{r^2}\frac{dt}{dr}\right) = \frac{1}{k_L a''} + \frac{1}{4\pi r^2 n_p}\left(\frac{1}{k_{SL}} + \frac{1}{k_R}\right) \tag{12.58}$$

Integration of this equation gives a relation between time and the radius of the particle. The latter can, in turn, be related to the fractional conversion. The various controlling mechanisms for this case are summarized in Table 12.2.

The following assumptions were made in this derivation.

1. The k_{SL} and $k_L a''$ values are not significantly affected by a decrease in the solid particle size.
2. All solid particles shrink uniformly in size as the reaction proceeds.

In the foregoing discussion the chemical reaction was assumed to be a first-order process. If the reactions are not first order, then an appropriate rate equation can be written. For these cases, however, the overall equations become nonlinear.

12.2.3. Examples: Solid–Liquid Systems

Reduction of Vat Dyes with Aqueous Alkaline Solutions of Sodium Hydrosulfite

The first step in the dyeing of fibers with vat dyes consists of the reduction and solubilization (vatting) of the quinonoid form to the soluble leuco form with aqueous alkaline solutions of sodium hydrosulfite. The rate of reduction of vat dyes, which are practically insoluble in aqueous solutions, to the leuco form plays an important role in the dyeing process, particularly in the case of pigment padding dyeing systems as well as in printing. The time of half reduction of a variety of vat dyes, under otherwise fairly uniform conditions, has been found to vary markedly, ranging from less than 5 sec to as high as 3000 sec. The following observations have been made (Peters, 1975).

1. There was practically no effect of caustic soda concentration in the range of about 5×10^{-5} to 1×10^{-3} mol/cm^3 on the rate of reduction of vat dyes.
2. For a range of dyes, the rate of reduction was found to increase by a factor of 3 when the sodium hydrosulfite concentration was increased from 2.3×10^{-5} to 1.15×10^{-4} mol/cm^3. This indicates that the rate of reduction does not vary linearly with the concentration of hydrosulfite.
3. An increase in the temperature from 40 to 60°C resulted in an increase in the rate of reduction by a factor of 3.
4. The effect of particle shape and size has not been clearly established. It is clear, however, that the rate of reduction does not vary linearly with the particle size. Further, milling the dye does not necessarily result in an increase in the rate of reduction. The particle shape (i.e., the crystal habit) evidently plays an important role. (The disk centrifuge method was employed to obtain the average size as well as the size distribution of the particles.) It

is likely that the larger crystals contain weak cleavage planes or are assemblages of small crystals, and as a consequence break down into much smaller particles when first attacked by the reducing agent.

From these data, which establish the fairly pronounced effect of temperature, hydrosulfite concentration, and crystal habit and size, it is clear that mass transfer factors are unlikely to be important and that the process appears to be surface reaction controlled. Further work is necessary to establish unambiguously the kinetics of the surface reaction.

Acidization of Dolomite, Calcite, and Feldspar with **HCl / HF** *Mixtures*

The productivity of petroleum wells can be considerably improved through the process of acidization, which is concerned with the application of acids and acid mixtures to dissolve porous and nonporous materials. The permeability of the formation is improved via matrix acidization and fracture acidization. For dolomite and calcite HCl can be used, but for sandstone HF/HCl mixtures have to be employed. Lund et al. (1973) and Fogler et al. (1975) have made a detailed study of the kinetics of the dissolution of dolomite, calcite, and feldspars in HCl/HF mixtures. In all these cases, the products of the various reactions are soluble in water.

Disks 5 cm (2 in.) in diameter and 0.635 cm ($\frac{1}{4}$ in.) thick were cut from the solid rock and polished. Disks were selected for the studies because mass transfer to rotating disks has been studied fairly extensively (and hence mass transfer factors can be easily taken into consideration). In order to suppress the evolution of gas, which may distort the mass transfer characteristics of rotating disks, the system was pressurized with N_2 up to about 42 atm in the case of dolomite. The speed of agitation was varied up to about 500 rev/min and the temperature was varied from 25 to 100°C. In addition, the acid concentration was varied over a wide range (HCl, 0.01–9 *M*; HF, 0.05–2.5 *M*). By varying the agitation speed, acid concentration, and temperature, the controlling mechanism could be discerned.

In the case of dolomite the speed of agitation had no effect on the rate of dissolution at 25 and 50°C. At 100°C, however, there was a significant effect of the speed of agitation on the rate of dissolution, which indicates the existence of diffusional resistance at 100°C. Thus at 25 and 50°C the dissolution was essentially surface reaction controlled. The dependence of the rate of dissolution on the concentration of the acid was found to vary with the temperature. The rate varied as the 0.44, 0.61, and 0.83 power of the HCl concentration at 25, 50, and 100°C, respectively. (For 100°C this power was obtained after accounting for diffusional resistance.) For surface-reaction-controlled cases the value of the activation energy was found to be high ($\simeq$ 15 kcal/mol). It appears that hydrogen ions are adsorbed on the solid dolomite surface and these react with the matrix. The adsorption of hydrogen ions can be described by a Freundlich isotherm.

Under conditions of practical relevance in reservoirs, mass transfer factors are expected to play an important role in the case of HCl–$CaCO_3$/dolomite systems. Some of the earlier data where mass transfer factors were important have been analyzed by Williams et al. (1970), who have proposed a model for liquid flow through a channel (where an acid mixture flows between parallel walls of calcium carbonate).

Fogler et al. (1975) have studied the dissolution of potassium and sodium feldspar in HCl–HF mixtures at 25 and 100°C. Here a pressure of 3.7 atm was adequate to prevent the evolution of gas. Silica reacts with HF to give SiF_4. The rates of dissolution were found to be independent of the speed of stirring, and hence diffusional factors were unimportant. The controlling mechanism was found to be the surface reaction. A strong influence of HCl concentration on the rate of dissolution was observed, and this was attributed to the adsorption of hydrogen ions on the mineral surface.

Reaction between Phosphate Rock and Mineral Acids

The manufacture of different types of phosphatic fertilizers, which is practiced on a very large scale, entails the reaction between ground phosphate rock and a strong acid. For the manufacture of phosphoric acid, acidulation with sulfuric acid is most extensively employed, since the product $CaSO_4$ (either as gypsum or hemihydrate) precipitates out and can be filtered. Here one of the products is insoluble. By contrast, in other methods, which make use of nitric acid and hydrochloric acid, the products are soluble in the aqueous medium. There is very limited information in the literature on the kinetics of these reactions.

Reaction with Sulfuric Acid (Andrew, 1979). Since the product $CaSO_4$ is insoluble, we have problems associated with the reaction between ground phosphate rock and sulfuric acid as well as with the crystallization of $CaSO_4$ (say, as gypsum or hemihydrate). Further, the reaction steps are different when phosphoric acid is initially present. In commercial practice magma recycle is carried out so that the initial acid mixture contains phosphoric acid and $CaSO_4$ particles are available for crystal growth.

The reaction steps are as follows:

$$Ca_3(PO_4)_2 + 4H_3PO_4 \rightleftharpoons 3Ca(H_2PO_4)_2 \quad \text{(i)}$$

$$Ca(H_2PO_4)_2 + H_2SO_4 + 2H_2O \rightarrow 2H_3PO_4 + CaSO_4 \cdot 2H_2O \quad \text{(ii)}$$

It is likely that the first step is faster than the second step, which involves precipitation. However, the first step is limited by an equilibrium that is dependent on the concentrations of calcium and phosphorous in the solution. If the attainment of equilibrium given by the first step becomes sufficiently fast, the attack rate will be governed by the rate of gypsum (or hemihydrate) precipitation, since this will displace the equilibrium and allow more rock to dissolve.

In case the initial acid mixture does not contain phosphoric acid and gypsum (hemihydrate), we will have considerably retarded rates of attack, since the formation of needlelike crystals of gypsum on the rock particles will interfere adversely with the reaction.

The particle size of the ground phosphate rock is very important. Thus factors that conduce to high rates of attack are (1) fine grinding of the phosphate rock; (2) the presence of a high concentration of phosphoric acid in the acid mixture; and (3) the presence of sufficient gypsum to ensure adequate surface for crystal growth.

Reaction with Nitric Acid. There is increasing interest all over the world, particularly where sulfur is not indigenous to the region, in the use of nitric acid in place of sulfuric acid, since then the nitrate value of the attacking acid can also be used. (In the case of sulfuric acid, sulfate part goes to a very low value product—gypsum.) Hussien and Seif (1980) have studied some aspects of the reaction of Egyptian rock with nitric acid. These authors have found that particle sizes in the ranges $-36 + 85$, $-85 + 120$, $-120 + 240$, and -240 mesh BSS show practically the same rate of attack and that particle size is therefore unimportant in the range covered. It is desirable to use 6 M HNO_3 and 10% excess acid over the stoichiometric requirement.

Separation of n-Paraffins from Isoparaffins and Other Substances by the Urea Adduction Process

The urea adduction process is used commercially for the manufacture of *n*-paraffins. Here a solid–liquid reaction system is involved. Yang and Manning (1970) have studied this problem and have, for the sake of convenience, used the system hexadecane/decane–urea–isopropanol. Seed crystals were added to most of the reacting solutions in order to simplify the analysis by avoiding complications arising from rates of nucleation. A stopped-flow reactor was used for kinetic studies.

The adduction rate was found to be inversely proportional to the initial supersaturation at constant seed density and inversely proportional to the logarithm of the seed density at constant initial supersaturation. Experimental data clearly show that the rate of adduction is controlled by diffusional factors. The predicted rate agreed with the experimental rate. Thus the diffusion of the reactive species to the reacting site controls the rate. It would be desirable to know which of the two reactants controls the rate. The molecular ratio in the adduct was about 11 for urea–hexadecane and about 8 for urea–decane. Further, the experimental solutions always contained less than 3 mol % urea and more than about 45% hexadecane and decane. Thus there will be an immediate deficiency of urea molecules at the reaction site and the rate will be controlled by the flux of urea. The diffusivity of urea may be affected by several factors, such as urea concentration, solvent concentration, and the interaction between urea and urea and urea and solvent. Thus the diffusion of polyurea molecules may be involved.

Manufacture of Cationic and Anionic Types of Ion-Exchange Resins

The common types of ion-exchange resins are manufactured from beads of copolymers of styrene and divinylbenzene (DVB). The sulfonated variety is used as the cationic type resin and the chloromethylated variety (after condensation with a suitable amine) is used as the anionic type resin.

Pepper (1951) has studied some aspects of the sulfonation of copolymer beads. It was observed that the rate of sulfonation of the copolymer beads (containing 5% nominal DVB) was dependent on the particle size. To attain a particular resin capacity, 30 to 50 μm and 100 to 150 μm particles took 20 and 90 minutes, respectively, under otherwise uniform conditions. It was observed that the resistance associated with the diffusion of sulfuric acid to the particle surface was unimportant.

Pepper et al. (1953) have studied some aspects of the chloromethylation of copolymer beads with chloromethyl methyl ether in the presence of stannic chloride as a catalyst. Here too it was observed that the resistance associated with the diffusion of this ether to the particle surface was negligible.

Manufacture of Organometallic Compounds: Grignard Reagents

Grignard reagents (alkyl magnesium halides) are used for the manufacture of fine chemicals. The manufacturing process consists of reaction between an alkyl halide and metallic magnesium in the presence of ether. There is little information in the literature on the kinetics of this type of reaction. A recent paper indicates that the rate of reaction is directly proportional to the magnesium surface area, concentration of ether, and concentration of alkyl halide (Horak et al., 1975). This indicates that the rate is controlled by a surface reaction; diffusional factors are unimportant.

Alkali Metal Alkyls. Lithium and sodium alkyls are made by dispersing Li or Na in alkyl chloride dissolved in a solvent such as benzene or petroleum ether. There is practically no information in the literature on the kinetics of this type of reaction. A related example of the manufacture of lithium aluminum hydride may also be cited, where the reaction between $AlCl_3$ dissolved in ether and suspended LiH is carried out:

$$4LiH(s) + \underset{\text{(solution in ether)}}{AlCl_3} \rightarrow LiAlH_4 + 3LiCl(s)$$

12.2.4. Examples: Gas–Liquid–Solid Systems

Reaction between Oxygen, Silver, and Cyanide Solutions

When oxygen, silver, and cyanide solutions are combined, the following reaction occurs:

$$O_2 + 4Ag + 8CN^- + 2H_2O \rightleftharpoons 4Ag(CN)_2^- + 4OH^-$$

The kinetics of this reaction has been investigated by Kakovsky and Kholmanskikh (1959). The reaction was found to be proportional to the concentration of cyanide ions in the range of $3.85–9.40 \times 10^{-6}$ mol/cm^3 and to be independent of the partial pressure of oxygen. The rate of reaction was also found to be influenced by the speed of stirring. This indicates that the process is governed by the transport of CN^- ions from the bulk of the solution to the silver metal surface. The mass transfer coefficient k_{SL} was found to be 2.89×10^{-3} cm/sec at 25°C. The corresponding mass transfer coefficient for a rotating disk under similar hydrodynamic conditions, calculated theoretically, was much higher than this value, which indicates that the process is not entirely controlled by the transport to the solid surface.

The process of oxidation can be assumed to be a two-step process represented as

$$M + CN^- \rightarrow M(CN) + e$$

$$M(CN) + CN^- \rightarrow M(CN)_2^-$$

The species formed in the first step, M(CN), forms an insoluble layer on the silver surface, and the cyanide ions have to diffuse through this insoluble layer so that they can react with the metallic silver. Hence there is an additional resistance to diffusion, which accounts for the low value of the mass transfer coefficient obtained experimentally.

When the cyanide concentration was above the critical value, the rate was found to be proportional to the oxygen pressure. This indicates that at high levels of cyanide concentrations, the transport of oxygen to the metal surface becomes the rate-controlling step.

The effect of temperature on the reaction rate was found to be as follows: below the critical cyanide concentration the energy of activation was about 1.52 kcal/mol at temperatures around 30°C. At higher cyanide concentrations the rate was only slightly dependent on temperature, since under these conditions the rate is limited by the transfer of O_2, and the solubility of O_2 decreases with an increase in temperature.

Kinetics of Dissolution of Copper and Cupric Sulfide in Aqueous Ammonia

Dissolution of Copper. Metallic copper is capable of dissolving in aqueous ammonia as a result of the formation of a cuprous complex, and the reaction can be used for the recovery of copper from ores and tailings containing about 0.4% Cu as a native metal. A similar reaction has been used to recover nickel and cobalt. The reaction can be represented as follows:

$$\tfrac{1}{2}O_2 + Cu + 4NH_3 + H_2O \rightleftharpoons Cu(NH_3)_4^{2+} + 2OH^-$$

No reaction occurs in the absence of oxygen. The mechanism of this process has been studied by Habashi (1963) on the basis of the electrochemical theory of leaching reactions. In this theory, it is assumed that the solid surface has some anodic areas at which an element oxidizes and cathodic areas at which the electrons are transferred to the oxidizing agent. On this basis, the total area S_e on which reaction occurs is divided into two parts: S_1, at which the cathodic reaction

$$\tfrac{1}{2}O_2 + H_2O + 2e \rightarrow 2OH^- \qquad \text{(a)}$$

occurs; and S_2, at which the anodic reaction

$$Cu + 4NH_3 \rightarrow Cu(NH_3)_4^{2+} + 2e \qquad \text{(b)}$$

takes place. We have:

$$S_e = S_1 + S_2$$

The rate of step (a) in terms of Cu oxidized, assuming the process to be diffusion controlled, is

$$2\frac{D_{O_2}}{\delta}S_1[O_2] = 2k_{SL}S_1[O_2]$$

The rate of step (b), assuming the process to be chemical reaction controlled, is

$$k_R S_2[NH_3]$$

where k_R is the surface reaction constant.

Under steady-state conditions the rates of the anodic and cathodic reactions must be equal:

$$\text{Rate of dissolution of copper} = 2k_{SL}S_1[O_2] = k_R S_2[NH_3]$$

Elimination of S_1 and S_2 results in the following equation:

Rate of dissolution of copper

$$= \frac{2k_{SL}k_R S_e[O_2][NH_3]}{2k_{SL}[O_2] + k_R[NH_3]}$$

The equation indicates that at high ammonia concentrations and low oxygen concentrations, the transport of O_2 to the solid surface will be controlling and the rate will be proportional to the partial pressure of oxygen and will be dependent on the speed of stirring in a mechanically agitated contactor.

When the ammonia concentration is low compared with the oxygen concentration, the term $k_R[NH_3]$ becomes controlling. The experimental data are in agreement with these predictions.

Leaching of Cupric Sulfide in Aqueous Ammonia. The hydrometallurgical route for the processing of sulfide ores of copper involves leaching with ammonia in the presence of O_2. Although some studies have been done, the mechanism of leaching with ammonia has not been unequivocally established. Reilly and Scott (1976) have studied the rate of dissolution of synthetic covellite (CuS) in ammoniacal solutions under oxygen pressure under such conditions that the chemical reaction rate controlled the overall rate. The range of variables covered was as follows: temperature, 5–85°C; oxygen pressure up to 68 atm; ammonia concentration, 2.5–7.0 M.

An interesting point that has been brought out is that the low yields reported in the literature at temperatures above 100°C are probably due to the hydrolysis of the soluble cupric amine salt. The mechanism is similar to that of the leaching of metallic copper.

An empirical equation can correlate the specific reaction rate per unit area quite accurately. The specific rate was found to vary as the one-third power of the dissolved O_2 concentration and the one-half power of the dissolved ammonia concentration.

Carbonation of a Suspension of MgO *(Changing Particle Size)*

Smithson and Bakhshi (1973) have studied the kinetics and mechanism of carbonation of MgO slurries in a small mechanically agitated contactor provided with a 4.5-cm four-blade propeller stirrer. Most of the experiments were done at an agitation speed of 1600 rev/min. The specific surface area of MgO particles varied from 12.1 to 80.8 m^2/g. The carbonation reaction was carried out at 9, 18, 28, and 38°C.

For all samples at 38°C, except that having a surface area of 12.1 m^2/g, the rates of carbonation were linear up to 80% conversion of MgO. It is clear that in such a case the rate-controlling step cannot be either surface reaction or solid–liquid film diffusion, since in both these cases the rate of carbonation is directly dependent on the surface area, which decreases with increasing percentage of conversion of MgO. It appears that the rate-controlling step is the transfer of CO_2 into the liquid phase (step 1 in Section 12.2.2).

At lower temperatures of 9, 18, and 28°C, under otherwise uniform conditions, the rate of carbonation did not vary linearly with the percentage of carbonation of MgO, and in fact the rate curves showed exponential behavior. An analysis of the experimental data shows that the rate-controlling step is the surface reaction. This can be easily deduced on the basis of a preliminary estimate of k_{SL} on the assumption that $k_{SL}d_p/D_A$ is equal to 2 (see Section 11.1.2). The activation energy for the surface reaction was found to be 7.2 kcal/mol.

Wet Oxidation of Nylon-66 (Changing Particle Size)

Some of the solid polymeric waste materials can be oxidized by air under wet conditons. Sundstrom et al. (1976) have studied the kinetics of the aqueous-phase oxidation of nylon-66 particles suspended in water at temperatures up to 190°C. A cylindrical disk of nylon-66 having a diameter of 5 cm (2 in.) was used so that the effect of mass transfer factors could be rationally considered. The speed of rotation was varied from about 50 to 250 rev/min. A kinetic rate expression was developed. The order of reaction with respect to the dissolved O_2 concentration was found to be 0.6.

Manufacture of Alkali Metal Hydrides: Reaction between H_2 *and Alkali Metal Suspended in a Solvent*

Alkali metal hydrides are manufactured by suspending the alkali metal in a high-boiling hydrocarbon solvent.

$$H_2 + 2M \rightarrow 2MH$$

It is known that good agitation increases the reaction rate. At temperatures higher than 97.5°C, Na metal will exist in the molten form, and we would then have a case of a gas–liquid–liquid reaction system.

Chlorination of Wood Pulp (Unchanging Particle Size)

The first stage in the bleaching of wood pulp is usually the chlorination of an aqueous suspension of wood pulp. This process is carried out at low as well as high pH. Karter and Bobalek (1971) have studied the mechanism of wood pulp chlorination at low pH. In this study the reaction was carried out in a pipeline reactor. An analysis of their experimental data, on the basis of a plot of the dimensionless conversion against the dimensionless time, indicates that diffusion through the product is the rate-controlling step.

Manufacture of Zinc Dithionite: Reaction between Dissolved SO_2 *and Zinc Particles Suspended in Water; Manufacture of Sodium Dithionite by the Formate Process*

Sodium hydrosulfite (dithionite) is generally manufactured from zinc dithionite, which in turn is manufactured by the reaction between SO_2 and fine zinc particles suspended in water.

$$2SO_2(aq) + Zn \rightarrow ZnS_2O_4$$

Here the product is soluble in water.

Szabo and Kaldi (1976) have studied the role of mass transfer in this reaction and some other aspects in three different types of reactors: (i) a 1.7-cm-i.d., 134-cm-long glass wetted wall reactor; (ii) a 1-liter mechanically agitated semibatch reactor; (iii) a 2.7-cm-diameter, 200-cm-long cocurrent horizontal pipeline reactor. The particle size of the zinc powder was in the range of 1–27 μm.

In the semibatch reactor the partial pressure of SO_2 was varied from 30 to 150 mm Hg and the temperature was maintained at 60°C. To study the effect of temperature, the partial pressure of SO_2 was maintained at 150 mm Hg and the temperature was varied from 30 to 60°C. The effects of temperature and partial pressure of SO_2, under otherwise comparable conditions, on the rate of dissolution were not very significant. The amount of zinc powder made a very substantial difference in the rate of dissolution. It appears that mass transfer associated with the solid–liquid film was the controlling step.

This reaction can be advantageously carried out in a cocurrent horizontal pipeline contactor.

Sastri and Epstein (1978) also studied the kinetics of dissolution of zinc in aqueous solutions of SO_2. A 0.90-cm-diameter zinc rod mounted on a shaft was used; the shaft speed could be varied up to 10,000 rev/min. The exposed length of the zinc rod was 5.5. cm and the area of contact 16.0 cm^2. These authors found that the speed of agitation had no effect on the rate of dissolution beyond 500 rev/min, under otherwise similar conditions. Thus diffusional resistance could be conveniently eliminated. The reaction was found to be first order in the dissolved SO_2. The temperature of reaction was varied from 11.9 to 48.9°C and the activation energy was found to be 3.5 kcal/mol.

Manufacture of Sodium Dithionite by the Formate Process. In recent years the manufacture of sodium dithionite (sodium hydrosulfite) by the reduction of SO_2 with sodium formate has acquired considerable importance, since sodium formate is available as a by-product from some processes and can also be conveniently manufactured by the absorption of CO in aqueous NaOH. Methanol is used as a solvent.

$$2SO_2 + NaOH + HCOONa \rightarrow Na_2S_2O_4 + CO_2 + H_2O$$

This reaction involves three phases: gas, liquid, and solid. It is not certain whether the reaction occurs in the liquid phase or at the solid–liquid interface. Ertl et al. (1979) have shown that the reaction involves an intermediate—$Na_2S_2O_5$. NaOOCH, which can be isolated and characterized by X-ray diffraction.

That the reaction probably occurs at the solid–liquid interface is indicated by the following observations:

1. The yield of dithionite decreases with an increase in water concentration, since this results in increasing the solubility of the intermediate product.
2. The stability of soluble dithionite is rather poor under operating conditions.
3. Microscopic examination reveals that initially transparent crystals of the $Na_2S_2O_5 \cdot$ NaOOCH double salt become cloudy with increasing concentration of dithionite.
4. The crystal habit of dithionite obtained from the formate process is different from that obtained from the zinc dust process, where the crystallization is done from aqueous solution.

REFERENCES

Andrew, S. P. S. (1979), The Design of Gas–Liquid Heterogeneously Catalyzed Reactors, private communication.

Ertl, G., Kiener, V., Ostertag, W., and Wunsch, G. (1979), *Angew Chem. Int. Ed. Engl.*, **18**, 313.

Fogler, H. S., Lund, K., and McCune, C. C. (1975), *Chem. Eng. Sci.*, **30**, 1325.

Habashi, F. (1963), *Ber. Bunsen-Ges.*, **67**, 402.

Hikita, H., and Asai, S. (1964), *J. Chem. Eng. Japan*, **2**, 77.

Horak, M., Palm, V., and Soogenbits, U. (1975), *Reaktsii Sposobu. Organ. Soedin.*, **11**(3), 709; *Chem. Abstr.* (1976), **84**, 73330.

Hussien, M., and Seif, S. (1980), *Chem. Econ. Eng. Rev.*, **12**(2), 39.

Juvekar, V. A., and Sharma, M. M. (1973), *Chem. Eng. Sci.*, **28**, 825.

Kakovsky, I. A., and Kholmanskikh, Yu. B. (1959), *Izvest. Akad. Nauk S.S.S.R., Otdel. Tekh. Nauk, Met. i Toplivo*, **5**, 97 (in Russian); *Chem. Abstr.* (1961), **55**, 13237.

Karter, E. M., and Bobalek, E. G. (1971), *Tappi*, **54**(11), 1882.

Lund, K., Fogler, H. S., and McCune, C. C. (1973), *Chem. Eng. Sci.*, **28**, 691.

Mahajani, V. V. (1976), *Indian Chem. Eng. (Trans.)*, **18**, 49.

Pepper, K. W. (1951), *J. Appl. Chem.*, **1**, 124.

Pepper, K. W., Paisley, H. M., and Young, M. A. (1953), *J. Chem. Soc.*, 4097.

Peters, R. H. (1975), *Textile Chemistry*, Vol. 3, *The Physical Chemistry of Dyeing*, Elsevier, Amsterdam, p. 598.

Phadtare, P. G., and Doraiswamy, L. K. (1965), *Ind. Eng. Chem. Process Design Dev.*, **4**, 274.

Phadtare, P. G., and Doraiswamy, L. K. (1966), *Ind. Eng. Chem. Process Design Dev.*, **5**, 351.

Ramachandran, P. A., and Sharma, M. M. (1969), *Chem. Eng. Sci.*, **24**, 1681.

Reilly, I. G., and Scott, D. S. (1976), *Ind. Eng. Chem. Process Design Dev.*, **15**, 60.

Sada, E., Kumazawa, H., and Butt, M. A. (1977a), *Chem. Eng. Sci.*, **32** 1165.

Sada, E., Kumazawa, H., and Butt, M. A. (1977b), *Chem. Eng. Sci.*, **32**, 1499.

Sada, E., Kumazawa, H., Butt, M. A., and Sumi, T. (1977c), *Chem. Eng., Sci.*, **32**, 972.

Sada, E., Kumazawa, H., and Butt, M. A. (1979a), *Chem. Eng. Sci.*, **34**, 715.

Sada, E., Kumazawa, H., Kudo, I., and Kondu, T. (1979b), *Chem. Eng. Sci.*, **34**, 719.

Sada, E., Kumazawa, H., and Butt, M. A. (1980), *Chem. Eng. Sci.*, **35**, 771.

Sastri, N. V. S., and Epstein, N. (1978), *Can. J. Chem. Eng.*, **56**, 124.

Smithson, G. L., and Bakhshi, N. N. (1973), *Ind. Eng. Chem. Process Design Dev.*, **12**, 99.

Sundstrom, D. W., Luciano, A. J., and Klei, H. E. (1976), *J. Appl. Polymer Sci.*, **20**, 207.

Szabo, M., and Kaldi, P. (1976), *Hungavian J. Ind. Chem.*, **4**, 39 (in English).

Tamhankar, S. S., and Chaudhari, R. V. (1979), *Ind. Eng. Chem. Fundam.*, **18**, 406.

Uchida, S., Koide, K., and Shindo, M. (1975), *Chem. Eng. Sci.*, **30**, 644.

Williams, B. B., Gidley, J. L., Guin, J. A., and Schechier, R. S. (1970), *Ind. Eng. Chem. Fundam.*, **9**, 589.

Yadav, G. D. (1980), Heterogeneous Reactions: Chlorination of Aqueous Phenols and Aromatic Sulfonic Acids; Effect of Diffusivity on True Gas-Side Mass Transfer Coefficient; Phase Transfer Catalysis, Ph.D. (Tech.) thesis, University of Bombay.

Yang, W.-C., and Manning, F. S. (1970), *Chem. Eng. Sci.*, **25**, 1423, 1431.

CHAPTER THIRTEEN

Mass Transfer Accompanied by Chemical Reaction in Fluid–Fluid Systems in the Presence of Solid Particles as Catalyst

A number of reactions of industrial importance, such as the hydrogenation of a variety of organic compounds, the hydrodesulfurization of petroleum fractions, and Fischer–Tropsch reactions, involve reaction between two fluids in the presence of a solid catalyst. Table 1.7 lists some such reactions, along with the type(s) of reactor that is (are) usually used. These reactions may be carried out in a variety of contactors, such as bubble (sparged) columns and mechanically agitated contactors (slurry reactors), and trickle-bed reactors. The liquid may contain the reactive species (as in, e.g., the hydrogenation of oils) or may be an inert medium to facilitate heat transfer (e.g., in the reaction between carbon monoxide and hydrogen to form light hydrocarbons). Sherwood and Farkas (1966), Satterfield (1970), Roberts (1976), Shah (1979), Deckwer and Alper (1980), Alper et al. (1980), and Chaudhari and Ramachandran (1980) have considered various aspects of slurry reactors.

In principle, gas–liquid reactions carried out in the presence of a colloidal metal or colloidal enzyme also fall in the category of slurry reactors. We may also have a situation where an immiscible liquid acts as the catalyst and this phase, under the operating conditions of the reactor, exists as fine droplets (diameter < 0.5 mm) that behave like rigid spheres. Molten salt media containing suspended catalyst particles have also been reported in the literature. Kelmers and Bennett (1976) have shown that Pt-based catalysts suspended in LiF–BeF_2–ThF_4 melts can reduce dissolved UF_5 to UF_4 when H_2 is used.

In recent years considerable attention has been given to the use of slurry adsorbers for a variety of applications. Slurry adsorbers offer a number of advantages over fixed-bed adsorbers in terms of easy adaptability to continuous operation, maintenance of isothermal conditions, longer life of adsorbents, and so on (Misic and Smith, 1971; Komiyama and Smith, 1975). The regeneration of powdered carbon from adsorbers can also be carried out under wet conditions in a slurry reactor (Charest and Chornet, 1976). A number of industrially important polymers are produced in heterogeneous systems involving suspended particles (McGreavy, 1972).

In Chapter 3 we considered many examples of reactions in which homogeneous catalysts based on expensive noble metals are used. Examples of such reactions are the carbonylation of methanol with CO to give acetic acid; the hydroformylation of olefins with CO and H_2 (oxo reaction) to give the corresponding aldehyde and/or primary alcohol; the conversion of ethylene to acetaldehyde, vinylacetate, and the like; and the hydrogenation of olefins. There are potential advantages in immobilizing these homogeneous catalysts with polymeric supports. Thus the catalyst can be easily separated from the reaction mixture and can possibly be used in continuous processes. Further, these heterogenized catalysts can be easily regenerated and reused. In addition, a hydrophobic matrix may protect the organometallic active center from deactivation by oxygen and water. There are distinct possibilities of conducting multistage reactions with a single catalyst (Leznoff, 1974; Manecke and Storck, 1978). A number of examples of potential interest have been reported by Manecke and Storck. In some cases in a homogeneous medium an organometallic compound may not act as a catalyst, but the same organometallic compound when heterogenized might work as a good catalyst. Terasawa et al. (1978) have shown that the *N*-benzylanthranilic acid complex of Pd(II) is inert in a homogeneous medium, whereas the bound catalyst displays very high activity.

McKillop and Young (1979) have also brought out the advantages of using supported reagents for carrying out a variety of organic reactions. In some cases it may be possible to realize a high selectivity that is not possible in homogeneous systems. Consider the bromination of a mixture of styrene and cyclohexene: When bromine adsorbed on molecular sieve 5A is used, α, β-dibromostyrene is formed in 95% yield; bromination of cyclohexene to a dibromo derivative does not occur. Thus we may deliberately decide to use slurry reactors for the types of reactions cited above.

In Section 3.1.16 we considered the example of phase transfer catalysts involving two liquid phases. In some cases it may be advantageous to use solid polymeric phase transfer catalysts. For instance, the loss of the catalyst can be drastically reduced. In Section 3.1.16 we cited an example of the conversion of *n*-octyl bromide to *n*-octyl cyanide by reaction with aqueous sodium cyanide solution. This reaction has also been studied with a polymeric heterogenized catalyst that showed comparable efficiency (Manecke and Storck, 1978).

In many cases of practical importance a liquid catalyst or a melt is supported on a porous solid support. Such catalysts are referred to as supported liquid-phase catalysts (SLPCs). Such catalysts have been used for vapor-phase solid-catalyzed reactions as well as for two-phase (gas–liquid and liquid–liquid) reactions (see Volume 1, Chapter 18). The best-known example of solid-catalyzed vapor-phase reactions is the conversion of SO_2 to SO_3 in the presence of a vanadium catalyst; in the case of gas–liquid reactions we can cite the alkylation of aromatic substances with olefins by using phosphoric acid on kieselguhr as a catalyst (a typical example is the reaction between benzene and propylene to give cumene).

Recently a novel application of the trickle-bed reactor (with cocurrent downflow) has been considered for the electrochemical production of propylene oxide (Boussoulengas et al., 1979). Here an aqueous electrolyte solution (1–3% w/w sodium bromide) and propylene are introduced at the top of a column stacked with packings (say, Raschig rings) made of graphite. An electrical potential is applied across the tower, and this induces bipolarity in each element of the packing (insulating nets of nylon are placed between each layer of packing). Electroregeneration of bromine occurs in the tower; propylene bromohydrin reacts with hydroxyl ions to give propylene oxide. This method appears to be promising.

The following steps are involved in the transfer of species A from the A phase to the B phase and subsequent chemical reaction in the presence of the solid particles as a catalyst.

1. Transfer of species A from the bulk A phase to the fluid–fluid interface. This resistance is unimportant if the A phase does not contain a diluent—that is, if it is pure and no volatile product is formed. Further, if A has very limited solubility in B (e.g., O_2 and H_2 in water and other solvents), then even for a dilute gas the resistance in the A phase becomes unimportant. Thus the resistance associated with this step is almost always unimportant in practice and can be safely ignored. However, if a more soluble gas, such as SO_2, is involved, then this resistance should be considered.
2. Transfer of species A from the fluid–fluid interface to the bulk of the B phase.
3. Transfer of dissolved A through the liquid film adjoining the solid particle to the solid surface.
4. Chemical reaction at the surface.

In the case of porous catalysts, species A may undergo diffusion and simultaneous chemical reaction in the interior of the catalyst and in such cases the effectiveness factor of the catalyst becomes important.

The concentration of the reactive species B is normally relatively high compared with that of A, and hence diffusion of B to the catalyst site is usually unimportant. It is not unlikely, however, that in some specific cases a situation may be encountered where the diffusion of species B to the catalyst surface becomes the controlling factor. (This matter is discussed in Section 13.1.8, Example 7.)

It has also been assumed that desorption of the product offers no resistance. This is generally valid, since in most cases in practice desorption occurs more readily than adsorption.

The concentration profiles for this case are shown in Figure 13.1. The relative merits of slurry reactors and trickle-bed reactors will be discussed later (see Section 14.4). Aspects of mass transfer associated with the gas–liquid film and the solid–liquid film in different types of contactor were considered in Chapter 11.

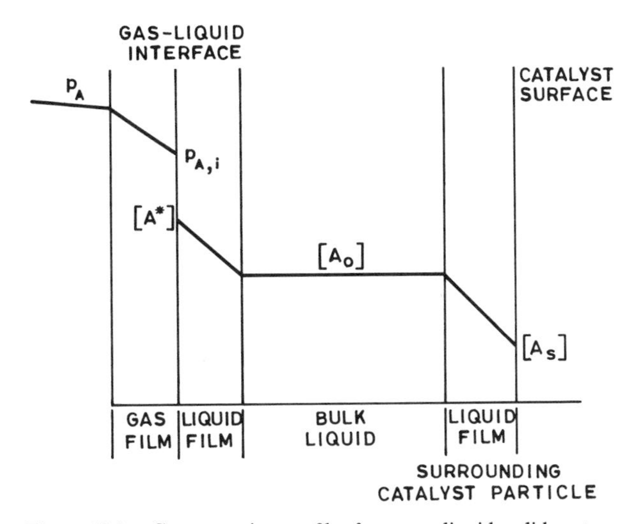

Figure 13.1. Concentration profiles for a gas–liquid–solid system where the solids act as a catalyst.

13.1. SLURRY REACTORS

13.1.1. General Considerations

Consider the case of systems where relatively fine catalyst particles are suspended in the liquid phase in a bubble column or a mechanically agitated contactor. We will assume that the reaction is first order in species A. (The situation where the reaction is not first order in A will be discussed later.) At steady state the rate equations for the various steps can be written as follows:

$$R'_A = k_L a''([A^*] - [A_o]) \quad \text{(for step 2)} \qquad (13.1)$$

$$= k_{SL} a_p([A_o] - [A_s]) \quad \text{(for step 3)} \qquad (13.2)$$

$$= k_R a_p [A_s] \quad \text{(for a first-order surface reaction on a nonporous catalyst; step 4).} \qquad (13.3)$$

It has been assumed that all the available surface in the catalyst is fully utilized. The situation when a porous catalyst is used and the effectiveness factor is less than 1 will be discussed later.

Elimination of $[A_o]$ and $[A_s]$ gives

$$\frac{[A^*]}{R'_A} = \frac{1}{k_L a''} + \frac{1}{k_{SL} a_p} + \frac{1}{k_R a_p}$$

$$= \frac{1}{k_L a''} + \frac{1}{a_p}\left(\frac{1}{k_{SL}} + \frac{1}{k_R}\right) \qquad (13.4)$$

If it is assumed that the catalyst particles and gas bubbles or dispersed-phase droplets are spherical and of uniform size of d_p and d_B, respectively, then Eq. 13.4 becomes

$$\frac{[A^*]}{R'_A} = \frac{d_B(1 - \epsilon_G)}{6 k_L \epsilon_G} + \frac{\rho_p d_p}{6w}\left(\frac{1}{k_{SL}} + \frac{1}{k_R}\right) \qquad (13.5)$$

since

$$a'' = \frac{6\epsilon_G}{d_B(1 - \epsilon_G)} \qquad (13.6)$$

$$a_p = \frac{6w}{\rho_p d_p} \qquad (13.7)$$

Equation 13.5 indicates that a plot of $[A^*]/R'_A$ against $1/w$ (the reciprocal of the catalyst loading) for a specified particle size should give a straight line. The intercept of this line will give $1/k_L a''$, while the slope will enable us to calculate $1/k_{SL} + 1/k_R$. It is interesting to note that plots of this type were first attempted more than 51 years ago by Davis et al. (1932). Such plots are helpful in analyzing the experimental data obtained for these systems. The following points should, however, be considered in the analysis of the experimental data:

1. It is assumed that the activity of the catalyst is maintained in all the experiments, that is, that no poisoning or deactivation of the catalyst occurs. The effect of poisoning of the catalyst on the rate of reaction would be relatively high at low catalyst loadings, and this might result in an upward curvature in the plot of $[A^*]/R'_A$ against $1/w$. Further, it is assumed that there is neither agglomeration nor disintegration of catalyst particles when the slurry is agitated. It is reasonable to presume that no disintegration of the catalyst particles occurs, since these are generally not friable. It is likely, however, that in practical situations, where relatively fine catalyst particles (say, smaller than 30 μm) are employed, some agglomeration of catalyst particles will occur.

It is assumed that solid particles are spherical. This should be actually checked by microscopic examination, since it is known that some catalyst particles are definitely not spherical. For instance, it is known that fine activated carbon particles are more nearly needle shaped than spherical (Bird, 1976; Chandrasekaran and Sharma, 1977). In the case of activated carbon particles sieve analysis does not give accurate particle size, and measured size may be 10 times the actual size for fine particles (Bird, 1976; see Section 13.1.8, Example 10). Active carbons are widely used as supports for Pt and Pd catalysts and it is of utmost importance to establish their particle size by proper techniques, such as use of an image analyzer or disk centrifuge.

2. It is assumed that the gas rate and/or mechanical agitation is sufficient to maintain the solid particles in suspension, that is, that there is no settling of catalyst particles and the entire surface area is available for the chemical reaction. There are reasons to believe that in some of the studies reported in the literature the solid particles were probably not kept in suspension (Sherwood and Farkas, 1966). The criteria for suspension of solid particles in agitated contactors were considered in Chapter 11. It is also assumed that the concentration of solid particles is uniform throughout the contactor. It must be ensured that this is in fact so. Hammer (1979) has shown that in gas-sparged slurry reactors a considerable variation in the axial solids concentration may be encountered.

3. It is assumed that d_B, ϵ_G and k_L are not affected by the variation in the catalyst loading and its size. However, it is likely that both ϵ_G and d_B are affected by the catalyst loading in the range normally encountered in practice. In fact, Slesser et al. (1968) have shown that in the case of gas–liquid–solid systems the holdup of the gas and the bubble size are affected by variation in the catalyst loading. Chandrasekaran and Sharma (1977) have shown that even 0.2% activated carbon particles can increase the value of $k_L a$ by about 30% as compared to that for an aqueous solution. One way to overcome the problem of the effect of catalyst loading on d_B, ϵ_G, and k_L is to use inert particles whenever possible in place of the catalyst particles (Zaidi et al., 1979). For example, if we are using a Pd/C catalyst, we can use carbon particles of identical characteristics as an inert material.

4. While conducting experiments in a bubble column reactor it is assumed that the gas phase moves in the plug flow manner, and while conducting experiments with a mechanically agitated reactor it is assumed that the gas phase is backmixed. These assumptions are irrelevant when the gas is pure. However, when the solute gas A is diluted with an inert gas and the outlet concentration of A is very different from the inlet concentration, then the validity of these assumptions becomes important. All the available evidence indicates that in laboratory bubble column reactors the assumption of plug flow for the gas phase is valid. In the case of a mechanically agitated contactor, however, caution must be exercised. It is known that in the absence of any fine solid particles the gas phase is essentially backmixed above a certain speed of agitation. However, when fine solid particles are present, then above a certain loading the gas phase may move in plug flow manner. Juvekar and Sharma (1973) have shown that in the carbonation of a slurry of lime, experimental data were better correlated with plug flow of the gas even under fairly intense agitation. Misic and Smith (1971) have also shown that for adsorption of benzene vapor in aqueous slurries of active carbons plug flow of the gas represents the data well. It is therefore necessary to ascertain the flow pattern of the gas with the actual system before it is accepted that the gas is backmixed or moves in plug flow. It may be noted that even when a pure gas is used and the reactant or one of the products is volatile, backmixing in the gas phase becomes important. For instance, in the reduction of aromatic nitro compounds with H_2 to the corresponding amino compound, water which is formed as a product of the reaction is desorbed.

5. It is assumed that the concentration of the fine solid particles in the fluid–fluid film is the same as that in the bulk. Since fine solid particles can sometimes show peculiar surface properties, it is possible that we will find cases where the concentration of solid particles in the film is greater than that in the bulk (Tsao, 1972).

6. It is assumed that no reaction occurs in the liquid film around the gas bubbles. Section 13.1.6 will deal with situations where the particle size may be smaller than the diffusion film thickness and a parallel reaction may occur while A diffuses.

Despite the limitations just pointed out, plots of $[A^*]/R'_A$ against $1/w$ are made in a routine way for the analysis of data from slurry reactors. If the resistance offered by the fluid–fluid film is relatively small compared to the overall resistance, the limitations listed will not materially affect the validity of these plots.

13.1.2. Procedure for Discerning the Controlling Mechanism

1. In any experimental study it is necessary to study the effect of the catalyst particle size and loading, and of the agitation speed in the case of a mechanically

agitated contactor or the superficial gas velocity in the case of bubble columns, on the overall rate of reaction. It must be ensured that in the range of the speed of agitation (or the superficial velocity) employed all catalyst particles are freely suspended and their concentration is uniform throughout the contactor.

If the value of a_p is very high or if $k_{SL}a_p$ and $k_R a_p$ are very high in comparison to $k_L a''$, the mass transfer of A from the A phase to the B phase becomes the controlling resistance. In these circumstances, the catalyst loading and the particle size will be unimportant and only factors affecting the dispersion characteristics of the system will be important. Thus in such cases the slope of the plot of $[A^*]/R'_A$ against $1/w$ for any specified particle size will be practically zero.

2. If the value of $k_L a''$ is very high in comparison to $k_{SL}a_p$ and $k_R a_p$, then the B phase will remain saturated with respect to the solute A. Here the plot of $[A^*]/R'_A$ against $1/w$ will show an insignificant value of the intercept. In such cases either the mass transfer to the solid surface or the chemical reaction at the catalyst surface will control the rate of reaction. The latter will be directly affected by the catalyst loading in such cases. At any given temperature, however, it is difficult to discern unambiguously whether diffusion through the liquid film adjacent to the solid particles or reaction at the surface is the controlling factor. The surface reaction rate constant k_R will be unaffected by the hydrodynamics of the system. In the turbulent regime the value of k_{SL} becomes independent of the particle size (see Section 11.1) and is substantially affected by the hydrodynamics (e.g., speed of agitation in mechanically agitated contactors).

When gas-sparged reactors are operated with relatively small catalyst particles and the particles' Reynolds number approaches 0, the value of k_{SL} would be expected to be inversely proportional to the particle size (see Section 11.1.2). The value of k_R is, however, independent of d_p and hence, in principle, if the gas–liquid resistance is absent, the effect of d_p on the rate at any specified catalyst loading may provide information on whether k_{SL} or k_R is controlling.

To get additional confirmation regarding the controlling mechanism, it may be necessary to study the effect of temperature on the rate of the reaction. A plot of $\ln[(1/k_{SL} + 1/k_R)^{-1}]$ against $1/T$ will give the value of the activation energy, ΔE, for the reaction. If the value of the activation energy is less than 5 kcal/mol, then mass transfer to solid particles is likely to control. On the other hand, if ΔE is greater than 10 kcal/mol, then the surface reaction would be controlling. In the range of ΔE from 5 to 10 kcal/mol, both k_{SL} and k_R are likely to be important. This discussion presumes that an increase in temperature does not result in activating the sites that were inactive at lower temperatures.

In some cases where catalysts, such as Pd or Pt on carbon, alumina, or molecular sieves, are used, it may be desirable to study, under otherwise the same conditions, the effect of the weight percentage of the active ingredient of the catalyst. In the case of a surface-reaction-controlled system the value of R'_A will be substantially affected by such a change; the rate may not vary linearly with the amount of the active species in the catalyst (e.g., the Pd or Pt content; Acres and Cooper, 1972). If k_{SL} is controlling, then variation in the percentage of the active ingredient should not have any significant influence on the value of R'_A.

3. The foregoing procedure is quite elaborate and time consuming. It may be worthwhile to examine the relative importance of different resistances on the basis of a single experiment under representative conditions (Sylvester et al., 1975). Thus if we can estimate with some certainty the values of $k_L a''$ and $k_{SL}a_p$, then the relative importance of different resistances can be seen and further experiments can then be accordingly planned. Goto (1976) has modified the procedure suggested by Sylvester et al. for batch reactors to cover the case of continuously operated slurry reactors.

Zero-Order Reactions

In the field of hydrogenation it is not uncommon to come across situations where the reaction is intrinsically zero order with respect to the concentration of hydrogen (Acres and Cooper, 1972). In this case instead of Eq. 13.3 the following equation will hold:

$$R'_A = k'_R a_p \tag{13.8}$$

(k'_R will have units of mol/cm^2 sec). We cannot get an explicit equation like 13.4 from Eqs. 13.1, 13.2, and 13.8. Here the rates of steps 2 and 3 will be directly affected by the total pressure of the system, since over the normal range of pressures employed in slurry reactors Henry's law holds. Thus the effect of pressure on R'_A can, in principle, be used as the basis for discerning the controlling mechanism. An increase in pressure will not affect the intrinsic rate, since the reaction is zero order in [A]. Thus up to a certain pressure value the rate of reaction may be directly proportional to the pressure, but thereafter the effect of pressure may be insignificant. Acres and Cooper (1972) have discussed such a case for the hydrogenation of dinitrotoluene dissolved in a suitable solvent (see Section 13.1.8, Example 3).

General-Order Reactions

For a general-order reaction when the order with respect to A is other than zero and one, an analytic equation like 13.4 cannot be obtained. The general procedure for assessing the importance of resistance associated with steps 2 and 3 can still be followed. For instance, if the speed of agitation has no effect on the value of R'_A (in the range where k_{SL} is also affected by the speed of agitation), then the controlling mechanism will be the surface reaction. Table 13.1 lists the effect of different variables that exercise major, minor, and negligible influence on R'_A.

Rigorous Procedure for Discerning Controlling Mechanism

The procedure outlined above, assumes, a priori, the order of reaction with respect to A. This is not very rational. It will be more realistic to first study the intrinsic kinetics of the reaction. This may be possible in most industrially important reactions. The procedure should be as follows.

1. Use a mechanically agitated contactor and operate it at relatively high speeds of agitation. For

TABLE 13.1. Controlling Mechanism in Slurry Reactors: Effect of Pertinent Variables on R'_A[a]

Controlling Resistance	Variables Whose Influence is		
	Major	Minor	Negligible
Gas–liquid mass transfer, $k_L a''$	[A*], type of impeller and stirring speed (mechanically agitated contactor), gas velocity (sparged contactor)	Temperature	$[B_o]$, d_p, w
Liquid–solid mass transfer of A, $k_{SL} a_p$ (for A)	d_p, w, [A*], stirring speed (mechanically agitated contactor, turbulent regime)	Temperature, gas velocity (sparged reactor, fine particles)	$[B_o]$
Liquid–solid mass transfer of B, $k_{SL} a_p$ (for B)	d_p, w, $[B_o]$, stirring speed (mechanically agitated contactor, turbulent regime)	Temperature, gas velocity (sparged reactor, fine particles)	[A*]
Surface reaction (pore diffusion negligible)	d_p, w, temperature, [A*], $[B_o]$; independent of [A*] for $m = 0$; independent of $[B_o]$ for $n = 0$		Type of impeller and stirring speed (mechanically agitated contactors); gas velocity (sparged contactors)
Surface reaction with pore diffusion	d_p, w, [A*], $[B_o]$, temperature[b]	Pore structure	Type of impeller and stirring speed (mechanically agitated contactors); gas velocity (sparged contactors)

[a]Adapted from Roberts (1976).
[b]The effect of temperature on R'_A is less pronounced in this case than for surface reaction where pore diffusion is negligible.

instance, for a 15-cm-i.d. fully baffled vessel provided with a turbine agitator about 8 cm in diameter, the speed of agitation should be in the range of 1000–5000 rev/min (i.e., impeller tip speeds should be in the range of 24,000–120,000 cm/min). For medium-pressure work it may also prove attractive to use a basket-type reactor (see Volume 1, Chapter 9). Kenney and Sedriks (1972) used such a reactor to study the hydrogenation of crotonaldehyde over palladium on an alumina catalyst (see Section 13.1.8, Example 6). Because of leakage problems with the gas, some serious experimental difficulties may be encountered for high-pressure reactions when a standard type of agitated reactor is employed. In such cases magnetically stirred autoclaves may be used. Turek et al. (1977) have pointed out that an integral confined-bed reactor, in which the gas and liquid flow cocurrently, may also be useful for laboratory studies.

The stirred basket reactor provides fairly high values of k_{SL}. Suzuki and Kawazoe (1975) and Teshima and Ohashi (1977) have made experimental measurements of k_{SL} in typical laboratory reactors by the technique of solid dissolution or adsorption of dissolved solute or ion exchange. Teshima and Ohashi have correlated their data with a Frössling-type equation and this should be helpful in making an estimate of the k_{SL} value.

In the case of liquid–liquid systems the value of the area of contact between two liquid phases can also be increased by increasing the fraction of the A phase. In general, up to a dispersed-phase fraction of about 0.3 the value of the effective interfacial area of contact is roughly proportional to the dispersed-phase fraction at impeller tip speeds greater than about 100 cm/sec.

2. Ensure that the diffusional resistances associated with steps 2 and 3 are eliminated. It is desirable to work with the finest catalyst particles possible (say 2–20 μm) and the highest practical loading of the catalyst. As a rule it is much easier to eliminate resistance associated with step 3, since the value of a_p can be made very large by both decreasing the particle size and increasing the catalyst loading.

3. The effect of pore diffusion should be eliminated by using very fine catalyst particles, as indicated above. This should be confirmed by studying the effect of particle size on the value of R'_A at a specified particle loading.

4. After ascertaining that all the diffusional resistances have been eliminated, the effect of the pressure of pure gas A in the case of gas–liquid systems on R'_A should be studied. From the foregoing data the order with respect to species A can be ascertained. In the case of liquid–liquid systems the mole fraction of A in the A phase should be varied to ascertain the order with respect to A. It should be ensured that there is no resistance to mass transfer in the A phase.

5. An additional check should be made by studying the effect of temperature on R'_A and noting the value of the activation energy, which should in general be greater than 10 kcal/mol for kinetically controlled reactions.

By following this procedure the intrinsic kinetics of the specified reaction can be established.

13.1.3. Effect of Temperature

Gas–Liquid and Liquid–Solid Mass Transfer Controlling

In cases where gas–liquid and liquid–solid mass transfer are rate controlling, with an increase in temperature the true k_L and k_{SL} values will nominally increase, since k_L is proportional to $D_A^{0.5}$ and k_{SL} to $D_A^{0.67}$. In most cases of gas–liquid systems the solubility of the gas decreases with an increase in temperature. However, H_2 gas behaves differently and its solubility actually increases with an increase in temperature. Thus in the case of hydrogen the solubility in soyabean oil increases by about 60% when temperature is raised from 20 to 100°C. Thus the overall effect in the case of reactions involving H_2 will be that the rate will increase significantly with an increase in temperature.

Surface Reaction Controlling

When surface reaction controls, the rate of reaction will increase very significantly with temperature when pore diffusional resistance is absent; the actual increase in the rate will depend on the value of the activation energy. When pore diffusional resistance is present the effect of temperature on the rate will be very much less than when there is no pore diffusional resistance.

13.1.4. Example for Discerning the Controlling Mechanism

The following data were obtained for the hydrogenation of an organic compound dissolved in a nonvolatile solvent in the presence of a noble metal catalyst in a 12.5-cm-i.d. mechanically agitated contactor provided with a 5.5-cm-diameter turbine impeller.

1. The rate of hydrogenation at a stirring speed of 1000 rev/min varied linearly with the absolute pressure of the system up to about 5 atm; thereafter it was independent of the pressure. The pressure at which this change in the dependence on the pressure occurred was lower at the higher speed of agitation of 1500 rev/min.
2. At a pressure of 8 atm the rate of reaction varied directly with the catalyst loading but there was no effect of the speed of agitation on the rate of reaction in the range from 1000 to 1500 rev/min. It is known that in this speed range the k_{SL} value is significantly affected.

What is the controlling mechanism?

It is clear that at an agitation speed of 1000 rev/min diffusional factors are eliminated above a pressure of 5 atm, since the rate of transfer of A from the gas phase to the liquid phase and the transfer of dissolved A from the bulk liquid phase to the catalyst particle surface will be directly affected by the pressure. Further proof is provided by the observation that the speed of agitation had no effect on the rate at 8 atm, even though both $k_L a''$ and $k_{SL} a_p$ would have been affected by the speed of agitation. The rate varied directly with the catalyst loading under these conditions. Thus the reaction is clearly surface reaction controlled and follows zero-order kinetics with respect to dissolved H_2. Below a speed of stirring of 1000 rev/min and a pressure of 5 atm diffusional factors are important.

13.1.5. Slurry Reactors Involving Reaction of Two Gases on a Suspended Catalyst

In some situations, two gases may be absorbed in a liquid medium containing a suspended catalyst and the two dissolved gases may react among themselves at the catalyst surface. For instance, carbon monoxide can be reacted with H_2 in an inert hydrocarbon medium containing an Ni–MgO catalyst to give methane ($CO + 3H_2 \rightarrow CH_4 + H_2O$). The oxidation of CO in the presence of cobalt oxide suspended in an inert liquid has also been studied (Ido et al., 1976). In general the reaction may be written as

$$A_1 + ZA_2 \xrightarrow{\text{catalyst}} \text{products} \tag{13.9}$$

For the sake of simplicity the reaction will be assumed to be first order with respect to A_1 as well as A_2.

The problem involves diffusion of two species, A_1 and A_2, from the gas phase to the solid surface via the liquid medium and subsequent chemical reaction on the surface. In some cases, the diffusion coefficients of A_1 and A_2 may be considerably different (like CO and H_2) and hence the mass transfer coefficients of A_1 and A_2 to the catalyst surface would be different. It will be assumed that k_L is proportional to the square root of D_A, and that k_{SL} is proportional to the two-thirds power of D_A. Therefore,

$$k_{L(A_2)} = k_{L(A_1)}\sqrt{\frac{D_{A_2}}{D_{A_1}}} = k_L\sqrt{\frac{D_{A_2}}{D_{A_1}}} \tag{13.10}$$

and

$$k_{SL(A_2)} = k_{SL(A_1)}\left(\frac{D_{A_2}}{D_{A_1}}\right)^{2/3} = k_{SL}\left(\frac{D_{A_2}}{D_{A_1}}\right)^{2/3} \tag{13.11}$$

The steps involved in the transport of A_1 to the solid surface are as follows (see the concentration profiles in Figure 13.2):

$$R'_{A_1} = k_L a''([A_1^*] - [A_{1,o}]) \tag{13.12}$$

for diffusion from gas phase into bulk liquid;

$$= k_{SL} a_p([A_{1,o}] - [A_{1,s}]) \tag{13.13}$$

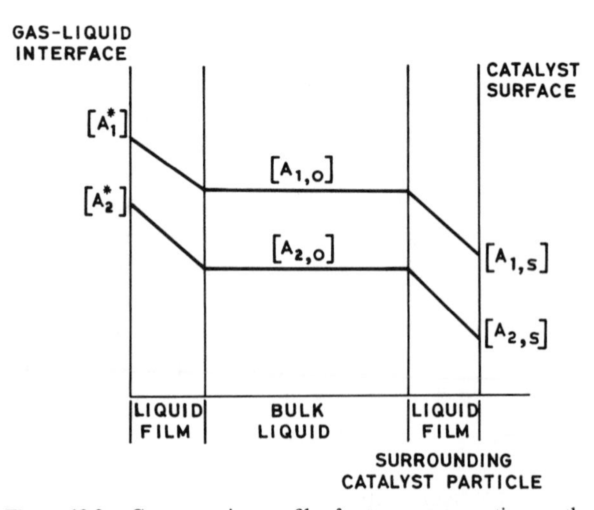

Figure 13.2. Concentration profiles for two gases reacting on the solid catalyst surface.

for diffusion from bulk liquid to catalyst surface; and

$$= k_R a_p [A_{1,s}][A_{2,s}] \quad (13.14)$$

for reaction at the catalyst surface. Eliminating the unknown term $[A_{1,o}]$, we obtain an expression for the concentration of A_1 at the catalyst surface as

$$[A_{1,s}] = [A_1^*] - R'_{A_1}\left(\frac{1}{k_L a''} + \frac{1}{k_{SL} a_p}\right) \quad (13.15)$$

The steps involved in the transport of species A_2 to the catalyst surface can be written similarly. Thus, the concentration of A_2 at the catalyst surface is given by

$$[A_{2,s}] = [A_2^*] - R'_{A_2}\left[\frac{1}{k_L a''}\sqrt{\frac{D_{A_1}}{D_{A_2}}} + \frac{1}{k_{SL} a_p}\left(\frac{D_{A_1}}{D_{A_2}}\right)^{2/3}\right] \quad (13.16)$$

At steady state,

$$R'_{A_2} = Z R'_{A_1} \quad (13.17)$$

Hence we obtain

$$[A_{2,s}] = [A_2^*] - Z R'_{A_1}\left[\frac{1}{k_L a''}\sqrt{\frac{D_{A_1}}{D_{A_2}}} + \frac{1}{k_{SL} a_p}\left(\frac{D_{A_1}}{D_{A_2}}\right)^{2/3}\right] \quad (13.18)$$

The rate of reaction at the solid surface is given by

$$R'_{A_1} = k_R a_p [A_{1,s}][A_{2,s}] \quad (13.19)$$

$$R'_{A_1} = k_R a_p \left\{[A_1^*] - R'_{A_1}\left(\frac{1}{k_L a''} + \frac{1}{k_{SL} a_p}\right)\right\} \times \left\{[A_2^*] - Z R'_{A_1}\left[\frac{1}{k_L a''}\sqrt{\frac{D_{A_1}}{D_{A_2}}} + \frac{1}{k_{SL} a_p}\left(\frac{D_{A_1}}{D_{A_2}}\right)^{2/3}\right]\right\} \quad (13.20)$$

Equation 13.20 is quadratic in R'_{A_1} in terms of the known quantities. The different cases that are possible are as follows.

Surface Reaction Very Rapid

Surface reaction is very rapid when the following condition is satisfied:

$$\frac{1}{k_R a_p} \ll \frac{1}{k_L a''} + \frac{1}{k_{SL} a_p} \quad (13.21)$$

(Here $k_L a''$ can be taken as the mean value of $k_{L(A_1)} a''$ and $k_{L(A_2)} a''$.) In this situation the reaction rate will be governed by the transport of either A_1 or A_2 or both A_1 and A_2 to the catalyst surface. The various cases are as follows.

1. $[A_{1,s}] = 0$, $[A_{2,s}]$ is finite, and the rate is controlled by the transfer of species A_1 when

$$[A_1^*] k_{L(A_1)} \ll [A_2^*] k_{L(A_2)} \quad (13.22)$$

2. $[A_{2,s}] = 0$, $[A_{1,s}]$ is finite and the rate is controlled by the transfer of species A_2 when

$$[A_2^*] k_{L(A_2)} \ll [A_1^*] k_{L(A_1)} \quad (13.23)$$

3. $[A_{1,s}] = 0$, $[A_{2,s}] = 0$, and the rate is controlled by the transfer of both A_1 and A_2 to the surface when

$$[A_1^*] k_{L(A_1)} = [A_2^*] k_{L(A_2)} \quad (13.24)$$

Surface Reaction Very Slow

This will be the case when

$$\frac{1}{k_R a_p} \gg \frac{1}{k_L a''} + \frac{1}{k_{SL} a_p} \quad (13.25)$$

(Here, $k_L a''$ can be taken as the mean value of $k_{L(A_1)} a''$ and $k_{L(A_2)} a''$.) For this case mass transfer factors will be unimportant and $[A_{1,s}]$ will be practically equal to $[A_1^*]$ and $[A_{2,s}]$ will be practically equal to $[A_2^*]$.

There is a dearth of information in the literature on experimental studies of systems falling in this category. Recently Kawakami et al. (1976) studied some aspects of the simultaneous hydrogenation of ethylene and propylene in a slurry reactor with Pt/C as a catalyst (see Section 13.1.8, Example 17). A more detailed discussion of this subject is presented by Ramachandran and Chaudhari (1979).

13.1.6. Catalyst Particles Smaller than Liquid (Gas–Liquid) Diffusion Film Thickness

In Section 12.1 we considered cases in which gas absorption is accompanied by an instantaneous reaction (or a fast reaction resulting in depletion of B) in a slurry containing sparingly soluble fine particles. In particular, we brought out the importance of simultaneous dissolution of solid particles in the film when the particle size is substantially smaller than the film thickness. The simultaneous dissolution of solid particles in the diffusion film can considerably enhance the specific rate of absorption accompanied by an instantaneous reaction. A somewhat similar situation can arise in slurry reactors, since in practice it is not uncommon to find catalyst particles in the micrometer and submicrometer range being used. Thus we can have a finite concentration of solid particles in the film. The constituent steps of diffusion of the solute from the gas–liquid interface to the bulk liquid and then through the liquid–solid film and subsequent surface reaction now become steps in parallel rather than in series as considered so far in this chapter (see Figure 13.3). In principle internal diffusion within catalyst pores may also be important, but in view of the very small size of the catalyst particles the effectiveness factor may well be very close to unity. Sada et al. (1977) have considered this situation with a generalized case of an effectiveness factor less than unity. A considerable enhancement in R'_A can occur as a result of the existence of fine catalyst particles in the film.

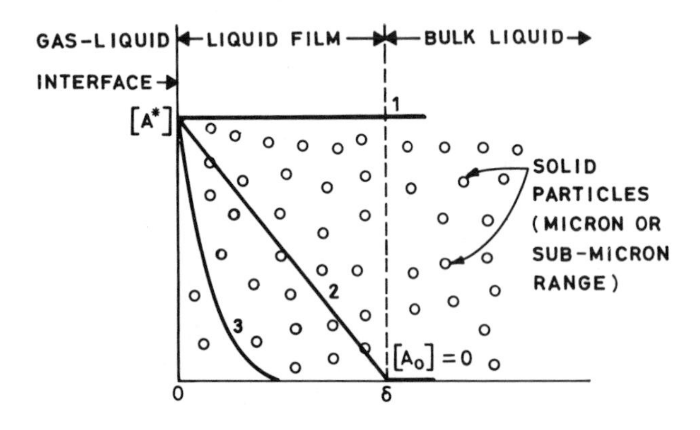

Figure 13.3. Concentration profiles for gas–liquid–solid (very fine particles): diffusion of solute A and the surface reaction are steps in parallel.

Alper et al. (1980b) have shown that finely powdered activated carbon increases the k_L value for O_2 considerably in a stirred cell; other particles such as those of quartz sand or acrylic beads did not increase the k_L value. The highly porous structure of activated carbon, which results in a high adsorption property, may be responsible for the increase in the value of k_L. It is postulated that a solid particle may move right into the diffusion film, adsorb some gas during its stay in the film, and go back into the bulk liquid. Thus we may well have an example of "facilitated" transport. These authors have also studied the absorption of O_2 in aqueous solutions of glucose where the oxidation reaction is catalyzed by Pt/C. The previous work of Lee and Tsao (1972) was considered and a lacuna in their analysis has been brought out, since it is quite likely that the enhancement in the rate of absorption of O_2 (observed by Lee and Tsao) was due to an increase in the value of k_L caused by carbon particles. In the work carried out by Alper et al. the carbon loading was kept the same but the Pt wt.% was varied. When the concentration of O_2 in the bulk liquid was finite no enhancement in the specific rate of absorption was observed. However, when no free O_2 existed in the bulk an increase in the catalyst concentration led to an enhancement by a factor of up to 2.

In principle we can have a fast reaction (regime 3) in a slurry reactor, where A completely reacts in the liquid film, which is further catalyzed by solid particles that happen to be very fine and smaller than the diffusion film thickness. Pal et al. (1982) have studied the oxidation of aqueous Na_2S, with and without carbon particles as a catalyst, at 80, 100, and 130°C in 14.5-cm-i.d. and 7.5-cm-i.d. stainless steel reactors that were operated as stirred cells (see Section 13.1.8, Example 10). In the absence of the catalyst the absorption of O_2 is accompanied by a fast pseudo-first-order reaction (regime 3) or conformed to the regime between 2 and 3. It appears that fine carbon particles can enhance the specific rate of absorption of O_2, indicating that a parallel reaction catalyzed by carbon particles also occurs in the film. In the case of a solution containing about 8×10^{-4} mol/cm^3 of Na_2S the value of R_A increased by a factor as high as about 13 at a catalyst loading as 1.0% w/w; the average catalyst particle size was 1.7 μm. There is need for further work in this area.

Pal et al. (1982) have proposed a model for this case where the reaction occurs in the diffusion film and is catalyzed by solid catalyst particles that are smaller than the diffusion film thickness (Figure 13.3).

The following differential equation holds for a fast pseudo-first-order reaction (Regime 3):

$$D_A \frac{d^2[A]}{dx^2} = k_1[A] + k_{SL}a_p[A] \quad (13.26)$$

where

$$k_1 = k_{1n}[B_o]^n \quad (13.27)$$

The second term on the right-hand side of Eq. 13.26 accounts for the reaction in the film due to catalyst particles. The following boundary conditions hold:

$$\text{At } x = 0, \quad [A] = [A^*], \quad \frac{d[B]}{dx} = 0 \quad (13.28)$$

$$\text{At } x = \delta, \quad [A] = 0 \quad (13.29)$$

The integration of Eq. 13.26 is straightforward and noting that $R_A = -D_A(d[A]/dx)_{x=0}$ leads to the following equation:

$$R_A = \frac{[A^*]\sqrt{D_A k_1 + D_A k_{SL} a_p}}{\tanh\left(\dfrac{\sqrt{D_A k_1 + D_A k_{SL} a_p}}{k_L}\right)} \quad (13.30)$$

When $(\sqrt{D_A k_1 + D_A k_{SL} a_p}/k_L)$ is greater than 3 the denominator term approaches unity and the following equation holds:

$$R_A = [A^*]\sqrt{D_A k_1 + D_A k_{SL} a_p} \quad (13.31)$$

From Eq. 13.31 it is clear that when $D_A k_1 \gg D_A k_{SL} a_p$ it reduces to

$$R_A \simeq [A^*]\sqrt{D_A k_1} \quad (13.32)$$

Here the contribution to the parallel reaction in film is negligible as the particle size is relatively very course leading to low values of a_p and k_{SL} (in the particle size relevant here k_{SL} will be inversely proportional to the particle size). Further when $D_A k_{SL} a_p \gg D_A k_1$ the following equation will hold:

$$R_A \simeq [A^*]\sqrt{D_A k_{SL} a_p} \quad (13.33)$$

Here R_A will be inversely proportional to d_p as both k_{SL} and a_p are inversely proportional to d_p. Further the activation energy will be substantially lower than when Eq. 13.32 holds. Equation 13.31 can be rewritten as:

$$\left(\frac{R_A}{[A^*]}\right)^2 = D_A(k_{SL}a_p + k_1)$$

$$\frac{1}{D_A}\left(\frac{R_A}{[A^*]}\right)^2 - k_1 = k_{SL}a_p$$

$$= \frac{2D_A}{d_p}\frac{6w}{\rho_p d_p} \quad \text{(for small size particles Sh = 2)}$$

$$= \frac{12}{\rho_p d_p^2} \times D_A w$$

$$= \alpha D_A w \quad (13.34)$$

where

$$\alpha = \frac{12}{\rho_p d_p^2} \quad (13.35)$$

A plot of $(1/D_A)(R_A/[A^*])^2 - k_1$ against $D_A w$ for a specified particle size should therefore be a straight line through origin having a slope of α. Thus data pertaining to different temperatures can be accommodated in a single plot.

Pal et al. have verified this theory for absorption of O_2 in aqueous solution of sodium sulfide at elevated temperature and pressure with fine activated carbon as a catalyst.

13.1.7. Slurry Reactors with Solid Particles as Reactants and Containing Two Immiscible Liquids

Solid Particles as Reactants

There are situations in practice when slurry reactors are employed for sparingly soluble solid reactant particles. For instance, the potassium salt of *m*-nitrobenzene sulfonic acid in an aqueous medium is reduced to metanilic acid in the presence of Ni/Pd/Pt-based catalyst (Ferrari and Garbei, 1969). Here an additional resistance associated with the dissolution of the solid particles becomes important. If the reactant particles are relatively coarse and their solubility is less than that of the gas, then the overall process may well be controlled by the dissolution of the solid reactant particles. This case can be easily analyzed on the basis of the available data on k_{SL} and solid reactant solubility. It is also conceivable that at low pressures [A*] may be less than [B_s] but that at higher pressures the converse may be true, since Henry's law is applicable.

A special situation arises when the solid reactant particles are insoluble but the actual reaction takes place between a decomposition product of this material that is soluble in the medium. A typical example is that of the hydrogenation of suspended cellulose or coal particles in an inert medium (see Section 13.1.8, Example 13).

Slurry Reactors Containing Two Immiscible Liquids

We have referred to the case of inert liquids being used to carry out a catalytic reaction. We may have yet another situation where for a reaction between a gas and a liquid reactant, in the presence of solid particles as catalyst, another immiscible liquid may be added in order to achieve certain results, which may, in part, be associated with the washing of poisons from the catalyst particles by the second liquid. Greenfield (1976) has shown that in the case of the hydrogenation of benzonitrile, with 5% Pt on carbon as a catalyst, at 100°C and pressure in the range of about 21–35 atm, the addition of water gives higher yields of dibenzylamine. Yields as high as 97% of dibenzylamine were realized with a 1 : 1 mol ratio of nitrile to water. It appears that water is able to prevent the poisoning of the catalyst. The reaction basically occurs in the liquid reactant phase.

Another interesting example of practical importance is concerned with the hydrogenation of epoxides, notably styrene oxide and α-olefin epoxides, directly to the corresponding primary alcohol. Here it has been shown that the presence of water, which is immiscible with the parent substance, in relatively large amounts gives almost quantitative yields of the relevant primary alcohol (Epoxides can isomerize to the corresponding methyl ketone and thus lead to the corresponding secondary alcohol; Newman et al., 1949). In the absence of water the yields of primary alcohol were low. The mechanistic aspects of this system have not been studied and deserve further attention. The presence of the second liquid phase is expected to change the mass transfer characteristics of the system.

13.1.8. Examples of Slurry Reactors

Some of the examples that have been reported in the literature are discussed in the following subsections.

1. Hydrogenation of α-Methyl Styrene (AMS) *and Phenyl Acetylene; Hydrogenation of Unsaturated Compounds with Polymer-Bound Catalysts*

***Hydrogenation of* AMS.** This reaction system has been adopted as a model reaction system by a number of authors for reasons of the simplicity of the system, the absence of by-product formation, and the ease with which the product can be analyzed. This system is also of some industrial importance in the manufacture of phenol by the cumene process where a small quantity of AMS is obtained as a by-product. Here AMS can be hydrogenated to cumene and thus can be recycled in the process.

Sherwood and Farkas (1966) have studied the hydrogenation of α-methyl styrene using Pd-black as the catalyst. The gas–liquid mass transfer was found to be relatively unimportant from a plot of the reciprocal of the rate of hydrogenation against the reciprocal of the catalyst loading (Figure 13.4). From the value of the activation energy, Sherwood and Farkas have shown that k_{SL} is the controlling factor and not k_R. From the intercept in the graphs of these authors, it is seen that $k_L a''$ increases as the temperature increases. A change in temperature from 27.8 to 65.5°C resulted in a 70% increase in $k_L a''$. Since k_L is proportional to $D_A^{0.5}$, this implies that the variation of $k_L a''$ with temperature is essentially due to the variation in k_L.

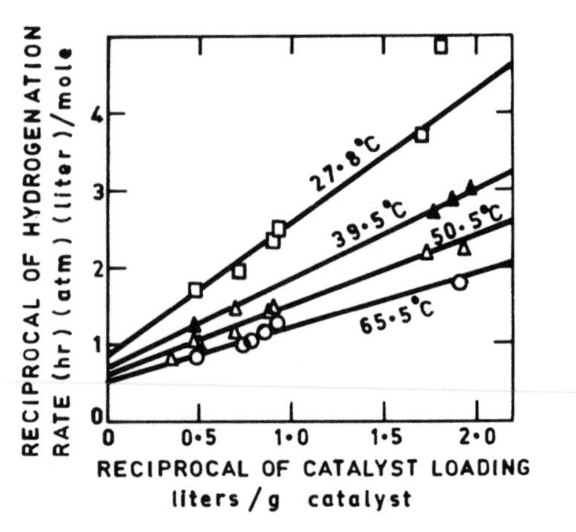

Figure 13.4. A plot of the reciprocal of the rate of hydrogenation against the reciprocal of the catalyst loading.

The k_{SL} value obtained from the experiments of Sherwood and Farkas does not, however, compare favorably with the k_{SL} value calculated independently on the basis of the correlation proposed by Friedlander (1961). Sherwood and Farkas had made their calculations on the basis of the estimated value of the diffusivity of hydrogen in cumene ($D_A = 1.1 \times 10^{-4}$ cm^2/sec). Subsequently the experimental value of the diffusivity of H_2 was obtained (1.7×10^{-4} cm^2/sec; Satterfield et al., 1968). With the experimental value of the diffusivity slightly better agreement between the predicted k_{SL} value and that calculated from the slurry reactor data is obtained. The major reason for this discrepancy is probably the lack of precise knowledge regarding the catalyst particle size in the reactor.

Pexidr et al. (1980) have also studied the hydrogenation of AMS in a gas-sparged slurry reactor with Pd/C as a catalyst. The weight percentage of Pd on C was varied and experiments were made at 30 and 60°C. It is clear from the experimental data that at 30°C as well as 60°C the dominant resistance was that due to the gas–liquid film. In a typical case, at 60°C with 5% Pd/C catalyst and a superficial gas velocity of 1.57 cm/sec and catalyst concentration of 1×10^{-3} g/cm^3, the values of $k_L a''$, $k_{SL} a_p$, and $k_R a_p$ were approximately 0.19, 1, and 1 sec^{-1}, respectively. These authors have clearly brought out the importance of particle size measurement and have shown that sieve analysis gives an unrepresentative picture of particle size. They have also made measurements in an agitated reactor (with a shaking arrangement), and here it was possible to almost eliminate the gas–liquid film resistance as well as the liquid–solid film resistance. Under these conditions the authors found a linear dependence of the rate on hydrogen pressure as well as Pd content (at less than a 4% Pd level).

Clarke et al. (1977) have studied liquid-phase hydrogenation with copper on magnesia–silica as a catalyst in the temperature range of 100–150°C. A 5.7-cm-i.d. 250-cm^3 stirred glandless autoclave was used. At lower temperatures and lower catalyst loading the overall rate was found to be chemically controlled. At higher temperatures and higher catalyst loadings, however, gas–liquid mass transfer resistance was found to be substantial. Under mass transfer limitations copper catalyst may show desirable characteristics for selective hydrogenation of olefinic compounds. In the case of Pd/C catalyst the gas–liquid mass transfer resistance was found to be dominant.

Satterfield et al. (1968) have studied the effectiveness factor of liquid-filled porous catalysts for the case of hydrogenation of α-methyl styrene using two sizes of catalyst pellets and powdered catalysts. The catalyst used was Pd–alumina, which is less active than Pd-black. For this case, it is likely that the chemical reaction is controlling. The effectiveness factor for 3.2-mm ($\frac{1}{8}$-in.) pellets (cylindrical) was found to be 0.07 with a tortuosity factor of 3.9. The effectiveness factor for finely crushed pellets was found to be unity.

Hydrogenation of Phenyl Acetylene. Kawakami and Kusunoki (1976) have studied the selective hydrogenation of phenyl acetylene to styrene in a 7.5-cm-i.d. 19.5-cm-high stirred basket reactor and a mechanically agitated slurry reactor with 0.5% $Pt\text{-}Al_2O_3$ catalyst.

$$H_2 + C_6H_5C{\equiv}CH \rightarrow C_6H_5CH{=}CH_2$$

$$H_2 + C_6H_5CH{=}CH_2 \rightarrow C_6H_5CH_2CH_3$$

These authors were able to easily eliminate external mass transfer resistances (gas–liquid and solid–liquid film resistances) when powdered catalyst was employed. Under kinetically controlled conditions, the intrinsic yield of styrene was found to be independent of both the initial concentration of phenyl acetylene and the dissolved H_2 concentration. When catalyst pellets were employed the rates of hydrogenation and the yields were significantly influenced by intraparticle diffusion. (Although this example is probably not of much industrial importance, related examples of practical relevance where a triple bond has to be selectively reduced to a double bond are known. For instance, the selective hydrogenation of butynediol to butenediol is of considerable industrial importance.)

Bizhanov et al. (1976) have also studied the hydrogenation of phenyl acetylene in the presence of a solvent, with different types of Raney nickel as catalyst, in a slurry reactor. It was established that the rate of hydrogenation was proportional to the amount of catalyst, indicating that either solid–liquid mass transfer or surface reaction was controlling the overall rate. The rate of hydrogenation at any specified pressure was independent of the concentration of phenyl acetylene up to a stage where 60–70% of the hydrogenation was observed. When 1 mol of H_2 was consumed per mole of phenyl acetylene, substantial amounts of ethyl benzene were produced. The different controlling mechanism for $Pt-Al_2O_3$ and Raney nickel can be attributed to the efficacy of the catalyst and the operating conditions.

Hydrogenation of Olefinic Compounds with Polymer-Bound Catalyst. Homogeneous catalysts are gaining increasing importance for hydroformylation, carbonylation, hydrogenation, and similar reactions. Some hydrogenation reactions have been promoted to such an extent that these are limited by diffusional resistance and in some cases reactions are complete in the diffusion film (see Section 3.4.11. under gas–liquid reactions). Further selective hydrogenations have also been achieved. The main disadvantages of this system are associated with the loss of expensive catalysts based on noble metals. Polymer-bound homogeneous catalysis can overcome the disadvantages of homogeneous catalysts while retaining their other attributes.

Terasawa et al. (1978) have used palladium-bound catalysts that were prepared by the reaction of palladium chloride with a phosphinated polystyrene. Under relatively mild conditions the hydrogenation of allenes, alkynes, and the like can be accomplished. The catalytic activity decreased in the following order: conjugated dienes > nonconjugated dienes > terminal olefins > internal olefins. Oxygen-containing solvents promoted the catalytic activity in a remarkable way. Under certain conditions the rate of hydrogenation was first order in H_2 and catalytic species and zero order with respect to the olefinic compound. Diffusional factors were found to be unimportant. At 25°C a value of the second-order rate constant of 4.12×10^4 $cm^3/mol\ sec$ for styrene was found; the corresponding value for 1,3-cyclooctadiene was found to be 3.79×10^4. Selective hydrogenation of conjugated dienes to monoenes could be relatively easily effected.

Recently Holy (1980) has reported that in the case of the hydrogenation of cyclohexene with anthranilic acid-anchored rhodium catalyst (on Rohm and Haas XAD-4 beads that are > 80% cross-linked) the reaction is diffusion controlled; agitation greatly influenced the rate of hydrogenation. This clearly indicates that the resistance associated with the gas–liquid film is important. It has been observed that the importance of diffusion control is not limited to polymers of one type of rigidity and indeed polymer-bound catalysts with no cross-linking also show similar behavior (Terasawa et al., 1978).

2. *Catalytic Hydrogenation of Fatty Oils*

The hydrogenation of unsaturated fatty oils results in eliminating some of the double bonds and at the same time a significant proportion of the remaining double bonds is isomerized through *cis–trans* conversion and positional shift. These changes result in shifting the melting range to higher temperatures, and stability to oxidation and flavor deterioration is improved. In current industrial practice stability to oxidation and flavor deterioration has acquired considerable importance because of the demand for softer margarines.

This subject has been extensively studied. Coenen (1960) has studied the catalytic hydrogenation of unsaturated fatty oils. The experimental data were correlated by a plot of $1/R'_A$ against $1/w$. The experimental data show that the transfer of hydrogen from the gas phase to the oil was rate controlling. The hydrogen concentration at the catalyst surface is practically zero under these conditions. Bern et al. (1975) have studied the kinetics of the hydrogenation of rapeseed oil in an 11-cm-i.d. 20-cm-high reactor provided with a turbine impeller 5 cm in diameter. Hydrogenations were carried out at 140–200°C and 0.3–10 atm hydrogen pressure in the presence of 0.087% nickel on kieselguhr catalyst (the nickel surface areas were 50–100 m^2/g). A detailed study of the effect of the transport steps was made. Bern et al. have shown that even under intense agitation the resistances associated with the gas–liquid and solid–liquid films are significant. In the case of approximately 10 μm catalyst particles the resistance associated with the transport of triglycerides and hydrogen in the pores of the catalyst was negligible.

Bern et al. (1976) have considered aspects of mass transfer and scale-up in fat hydrogenation. They considered laboratory, pilot, and industrial reactors of 30-, 500-, and 24,000-liter capacities. The resistance associated with the gas–liquid film plays an important role and any scale-up criterion should take this fact into consideration. Often a high value of $k_L a''$ may be realized in the laboratory reactor (a value up to about 2 sec^{-1} has been reported) but prohibitive power consumption will be required in order to ensure high values in the industrial reactor. In general industrial reactors are designed to give $k_L a''$ values of the order of 0.05 sec^{-1}. Further, for the speeds of agitation that are normally employed in practice the superficial gas velocity also affects the value of $k_L a''$.

Marangozis et al. (1977) have analyzed in detail their own new data and published data on the hydrogenation of cottonseed oil. A generalized model for hydrogenation has been presented. Their analysis shows that mass transfer resistances can be properly accounted for and that the chemisorption of H_2 on the catalyst surface significantly retards the reaction only at H_2 pressures greater than 10 atm. At lower pressures the reaction was pseudo-second order for a given catalyst concentration (first order in H_2 and first order in unsaturated oil).

Recently Coenen (1976, 1978) has reviewed this subject and brought out a number of points of practical relevance.

Selectivity in the Hydrogenation of Fatty Oils Containing Three Double Bonds (Albright, 1973). In the hydrogenation of unsaturated fats for edible purposes it is essential to hydrogenate the linolenic acid, which contains three double bonds (UUU). Many times it is desired that the hydrogenation be selective in such a way that all the UUU is completely hydrogenated but only limited hydrogenation of the diunsaturated (UU) and monounsaturated (U) compounds occurs:

$$\text{UUU} \xrightarrow{k_2} \text{UU} \xrightarrow{k_2'} \text{U} \xrightarrow{k_2''} \text{saturated compound}$$

A selectivity ratio defined as k_2/k_2', as high as 100 can be realized in practice. It appears that the double bond located in either UU or UUU is more strongly adsorbed than the double bond located in U. This preferred adsorption of the double bond in UU or UUU appears to be responsible for the selective hydrogenation.

Under industrial conditions the conversion of UUU to UU is essentially controlled by mass transfer resistance associated with the gas–liquid film. Thus the nature and the amount of the catalyst will not be so important for the conversion of UUU to UU as in the case of the conversion of UU to U and U to a saturated compound, since in the latter case a major part of the resistance is associated with the surface reaction. In view of the foregoing, a less active catalyst (like copper-based catalysts) can possibly permit selective hydrogenation of the UUU to UU. Further, a lower degree of agitation and/or higher catalyst concentration would lead to the hydrogenation being controlled by the resistance associated with the gas–liquid film. These factors will also ensure a higher selectivity. Higher temperatures will have a favorable effect on the selectivity, since the activation energy for the chemical process is very much higher than that for mass transfer processes and therefore diffusional resistance would increase if it were not completely dominating. However, higher temperatures may result in undesirable side reactions, namely, polymerization and cyclization. The conversion of UU to U is half order in hydrogen (Hashimoto et al., 1971b) and hence lower pressure will tend to favor a higher selectivity. A model has been proposed by Hashimoto et al. (1971a) for correlating selectivity in these cases.

Cordova and Harriott (1975) have also studied some aspects of selectivity in the hydrogenation of methyl linoleate in the presence of 1% Pd on carbon as a catalyst. Although Pd/C catalyst is not used in industrial practice it is instructive to consider the results obtained in this work. Experiments were carried out in a mechanically agitated 16-cm-i.d. 25-cm-high (approximately) fully baffled stainless steel autoclave. The effects of particle loading and particle size were studied. Most of the experiments were carried out at a temperature of 121°C and a pressure of (approximately) 3 atm. The rate of formation of the stearate was insignificant until all the linoleate was converted to oleate. Thus, very high selectivity can be realized.

Plots of reciprocal R_A' against reciprocal catalyst loading are reported for different sizes of particles, and from these plots it is clear that a part of the resistance was due to the gas–liquid film. It is also clear from these plots that some resistance was contributed by the solid–liquid film.

The rate of hydrogenation of methyl oleate to methyl stearate was also studied after all the linoleate had reacted. There were some nominal gas–liquid film resistance but the solid–liquid film resistance was negligible except in the case of the largest particles, where it was about 4%.

***Selectivity in the Hydrogenation of* UU *to trans*-U.** As pointed out earlier, lower concentrations of hydrogen at the surface improve the selectivity of UU to U. It is striking that this situation also promotes specific isomerization to *trans*-U (i.e., the number of *trans* double bonds formed per double bond hydrogenated improves). Coenen (1976, 1978) has shown that the improved selectivity is caused by the polyunsaturated fatty acids being more strongly bonded to the nickel surface than the monoenoic acids. This will result in the catalyst surface being monopolized by UU as long as there is a finite concentration of UU in the oil. Further details can be obtained from the papers of Coenen (1976, 1978).

Importance of the Diffusion of Triglycerides. Transport of triglyceride molecules, which are large molecules having a molecular weight around 1000, plays an important role, since their dimensions are in the same range as the pore widths commonly encountered in commercial nickel catalysts. Thus we can well have a situation where over a narrow pore-width range the effective diffusion coefficient of glyceride molecules drops from the bulk value to zero. In situations where intermediate pore widths of 2–3 nm are encountered we can run into some problems. Here steep concentration gradients will exist along the pores and accumulation of an intermediate product will take place. Thus the selectivity for the desired product will be adversely affected. An increase in the speed of agitation can lead to higher concentrations of the dissolved hydrogen in the bulk liquid and this will establish steeper concentration gradients in the pores and the selectivity will be even more adversely affected than the case cited above.

3. Hydrogenation of Nitro Compounds to Corresponding Amines

Nitroaromatic Compounds: Nitrobenzene, Dinitrobenzene, Dinitrotoluene. The vapor-phase reduction of nitrobenzene with hydrogen to aniline is a well-established industrial process. However, the dinitro compounds have relatively high boiling points and are also thermally unstable; hence it becomes necessary to use the liquid-phase process (the conventional iron–acid reduction process is relatively expensive and poses environmental problems). Dovell et al. (1970) have studied the reduction of dinitrotoluene (DNT, a commercial mixture of isomers) and *m*-dinitrobenzene (DNB), using palladium and platinum supported on alumina or carbon as catalysts. Experiments were carried out in batch autoclaves, and a variety of solvents, such as methanol, 2-propanol, and aromatic hydrocarbons, were used. The temperature of the reaction was varied from 70° to 120°C and the total pressure was varied from about 8 to 70 atm. The effect of the intensity of agitation was also studied.

For temperatures greater than 80°C the rate of reaction was found to be independent of the concentrations of DNT and DNB and directly proportional to hydrogen pressure. Further, the rate of reaction increased with an increase in the speed of stirring. It is thus clear that the rate of the reaction is controlled by diffusional factors. At lower catalyst loadings the controlling resistance was partly due to the transport of H_2 from the gas phase into the liquid phase and partly due to the transport of dissolved hydrogen to the catalyst surface. However, at higher catalyst loadings, as would be expected, the controlling step was found to be the diffusion of hydrogen from the gas phase to the liquid phase. Since diffusion of H_2 is the controlling step, the rate of reaction would be expected to be independent of the DNT or DNB concentration and would be practically the same for the dinitro compounds. Experimental data confirm these predictions. It is likely that at temperatures below 80°C the diffusional factors will be relatively unimportant. The experimental data show that at 70°C the rate of reaction was dependent on the concentration of the dinitro compounds.

Acres and Cooper (1972) have also studied the hydrogenation of nitrobenzene (NB) dissolved in methanol, and of DNT dissolved in 6 : 1 isopropyl alcohol–water, in the presence of carbon-supported palladium catalysts in stirred autoclaves. Four types of catalyst were used, and these differed in their degree of metal dispersion. In the lower range of NB concentration the rate of hydrogenation was independent of the NB concentration. Their experimental data indicated that the resistance associated with gas–liquid film was unimportant. The diffusion of dissolved hydrogen to the catalyst surface was found to be the rate-controlling step.

Acres and Cooper have obtained some interesting results on the hydrogenation of DNT (2,4-dinitrotoluene) dissolved in isopropanol–water with 5% Pd on carbon as a catalyst. Here the rate of hydrogenation was found to vary linearly with the hydrogen pressure up to a pressure of about 8.5 atm and thereafter the rate became independent of the hydrogen pressure (Figure 13.5). Further, the values of the

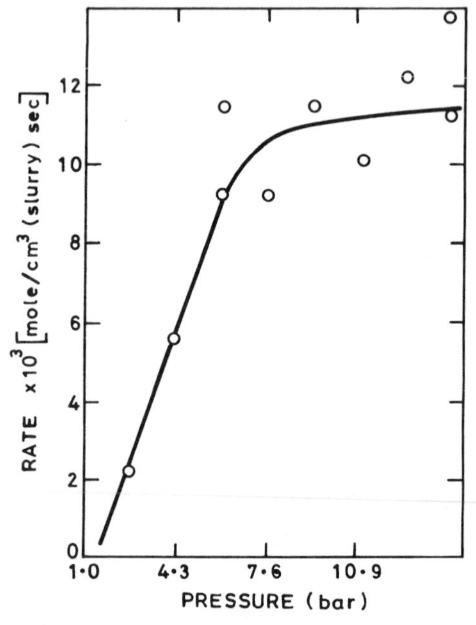

Figure 13.5. The effect of pressure on the reaction rate: hydrogenation of DNT at 383°K.

activation energy at pressures of about 7 and 16 atm were found to be 1.697 kcal/mol and 10.54 kcal/mol, respectively. This example clearly brings out the situation in which, for a reaction that is intrinsically zero order in hydrogen, the diffusional resistance is eliminated by an increase in the pressure of the solute gas (the rate of transfer of H_2 will be directly proportional to the pressure but the rate of the intrinsic reaction will be independent of H_2 pressure).

Some unique observations have been made by Acres and Cooper as regards the isomer composition at 50% hydrogenation (at the level of the conversion of one—NO_2 group to —NH_2 group we can get either *o*-nitro-*p*-toluidine, ONPT, or *p*-nitro-*o*-toluidine, PNOT). Under hydrogen-diffusion-controlled conditions (e.g., at a pressure of 6 atm (gauge) and 120°C) the proportion of ONPT is less ($\approx$ 8.4%) but is substantially increased ($\approx$ 25.5%) by operating under kinetically controlled conditions (e.g., at 14.3 atm (gauge) and 80°C). This effect is remarkable and brings out the possibility of exploiting the role of diffusional factors to achieve the desired selectivity (see the next example, on the manufacture of hydroxylamine from the reduction of nitrite ions with H_2). The change in the behavior of the catalyst under diffusion-controlled and kinetically controlled conditions may be attributed to the characteristics of the Pd catalyst under these conditions. Under kinetically controlled conditions the concentration of dissolved H_2 at the catalyst surface would be expected to be equal to the saturation concentration and hence Pd probably exists as a hydride. By contrast, under diffusion-controlled conditions the concentration of the dissolved H_2 at the catalyst surface will be practically zero and no hydride can be formed.

Hydrogenation of Nitrobenzene with a New Type of Catalyst. A new type of catalyst, consisting of small noble metal particles dispersed within a swollen *nonporous* polymer gel, has been studied for the hydrogenation of nitrobenzene dissolved in such solvents as acetic acid and methanol and their mixtures. Small palladium particles were entrapped within a gel prepared by cross-linking polymerization of 2-hydroxy ethyl methacrylate (Tong et al., 1978). Experiments were made in shake flasks and the resistance associated with the gas–liquid film could be eliminated. Considerable resistance was offered by the solid–liquid film. The rate of hydrogenation varied linearly with H_2 pressure only up to a certain value. The rate of hydrogenation was independent of the nitrobenzene concentration beyond a value of 2×10^{-5} mol/cm^3, indicating that under these conditions the diffusional resistance associated with the transport of nitrobenzene to the catalyst surface was absent.

Nitrocaprolactam. van Direndonck and Nelemans (1972) have studied the hydrogenation of α-nitrocaprolactam to aminolactam in the presence of a catalyst in mechanically agitated contactors, which is a part of the process of manufacturing L-lysine:

$$3H_2 + \begin{array}{ccc} & CH_2 & \\ H_2C & & HC{-}NO_2 \\ | & & | \\ H_2C & & C{=}O \\ | & & | \\ H_2C & \text{---} & NH \end{array} \xrightarrow[85^\circ C]{\text{catalyst}} \begin{array}{ccc} & CH_2 & \\ H_2C & & CHNH_2 \\ | & & | \\ H_2C & & C{=}O \\ | & & | \\ H_2C & \text{---} & NH \end{array} + 2H_2O$$

$$(\Delta H = -125.48 \text{ kcal/mol})$$

Owing to the low solubility of H_2 in water (Henry's constant $= 7 \times 10^{-7}$ mol/cm^3 atm at about 85°C) it is desirable to carry out the reaction under a pressure of about 20 atm. The desirable temperature range is 70–100°C. (Higher temperatures lead to the hydrolysis of the aminolactam to undesirable products.)

It was observed that at a specified stirrer speed the rate of hydrogenation varied linearly with the hydrogen pressure up to a certain level and thereafter there was no effect of the pressure. Here again we have a situation where the intrinsic kinetics of the reaction shows zero order with respect to the dissolved H_2 and therefore the diffusional resistance associated with the transfer of H_2 can possibly be eliminated by increasing the pressure. Under conditions such that the transfer of H_2 is not important it was found that the rate varied directly with the catalyst loading and the concentration of nitrolactam provided that the latter was lower than 1×10^{-4} mol/cm^3.

Under conditions of industrial importance hydrogen transfer rates become important, and the scale-up then requires a knowledge of $k_L a''$. Some aspects of scale-up up to a reactor capacity of 9000 liters have been considered by these authors. Because of the surface-active nature of the aminolactam, $k_L a''$ values as high as 2 sec^{-1} were obtained.

4. *Manufacture of Hydroxylamine Salts by the Reduction of Nitrite / Nitrate with* H_2

Hydroxylamine salts are required in the manufacture of caprolactam (monomer for nylon-6) where cyclohexanone oxime is made by the reaction between cyclohexanone and hydroxylamine. In the conventional process for the manufacture of hydroxylamine by the reduction of ammonium nitrite with SO_2 a large quantity of ammonium sulfate is obtained as a by-product, which is undesirable. Ammonium nitrite can be reduced with H_2 in the presence of noble-metal-based catalysts. Here if the reduction is not controlled hydroxylamine may be further reduced to ammonia. Acres et al. (1974) have pointed out that selectivity with respect to hydroxylamine can be realized by working under hydrogen-transport-controlled conditions, which can be created by, for instance, working with H_2 at a subatmospheric pressure. From a practical point of view it would be more attractive to modify the catalyst in such a way that H_2 transport is controlling and to operate the reactor at higher pressures.

van Goolen (1976) has made a study of the reduction of aqueous ammonium nitrate ($\simeq$ 20%) in phosphoric acid media ($\simeq$ 23%) with H_2 in the presence of a noble metal catalyst dispersed in active carbon in mechanically agitated contactors of 1- and 30-liter capacities. The pH was maintained at about 1.8.

$$3H_2 + 2H_3PO_4 + NH_4NO_3 \xrightarrow{\text{catalyst}} (NH_3OH)H_2PO_4 + NH_4H_2PO_4 + 2H_2O$$

The temperature was varied from 30 to 90°C and the pressure from about 1 to 10 atm. The catalyst concentration was about 0.4–2.0 g of Pd per liter. Mass transfer factors were found to play an important role.

For the commercial-scale plant a reaction volume of 60,000–90,000 liters was required and it was recommended that a bubble column rather than a mechanically agitated contactor be used. This recommendation was based on considerations of (1) the hazards of catalyst attrition in the large-scale mechanically agitated contactor; and (2) problems of shaft seal and its reliability.

5. *Fischer–Tropsch Reaction: Conversion of* CO + H_2 *to* CH_4 *and Paraffins*

Calderbank et al. (1963) have studied the Fischer–Tropsch reaction by bubbling the synthesis gas (a mixture of CO and H_2) through a slurry of iron catalyst suspended in molten wax. It was found that the diffusion of hydrogen in the liquid phase and the rate of catalytic reaction determine the overall rate.

Kölbel et al. (1964) have studied the hydrogenation of CO to CH_4 in bubble columns containing Ni–MgO catalysts suspended in paraffinic hydrocarbons. Zaidi et al. (1979) have made a fairly exhaustive study of this reaction for the manufacture of C_6 to C_{11} hydrocarbons, with selective conversion to olefins. The basic reactions are as follows:

$$CO + 2H_2 \rightarrow —CH_2— + H_2O$$

$$CO + H_2O \rightarrow CO_2 + H_2$$

Slurry reactors are likely to be more attractive than fixed-bed reactors, since in the former temperature control can be easily accomplished. Molten paraffin wax medium in the temperature range of 250–300°C was used. For convenience the water–gas shift reaction was used as the model reaction system with low-temperature shift conversion catalyst (Girdler 66B catalyst); this reaction is also representative. The weight percentage of catalyst was varied from 1.5 to 10.45%; the total weight percentage of solid particles was kept constant by using an appropriate amount of inert solid support particles (alumina).

Experiments were carried out in a 4.14-cm-i.d. 209-cm-high column and the superficial gas velocity was varied from 0.7 to 3.8 cm/sec. Plots of $[A^*]/R'_A$ against $1/w$ were made (the pressure was 900 kPa) and straight lines with finite slopes were obtained. Values of $k_L a''$ varied from about 0.08 to 0.2 sec^{-1}.

It appears that under conditions of industrial importance the process is likely to be controlled by a slow reaction and that diffusional factors will play an insignificant role. Thus an increase in the superficial gas velocity will result in a decreased percentage of conversion per pass of the solute gas. The authors obtained an optimum value of the superficial gas velocity through a simple optimization procedure.

Satterfield and Huff (1980) have also analyzed the available data on Fischer–Tropsch synthesis using nitrided fused iron catalyst. However, these authors have concluded that at higher synthesis temperatures

(> 235°C) for this catalyst gas–liquid mass transfer becomes the controlling step.

6. Hydrogenation of Crotonaldehyde: Effectiveness Factor

The hydrogenation of crotonaldehyde in industrial practice is usually carried out in the vapor phase. However, it is a convenient system for studying some aspects of slurry reactors. Kenney and Sedriks (1972) have studied this reaction with palladium on porous alumina as a catalyst in a modified form of the Carberry basket reactor. Experiments were conducted at atmospheric pressure and in the temperature range of 30–70°C. The catalyst was used in the form of about 5-mm ($\frac{3}{16}$-in.) cylindrical pellets and powdered pellets whose mean particle size was of 30 μm. These authors successfully eliminated diffusional resistances associated with gas–liquid and solid–liquid films. The value of the activation energy was found to be 11 kcal/mol when the powdered catalyst was used. The reaction was found to be first order in hydrogen. The effectiveness and tortuosity factors were found to be about 0.1 and 1.6, respectively.

7. Hydrogenation of Allyl Alcohol Dissolved in Water and Ethanol and of Fumaric Acid Dissolved in Ethanol

This example illustrates the importance of the diffusion of species B to the catalyst surface. Ruether and Puri (1973) have studied the hydrogenation of allyl alcohol dissolved in water and ethanol and of fumaric acid dissolved in ethanol in the presence of fine ($\simeq$ 10 μm) Raney nickel catalyst particles. These systems served as convenient model systems for studying some aspects of mass transfer in slurry reactors. In all cases the rate of hydrogenation was zero order with respect to reactant B when the concentration of B was greater than about 1×10^{-5} mol/cm^3. However, at lower concentrations of B the rate of hydrogenation was found to be first order in B. This implies that diffusional resistance associated with the transport of species B to the catalyst surface is unimportant at concentrations of B greater than 1×10^{-5} mol/cm^3. Further, at very low concentrations of B, the diffusion of B to the catalyst surface is the rate-controlling step. Here the rate of transfer of A to the catalyst surface becomes much greater than the rate of transfer of B to the catalyst surface.

Hydrogenation of Xylose. Wisniak et al. (1974a, b) have studied the kinetics of hydrogenation of xylose to xylitol in the presence of Raney nickel, Ru, Rh, and Pd catalysts over a wide range of temperature, pressure, and catalyst concentrations in a small mechanically agitated autoclave. (Xylitol may prove to be a good sweetener, since it has no insulin requirement.) In the case of the Raney nickel catalyst the diffusional factors could be eliminated by operating at higher speeds of agitation. The reaction follows pseudo-first-order kinetics and the rate-controlling step involved the surface reaction between chemisorbed atomic hydrogen and adsorbed or unadsorbed xylose, depending on the temperature level. The effect of pressure on the pseudo-first-order reaction constant shows striking differences in behavior as the temperature and pressure are increased. At 100°C the rate goes through a maximum at about 20 atm absolute pressure; at 125°C the rate continues to increase up to about 35 atm. This behavior can be partly explained on the basis of the mechanism of the reaction. In the case of Ru, Rh, and Pd catalysts the rate increases up to a pressure of about 40 atm and thereafter it remains constant. Further, in the case of Rh and Pd catalysts the rate drops to negligible values below about 14–21 atm absolute pressure. This indicates that for these catalysts hydrogen is not adsorbed in significant amounts at lower pressures.

9. Oxidation of SO_2 with Air in Aqueous Suspensions of Activated Carbon

The removal of SO_2 in the presence of O_2 from off-gases is becoming increasingly important. Some work has been reported by Hartman and Coughlin (1972) for trickle-bed reactors where the column was packed with activated carbon (see Example 6 in Section 13.2.7). It is known that some varieties of activated carbon catalyze the oxidation of SO_2 to H_2SO_4. Twelve samples of activated carbon were first tested under identical conditions by Seaburn and Engel (1973) to assess their wet adsorption characteristics, and it was found that the slurries showed substantially different performance even when the carbons had similar physical properties. However, all suspensions exhibited greatly enhanced SO_2 removal ability when compared to water. When oxygen was also present along with SO_2 then some of the carbons showed catalytic activity even at ambient conditions for the conversion of SO_2 to H_2SO_4. It appears that under the conditions employed by these authors the surface reaction between adsorbed SO_2 and O_2 was the rate-controlling step.

Komiyama and Smith (1975) have made a systematic study of dissolved SO_2 oxidation with a Pittsburgh Carbon Co. type BPL activated carbon having a particle size of 0.03 mm. Experiments were carried out in a 10-cm-i.d., 10-cm-high glass mechanically agitated contactor. They were able to eliminate mass transfer resistance and study the intrinsic kinetics. The reaction was found to be first order with respect to O_2 and zero order with respect to SO_2.

It appears that the gas phase moves essentially in the plug flow manner in slurry reactors even under conditions of fairly intense agitation. A similar observation has been made by Juvekar and Sharma (1973) for the carbonation of a suspension of lime (see Section 12.1.4).

Goto and Smith (1978a) have considered the design of slurry, trickle-bed, and packed-column reactors for this system. Equations are derived for slurry reactors where the gas phase moves in the plug flow manner as well as when it is backmixed; the liquid phase was assumed to be backmixed. The available experimental data were well correlated by the equations derived by them.

10. Oxidation of Aqueous Sodium Sulfide (Black Liquor) in the Presence of Activated Carbon as Catalyst

We have considered the example of air oxidation of black liquor (see Section 3.3.3). It is known that activated carbon particles act as catalyst. Chandrasekaran and Sharma (1977, 1978) have made a study of this system in a 13-cm-i.d. mechanically agitated reactor. Different brands of the activated carbon particles (BDH, Darco G-60, and Norit) were used. Oxidation experiments were carried out at 70°C.

It was observed that the rate of oxidation was much greater than that observed in the absence of catalyst particles. The rate of oxidation per unit volume of the slurry with 0.2% carbon particles continued to increase even up to a speed of 2000 rev/min. Thus it is clear that the resistance associated with O_2 transfer from the gas to the liquid phase (i.e., liquid-film resistance) and/or the transfer of dissolved O_2 to the catalyst surface (i.e., solid–liquid-film resistance) is controlling. Further experiments on the effect of catalyst loading in the range of 0.02–2% at a stirring speed of 1600 rev/min showed that above a loading of 0.2% the particle loading had no effect (Figure 13.6). From this observation it is clear that the controlling resistance is associated with the liquid film adjacent to the gas–liquid interface above a loading of about 0.2%. The value of $k_L a''$ at a stirring speed of 1600 rev/min was found to be about 2.4 sec^{-1}.

Experimental data indicated unequivocally that resistance associated with the solid–liquid film above 0.2% catalyst loading is negligible. The particle size of active particles assessed on the basis of sieve analysis is completely misleading in the case of active carbon particles. The Johnson-Matthey Co. of Great Britain carried out an extensive study of the characteristics of

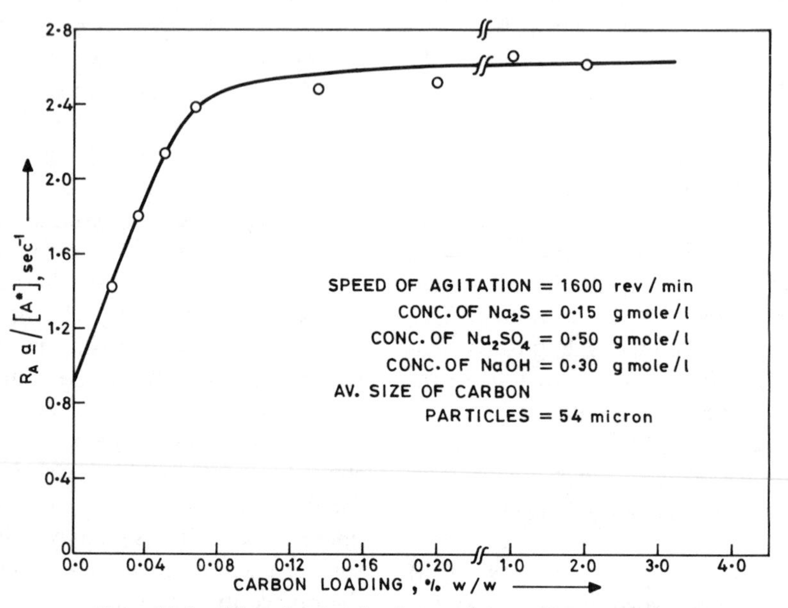

Figure 13.6. Effect of carbon loading on the rate of absorption in an agitated contactor 13 cm i.d.) at 70°C.

active carbons (Bird, 1976). For the Darco G-60 carbon used in the work just described the external area of the particles is around 1.7 m^2/g. With this external area value and the corresponding average particle size, it can easily be shown that the calculated value of $k_{SL} a_p$ at 0.2% carbon loading is very much greater than $k_L a''$, and hence the experimental observation that gas–liquid-film resistance is controlling is rational.

Pal et al. (1982) have made a systematic study of catalysis by carbon particles at higher temperatures (up to 150°C) in a mechanically agitated contactor as well as a stirred cell operated under pressure. When the carbon particles are smaller than the diffusion film thickness (e.g., in a stirred cell with particles smaller than 50 μm) then a parallel reaction can occur in the film (see Section 13.1.6).

Thus we have an interesting situation where catalysis by activated carbon particles at lower temperatures (around 70°C) first changes the controlling regime from the kinetically controlled very slow reaction case (regime 1) to the mass-transfer-controlled case (regime 2). At higher temperatures (80–130°C) and lower k_L values ($\simeq$ 5–8 $\times 10^{-3}$ cm/sec), even without catalyst, the system may belong to the fast pseudo-first-order reaction regime (regime 3). Fine carbon particles (1.7–4.7 μm) can further enhance the specific rate of absorption of the system originally belonging to regime 3 and this enhancement factor may be as high as 13.

Recently Mahajani (1979) has studied the use of a copper-based catalyst for this oxidation reaction under conditions very similar to those employed for active carbon as catalyst. It appears that here too the controlling mechanism is the transfer of O_2 into the liquid.

A related case of the oxidation of calcium polysulfide (CaS_x) suspended in water can be cited. There is a finite solubility of CaS_x in water. This system is of some relevance in treatment of wastewater for the removal of heavy metal ions such as Hg^{2+}, Cd^{2+}, Zn^{2+}, Ph^{2+}, and Cu^{2+} (Yahikozawa et al., 1977).

11. Oxidation of Alcohols in Aqueous Alkaline Media with Pd*-Based Catalysts*

It is known that noble metal catalysts can convert ethanol in aqueous alkaline media to sodium acetate. This type of reaction may be a good model system and also has some potential practical importance. Hsu and Ruether (1978) have studied the kinetics of ethanol oxidation in an aqueous alkaline media with pelleted and powdered Pd/Al_2O_3 catalyst. Under certain conditions they were able to eliminate diffusional resistances, and under these conditions they found the reaction to be first order in O_2.

Mahajani (1979) has studied the oxidation of *n*-butanol dissolved in aqueous alkaline solutions in a 9.5-cm-i.d. mechanically agitated slurry reactor with a Pd/C catalyst. He was able to eliminate diffusional resistances and found the reaction to be zero order in O_2.

The foregoing reaction systems may also serve a useful purpose in laboratory studies of slurry reactors.

12. Reduction of Uranium(V) *by* H_2

In the molten salt breeder reactor technology the reduction of UF_5 dissolved in an $LiF–BeF_2–ThF_4$ melt (72–16–12 mol %), to UF_4 is a necessary step in fuel reprocessing. In the absence of a catalyst the reaction takes place very slowly and is apparently zero order in H_2 and UF_5. The diffusional factors were unimportant. Kelmers and Bennett (1976) have shown that platinum can effectively catalyze this reduction reaction and a 10- to 100-fold increase in the reaction rate was achieved at 550°C. The physical form of the catalyst was found to be unimportant, since either platinum black or granular platinum sponge were equally effective. The controlling mechanism has not been established. (This example is cited because of its novel features and possible practical applications.)

13. Hydrogenation and Hydrocracking of α-Cellulose (also Powdered Coal) to Liquid and Gaseous Fuels

Gupta et al. (1976) have shown that α-cellulose as well as powdered newspaper slurried in paraffin oil can be hydrogenated and hydrocracked to liquid and gaseous fuels in the presence of 0.2 wt. % nickel hydroxide catalyst. The reaction can be carried out in the temperature range of 343–482°C and total pressure in the range of 30–70 atm. This is a special type of reaction system, since the solid reactant particles, which are insoluble in the medium, are suspended along with catalyst particles. Experiments were carried out batchwise in a 1-liter stirred autoclave or a 750-cm^3 rocking autoclave. The ground cellulose was dispersed as a 30% slurry. Most of the kinetic runs were made at a pressure of about 54 atm.

Experimental data show that up to a catalyst loading of 0.75 wt. % mass transfer resistance is negligible. However, at a catalyst loading of about 1 wt. % there is some mass transfer resistance. Further, the reaction was found to be zero order in H_2. At a low H_2 pressure (say, less than 30 atm) there was some mass transfer resistance and hence some effect of H_2 pressure on the rate of reaction could be seen. The reaction also behaves as first order in unconverted carbon. The following consecutive reactions occur:

$$\text{Cellulose} \rightarrow \text{pyrobitumens} \rightarrow \text{oil} \rightarrow \text{gas}$$

The reaction mechanism was postulated to be dissociation of hydrogen at the nickel metal sites followed by reaction with partially pyrolyzed cellulose fragments that diffuse through the reaction medium.

The foregoing work, in principle, should also be applicable to the hydrogenation of coal particles suspended in an oil medium.

14. Dehydrogenation of Secondary Alcohols to Ketones

The dehydrogenation of secondary alcohols, such as isopropanol and *sec*-butanol, to the corresponding ketone in a slurry reactor has been adopted in practice. Here an inert high-boiling-point solvent is used and dehydrogenation is conducted at around 150°C. An important advantage of this process, apart from the ease of heat transfer, is that equilibrium displacement is ensured by the continuous removal of ketone and H_2 as fast as these are formed.

Epoxidation of Olefins. Hydroperoxides such as those based on isobutane, ethyl benzene, cumene, and the like, can be used to epoxidize olefinic compounds. This type of reaction has become industrially important in the context of the manufacture of propylene oxide where the coproduct *tert*-butyl alcohol or phenyl methyl carbinol, obtained with the hydroperoxide of isobutane or ethyl benzene, respectively, can be dehydrated to give isobutylene or styrene. (This is commercially known as the Oxirane process.) It has been reported that both heterogeneous and homogeneous catalysts based on Mo, W, Co, and the like can be employed.

Raval and Sharma (1980) have studied epoxidation of styrene, 1-hexadecene, undecylenic acid (or its methyl ester), and so on with cumene hydroperoxide with Mo sulfide and oxide as catalysts. Experiments were made in an 8.5-cm-i.d. agitated contactor at a temperature of about 95°C. The effect of particle loading, particle size, and speed of stirring clearly revealed that diffusional resistance was absent. (Estimates of $k_{SL}a_p$, assuming the Sherwood number to be 2, also indicated that solid–liquid-film resistance was negligible.) In a typical case of 1-hexadecene (2.4×10^{-3} mol/cm^3) and cumene hydroperoxide (4×10^{-4} mol/cm^3) with a 0.288 wt. % loading of very fine Mo sulfide particles (particle sizes were 0.5–4 μm) well over 90% yields of epoxide based on cumene hydroperoxide conversion were realized.

In principle we can except a situation where one of the reactants interacts with the catalyst particles and forms an intermediate (complex), which may be soluble or insoluble in the liquid medium containing reactant B, and then reacts with the reactant B. A reference may be made to the epoxidation of olefins such as propylene, butylene, and styrene with hydroperoxides, such as *tert*-butyl hydroperoxide, ethylbenzene hydroperoxide, and cumene hydroperoxide, in the presence of molybdenum oxide/sulfide as a catalyst (Sheldon, 1973; Raval and Sharma, 1980). From the studies of Raval and Sharma it appears that the rate of decomposition of the hydroperoxide does not correlate with the rate of epoxide (and other products) formation. However, after a time lag in batch experiments of 1-hexadecene it was found that the yields of α-olefin epoxide were 90%, compared to a 50% yield, 6 hr after the start of the experiment. The rate of decomposition of the hydroperoxide was dependent on the catalyst loading as well as the particle size but was independent of the speed of agitation in a 7-cm-diameter fully baffled mechanically agitated contactor provided with a 2.5-cm-diameter turbine impeller in the range of 2200–2900 rev/min. A plausible explanation is that first some complex between the hydroperoxide and the catalyst is formed, which then reacts with the olefin. This explanation is based on the premise that the yields of epoxide and isomerized products go to much higher levels after a lapse of some time. If the hydroperoxide decomposition occurred without making active oxygen available, such an increase would not be observed and the epoxide yields would be relatively low.

A rational analysis of such cases in slurry reactors where the olefin may well be gaseous (e.g., propylene) has not been reported and deserves consideration.

Here the constitutent steps are *not* in series as visualized in Section 13.1.

Isomerization of Epoxides. Isomerization of epoxides is of considerable importance. For instance, styrene oxide can be isomerized to phenyl acetaldehyde or acetophenone (the latter is undesirable). Epoxides of tertiary olefins can isomerize to aldehyde only, since the structure would clearly indicate such a behavior. There is a dearth of data on the kinetics of such reactions.

16. Slurry Polymerization: Polymerization with Ziegler–Natta Catalysts

Ziegler–Natta catalysts, which generally consist of a transition metal halide (such as $TiCl_4$ or α-$TiCl_3$) and an organometallic compound (such as alkylhalide or trihalide of aluminum) permit the polymerization of olefins to be conducted at pressures close to atmospheric pressure. The polymers produced by using these catalysts have certain distinctive properties. For instance, highly linear polyethylene having a high molecular weight and high density can be produced with these catalysts. Here hydrocarbon solvents are used and gas is introduced into the reactor. The catalyst particles are suspended in the solvent and hence the system is equivalent to a slurry reactor. There is, however, an important difference between slurry polymerization reactors and conventional slurry reactors. In the case of slurry polymerization the polymer grows on the catalyst particles and hence the monomer has to diffuse through the product polymer layer. The catalyst particles usually have to grow more than 10,000-fold in volume during polymerization: the initial size of the particles is generally in the range of 0.06–0.3 μm. This is deliberate, since catalysts are much more expensive per unit weight than the polymer they produce and it becomes necessary to have such a large increase in volume (Schmeal and Street, 1971). Further, as the polymer particle grows, the catalyst breaks into small fragments that are covered by the polymer and convected outward. This causes movement of active sites of the catalyst.

Apart from polymerization based on Ziegler–Natta catalysts we may also have situations that involve insoluble polymers like polyphenylene oxide.

The Ziegler–Natta polymerization catalysts yield polymers that have a broad molecular weight distribution. (The ratio of the weight-average molecular weight to the number-average molecular weight lies between 4 and 40.) An unusually broad molecular weight distribution adversely affects such polymer properties as resistance to environmental stress cracking and crazing and melt processing characteristics.

The kinetics of polymerization in the system described in the first paragraph has been studied fairly extensively. However, there are inconsistencies in rates and orders of reaction. For instance, rates of reaction have been found to increase, decrease, or remain essentially constant with time. Even the order of the reaction with respect to the monomer has been found to vary between first and second (Singh and Merrill, 1971). It appears that a rational model of polymerization can possibly explain most of the observed facts (Begley, 1966; Singh and Merrill, 1971; Schmeal and Street, 1971). Since additional parameters associated with a growing catalyst particle are involved in slurry polymerization, we shall discuss the salient features of the proposed models.

Characteristics of Ziegler–Natta Catalysts. Ziegler–Natta catalysts are prepared by the reaction of an organometallic compound and a transition metal halide in an inert solvent such as *n*-heptane. The system should be dry and oxygen free. For instance, $TiCl_4$ reacts with aluminum alkyls in an *n*-heptane medium to give a new solid phase containing Ti in its various valence states. It is generally believed that the catalyst consists of aggregates of particles ranging in size from 100 to 1000 Å. Polymer grows on this catalyst species, and in the process the aggregates of catalyst break up and are dispersed as small pieces in the polymer (Schmeal and Street, 1971).

Ziegler–Natta Catalyst Polymerization Models. Begley (1966), Singh and Merrill (1971), and Schmeal and Street (1971) have suggested different polymerization models, some of which are common. Schmeal and Street have given a comprehensive review of this subject and have suggested a few models:

1. *Even distribution of the catalyst in the polymer* is considered the base model, and here particle growth is ignored and catalyst sites are assumed to be dispersed evenly in a spherical matrix of the polymer. On the basis of this model a narrow molecular weight distribution (MWD) is predicted for small values of the Thiele modulus (reaction control) and a broader MWD for large values of the Thiele modulus (diffusion control).

2. In the *solid core model* the polymer is assumed to accumulate about a catalyst sphere the surface of

which supports the polymerization. In this case the monomer has to diffuse through the growing polymeric coat. Begley (1966) has also suggested this model for the polymerization of propylene with Phillips (United States) catalyst. As the relative radius of the polymer coat increases the rate will decrease and eventually reach an asymptotic value. For small values of the Thiele modulus the predicted rate will be the same as that given by the base model. A narrow MWD will be obtained if this model holds.

3. The catalyst sites in the *polymeric core expansion model* are assumed to move outward in the polymer matrix with negligible velocity. This resembles the solid core model, but here the core is assumed to be polymeric and sites are distributed evenly throughout the polymeric core. The MWD will be the same as predicted by the base model.

4. In the *flow expansion model* the sites are assumed to move outward without being affected by the expanding polymer matrix. This model predicts a broader MWD for large values of the Thiele modulus and quantitatively predicts the same behavior as the polymeric core model.

The same rate behavior and MWD is predicted by all these models for small values of the Thiele modulus (reaction control).

Importance of External Diffusional Factors. The rate of transport of the olefin into the solvent is expected to be very high in view of the relatively high solubility and low rates of reaction, and hence the resistance associated with the liquid film next to the gas–liquid interface can be considered negligible. Further, since the particle size is very small, the $k_{SL}a_p$ value will be relatively high, and in most practical situations the resistance associated with the liquid film on the solid particles will also be negligible. However, with the exceptionally active catalysts reported in the most recent patent literature the diffusional factors may well become important. Some aspects of diffusional resistance have also been discussed by Reichert (1977).

Catalyst Site Decay Model. Begley (1966) has suggested that the decline in the rate of polymerization with increasing time can also be satisfactorily explained by another model, which is based on the decline in the number of active sites on the catalyst surface. Since the rates are a function of time, care should be exercised in analyzing the experimental data.

Methods for Obtaining Narrow MWDs. For many applications in practice a narrow MWD is preferred. Singh and Merrill (1971) have indicated how a narrow MWD can be obtained. The width of the MWD can be decreased if the monomer bypasses the surface and goes to an inner site. This can be accomplished by destroying the sites near the surface after a predetermined degree of polymerization. The deactivation of the sites near the surface can be achieved by using controlled quantities of terminating agents, such as water or alcohol, that contain an active hydrogen. Some processes that employ this strategy have been patented.

It may also be possible to increase the rate of transport of monomer to the central core by steadily increasing the monomer pressure, and this should result in improving the MWD.

17. Simultaneous Hydrogenation of Ethylene and Propylene

Kawakami et al. (1976) have covered some aspects of the individual and competitive hydrogenations of ethylene and propylene in a slurry reactor with water as the liquid medium. (This system is not industrially important.) A 7.5-cm-i.d. 18-cm-high fully baffled reactor provided with a glass impeller having four flat turbine blades was used. The stirring speed was kept constant at 1800 rev/min. The catalyst was 5% Pt on carbon having an average particle diameter of 6 μm. The catalyst loading was varied from 1 to 5×10^{-4} g/cm^3. Temperature was varied from 5 to 35°C and pressure was atmospheric. In the region of excess concentration of dissolved H_2 the rates of hydrogenation of the individual olefin were found to be controlled by the gas–liquid and liquid–particle mass transfer of olefin. By contrast, in the region of excess concentration of dissolved olefin the rate was influenced by a combination of chemical reaction and pore diffusion in addition to mass transfer factors. For the case of the competitive hydrogenation of C_2H_4 and C_3H_6 in the region of excess concentration of dissolved H_2 the selectivity was governed solely by the ratio of the mass transfer rate of propylene to that of ethylene.

18. Absorption of CO_2 in Aqueous Buffer Solutions Containing Carbonic Anhydrase

Dean et al. (1977) have studied absorption of CO_2 in aqueous alkaline buffer solutions containing free carbonic anhydrase enzyme as well as this enzyme microencapsulated in cellulose nitrate microcapsules in a slurry reactor. It was possible to obtain values of $k_L a$ and the effectiveness factor for the microencapsulated enzyme. Alper et al. (1980b) have also studied the absorption of CO_2 in buffer solutions containing carbonic anhydrase.

13.2. FIXED-BED REACTORS

In this type of reactor we use coarse catalyst particles ($\simeq 1 \times 1$ mm to 10×10 mm size) in a packed bed where the gas and liquid flow cocurrently or countercurrently. The most common mode of operation is cocurrent downflow, since it avoids problems associated with the flooding of the column. In some special cases, however, where some restriction is imposed by equilibrium considerations, the countercurrent mode of operation may be adopted. Since the liquid flow over the packings is comparatively slow in the film flow regime, this mode of operation is referred to as *trickle flow* and the reactor is usually called a trickle-bed reactor. Bondi (1971), Goto et al. (1976), and Hofmann (1977) have considered some aspects of fixed-bed reactors, and Satterfield (1975), Hofmann (1978), and Shah (1979) have published very comprehensive reviews on these reactors.

The trickle-bed reactor may also be used for solid-catalyzed vapor-phase reactions where it is desired to remove the heat by introducing an inert liquid that may also wash off the catalyst poisons. In some cases the reactant or product in the liquid state may be capable of washing out polymeric or tarry materials formed by the reaction; this enhances the reaction rate and gives more stable performance of the catalyst (Germain et al., 1974). In principle, a second immiscible liquid phase may also be introduced to wash undesirable materials off the catalyst.

For reversible reactions where the conversion is limited by equilibrium considerations, the introduction of liquid may substantially improve the conversion if the product is more soluble in the liquid than the reactant. For instance, in the manufacture of isopropanol by catalytic hydration of propylene, both the vapor-phase and mixed-phase operations can be adopted. Here the conversion of propylene is much higher with the mixed-phase operation than with the vapor-phase operation. The solubility of the hydration product, isopropanol, is very much higher in water (present in excess) than that of propylene, and hence the equilibrium conversion goes up. In principle a similar advantage can be realized in catalyzed liquid-phase reactions, where an immiscible phase can be added that preferentially extracts the product of the reaction. Fixed-bed reactors are operated adiabatically, and in some cases cold fluid is used as a quench at predetermined locations.

13.2.1. Flow Regimes and Mass Transfer Characteristics

The various steps involved in fixed-bed reactors are the same as in slurry reactors. However, there are some complications. To start with, we can vary the particle size over an extremely limited range. The hydrodynamics of liquid flow is rather complicated, since with an increase in the liquid flow rate the wetted area increases in the trickle (film) flow regime until complete wetting is attained. The effect of liquid flow rate on $k_L a$ and $k_{SL} a$ is also complicated, since the liquid flow rate affects k_L, k_{SL}, and a separately and differently. Further, depending on the values of the superficial liquid and gas velocities, physical properties of the liquid, and the size of the catalyst particles, a variety of flow regimes—trickle (film) flow, pulse flow, bubble flow, and spray flow—are possible (Figure 13.7; Sato et al., 1973; Charpentier and Favier, 1975; Charpentier, 1976; Talmor, 1977; Morsi et al., 1978; Gianetto et al., 1978; Hofmann, 1978; Sicardi et al., 1979). In some cases, foaming may also be observed. The functional dependence of mass transfer coefficients and interfacial area on operating parameters is different in various flow regimes. Charpentier and Favier (1975) have pointed out the following flow regimes: for nonfoaming systems: trickle (film) flow, pulsing flow, bubble flow, and spray flow; for foaming systems: foaming, foaming–pulsing, pulsing, and spray.

Trickle (film) flow regime: Here the liquid flows as a laminar film over the packings in the continuous gas phase.

Pulse flow: Here alternate gas-rich and liquid-rich parts pass through the column.

Bubble flow: In this case the liquid phase constitutes the continuous phase and the gas passes as bubbles.

Spray flow: Here the liquid is dispersed in the form of fine droplets in the continuous gas phase; a part of the liquid continues to flow as a film over the packings.

It is necessary to know in which flow regime the system in question falls. Charpentier and co-workers

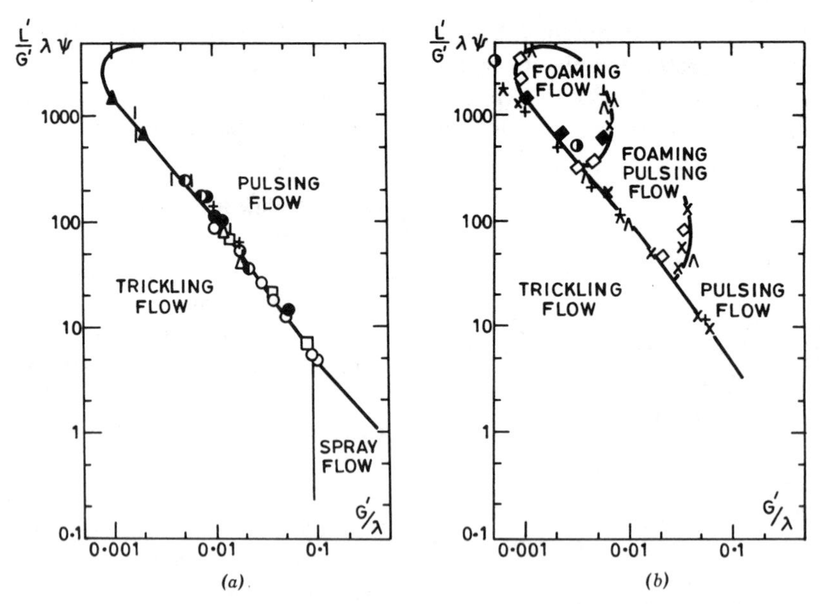

Figure 13.7. (*a*) Flow pattern diagram for nonfoaming liquids. (*b*) Flow pattern diagram for foaming liquids.

have given charts that permit delineation of the flow regimes for 3-mm glass and alumina spheres and 1.5 × 5 mm alumina pellets. At low liquid flow rates (< 2–5 kg/m^2 sec) insufficient liquid is present to completely wet the packing, and the pulse flow regime is not realized. Additional complications arise when the liquid shows foaming tendencies (e.g., in the case of some hydrocarbon systems).

Recently Talmor (1977) made a systematic study of this subject and provided charts for the delineation of flow regimes for nonfoaming and foaming systems (Figures 13.8 and 13.9). Talmor has shown that the correlating parameters are the volumetric gas-to-liquid ratio, and a force ratio relating inertia plus gravity forces to interface plus viscous resistances given by $(1 + 1/\mathrm{Fr})/(\mathrm{We} + 1/\mathrm{Re})$. The force ratio is dependent on the packing size and bed voidage, the liquid and gas superficial mass flow rates, and the density, viscosity, and surface tension of the liquid. Apparently the bed diameter or liquid height does not affect the flow regime under otherwise specified conditions.

Charpentier and Favier (1975), Midoux et al. (1976), Talmor (1977), and Morsi et al. (1978) have clearly brought out the differences in liquid holdup for foaming and nonfoaming systems under otherwise uniform conditions. They have shown that the free liquid holdup in the case of a nonfoaming liquid exhibits the following behavior when for a given liquid flow rate the gas flow rate is increased. The free holdup remains approximately constant in the trickling flow regime, then increases sharply in the pulsing flow and decreases slightly with the spray flow. For the corresponding situations for foaming liquids the free liquid holdup remains approximately constant for trickling flow, then decreases sharply with the foaming flow and pulsing–foaming flow, then slightly increases or remains constant in the transition from pulsing–foaming flow to pulsing flow, then decreases again with the pulsing flow. Many authors recommend that the pressure drop for the specified system and packing be measured in a small laboratory column. Schwartz et al. (1976) and Talmor (1977) have also pointed out that it is still not possible to predict holdup and pressure drop accurately in different fixed-bed reactors. In addition, Chou et al. (1977) have studied the transition to pulsed flow in a 6.35-cm-i.d. column packed with 2.9-mm glass beads. The wetting characteristics of the packing were changed by coating glass beads with a silicone oil (Dow Corning 550 silicone oil). Foaming and nonfoaming systems were studied. These authors also stress that flow maps based on an air–water system cannot be used for other systems, and there is need for further work in this area. Morsi et al. (1978) have extended the work of Charpentier and Favier (1975) and Charpentier (1976) and have further confirmed the flow pattern diagrams and correlations proposed by these authors. The correlation suggested by Charpentier and co-workers also holds for porous spherical par-

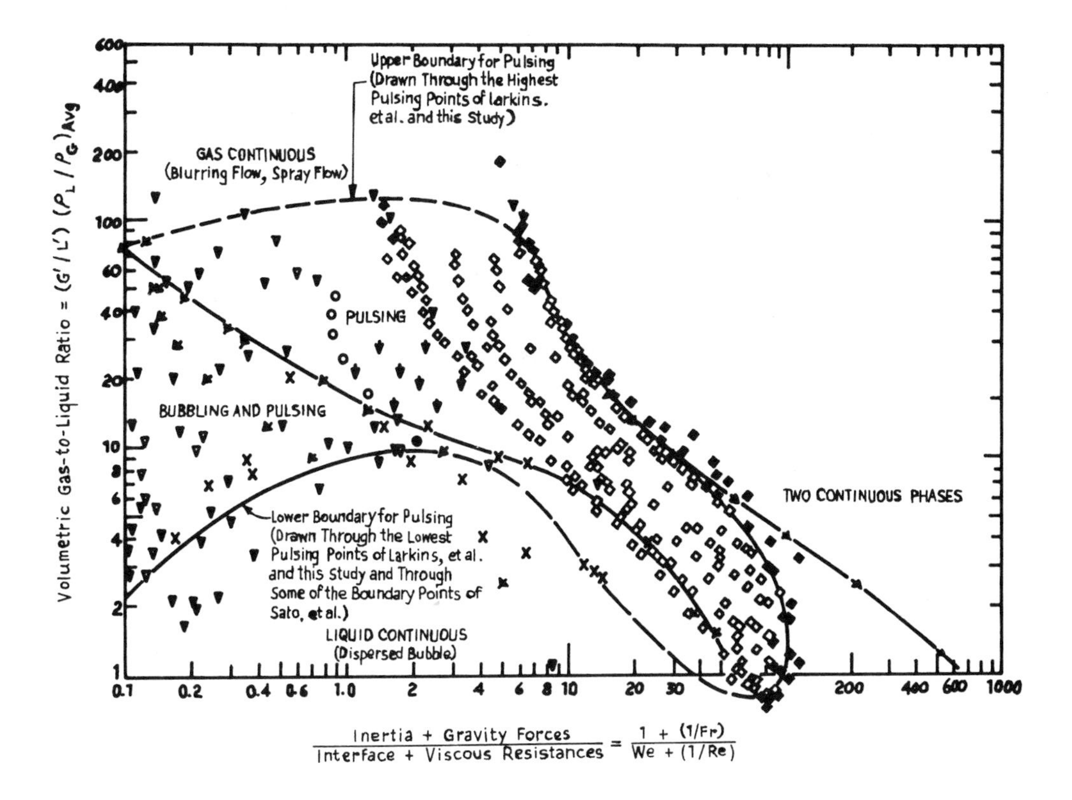

Symbol	Source	Packing	Dp. cm	ϵ	Bed Dia., cm	Bed Height, m	System
▼	Beimesch and	Beads	0.470	0.387	7.62	1.22	Air/Water
	Kessler (1971)	Spheres	0.645	0.444	7.62	1.22	Air/water
⊿ ✖	Larkins,	Beads	0.300	0.364	5.08	1.92	CO_2/Hexane
✖ ✖	et al. (1961)	Beads	0.300	0.371	5.08	1.25	Nat. Gas/CO_2/Lube Oil
▽ ▼	↓	Raschig R.	0.582	0.530	10.2	2.22	Air/Water/DEG
		Spheres	0.317	0.357	↓	↓	↓
		Cylinders	0.952	0.362			
×	Salo, et al.	Spheres	0.259	0.370	6.58	1.00	Air/Water
	(1973a)	↓	0.801	0.408	6.58	↓	↓
	↓		0.801	0.382	12.2		
○ ●	Clements and Schmidt (1976)	Cylinders	0.104	0.361	5.08	1.43	Freon-12/Silicone Oil
◇ ◆	This Study	Cylinders	0.350	0.366	29.2	1.22	Air/0-46% Glycerine Solutions

Open Points Represent Visually Pulsing or Slugging or Oscillatory Local Pressure Drop Runs

Solid Points Represent Visually Homogeneous Flow Runs;
✖ - Two Continuous Phases, ✖ - Bubbling

Data Points of Sato, et al. (1973a) are for a Boundary Between Dispersed Bubble and Pulsing Flow Patterns

$0.000413 \leqslant Fr \leqslant 191$
$0.0000541 \leqslant We \leqslant 18.1$
$0.0196 \leqslant Re \leqslant 967$

Figure 13.8. Flow map for two-phase downflow through packed beds, for nonfoaming liquids (TCS < 3 sec); from Talmor, 1977). The original reference may be consulted for the references cited here.

ticles. The correlation suggested by Morsi et al. takes into consideration the effect of the liquid viscosity on holdup. These correlations hold for particles having a diameter larger than 2 mm.

Sicardi et al. (1979) have suggested that it would be useful to classify flow regimes into two main classes: poor interaction and high interaction regimes. For nonfoaming systems they have analyzed the available data along with their own data and have proposed a simplified flow map that delineates the flow regimes into low and high interaction regimes (Figure 13.10; see Tables 13.2 and 13.3). The most

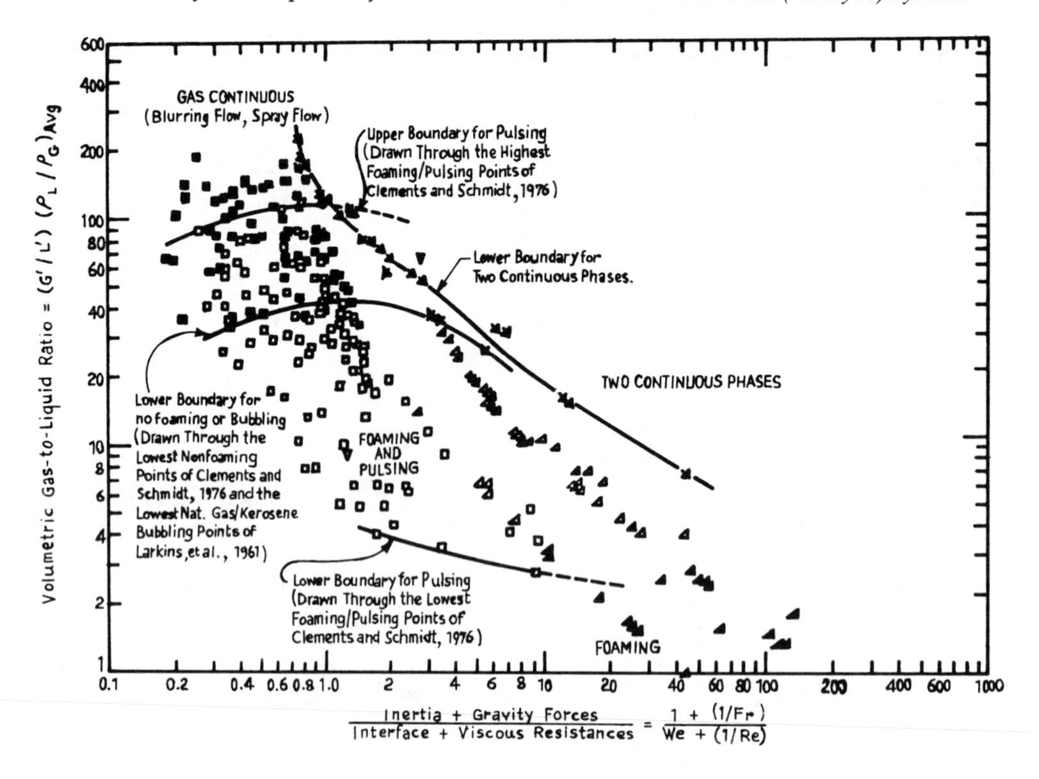

Symbol	Source	Packing	D_p, cm	ϵ	Bed Dia., cm	Bed Height, m	System
□ ■	Clements and Schmidt (1976)	Cylinders	0.137	0.357	3.40	0.915	Air/Silicone Oil
			0.192	0.365			
			0.213	0.370			
			0.350	0.368			
			0.104	0.361	5.08	1.43	
			0.292	0.318			
		Spheres	0.158	0.388			
		Cylinders	0.189	0.350	10.2	0.610	
◿ ◢	Larkins, et al., (1961)	Pellets	0.317	0.357	5.08	2.44	Nat. Gas/Kerosene
		Beads	0.300	0.364	5.08	1.25-2.35	Nat. Gas/Kerosene
				0.375			
▽		Cylinders	0.317	0.357	10.2	2.22	Air/0.5% Methocel Solution

Open Points Represent Visual Foaming and Pulsing (Clements and Schmidt, 1976) or Slugging (Larkins, et al., 1961)
Solid Points Represent no Foaming (Clements and Schmidt, 1976) or Homogeneous Flow Without Pressure Surges (Larkins, et al., 1961); Two Continuous Phases, ◢ Foaming, Bubbling

$0.00432 \leqslant Fr \leqslant 124$
$0.000156 \leqslant We \leqslant 1.06$
$0.102 \leqslant Re \leqslant 32.9$

Figure 13.9. Flow map for two-phase downflow through packed beds for foaming liquids (from Talmor, 1977). The original reference may be consulted for the references cited here.

important advantage of this flow map is that the ordinate reflects only the liquid flow rate, unlike the other charts (Figures 13.7–13.9) where it contains the ratio of the liquid to gas flow rates. The abscissa represents the gas flow rate term and omits any liquid flow rate term. Some aspects of liquid flow in trickle-bed reactors have been considered by Crine et al. (1980).

In general, industrial reactors operate in the trickle flow regime. However, in the petroleum and petrochemical industries where hydroprocessing is involved (see Section 13.2.7, Example 4) and where relatively high liquid and gas flow rates are encountered, we may well have a pulsing flow regime. In such flow regimes the functional dependence of a, $k_L a$, and $k_{SL} a_p$ on the operating variables is differ-

TABLE 13.2. Characteristic Properties of the Systems Studied in Figure 13.10

Column Diameter T (cm)	Packing Type	Nominal Packing Diameter d_p (cm)	$\frac{T}{d_p}$	ϵ	a_p (cm^{-1})	Column Height (cm)	Gas Phase	Liquid Phase	$\frac{\mu_L}{\mu_w}$	$\frac{\sigma_L}{\sigma_w}$	Gas Superficial Velocity V_G (cm/sec)	Liquid Superficial Velocity V_L (cm/sec)	Symbol
30	Raschig rings	1.0	30	0.62	5.10	391	Air	Water	1	1	4.6–49.2	1.5–3.8	●
							Air	Water + 0.5 ppm Lutensol LF711	1	0.9	4.6–49.2	1.5–3.8	○
							Air	Water + Tylose 1%	4	1	4.6–49.2	1.5–3.8	◐
30	Ceramic cylinders	1.2	25	0.406	2.91	391	Air	Water	1	1	0.5–38	0.5–2.7	▼
15	Ceramic cylinders	0.6	25	0.41	6.16	385	Air	Water	1	1	2.4–48.9	0.32–5.11	▲
8	Ceramic cylinders	0.5	16	0.41	9.06	408	Air	Water	1	1	7.6–12.5	0.3–1.8	■

TABLE 13.3. Characteristic Properties of the Systems Studied in Figure 13.10

Column Diameter T (cm)	Packing Type and Shape	d_p (cm)	$\frac{T}{d_p}$	Gas and Liquid Systems	Curve Number
5.00	Catalyst spheres	0.3	17	Air, CO_2–water, cyclohexane	1
	Catalyst cylinders (I)	0.18 × 0.6	13	He,N_2–petroleum, ether, gasoline	
	Catalyst cylinders (II)	0.14 × 0.5	16		
6.35	Beads	0.29	22	Air–water, –water + alcohol, etc.	2
8.00	Glass spheres	0.6	13	Air–water	3
	Raschig rings	0.6			
	Berl saddles	0.6			
6.60–12.20	Glass beads	0.259–1.65	25–7.5	Air–water	4
8.00	Glass spheres	0.6	13	Air–water	5
	Glass cylinders	0.27	30	Air–water + glycerol	
	Glass cylinders	0.54	15		
7.62	Glass spheres	0.47	16	Air–water	6
	TCC beads	0.38	20		
	Alumina beads	0.65	12		
10.00	Raschig rings	0.64	16	Air–water	7
	Raschig rings	1.03	9.7		
20.00	Raschig rings	2.2	9		
29.20	Cylinders	0.35	83	Air–water	8

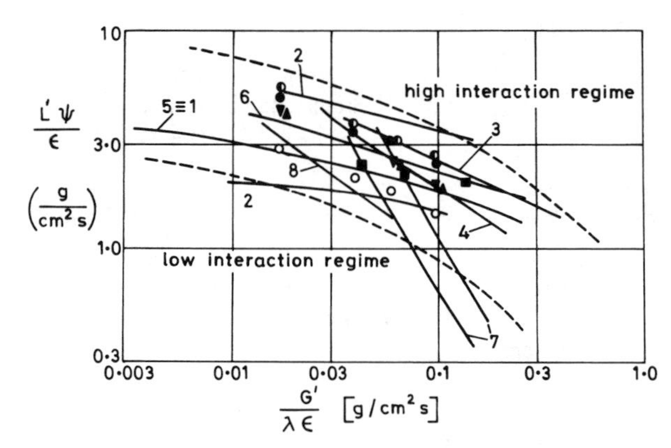

Figure 13.10. Simplified flow map for nonfoaming liquids in a trickle-bed reactor (Sicardi et al., 1979):

$$\psi = \frac{\sigma_W}{\sigma_L}\left[\left(\frac{\mu_L}{\mu_W}\right)\left(\frac{\rho_W}{\rho_L}\right)^2\right]^{0.33}$$

$$\lambda = \left(\frac{\rho_G \rho_L}{\rho_{air}\rho_W}\right)^{0.5}$$

ent, and in fact the value of k_L may even vary by a factor of 10 and k_{SL} may vary by a factor of 5. In the case of bubble flow, the value of a_p for solid–liquid mass transfer will be that corresponding to the geometric area of the packing but the value of a for gas–liquid mass transfer will be that provided by the bubbles.

Some complications also arise in scaling-up of reactors. Generally pilot-plant work is carried out with reactors of 2.5-cm i.d. that are about 0.5–2 m long at about the same liquid hourly space velocity as envisaged for the commercial units, which may have a total catalyst depth of 20–25 m. Thus, the superficial liquid velocity in the pilot-plant reactor may be less than 10% of that in the commercial reactor (the corresponding superficial gas velocity will also be lower), and this may result in a situation where the flow regime is different and diffusional factors may become important. Further, the backmixing characteristics in the pilot-plant reactor will also be different, because of the low values of the ratio of the height of the reactor to the diameter of the reactor.

In the trickle flow regime it is reasonable to assume that the value of a for gas–liquid and solid–liquid mass transfer is the same. It is not unlikely that for higher liquid flow rates with viscous liquids, the contribution of liquid holdup at packing junctions will cause the effective interfacial area for gas–liquid mass transfer to be higher than that for liquid–solid mass transfer. For other flow regimes the value of a for the gas–liquid and liquid–solid mass transfer would be expected to be different.

Pulsing Flow Regime

In some examples of industrial importance we encounter pulsing flow, which has some unique properties. The inception of this regime has been physically interpreted as being due to the formation of very large-amplitude waves that occlude the packing channels (Sicardi et al., 1979). In this flow regime we may get attractive values of $k_L a$ and $k_{SL} a$. There is some information in the literature suggesting that higher values of a may be realized in this flow regime than in the bubble flow regime (Mahajani and Sharma, 1979, 1980). At the transition from trickle flow to pulse flow we may get a sharp rise in the values of $k_L a$ and a. This flow regime is not likely to be favored in practice due to fluctuating pressure drop.

13.2.2. Packed Bubble Column Reactors

As mentioned earlier, in packed bubble column reactors the column is flooded and the catalyst particles also act as packings. In some cases the conversion in flooded reactors may be higher than that obtained with trickle-bed reactors. Snider and Perona (1974) have reported that in the reduction of uranyl(VI) to uranyl(IV) with H_2 in the presence of a Pd-based catalyst higher conversions are realized in a flooded reactor than in trickle-bed reactors. These authors have also observed that in the presence of gas flow liquid–solid mass transfer coefficients under flooded conditions can be as high as five times the value obtained when only liquid flows. If the catalyst is deactivated by the deposition of tarry or polymeric materials, then this type of reactor may show superior performance, since the impurities are more easily washed out in flooded reactors.

The intrinsic kinetics of the reaction can sometimes be studied in a liquid-filled reactor. The effect of different particle size will indicate the importance of liquid–solid mass transfer resistance and intraparticle diffusional resistance (Levec and Smith, 1976; see Example 5—on the treatment of wastewater in trickle-bed reactors—in Section 13.2.7). This type of reactor will have a much higher pressure drop than trickle-bed reactors. Further, if the catalyst is soft or deformable, catalyst particles may cement. In those situations where the reactant is present in the vapor as well as the liquid phase (see the example on the hydrogenation of crotonaldehyde and benzene) and diffusional factors are important, this type of reactor will give a lower reaction rate than a partially wetted trickle-bed reactor, since here the catalyst particles are completely surrounded by a liquid that offers resistance to the transport of the dissolved gas. Hofmann (1978) has discussed various aspects of packed bubble column reactors.

13.2.3. Use of Inert Particles in Trickle-Bed Reactors and Packed Bubble Column Reactors

If there is significant resistance associated with the gas–liquid film, higher rates of reaction per unit amount of catalyst can be realized by mixing an inert material with the catalyst. This suggestion may be particularly useful when expensive catalysts based on noble metals are used. Further, if it is desired that some free dissolved gas be present in the bulk liquid, then too the foregoing modification will hold. It has been claimed that this modification is useful in the manufacture of H_2O_2 by the ethyl anthraquinone route, where the ethyl anthraquinone has to be hydrogenated. The mixing of an inert material with the catalyst should also be useful for packed bubble column reactors.

13.2.4. Backmixing in Trickle-Bed Reactors

It is known that in pilot-plant reactors there is significant backmixing in the liquid phase, which adversely affects the performance of the reactor. In commercial reactors, however, the backmixing in the liquid phase may be unimportant because the beds in commercial reactors are deeper. For small deviations from plug flow the axial dispersion model may be employed to quantitatively take into account the effect of backmixing in the liquid phase. Mears (1971); Schwartz and Roberts (1973), Goto et al. (1976), Hofmann (1977, 1978), Gianetto et al. (1978), and Shah et al. (1978) have considered various aspects of backmixing. Mears has shown that backmixing is unimportant when the following inequality is satisfied:

$$\frac{h_t}{d_p} > \frac{20n}{\mathrm{Pe_L}} \ln\left(\frac{[\mathrm{B_o}]_i}{[\mathrm{B_o}]_f}\right) \tag{13.36}$$

(n is the order of the reaction; $\mathrm{Pe_L} = d_p V_L / D_c$ where V_L is in cm/sec and D_c, the axial dispersion coefficient is in cm^2/sec). In commercial reactors h_t is typically about 5–10 times that in the pilot-scale reactor; therefore, it is easier to satisfy this inequality in commercial reactors than in pilot-scale reactors.

It appears that the one-dimensional dispersion model may not be able to explain the performance of trickle-bed reactors satisfactorily because of the existence of stagnant zones, particularly in the case of porous catalysts (Hofmann, 1977, 1978; Gianetto et al., 1978; Shah et al., 1978). A modified cross-stream model has been suggested in which the liquid phase is divided into stagnant and free-flowing fractions. There are reasons to believe that the low space-time yields of the trickle-bed reactor as compared with those of classical solid-bed reactors are caused more by an unsatisfactory exchange rate between the active and inactive liquid holdup than by a strong spreading of the residence time on the freely flowing liquid.

13.2.5. Effect of Temperature

As regards the effect of temperature, the same considerations hold as were discussed in the case of slurry reactors (Section 13.1.3). However, care must be exercised when the reactant B is volatile, since in such cases a substantial part of the reaction may occur on the dry portions of the catalyst. In this case, the effect of temperature will be very different from the case in which B is nonvolatile (see Section 13.2.7, Example 2).

13.2.6. Procedure for Discerning the Controlling Mechanism

In the following subsections, which present procedures for discerning the controlling mechanism in various types of fixed-bed reactors, it is assumed that gas-side resistance is absent.

Trickle-Bed Reactors (Trickle (Film) Flow Regime)

As pointed out earlier, the accurate characterization of trickle-bed reactors poses a number of problems because of the interaction of numerous phenomena: two-phase flow, convective and diffusive mass transfer, heat transfer, chemical reaction, activation and deactivation of the catalyst, and so on (Germain et al., 1974). The following procedure may, however, be followed to discern the controlling mechanism.

1. Establish the intrinsic kinetics of the reaction by the same procedure as outlined for slurry reactors (Section 13.1.2) and obtain the order of the reaction with respect to the reactants, rate constant, and activation energy.
2. If the reactant has a finite vapor pressure at the operating temperature of the reactor, then separately study the intrinsic kinetics of the solid-catalyzed vapor-phase reaction by following the established procedures.

3. Ensure that, as far as possible, the ratio of the tube diameter to the size of the catalyst pellet is more than 10. A proper distributor for the liquid must be used.

4. Study the effect of the liquid flow rate on the rate of reaction after the catalyst particles have been completely wetted (which should be scrupulously established). An increase in the rate of reaction with an increase in the liquid flow rate will indicate that either the gas–liquid-film resistance or liquid–solid-film resistance is important. If the liquid flow rate has no effect on the rate of reaction, external diffusional resistances are absent. In such a case a study of the effect of catalyst particle size on the rate of reaction will indicate whether intraparticle diffusional resistance is important. In the case where gas–liquid-film resistance or liquid–solid-film resistance is important, there will be no effect of the concentration of species B on the rate of reaction provided that the concentration of B is far in excess of [A*]. It should be ascertained that the effect of liquid flow rate is not due to a possible increase in the liquid holdup.

If reducing the particle size has no effect on the rate of reaction per unit area of the catalyst particles, pore diffusional resistance is absent.

van Klinken and van Dongen (1980) have brought out the importance of catalyst dilution in laboratory reactors to obviate the problems associated with the maldistribution of liquid. In the specific case of hydrodenitrogenation of a vacuum distillate, where an $Ni-Mo/Al_2O_3$ catalyst (of 1.5-mm particles) is used, it was found desirable to use 0.2-mm silicone carbide powder as a diluent. The addition of small inert particles reduces axial dispersion substantially, and the liquid moves in an essentially plug flow manner. Further, the relatively higher holdup of the diluted bed leads to better wetting and hence improved utilization of the catalyst (see point 5).

5. The functional dependence of k_L and k_{SL} on the liquid flow rate is not very different (both will vary approximately as the 0.3–0.4 power of the superficial liquid velocity) and it becomes difficult to distinguish between these two cases, particularly since the values of k_{SL} and k_L are also comparable. The effect of an increase in the gas flow rate, at higher values of superficial gas velocity and nearly complete wetting, on the rate of reaction per unit volume of the reactor may, in principle, give some indication whether gas–liquid or solid–liquid mass transfer is important. An increase in the superficial gas velocity, after nearly complete wetting, will result in increasing the value of $k_L a$, since the liquid is dispersed as droplets and contributes to a higher value of a. By contrast, the area for solid–liquid mass transfer may decrease with an increase in the superficial gas velocity.

6. It may be useful to study the effect of replacing the active catalyst particles with nonactive particles having the same size and shape. If with (say) 30% of the active particles replaced by nonactive particles some effect on the overall rate of reaction is observed, then we may conclude that surface reaction is important (Enright and Chuang, 1978). We can also change the percentage of the active ingredient in the catalyst (e.g., the Pd or Pt content of catalysts based on these noble metals) and study the effect of this change on the rate of reaction under otherwise uniform conditions (Morita and Smith, 1978). A surface-reaction-controlled system will be substantially affected by this change, but there would be no effect on systems that are controlled by gas–liquid mass transfer or solid–liquid mass transfer resistance. This procedure involving a change in the percentage of active catalyst was also suggested in the case of slurry reactors (see Section 13.1.2).

Table 13.4 lists the effect of different variables that exercise major, minor, and negligible influence on $R_A a$ (mol/cm^3 of column volume sec).

Packed Bubble Column Reactor (Flooded Reactor)

Study the effect of the gas flow rate on the rate of reaction. If there is a substantial effect (the rate is approximately proportional to about the 0.5 power of the superficial gas velocity), then external diffusional resistance is important. If there is no effect beyond a certain minimum superficial gas velocity, it is indicative of the absence of external diffusional resistance. The superficial liquid velocity may also have a significant effect on the k_{SL} value for small particles (Snider and Perona, 1974). With 0.29-cm alumina spheres k_{SL} has been reported to vary as the 0.5 power of the superficial liquid velocity. However, there is some controversy on this subject, and Mochizuki and Matsui (1974) have found no effect of liquid flow rate on $k_{SL} a_p$ with 5 mm × 5 mm packings up to a liquid Reynolds number of 5 (see Section 11.1.5).

It must be ensured that the gas flow rate is not increased beyond a level that causes a change in the flow regime to pulse flow.

The $k_L a$ and $k_{SL} a_p$ values are of comparable

TABLE 13.4. Controlling Mechanism in Trickle-Bed Reactors (Film Flow Regime): Effect of Pertinent Variables on $R_A a$

Controlling Resistance	Variables Whose Influence is: Major	Minor	Negligible
Gas–liquid mass transfer, $k_L a$	[A*], d_p, superficial liquid velocity	Temperature	[B_o], superficial gas velocity (at lower values), replacement of active by inactive catalyst particles
Liquid–solid mass transfer, of A, $k_{SL} a_p$ (for A)	d_p, [A*], superficial liquid velocity	Temperature	[B_o], superficial gas velocity (at lower values), replacement of active by inactive catalyst particles
Liquid–solid mass transfer, of B, $k_{SL} a_p$ (for B)	d_p, [B_o], superficial liquid velocity	Temperature	[A*], superficial gas velocity[a]
Surface reaction (pore diffusion negligible)	d_p, [A*], [B_o], temperature, replacement of active by inactive catalyst particles	Superficial liquid velocity (above certain minimum)	Superficial gas velocity[a]
Surface reaction with pore diffusion	d_p, [A*], [B_o], temperature,[b] replacement of active by inactive catalyst particles	Superficial liquid velocity (above certain minimum)	Superficial gas velocity[a]

[a] It is assumed that this does not cause any charge in the flow regime.
[b] The effect of temperature on $R_A a$ is less pronounced in this case than for surface reaction where pore diffusion is negligible.

magnitude. Further, in order to arrive at a definite conclusion whether $k_L a$ or $k_{SL} a_p$ is dominating, the functional dependence of $k_L a$ and $k_{SL} a_p$ on the superficial gas velocity may not be substantially different. However, it is likely that a substantial reduction in the size of the particles will affect the $k_{SL} a_p$ value much more than the $k_L a$ value. If the effect of reducing the particle size to one-half makes an almost proportionate difference to the rate, it may be indicative of the absence of gas–liquid film resistance. The effect of replacing active particles with nonactive particles and of varying the percentage of active ingredient in the catalyst can also be studied in the manner indicated earlier for trickle-bed reactors.

There is need for further work on the mass transfer characteristics of trickle-bed reactors and bubble column reactors, particularly in large diameter reactors, with the types of catalyst particles and fluids that are employed in practice. Some aspects of the process design of reactors have been considered by Goto and Smith (1978b).

13.2.7. Examples of Fixed-Bed Reactors

1. Hydrogenation of α-Methyl Styrene (AMS) *in a Trickle-Bed Reactor and a Packed Bubble Column Reactor (Flooded Reactor); Selective Hydrogenation of Phenyl Acetylene*

We have considered this system under slurry reactors (Section 13.1.8, Example 1). Satterfield et al. (1969) have studied the hydrogenation of AMS in a trickle-bed reactor consisting of a single vertical column of spherical porous Pd (1%) on alumina catalyst particles 0.825 cm in diameter in the temperature range of 20–50°C. The intrinsic kinetics as well as the effectiveness factor were studied using powdered catalyst as well as in a reactor where the catalyst pellets were swirled. The liquid flow rate had practically no effect on the reaction rate, indicating that diffusional resistances associated with the gas–liquid and liquid–solid films were insignificant. The apparent activation energy was found to be 5.08

kcal/mol; from intrinsic kinetics the activation energy value was found to be 7.6 kcal/mol. These data indicate that pore diffusion factors are important.

Germain et al. (1974) have also studied the hydrogenation of AMS under trickle-bed conditions as well as in the vapor phase with Pd on γ-alumina catalyst. They have shown that the catalyst activity is strongly dependent on the purity of the AMS. They have also brought out some novel aspects connected with the performance of the partially wetted reactor (see the next example), and the existence of two steady states, which is discussed just after the next example.

White et al. (1974) have studied the kinetics of the hydrogenation of AMS to cumene using a rotating-disk catalytic reactor. The catalyst was palladium film deposited on a stainless steel disk 6.3 cm (2.5 in.) in diameter and 1.9 cm (0.75 in.) thick. In the temperature range of 40–115°C, at a hydrogen pressure of 4 atm and disk speed of 5–42 radian/sec the reaction was partly diffusion and partly surface reaction controlled. The kinetic parameters were also obtained, and these agreed with the published data.

Snider and Perona (1974) have studied the hydrogenation of AMS in a 3.8-cm jacketed upflow flooded reactor containing Pd on alumina catalyst particles having an average diameter of 0.29 cm. The reaction was carried out at a pressure of 18 atm and the temperature was varied from 24 to 40.5°C. There was practically no effect of the concentration of AMS in the cumene nor of temperature on the rate of hydrogenation, indicating that diffusional resistance played a dominant role. Furthermore, experiments showed that resistance to mass transfer was located in the liquid–solid film. The values of the solid–liquid mass transfer coefficient in the presence of gas were as much as five times those obtained with only liquid flow in the reactor.

Mochizuki and Matsui (1976) have studied the selective hydrogenation of phenyl acetylene to styrene in a 3.2-cm-i.d. cocurrent upflow reactor with Pd on alumina as a catalyst. Mass transfer from liquid to the catalyst surface was found to be important.

Morita and Smith (1978) have also studied the hydrogenation of AMS in a 2.54-cm-i.d. 30-cm-long reactor provided with 0.141-cm (10–14 mesh) Pd/Al_2O_3 catalyst (Pd content 0.5 and 2.5% w/w). To start with, a liquid-filled mode of operation was adopted to study the intrinsic kinetics, since with this method of working diffusional resistances can be more readily eliminated. The temperature was varied from 32 to 52°C and the pressure was atmospheric. A batch-recycle system was used so that substantial conversions occurred. Experiments were made in such a way that appropriate plots could be made to obtain the liquid–solid mass transfer coefficient values. The content of active Pd was also varied, since this change affects the kinetics of the surface reaction but does not affect the solid–liquid mass transfer coefficient.

The fraction f of the particle surface covered by liquid did not vary significantly with the liquid flow rate. The average value of f was 0.89. The most important conclusion drawn by the authors is that the mass transfer coefficients obtained from their experiments were about one-fourth of those based on mass transfer from nonporous particles. This difference may well be due to a lower area for mass transfer in the reaction case. The dry portions of the catalyst also contribute to the reaction, and this complicates the issue further.

2. *Hydrogenation of Crotonaldehyde and Benzene; Hydrogenation of* AMS *(Importance of the Reaction Occurring in the Vapor Phase)*

Sedriks and Kenney (1973) have studied the hydrogenation of crotonaldehyde to butyraldehyde at 30°C and atmospheric pressure in a 4.3-cm-diameter jacketed trickle-bed reactor. The catalyst used was pelletized palladium on alumina (0.476 cm × 0.476 cm ($\frac{3}{16}$ in. × $\frac{3}{16}$ in.)). The superficial liquid flow rate was 0.0045 cm/sec, which implies that the catalyst pellets were very poorly wetted. At 31°C the vapor pressure of crotonaldehyde is 0.07 atm and hence there was a substantial concentration of crotonaldehyde in the vapor phase. Sedriks and Kenney have established that a substantial part of the reaction occurred in the vapor phase. In fact, their experimental data revealed that the reaction in the vapor phase was dominant. It is likely that for exothermic reactions dry areas of the catalyst may provide seats of hot spots and potential sites for local temperature runaway. It may be emphasized that if the reactant has negligible vapor pressure, then the question of the reaction occurring in the vapor phase does not arise.

Satterfield and Özel (1973) have studied the hydrogenation of benzene at 76°C (4°C below its boiling point) on 2% Pt on alumina spherical catalyst pellets 0.635 cm in diameter in a glass reactor. The superficial liquid velocity was varied between 0.11 and 0.37 cm/sec. It was observed visually that all the catalyst pellets were wet. However, a careful observation indicated that part of the liquid flowed as rivulets that maintained their position. Thus some catalyst pellets were covered with a trickling liquid film whereas others lacked a liquid film even though they were wet. The experimental work of these authors clearly shows that the overall steady-state conversion, expressed as moles per second per cubic centimeter of catalyst [mol/(sec) (cm^3 of catalyst)], decreased by about 25% when the liquid flow rate was increased threefold. This is contrary to the expected results and clearly brings out the importance of the reaction occurring in the vapor phase. With an increase in the liquid flow rate the extent of reaction in the vapor phase will decrease, whereas that in the liquid phase will increase. However, the relative contribution of the reaction in the vapor phase is greater, since the presence of the liquid phase introduces additional diffusional resistance. Thus a partially wet trickle bed may exhibit a higher reaction rate than a completely wet reactor.

Germain et al. (1974) have made similar observations in the case of the hydrogenation of AMS. They have also pointed out that because of capillary forces partial wetting of the catalyst pellets may be enough to ensure good availability of AMS to the reaction sites. It is conceivable that liquid AMS enters a partly wet pellet at one side, is hydrogenated to cumene near the gas–liquid interface, and reaches the gaseous phase. (Here, the reaction product is more volatile than the reactant.)

Herskowitz et al. (1979) have made a study of hydrogenation of AMS in a 2.54-cm-i.d. trickle-bed reactor with a Pd/Al_2O_3 catalyst. In the case of the catalyst containing 2.5% Pd higher rates of hydrogenation were found at low liquid velocities than at high liquid velocities. This behavior can again be attributed to hydrogenation of AMS vapor by dry portions of the catalyst.

3. *Existence of Two Steady States in the Hydrogenation of* AMS

Germain et al. (1974) have studied the hydrogenation of AMS over a Pd on γ-alumina catalyst in a trickle-bed reactor, a mechanically agitated contactor (slurry reactor), and in vapor phase. In the case of the trickle-bed reactor at a temperature greater than 35°C they found that the dependence of the rate of reaction on the liquid flow is not uniform. For some experiments the reaction rate was found to increase with a decrease in the liquid flow rate (contrary to the normal behavior) and in this sequence of experiments if the liquid flow rate is increased, much higher rates of reactions were realized than those measured separately. Further, in some cases the value of the rate of reaction per unit mass of catalyst measured in the slurry reactor was less than that realized in the trickle-bed reactor.

Germain et al. have pointed out the possible existence of two steady states: one on the basis of the rate being limited by mass transfer in the film of liquid trickling on the *uniformly wet catalyst pellets*; and the second on the basis that reaction takes place on partly wet pellets. The role of liquid was found to be essential in maintaining the catalyst activity by dissolving the polymeric substances formed by the reaction. Thus a cyclic behavior of the catalyst pellets may arise as a result of alternate operation in the gaseous and liquid phases.

4. *Hydrodesulfurization of Petroleum Fractions; Hydrodemetallization of Residual Oils*

Hydrodesulfurization of Petroleum Fractions. The most important industrial application of trickle-bed reactors is in the field of hydrodesulfurization of petroleum fractions where the sulfur in the organic compounds is converted to H_2S. For relatively heavy feedstocks (high viscosity and high boiling point) a typical value of the superficial liquid velocity is about 0.17 cm/sec. By contrast, for naphtha and light gas oils the superficial liquid velocity value can approach about 2 cm/sec. It may also be desired to reduce the sulfur content to a very low level. It is likely that under certain conditions the diffusion of the sulfur compound to the catalyst surface may become the controlling step. Under these conditions the degree of mixing at the exit of each catalyst particle may have a profound effect on its performance.

van Deemter (1965) has given the case history of Shell's process for the hydrodesulfurization of petroleum fractions. Experiments were made with a straight-run heavy gas oil containing 1.5% of sulfur on a commercial $Co\text{–}Mo/Al_2O_3$ catalyst. The particle size was varied from 0.35 to 5 mm. The thickness of the liquid film (i.e., its physical thickness) on the catalyst particles is expected to vary from about 0.01 to 0.1 mm, depending on the overall flow conditions. Thus the thickness of the liquid film is much smaller than the radius of the catalyst pellets and the diffusional resistance associated with the transport of H_2 to the catalyst surface is most unlikely to be important. The diffusional resistance associated with the transport of sulfur compounds can be important. Experimental data show that the catalyst size is very important under otherwise uniform conditions. For 0.35-mm-diameter particles there was practically no resistance associated with diffusion in the pores. In the case of 5-mm-diameter particles, however, only 36% of the internal active surface was utilized. A separate series of experiments were made in a continuous well-stirred reactor where the resistance associated with pore diffusion could be eliminated. It was found that no single reaction of any order fitted the data; a better agreement was observed with a system of two simultaneous first-order reactions with rate constants equal to 100 hr^{-1} and 10 hr^{-1}.

Schuit and Gates (1973) have also given a comprehensive review of the chemistry and engineering aspects of hydrodesulfurization. These authors have also reported, on the basis of the available experimental data, that external mass transfer factors are unimportant.

The amount of H_2 that is used in the reactors is usually much greater than that required stoichiometrically and is fixed on the basis of the requirements of temperature control and in some cases to improve the liquid flow characteristics. The excess hydrogen is recirculated after removal of H_2S and mercaptans.

Shimizu et al. (1970) have studied the kinetics of hydrodesulfurization of Khafji residual oil at 370–420°C and 51–131 atm of pressure in a double-tubestainless steel reactor (length, 3 m; i.d. of inner tube, 8 mm; o.d. of inner tube, 15 mm; i.d. of outer tube, 25 mm). The inner tube was packed to a depth of about 2 m with catalyst pellets. The sulfur content of the oil was about 4% w/w and the average molecular weight was in the range of 460–507. Co–Mo–alumina and Co–Mo–silica–alumina spherical pellets 0.8 mm in diameter were used as catalyst. The reaction was found to be kinetically controlled and second order with respect to the sulfur concentration.

Henry and Gilbert (1973) have considered some aspects of the scale-up of pilot-plant data for catalytic hydroprocessing (hydrodesulfurization, hydrocracking, hydrodenitrogenation, etc.). Their model is based on the holdup of the liquid and is able to correlate the experimental data well. Satterfield (1975) has pointed out that the physical premise on which this model is based is not very sound.

Crine et al. (1980) have analyzed the published data on the hydrodesulfurization of petroleum fractions with a single wetting parameter that is independent of the temperature and the nature of the reaction investigated. The suggested wetting parameter depends on the fluid properties and catalyst size. This parameter logically correlates the dependence on the operating parameters.

Weekman (1976) has reviewed various aspects of the hydroprocessing of petroleum fractions.

In the case of the hydrodesulfurization of heavy residual oil complications arise because of the presence of soluble organometallic compounds (chiefly based on nickel, present at a level of about 15 ppm, and vanadium, present at a level of about 50 ppm), which deactivate the catalyst. Shah and Paraskos (1975) have considered some aspects of this problem and have shown that a catalyst that performs best initially is not necessarily best for the longer run. Montagna and Shah (1975) have considered the various models for analyzing the experimental data on the hydrodesulfurization of heavy residual oils and have shown that the models of Mears and of Henry and Gilbert, although based on different premises, correlate the data.

Hydrodemetallization of Residual Oils. Heavier petroleum fractions containing asphaltenes comprise significant amounts of organic metallic compounds, particularly those of vanadium and nickel (0–2000 ppm). It is desirable to demetallize these heavier fractions so that subsequent hydroprocessing becomes more efficient.

Hydrodemetallization is an interesting solid-catalyzed reaction where the organometallic reactant leaves an easily identifiable deposit on the catalyst surface at a site where the reaction occurred. Further, this deposit, which when sulfur is also present in the heavy fractions is usually in the form of sulfides of the relevant metal, may also catalyze the hydrodemetallization reaction. The deposition of metals can plug the pore mouths of the catalyst, resulting in substantial deactivation. Further, the resistance associated with diffusion in the pores will increase.

A systematic study of this system has been made. A noteworthy feature of this system is that measurements of metal concentration profiles in the spent catalysts can be made with different particle sizes. There is enough evidence to suggest that pore diffusional resistance associated with the transport of the organometallic compounds is dominant. Thus catalyst pore size and particle size will play important roles (Bridge and Green, 1980).

5. Use of Trickle-Bed Reactors for the Treatment of Wastewater; Air Oxidation of Dilute Formic Acid and Acetic Acid

The removal of organic matter from wastewater by aerobic treatment in trickling filters has been practiced for a long time (see below). It has been suggested that some catalysts based on copper oxide, zinc oxide, iron oxide, and the like might work well in trickle-bed reactors for the oxidation of organic pollutants (Goto et al., 1977). Goto and Smith (1975) have reported data on the air oxidation of formic acid with CuO–ZnO catalyst (particle size 0.291 and 0.0541 cm) in the temperature range of 212–242°C. These catalysts are not active at lower temperatures, and hence a temperature in the range of 210–250°C has to be employed, which means that the oxidation has to be carried out under pressure. Experiments were carried out at 48 atm in a 2.54-cm-i.d. trickle-bed reactor. The intrinsic kinetics of the reaction was also studied. It was observed that gas–liquid mass transfer resistance is important.

Levec and Smith (1976) have studied the air oxidation of dilute acetic acid solutions. Since acetic acid is a relatively refractory pollutant, the temperature had to be kept at the higher level of 252–286°C and ferric oxide particles were used as catalyst. The pressure was varied from 67 to 72.5 atm. The trickle-bed reactor had an inside diameter of 2.54 cm and was 30 cm long. Experiments were also carried out with a liquid-filled reactor that had an inside diameter of 0.93 cm and was 25 cm long and here the liquid flow rate was varied from 0.48 to 0.81 cm^3/sec. In the liquid-filled reactor the catalyst particle size was varied from 0.0384 to 0.238 cm and the acetic acid concentration from 8.3 to 70.8×10^{-7} mol/cm^3. In the case of the trickle-bed reactor the catalyst particle size was varied from 0.054 to 0.238 cm and the liquid flow rate from 0.38 to 1.32 cm^3/sec; the gas flow rate was varied from 1.6 to 5.9 cm^3/sec.

In the case of the liquid-filled reactor the intrinsic kinetics could be studied, since no intraparticle diffusion or liquid-to-particle mass transfer resistances were observed on the basis of experiments with different sizes of particles. The rate of oxidation was found to be one-half order in O_2 and first order in acetic acid in the concentration range of 50–500 ppm. However, at higher concentrations of acetic acid the reaction was found to be zero order with respect to acetic acid.

In the trickle-bed reactor some interesting results were obtained. Mass transfer resistance associated with the transfer of O_2 was found to be important. Since the reactor was operated at a specified total pressure, an increase in temperature resulted in a reduction in the effective partial pressure of O_2 because of the high vapor pressure of water. The global rate agreed reasonably with the calculated value on the basis of resistances offered by the gas–liquid and solid–liquid film at lower temperatures. At higher temperatures, however, the experimental values were much higher than the predicted values, presumably because of the local vaporization of a part of the water on the catalyst surface, which reduced mass transfer resistances. Further, in deep beds the experimental values of conversion were less than the predicted values at low liquid rates, perhaps because of increased channeling of liquid at low flow rates in deep beds.

Levec et al. (1976) have studied the performance of a new active catalyst for the oxidation of acetic acid that is based on Cu, Mn, and lanthanum on zinc aluminate spinel. This catalyst is much more active than the Fe_2O_3 catalyst.

Trickling Filters for Treatment of Wastewater. The trickling filter is a fixed-bed biological reactor consisting of a large shallow tank filled with packing. Wastewater is introduced by stationary or rotating-arm distributors and percolates down through the packing to be discharged at the bottom. The packing is inert; it acts as a support for biological growth (the slime layer) and serves as a filler with connecting void spaces so that liquid and air can flow through the bed simultaneously. The slime layer adsorbs dissolved organic matter from the wastewater and O_2 is absorbed from air.

The nutrients and oxygen are used by the microorganisms to form additional cell matter. Cell mass accumulates and forms the above-mentioned slime layer. Excess cell mass is periodically sloughed off and removed with the effluent. The sloughed cell material is eventually removed from the treated wastewater by settling. From a mechanistic viewpoint, the trickling filter is analogous to a trickle-bed reactor. The most important difference is in the characteristics of the catalytic surface, namely, the slime layer. The slime layer consists of a gelatinous matrix interpersed with microorganisms; it is formed within the first few days of operation and covers all the exposed surfaces in the bed. Total accumulation and composition of the slime varies widely both within a given bed and from plant to plant. Although the designs and operating experience for the trickling filters are well documented in the sanitary engineering literature, most of these descriptions and discussions are of an empirical nature. In recent years, however, there have been increasing efforts in the direction of simulating and modeling trickling filters. Although the terminology differs, the modeling and analysis of the mechanistic phenomena are done on lines essentially parallel to those in the case of trickle-bed reactors.

Atkinson and Ali (1976) have modeled these types of reactors and have also made an experimental study of the performance of a new type of plastic packings (Biopoc of Hydronyl—now Norton—in England). These authors have found that neither the gas–liquid nor solid–liquid film mass transfer resistance was significant under the conditions employed by them, which are representative of those employed in practice. Thus the kinetic coefficients provide the basis for the design.

6. *Oxidation of* SO_2

It is known that the oxidation of dissolved SO_2 with O_2 is catalyzed by active carbon (see Example 9 in Section 13.1.8). It would be advantageous if the oxidation of lean SO_2 could be carried out in a continuously operated trickle-bed reactor packed with active carbon catalyst. Hartman and Coughlin (1972) have made experiments in a 3.15-cm-i.d. column packed with 4.5×5.7 mm pellets. The column was operated countercurrently. Experiments were also made in a well-stirred tank containing about 4000 cm^3 of liquid and a small amount of active carbon pellets. The conditions in the stirred-tank reactor were chosen in such a way that mass transfer resistances were unimportant and the concentration of dissolved SO_2 and O_2 at the catalyst surface corresponded to the saturation concentration. It was found that both the rate of transport of O_2 to the catalyst surface and the surface reaction were important.

Goto and Smith (1978a, b) have analyzed the performance of trickle-bed reactors operated cocurrently and packed-column reactors operated countercurrently for this system. The available experimental data are well correlated by the equations derived by Goto and Smith.

7. *Methanation for Purification of Ammonia Synthesis Gas*

The final purification of ammonia synthesis gas, consisting of a stoichiometric mixture of nitrogen and hydrogen containing CO and CO_2 at a ppm level, is generally accomplished by methanation over an Ni or Ru/Ni catalyst. The common mode of working is based on adiabatic operation with a pelleted catalyst (a solid-catalyzed vapor-phase reaction). The rise in temperature has a detrimental effect due to equilibrium considerations. Recently it has been claimed that heat can be removed by injecting an evaporating liquid, such as water (Wyatt, 1979).

8. *Deuterium Exchange between* H_2 *and Water*

Deuterium exchange between H_2 and water is of great practical importance in the nuclear power industry. The dual temperature catalyzed exchange of deuterium between H_2 and water is potentially an attractive chemical separation method.

$$\mathrm{HD} + \mathrm{H_2O}(vap) \rightleftharpoons \mathrm{HDO}(vap) + \mathrm{H_2} \qquad \text{(i)}$$

$$\mathrm{HDO}(vap) + \mathrm{H_2O}(liq) \rightleftharpoons \mathrm{H_2O}(vap) + \mathrm{HDO}(liq) \qquad \text{(ii)}$$

$$\mathrm{HD} + \mathrm{H_2O}(liq) \rightleftharpoons \mathrm{HDO}(liq) + \mathrm{H_2} \qquad \text{(iii)}$$

Reaction (i) occurs at the catalyst site. A number of catalysts have been considered, and it appears that Pd/C is quite attractive (Enright and Chuang, 1978). It is necessary to waterproof the catalyst, and this was achieved by coating with Teflon. Carbon particles were of 0.1 μm size and contained 0.2% Pt. These particles were duly waterproofed and bonded to 1.27-cm ceramic Intalox saddles. A 20-cm-diameter column 315 cm high was used, and since the reaction is reversible the countercurrent mode of operation was adopted to realize a larger driving force for mass transfer in comparison to that in the cocurrent mode of operation.

The region of industrial importance calls for the overall mass transfer coefficient to be in the range of 0.5–5 sec^{-1}. Mass transfer plays an important role, and under otherwise uniform conditions there was a substantial gas flow rate effect and small liquid flow rate effect.

Since the packings were hydrophobic the liquid flow distribution would be expected to be poor and hence the technique of dilution with the same ceramic Intalox saddle support, which is hydrophilic, was adopted, particularly because Pt is expensive and this technique might reduce inventory costs. It was found that the performance of the diluted catalyst was as good as or even better than that obtained when the hydrophobic catalyst was used alone. External mass transfer is expected to improve with better liquid distribution. In any case, even under otherwise uniform conditions the same external mass transfer coefficient value will be realized with a diluted catalyst and hence expensive catalyst can be saved. Internal mass transfer was also found to be important.

REFERENCES

Acres, G. J. K., and Cooper, B. J. (1972), *J. Appl. Chem. Biotechnol.*, **22**, 769.

Acres, G. J. K., Bird, A. J., and Davidson, P. J. (1974), *Chem. Eng. (London)*, No. 283, p. 145.

Albright, L. F. (1973), *J. Am. Oil Chem. Soc.*, **50**, 255.

Alper, E., Wichtendahl, B., and Deckwer, W.-D. (1980), *Chem. Eng. Sci.*, **35**, 217.

Atkinson, B., and Ali, M. E. A. R. (1976), *Trans. Inst. Chem. Eng.*, **54**, 239.

Begley, J. N. (1966), *J. Polymer Sci.*, Part A-1, **4**, 319.

Bern, L., Hell, M., and Schöön, N.-H. (1975), *J. Am. Oil Chem. Soc.*, **52**, 182, 391.

Bern, L., Lidefelt, J.-O., and Schöön, N.-H. (1976), *J. Am. Oil Chem. Soc.*, **53**, 463.

Bird, A. J. (1976), private communication.

Bizhanov, F. B., Fasman, A. B., Sokol'skii, D. V., and Kozhakulov, A. (1976), *Int. Chem. Eng.*, **16**, 650.

Bondi, A. (1971), *Chem. Tech.*, **1**, 185.

Boussoulengas, A. V., Ehdaie, S., and Jansson, R. E. W. (1979), *Chem. Ind. (London)*, No. 19, 670.

Bridge, A. G., and Green, D. C. (1980), Paper presented at ChemTech., Bombay.

Calderbank, P. H., Evans, F., Farley, R., Jepson, G., and Poll, A. (1963), *Proc. Symp. Catalysis in Practice* (Inst. Chem. Eng., London), p. 66.

Chandrasekaran, K., and Sharma, M. M. (1977), *Chem. Eng. Sci.*, **32**, 669.

Chandrasekaran, K., and Sharma, M. M. (1978), *Chem. Eng. Sci.*, **33**, 1294.

Charest, F., and Chornet, E. (1976), *Can. J. Chem. Eng.*, **54**, 190.

Charpentier, J. C. (1976), *Chem. Eng. J.*, **11**, 161.

Charpentier, J. C., and Favier, M. (1975), *AIChE J.*, **21**, 1213.

Chou, T. S., Worley, F. L., and Luss, D. (1977), *Ind. Eng. Chem. Process Design Dev.*, **16**, 424.

Chaudhari, R. V., and Ramachandran, P. A. (1980), *AIChE J.*, **26**, 177.

Clarke, A., Lloydlangston, J., and Thomas, W. J. (1977), *Trans. Inst. Chem. Eng.*, **55**, 93.

Coenen, J. W. E. (1960), in De Boer, J. H. (Ed.), *The Mechanism of Heterogeneous Catalysis*, Elsevier, Amsterdam, p. 126.

Coenen, J. W. E. (1976), *J. Am. Oil Chem. Soc.*, **53**, 382.

Coenen, J. W. E. (1978), *Chem. Ind. (London)*, No. 18, 709.

Cordova, W. A., and Harriott, P. (1975), *Chem. Eng. Sci.*, **30**, 1201.

Crine, M., Marchot, P., and L'Homme, G. A. (1980), *Chem. Eng. Sci.*, **35**, 51.

Davis, H. S., Thomson, G., and Crandall, G. S. (1932), *J. Am. Chem. Soc.*, **54**, 2340.

Dean, D. N., Fuchs, M. J., Schaffer, J. M., and Carbonell, R. G. (1977), *Ind. Eng. Chem. Fundam.*, **16**, 452.

Deckwer, W.-D., and Alper, E. (1980), *Chem. Ing.-Tech.*, **52**, 219.

Dovell, F. S., Ferguson, W. E., and Greenfield, H. (1970), *Ind. Eng. Chem. Prod. Res. Dev.*, **9**, 224.

Enright, J. T., and Chuang, T. T. (1978), *Can. J. Chem. Eng.*, **56**, 246.

Ferrari, G., and Garbei, A. (1969), Fr. 1, 570, 990 (June, 1969); *Chem. Abstr.* (1970), **72**, 100282.

Friedlander, S. K. (1961), *AIChE J.*, **7**, 347.

Germain, A. H., Lefebvre, A. G., and L'Homme, G. A. (1974), *Adv. Chem. Ser.*, **133**, 164.

Gianetto, A., Baldi, G., Specchia, V., and Sicardi, S. (1978), *AIChE J.*, **24**, 1087.

Goto, S. (1976), *Can. J. Chem. Eng.*, **54**, 126.

Goto, S., and Smith, J. M. (1975), *AIChE J.*, **21**, 706, 714.

Goto, S., and Smith, J. M. (1978a), *AIChE J.*, **24**, 286.

Goto, S., and Smith, J. M. (1978b), *AIChE J.*, **24**, 294.

Goto, S., Watabe, S., and Matsubara, M. (1976), *Can. J. Chem. Eng.*, **54**, 551.

Goto, S., Levec, J., and Smith, J. M. (1977), *Catal. Rev. Sci. Eng.*, **15**, 187.

Greenfield, H. (1976), *Ind. Eng. Chem. Prod. Res. Dev.*, **15**, 156.

Gupta, D. V., Kranich, W. L., and Weiss, A. H. (1976), *Ind. Eng. Chem. Process Design Dev.*, **15**, 256.

Hammer, H. (1979), *Chem. Ing.-Tech.*, **51**, 295.

Hartman, M., and Coughlin, R. W. (1972), *Chem. Eng. Sci.*, **27**, 867.

Hashimoto, K., Teramoto, M., and Nagata, S. (1971a), *J. Chem. Eng. Japan*, **4**, 150.

Hashimoto, K., Muroyama, K., and Nagata, S. (1971b), *J. Am. Oil Chem. Soc.*, **48**, 291.

Henry, H. C., and Gilbert, J. B. (1973), *Ind. Eng. Chem. Process Design Dev.*, **12**, 328.

Herskowitz, M., Carbonell, R. G., and Smith, J. M. (1979), *AIChE J.*, **25**, 272.

Hofmann, H. (1977), *Int. Chem. Eng.*, **17**, 19.

Hofmann, H. (1978), *Catal. Rev. Sci. Eng.*, **17**(1), 71.

Holy, N. L. (1980), *Chem. Tech.*, **10**, 366.

Hsu, S.-H., and Ruether, J. A. (1978), *Ind. Eng. Chem. Process Design Dev.*, **17**, 524.

Ido, T., Teshima, H., and Shindo, S. (1976), *Int. Chem. Eng.*, **16**, 695.

Juvekar, V. A., and Sharma, M. M. (1973), *Chem. Eng. Sci.*, **28**, 825.

Kawakami, K., and Kusunoki, K. (1976), *J. Chem. Eng. Japan*, **9**, 469.

Kawakami, K., Ohgi, Y., and Kusunoki, K. (1976), *J. Chem. Eng. Japan*, **9**, 475.

Kelmers, A. D., and Bennett, M. R. (1976), *Inorg. Nucl. Chem. Letters*, **12**, 333.

Kenney, C. N., and Sedriks, W. (1972), *Chem. Eng. Sci.*, **27**, 2029.

Kölbel, H., Hammer, H., and Meisl, V. (1964), *Proc. 3rd European Symp. Chem. React. Eng.*, p. 115.

Komiyama, H., and Smith, J. M. (1975), *AIChE J.*, **21**, 664, 670.

Lee, Y. Y., and Tsao, G. T. (1972), *Chem. Eng. Sci.*, **27**, 1601.

Levec, J., and Smith, J. M. (1976), *AIChE J.*, **22**, 159.

Levec, J., Herskowitz, M., and Smith, J. M. (1976), *AIChE J.*, **22**, 919.

Leznoff, C. C. (1974), *Chem. Soc. Rev.*, **3**, 65.

McGreavy, C. (1972), *J. Appl. Chem. Biotechnol.*, **22**, 747.

McKillop, A., and Young, D. W. (1979), *Synthesis*, **6**, 401; **7**, 481.

Mahajani, V. V. (1979), Heterogeneous Reactions, Ph.D. (Tech.) thesis, University of Bombay.

Mahajani, V. V., and Sharma, M. M. (1979), *Chem. Eng. Sci.*, **34**, 1425.

Mahajani, V. V., and Sharma, M. M. (1980), *Chem. Eng. Sci.*, **35**, 941.

Manecke, G., and Storck, W. (1978), *Angew. Chem. Int. Ed. Engl.*, **17**, 657.

Marangozis, J., Keramidas, O. B., and Paparisvas, G. (1977), *Ind. Eng. Chem. Process Design Dev.*, **16**, 361.

Mears, D. E. (1971), *Chem. Eng. Sci.*, **26**, 1361.

Midoux, N., Favier, M., and Charpentier, J. C. (1976), *J. Chem. Eng. Japan*, **9**, 350.

Misic, D. M., and Smith, J. M. (1971), *Ind. Eng. Chem. Fundam.*, **10**, 380.

Mochizuki, S., and Matsui, T. (1974), *Chem. Eng. Sci.*, **29**, 1328.

Mochizuki, S., and Matsui, T. (1976), *AIChE J.*, **22**, 904.

Montagna, A. A., and Shah, Y. T. (1975), *Chem. Eng. J.*, **10**, 99.

Morita, S., and Smith, J. M. (1978), *Ind. Eng. Chem. Fundam.*, **17**, 113.

Morsi, B. I., Midoux, N., and Charpentier, J. C. (1978), *AIChE J.*, **24**, 357.

Newman, M. S., Underwood, G., and Renoll, M. (1949), *J. Am. Chem. Soc.*, **71**, 3362.

Pal, S. K., Sharma, M. M., and Juvekar, V. A. (1982), *Chem. Eng. Sci.*, **37**, 327.

Pexidr, V., Krejcirik, A., and Pasek, J. (1980), *Int. Chem. Eng.*, **20**, 84.

Ramachandran, P. A., and Chaudhari, R. V. (1979), *Ind. Eng. Chem. Process Design Dev.*, **18**, 703.

Raval, R. P., and Sharma, M. M. (1980), Unpublished work.

Reichert, K. H. (1977), *Chem. Ing.-Tech.*, **49**, 626.

Roberts, G. W. (1976), in Rylander, P. N., and Greenfield, H. (Eds.), *Catalysis in Organic Syntheses*, Academic Press, New York.

Ruether, J. A., and Puri, P. S. (1973), *Can. J. Chem. Eng.*, **51**, 345.

Sada, E., Kumazawa, H., and Butt, M. A. (1977), *Chem. Eng. Sci.*, **32**, 970.

Sato, Y., Hirose, T., Takahashi, F., Toda, M., and Hashiguchi, Y. (1973), *J. Chem. Eng. Japan*, **6**, 315.

Satterfield, C. N. (1970), *Mass Transfer in Heterogeneous Catalysis*, MIT Press, Cambridge, Massachusetts.

Satterfield, C. N. (1975), *AIChE J.*, **21**, 209.

Satterfield, C. N., and Huff, G. A. Jr. (1980), *Chem. Eng. Sci.*, **35**, 195.

Satterfield, C. N., and Özel, F. (1973), *AIChE J.*, **19**, 1259.

Satterfield, C. N., Ma, Y. H., and Sherwood, T. K. (1968), *Proc. Symp. Tripartite Chem. Eng. Conf.* (Montreal), p. 22.

Satterfield, C. N., Pelossof, A. A., and Sherwood, T. K. (1969), *AIChE J.*, **15**, 226.

Schmeal, W. R., and Street, J. R. (1971), *AIChE J.*, **17**, 1188.

Schuit, G. C. A., and Gates, B. C. (1973), *AIChE J.*, **19**, 417.

Schwartz, J. G., and Roberts, G. W. (1973), *Ind. Eng. Chem. Process Design Dev.*, **12**, 262.

Schwartz, J. G., Weger, E., and Dudukovic, M. P. (1976), *AIChE J.*, **22**, 894, 953.

Seaburn, J. T., and Engel, A. J. (1973), *Am. Inst. Chem. Eng. Symp. Ser.*, **69**(134), 71.

Sedriks, W., and Kenney, C. N. (1973), *Chem. Eng. Sci.*, **28**, 559.

Shah, Y. T. (1979), *Gas–Liquid–Solid Reactor Design*, McGraw-Hill, New York.

Shah, Y. T., and Paraskos, J. A. (1975), *Ind. Eng. Chem. Process Design Dev.*, **14**, 368.

Shah, Y. T., Stiegel, G. J., and Sharma, M. M. (1978), *AIChE J.*, **24**, 369.

Sheldon, R. A. (1973), *Recl. Trav. Chim. Pays-Bas*, **92**, 253, 367.

Sherwood, T. K., and Farkas, E. J. (1966), *Chem. Eng. Sci.*, **21**, 573.

Shimizu, Y., Inoue, K., Nishikata, H., Koenuma, Y., Takemura, Y., Aizawa, R., Kobayashi, S., Egi, K., Matsumoto, K., and Wakao, N. (1970), *Bull. Japan Petrol. Inst.*, **12**, 10.

Sicardi, S., Gerhard, H., and Hofmann, H. (1979), *Chem. Eng. J.*, **18**, 173.

Singh, D., and Merrill, R. P. (1971), *Macromolecules*, **4**, 599.

Slesser, C. G. M., Allen, W. T., Cuming, A. R., Fawlowsky, U., and Shields, J. (1968), *Proc. 4th European Symp. Chem. React. Eng.* (Suppl. to *Chem. Eng. Sci.*), p. 41.

Snider, J. W., and Perona, J. J. (1974), *AIChE J.*, **20**, 1172.

Suzuki, M., and Kawazoe, K. (1975), *J. Chem. Eng. Japan*, **8**, 79.

Sylvester, N. D., Kulkarni, A. A., and Carberry, J. J. (1975), *Can. J. Chem. Eng.*, **53**, 313.

Talmor, E. (1977), *AIChE J.*, **23**, 868, 874.

Terasawa, M., Kaneda, K., Imanaka, T., and Teranishi, S. (1978), *J. Catal.*, **51**, 406.

Teshima, H., and Ohashi, Y. (1977), *J. Chem. Eng. Japan*, **10**, 70.

Tong, S. B., O'Driscoll, K. F., and Rempel, G. L. (1978), *Can. J. Chem. Eng.*, **56**, 340.

Tsao, G. T. (1972), *Chem. Eng. Sci.*, **27**, 1593.

Turek, F., Oertel, R., and Lange, R. (1977), *Int. Chem. Eng.*, **17**, 84.

van Deemter, J. J. (1965), *Chem. Eng. Sci.*, **20** (Special Suppl.), 215.

van Direndonck, L., and Nelemans, J. (1972), *Proc. 5th European/2nd Int. Symp. Chem. React. Eng.*, B6-45.

van Goolen, J. T. J. (1976), *Proc. 4th Int./6th European Symp. Chem. React. Eng.*, IX-399.

van Klinken, J., and van Dongen, R. H. (1980), *Chem. Eng. Sci.*, **35**, 59.

Weekman, V. W. Jr. (1976), *Proc. 4th Int./6th European Symp. Chem. React. Eng.*, p. 615.

White, D. E., Litt, M., and Heymach, G. J. (1974), *Ind. Eng. Chem. Fundam.*, **13**, 143.

Wisniak, J., Hershkowitz, M., Leibowitz, R., and Stein, S. (1974a), *Ind. Eng. Chem. Prod. Res. Dev.*, **13**, 75.

Wisniak, J., Hershkowitz, M., and Stein, S. (1974b), *Ind. Eng. Chem. Prod. Res. Dev.*, **13**, 232.

Wyatt, M. (1979), Brit. U.K. Pat. 2,008,147.

Yahikozawa, K., Aratani, T., Ito, R., Sudo, T., and Yano, T. (1977), *Bull. Chem. Soc. Japan*, **51**, 613.

Zaidi, A., Louisi, Y., Ralek, M., and Deckwer, W.-D. (1979), *Ger. Chem. Eng.*, **2**, 94.

CHAPTER FOURTEEN

Types of Contactors and Their Relative Merits

14.1. GAS–LIQUID CONTACTORS

Most industrial contactors can be classified into three broad categories (van Krevelen, 1950).

1. Contactors in which the liquid flows as a thin film:
   a. packed columns;
   b. trickle-bed reactors;
   c. thin-film reactors;
   d. disk reactors.
2. Contactors with dispersion of gas into liquids:
   a. plate columns (including controlled-cycle contactors);
   b. mechanically agitated contactors;
   c. bubble columns;
   d. packed bubble columns;
   e. sectionalized bubble columns;
   f. two-phase horizontal cocurrent contactors;
   g. coiled reactors;
   h. plunging jet reactors; jet reactors;
   i. vortex reactors.
3. Contactors where liquid is dispersed in the gas phase:
   a. spray columns;
   b. venturi scrubbers;

This classification is rather broad, and we do have situations in practice where there is some overlap of the categories. For instance, in the case of a sieve-plate absorption column, operated at a relatively high superficial gas velocity, a part of the liquid exists in the form of droplets and we have an overlap between categories 2 and 3. A similar situation is encountered in horizontal pipeline contactors operated in the annular flow regime. Figures 14.1–14.3 illustrate the more important types of contactor. Table 14.1 gives some salient features of typical gas–liquid contactors and includes representative values of $k_L a$ and a that are provided by fluids like air and water. In addition, typical superficial gas velocity values, the residence time distribution characteristics of the gas and liquid phases, and the residence time of the liquid and fractional liquid holdup are also indicated in Table 14.1.

The mass transfer characteristics of some of the important contactors have been reviewed by Danckwerts (1970). Shah et al. (1978) have given a comprehensive review of backmixing in a variety of the reactors covered in this chapter. Nagel and coworkers have published a number of papers on the subject of interfacial area, the liquid-side mass transfer coefficient, and their relationship with energy dissipation per unit volume. Nagel et al. (1978) have considered criteria for the choice and designs of gas–liquid reactors. A wide variation in the values of a and $k_L a$ can be seen in a variety of gas–liquid contactors, and in fact these variations can be several orders of magnitude. The way in which the volume-specific conversion can be altered by variation of the volume-specific mass transfer area depends on the rate of the chemical reaction. More power input per unit volume of liquid is required when we desire to have higher values of a. Levels of conversion as well as yield can vary substantially for a variety of reaction systems when values of a and k_L are varied. In particular, the case of parallel and consecutive reactions can be cited. For economic optimization of reactors, the power required for mixing and the investments in reactor volume are important.

The selection of a contactor for a specified duty will depend on a number of factors: residence time of

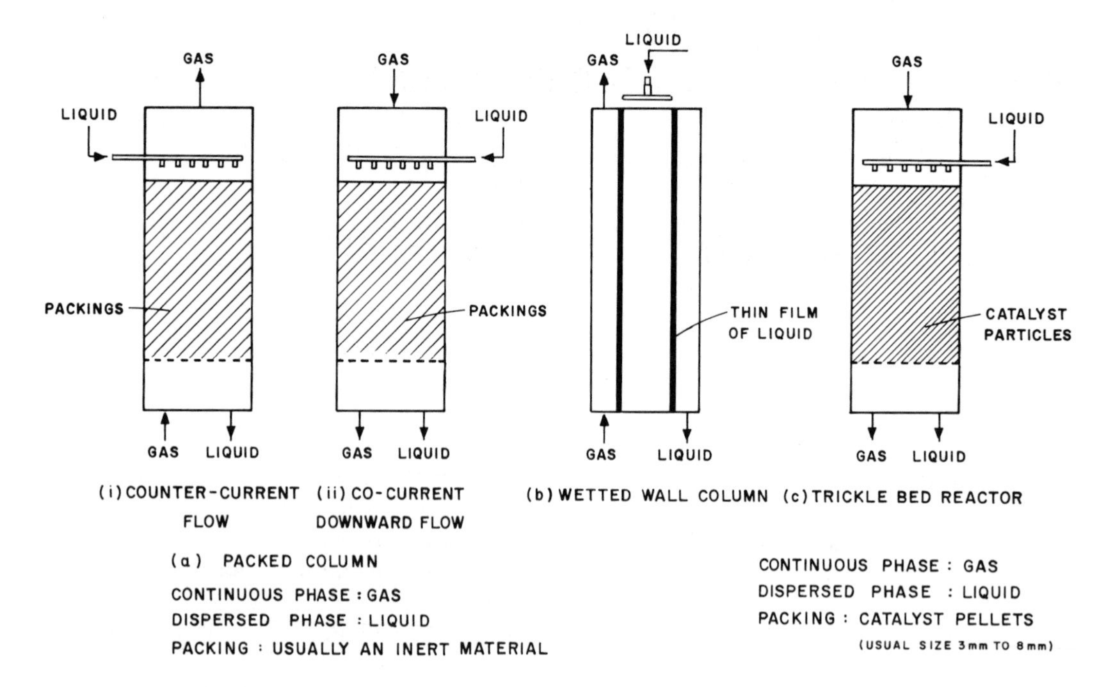

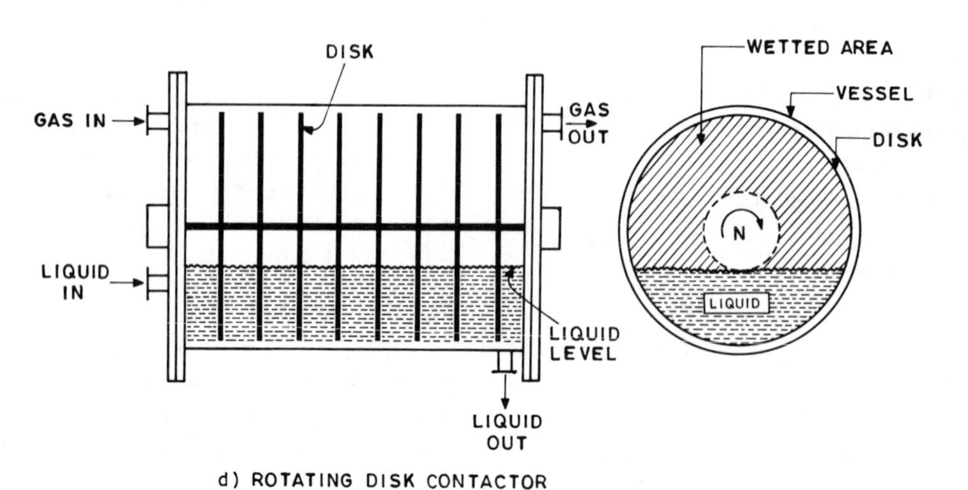

Figure 14.1. Liquid dispersed as a thin film: (*a*) packed column; (*b*) wetted-wall column; (*c*) trickle-bed reactor; (*d*) rotating disk contactor.

the liquid phase; allowable pressure drop; relative flow rates of gas and liquid; countercurrent or cocurrent mode of operation; need to remove or supply heat; corrosion; presence of solid particles; foaming behavior; micromixing; selectivity; rheological behavior (if non-Newtonian systems are encountered); and so on. We shall discuss salient characteristics of various contactors in the light of these and other factors.

14.1.1. Contactors in Which the Liquid Flows as a Thin Film

(*a*) *Packed Columns*

Packed columns (Figure 14.1*a*) are used in practice because of their simplicity and ability to withstand corrosive conditions. Further, the total pressure drop through the column is relatively low as compared to

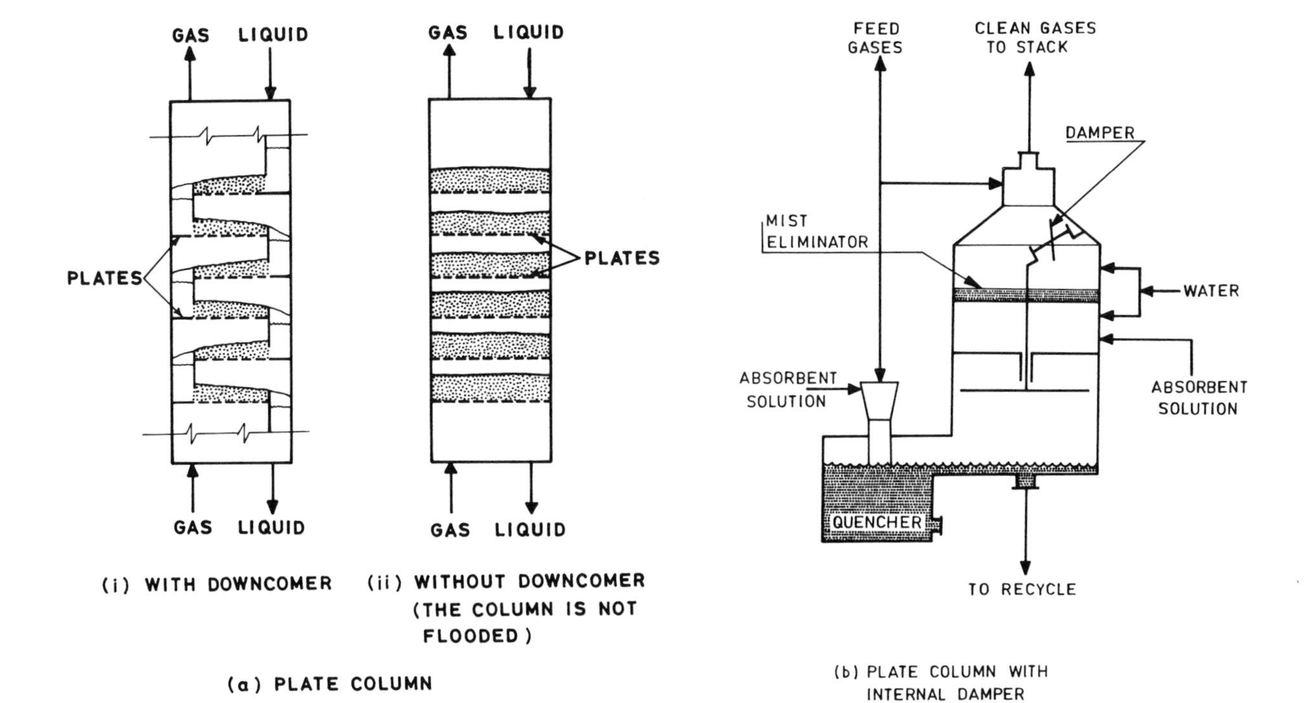

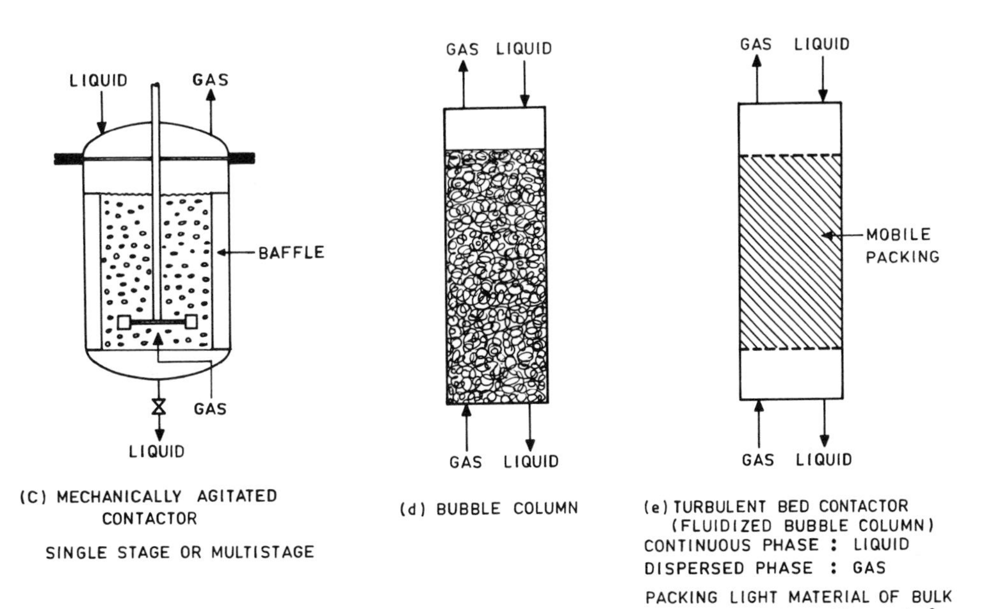

Figure 14.2. Gas dispersed in a continuous liquid phase: (*a*) plate column; (*b*) plate column with internal damper; (*c*) mechanically agitated contactor; (*d*) bubble column; (*e*) turbulent-bed contactor; (*f*) packed bubble column; (*g*) bubble column with perforated or grid plates; (*h*) horizontal sparged contactor; (*i*) packed bubble column with downcomer; (*j*) flow patterns in two-phase cocurrent horizontal pipeline contactor; (*k*) vortex reactor.

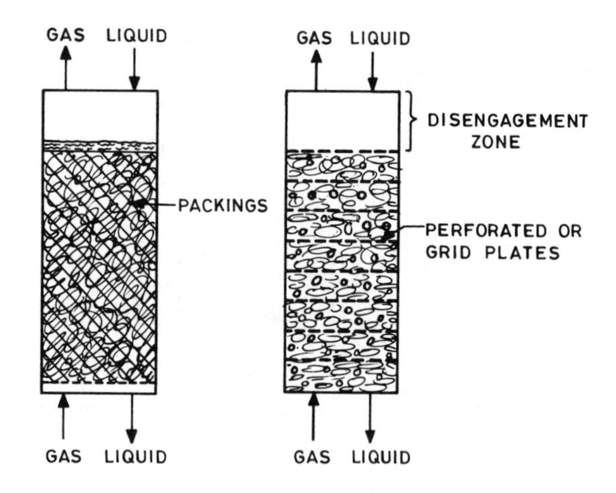

CONTINUOUS PHASE : LIQUID
DISPERSED PHASE : GAS
MODE OF OPERATION: SEMIBATCH OR CONTINUOUS CO-CURRENT / COUNTER-CURRENT

Figure 14-2. *(Continued)*

that in the case of (say) a plate or bubble column. A variety of packings in different sizes, shapes, and materials of construction is available. It is usually easy to choose packings that can withstand the stipulated column atmosphere for extended periods. However, it would be necessary to use a suitable construction material for the shell and other column internals, like the packing support and liquid distributor. In the case of the shell, a suitable lining on mild steel might prove satisfactory.

The most commonly employed packings are Raschig rings, Pall rings (common and Hy-pack varieties) and Intalox saddles (common and super varieties). Raschig rings and Pall rings are available in ceramic, metals, alloys, and plastics; Intalox saddles are available in ceramic and plastics; a new variety of saddle is available in metals and alloys (Strigle and Rukovena, 1979). Mass Transfer Ltd. of England has introduced a type of packing—the Cascade Mini-Ring—that is claimed to offer lower pressure drop and higher values of mass transfer coefficient as compared with other available packings.

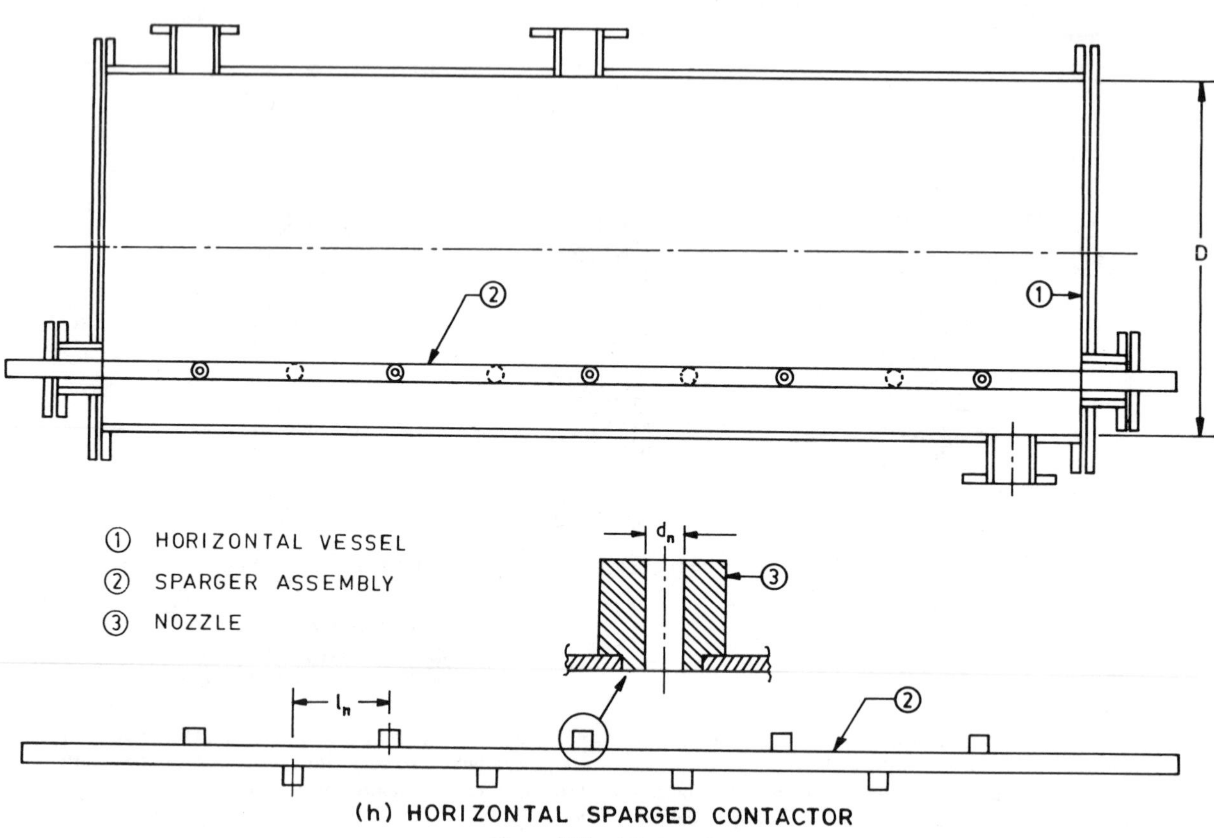

Figure 14.2. *(Continued)*

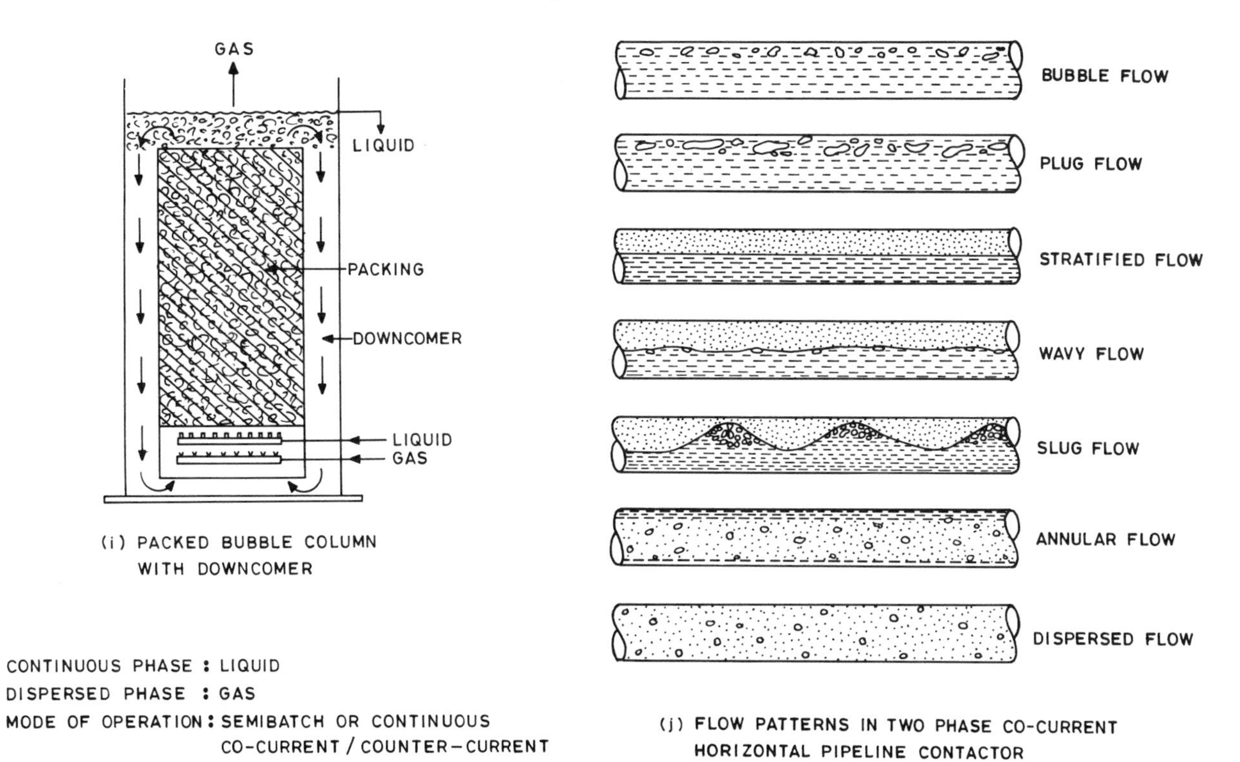

Figure 14.2. (*Continued*)

This packing basically belongs to the Raschig ring and/or Pall ring family and appears to have a relatively low height-to-diameter ratio (0.2–0.4 compared to the usual value of 1) (Mass Transfer Ltd., Bulletin on Cascade Mini-Rings, p. 63). Chem-Pro Equipment Corporation have introduced a new type of packing, called Saddelox, that is formed basically by cutting Pall rings in half (Chem-Pro Equipment Corporation, Bulletin 700).

New types of packing (e.g., Diamond grid and Sulzer packings, multifilament gauze packing such as Goodloe packing, and Koch Flexipac packings), which are sometimes referred to as regular packings, have also been introduced, and these offer relatively low pressure drop (Billet, 1969; Koch Engineering Co. Bulletin KFP-11). With the availability of newer types of packings, like Pall rings, Intalox saddles, Cascade Mini-Rings, and regular packings, it is now

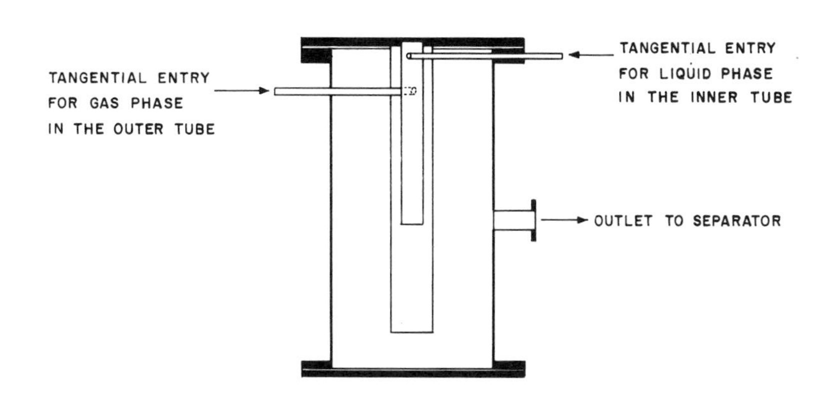

Figure 14.2. (*Continued*)

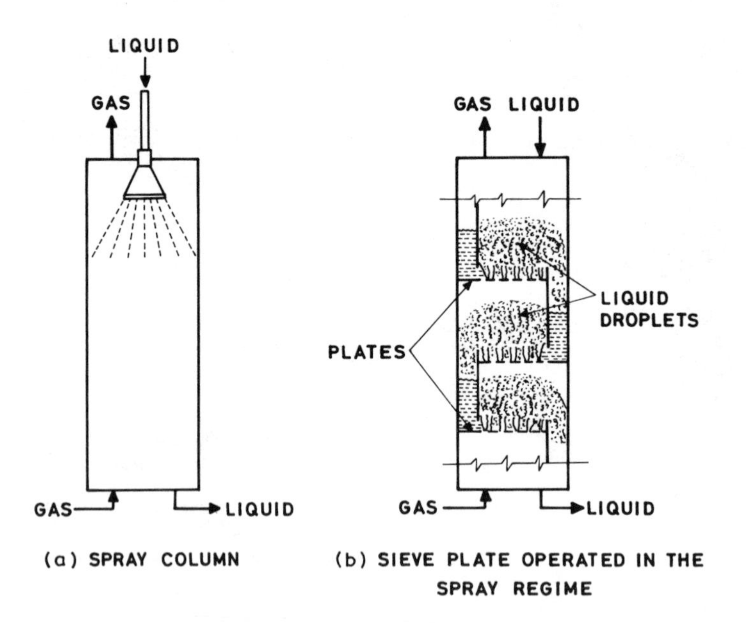

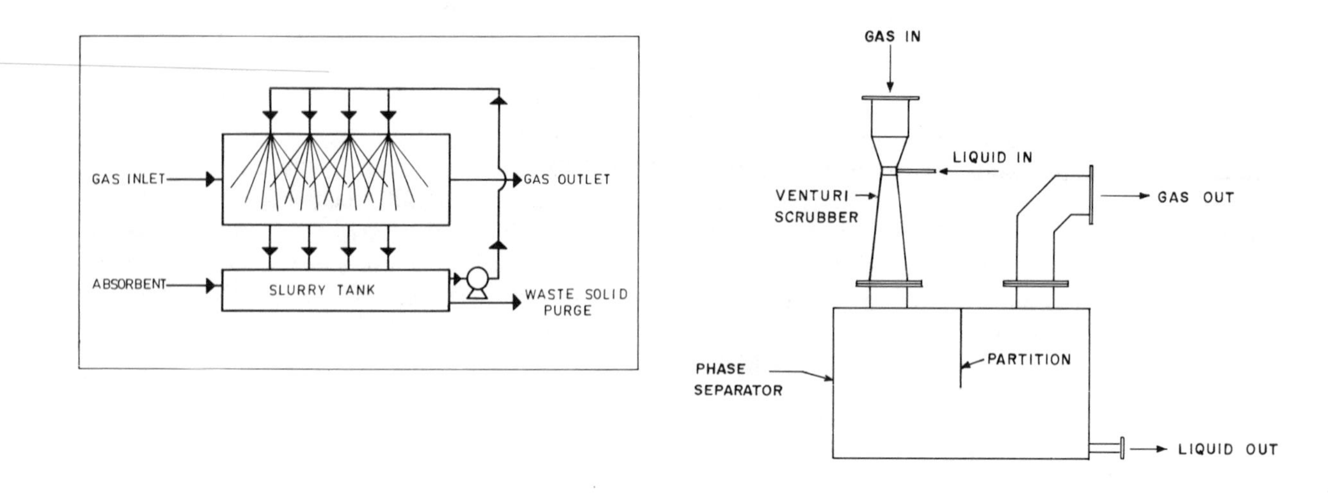

Figure 14.3. Liquid dispersed as droplets; (*a*) Spray column; (*b*) sieve plate operated in the spray regime; (*c*) horizontal spray absorber; (*d*) venturi scrubber.

possible to design packed columns as large as 9–10 m in diameter.

In recent years, polypropylene Pall rings and Intalox saddles have gained considerable importance for gas absorption operations, primarily as a result of their ability to withstand corrosive atmosphere. (For special cases fluoroplastics can be employed.) It is reported that some special grades of polypropylene Pall rings and Intalox saddles have been successfully used for the absorption of CO_2 in aqueous alkanolamines and potash solutions and in the adjunct desorption columns. In these operations, temperatures as high as 120–130°C are encountered. Further, since the plastic packings have thinner walls than their ceramic counterparts, the former can be operated at relatively higher velocities without flooding

TABLE 14.1. Salient Features of Gas–Liquid Contactors[a]

Type of Absorber	Typical Superficial Gas Velocity Values (cm/sec)	RTD G	RTD L	R_L	ϵ_L	$k_L \times 10^2$ (cm/sec)	a (cm^2/cm^3 of contactor volume)	$k_L a \times 10^2$ (sec^{-1})
Film-type								
Packed columns and Trickle-bed reactors	10–100	P	P	Very low	0.05–0.1	0.3–2	0.2–3.5	0.06–7
With gas dispersed as bubbles in liquid								
Bubble columns	1–30	P	M	Unlimited	0.6–0.8	1–4	0.25–10	0.25–40
Packed bubble columns	1–20	P	PM	Unlimited	0.5–0.7	1–4	1–3	1–12
Bubble cap plate columns	50–200	P	M*	Unlimited	0.7–0.8	1–4	1–4	1–16
Plate columns without downcomers	50–300	P	M*	Limited variation	0.5–0.7	1–4	1–2	1–8
Mechanically agitated contactors	0.1–2	M or PM	M	Unlimited	0.5–0.8	1–5	2–10	2–50
Horizontal pipeline contactors	5–300	P	P	Low	0.1–0.8	2–6	1–4	2–24
With liquid dispersed in gas								
Spray columns	5–300	PM	P	Very low		0.5–1.5	0.2–1.5	0.1–2.25
Sieve plate operated in the spray regime	100–300	P	PM*	Unlimited		1–3	0.5–2	0.5–6
Venturi scrubbers	Superficial gas velocity at throat = 40–110 m/sec	P	P	Very low	0.05–0.1	5–10	1–2	5–20

[a]*Notation used in the table*: RTD, residence time distribution; R_L, residence time of liquid; ϵ_L, fractional liquid holdup (fraction of the effective volume of the contactor occupied by the liquid); G, gas; L, liquid; P, plug; M, completely backmixed; PM, partially mixed; M*, good mixing on plate, no mixing between the plates; PM*, partial mixing on plate, no mixing between plates.

under otherwise identical conditions. In addition, there is no danger (as there is with ceramic packings) that the packings will chip. The mass transfer characteristics of 15-mm, 1-in., $1\frac{1}{2}$-in., and 2-in. plastic packings have been reported in the literature (Danckwerts and Rizvi, 1971; Sahay and Sharma, 1973; Linek et al., 1974; Kolev, 1974). The main disadvantage of the plastic packings is that water does not wet them. However, Linek et al. (1974, 1977) have found that the effective interfacial area provided by plastic packings can be increased by properly treating the packings, which makes them more wettable. Polyethylene and polypropylene packings can be hydrophilized by oxidation with a mixture of sulfuric acid and potassium dichromate in the presence of a trivalent chromium catalyst at an elevated temperature. Such treatment increased the effective interfacial area of 15-mm Raschig rings of polyethylene and polypropylene by a factor of 2.5, bringing these values close to those provided by ceramic packings.

Recently, regular packings in plastics, metals, and ceramic have been introduced. Bomio (1977, 1979) has reported some data on Sulzer-type packings made from plastic or wire gauze or corrugated perforated metal or plastic panels and has shown that these are superior to (say) 50-mm (2.5-mm-thick) plastic Pall rings. Multifilament gauze packings are also available in polypropylene and mixed fabric woven from polypropylene and polyacrylonitrile threads. These packings can be easily used at temperatures up to 80°C. There are claims in the literature that these packings give good performance. An example of the removal of methyl mercaptan by absorption in an aqueous solution of caustic soda has been cited (Norris, 1975). For absorption of lean CO_2 and SO_2 in aqueous solutions of sodium hydroxide the Sulzer plastic packing (type BX) gives mass transfer coefficient values that are sometimes even more than a factor of 3 times those obtained with 50 × 50 mm plastic Pall rings, under otherwise uniform conditions. For duties where gas flow rates are very high and liquid flow rates are relatively low this Sulzer packing gives high values of a (Bomio, 1979). It is of utmost importance that when these regular packings are used the liquid distributor be very carefully designed and that leveling of the distributor and placement of the packing in the column be perfect. A very good and even distribution of liquid at the top is of crucial importance (Huber and Meier, 1975).

The selection of the size and type of packing will depend on a number of factors. The effective interfacial area per unit of packed volume for any type of packing decreases with an increase in the size of the packing. On the other hand, with an increase in the size of the packing the flooding velocity increases. Thus with an increase in the size of the packing a relatively smaller-diameter column can be used, but the height will have to be much higher than that in the case of a column packed with smaller packings. The selection of the type of packing, therefore, requires a careful economic analysis. The common packing sizes used in practice are 25 and 38 mm (1 and $1\frac{1}{2}$ in.). An analysis by Eckert (1970) indicates that in large columns a 50-mm (2-in.) size might be the most economical.

Packed columns are particularly suited for those applications where the gas rate is relatively low and the liquid rates are high. In such cases, the performance of the plate or bubble columns will be relatively poor. Further, the residence time of the liquid and the liquid holdup are small. An important advantage offered by the packed column is that the gas and the liquid move essentially in the plug flow manner. Thus, when it is desired to reduce the solute content to a very low value then some advantage may be offered by the packed column. In the case of plate columns too the gas moves in the plug flow manner. In the case of bubble columns, however, there is some backmixing in the gas phase, and in the case of mechanically agitated contactors, there is a substantial backmixing in the gas phase.

The normal values of $k_L a$ in packed columns are significantly lower than in those contactors, where gas is dispersed in the liquid (see Table 14.1). The values of a in packed columns are also, in general, lower than in contactors where gas is dispersed in the liquid. The value of a for any specified packing is primarily dependent on the superficial liquid flow rate, and relatively large variations in the viscosity, ionic strength, and so on of the liquid phase do not significantly influence the values of a. However, at lower liquid flow rates, the surface tension of the liquid may affect the values of a. Thus when the system conforms to any regime between 2 and 4, it would be necessary to use a larger reactor volume in the case of a packed column than in (say) the plate or the bubble columns. It is presumed that the gas moves in plug flow. However, if a mechanically agitated contactor is used, where gas and liquid phases are almost completely backmixed, then the situation will be very different. This matter is further discussed in Section 14.1.2. Relatively low values of k_L in packed columns also imply, as indicated by conditions given by expression 2.79, that a specified system may conform to regime 4 in the case of a packed column, but may conform to regime 3 in the case of (say) a plate column. The specific rate of mass transfer is highest when a system conforms to regime 3.

It is conceivable that in view of relatively high values of k_L in contactors such as plate columns and bubble columns, a system may conform to regime 2, but in the case of packed columns it may conform to regime 3. Thus in packed columns the solute gas will be completely consumed in the film and no free A would exist in the bulk. By contrast, in plate columns no A would have reacted in the film and in the bulk B phase other reactions of A may occur. For instance, in some reactions based on ozone we might benefit by using packed columns.

There are some systems where packed columns and other contactors, such as plate columns or bubble columns, can be used. However, a packed column may be preferred if it is desired for reasons of safety to keep a low liquid holdup in the system.

It is conceivable that in some cases the packing may also act as a catalyst. For instance, in the chlorination of CS_2 to CCl_4 the packing acts as a catalyst.

Packed columns are generally not satisfactory in the following circumstances:

1. When the gas or the liquid contains suspended impurities or solids are formed *in situ* as a product of the reaction.
2. The system conforms to regime 1 (very slow reaction) or the regime between 1 and 2. In

such a case the holdup and the residence time of the liquid should be high, but in packed columns these values are very low. In the specific case of the oxidation of black liquor by air, where the pressure drop of the gas is important and the reaction is relatively slow (between regime 1 and 2) and requires sufficient residence time of the liquid, the problem was overcome to some extent by using a special design of corrugated asbestos cement sheets as packings (Collins, 1962).

3. For very low liquid rates, in which case the wetting of the packing will be very poor.
4. When it is necessary to remove or supply heat. In this case it is sometimes possible to use a contactor made up of a number of wetted-wall columns where the liquid to be contacted flows outside the tube and the heating or cooling medium passes through the tube (see Figure 14.1*b*). (Also see the material on tube columns given in this section.)

Stacked versus Random Packings. Sometimes the gas to be absorbed is available at a nominal pressure and the pressure drop through the absorber becomes a critical factor. For instance, in the manufacture of H_2SO_4 by the contact process, the pressure drop through the absorption column for the absorption of SO_3 in 96–98% H_2SO_4 (or a higher concentration of H_2SO_4) should be as low as possible. It is well known that at the same gas and liquid flow rates the pressure drop through the stacked column is substantially lower than that in the case of random packings. Stacked packings are generally used only when the packing size is greater than 5 cm (2 in.) and the column diameter is greater than 100 cm. However, with the availability of newer packings, like Intalox saddles, which offer much lower pressure drop under otherwise comparable conditions, stacked packings are being replaced by random packings whose mass transfer characteristics are superior because of better distribution of the liquid in the column.

Cocurrent versus Countercurrent Operation. When mass transfer is accompanied by an irreversible reaction, then the overall driving force will be unaffected by the mode of the operation—that is, cocurrent or countercurrent—of the packed column. An important advantage of operating a packed column in the cocurrent manner is that no restriction on the gas flow rate can be employed, since there would not be any flooding in the cocurrently operated column. Dodds et al. (1960) have shown that liquid and gas rates as high as 30,000 and 1500 lb/hr ft^2, respectively, can be successfully used, as compared to the corresponding normal rates of 8000 and 1000 lb/hr ft^2 in the countercurrent column. For operations where an irreversible reaction takes place in the liquid phase, (for instance, absorption of lean SO_2 or Cl_2 in aqueous NaOH solutions) the cocurrent operation can sometimes be advantageously employed. Power consumption in the case of the cocurrent operation will be lower than that in the case of the countercurrent operation under otherwise comparable conditions because of lower pressure drop in the case of the cocurrent mode of operation.

When absorption is carried out at higher pressures some advantage may be realized by operating the column cocurrently. Since relatively higher gas velocities can be employed, cocurrent operation permits a decrease in the diameter of the column. The use of smaller-diameter columns implies that the shell thickness can be smaller. Turpin and Huntington (1967), Sweeney (1967), Reiss (1967), Hochman and Effron (1969), Gianetto et al. (1970, 1973), Shende and Sharma (1974), Fukushima and Kusaka (1977a, b), and Mahajani and Sharma (1979, 1980) have reported data on performance characteristics of cocurrently operated columns.

In general, under otherwise uniform conditions, the cocurrent mode of operation gives slightly higher values of a, $k_L a$, and $k_G a$ at relatively high values of v_G; at low v_G values the values of the mass transfer coefficients are practically the same. Depending on the relative flow rates of the two phases and physical properties of gas and liquid phases, we can get different flow regimes; this matter was discussed at some length in Section 13.2. We can have a shift to a flow regime where liquid becomes the continuous phase and gas the dispersed phase. In between we have the pulse flow regime. Mahajani and Sharma (1980) have shown that remarkably high values of a (of up to even 16 cm^2/cm^3) may be realized in the pulse flow regime with stainless steel multifilament gauze packings. It is very likely that such packings made in plastic offer comparable performance. Thus the new type of plastic packings may prove to be valuable in many process applications.

There are some special circumstances where the cocurrent mode may be advantageous. Thus in the oxidation of black liquor with air the losses of sulfur compounds in the form of H_2S and RSH can probably be reduced if the cocurrent mode of operation is adopted. This is because the oxidation of Na_2S results in the formation of NaOH, which in turn will increase the pH of the solution and help in absorbing any H_2S and RSH that might have been stripped out by air (reaction: $2Na_2S + 2O_2 + H_2O \rightarrow Na_2S_2O_3 + 2NaOH$). In countercurrent operation any stripped H_2S will come in contact with the solution, which has a much lower capacity to absorb H_2S (Collins, 1962). In another case of simultaneous absorption of NH_3 and CO_2 from an inert gas the cocurrent mode of contacting will be expected to be beneficial when it is desired to promote the absorption of CO_2. This arises out of the fact that the mass transfer coefficient for the absorption of CO_2 increases with an increase in the free ammonia concentration. If on the other hand selectivity with respect to ammonia is desired, then higher selectivity will be realized when the countercurrent mode of operation is adopted, since most of ammonia will be absorbed in the lower section of the column. In yet another case of reaction between HCl gas and SO_3 to form chlorosulfonic acid we can benefit from the cocurrent mode of operation, since a slight excess of HCl is normally used.

In some cases the countercurrent operation may favorably affect the shift in chemical equilibrium. For instance, in the transesterification of dimethyl terephthalate with ethylene glycol countercurrent operation favorably affects the chemical equilibrium.

Selectivity. When complex reactions, such as consecutive or consecutive/parallel, are involved, we may have a change in selectivity with the change in the flow regime due to large variations in the k_L value (see, e.g., Chapter 4).

Tube Columns with Packings (Packed-Tube-Type Columns). A new type of packed column has been suggested by Billet et al. (1978); in it, as in a multitubular reactor or shell-and-tube heat exchanger, we have a large number of tubes fixed on a tube sheet. Packings such as Pall rings are snugly fitted in the tube. Billet et al. have reported measurements of $k_G a$ for cocurrent as well as countercurrent modes of operation by absorbing lean SO_2 in aqueous caustic solutions. These authors have brought out the advantages of this type of contactor: large capacity, low pressure drop, high mass transfer coefficient, and the like. It appears that the cocurrent mode of operation gives better performance. Patil and Sharma (1981) have measured values of a (also of $k_L a$ in some cases) in a 2.5-cm-i.d. column provided with 25-mm (1-in.) Pall rings as well as multifilament gauze packings. Cocurrent downflow operation was adopted. Different flow regimes (film flow, pulsating flow, etc.) were covered (see Section 13.2). Under some conditions of high superficial liquid velocity values (1–2 cm/sec) and superficial gas velocity (1–2 m/sec) values of a were found within the range of 5–16 cm^2/cm^3 that appear to be very attractive. Further work is necessary before definite recommendations can be made.

Cross-Flow Columns. Cross-flow columns can handle much higher gas velocities as compared to countercurrent columns, and the pressure drop is relatively low. Cross-flow cooling towers are widely used in practice but little attention has been paid to cross-flow absorption or stripping columns. In some specific cases it may be possible to advantageously employ cross-flow packed absorption or stripping columns. The utility of these types of columns is restricted to cases where air is used for oxidation-type reactions. Wnek and Snow (1972) have given a design procedure for cross-flow columns. Hayashi et al. (1978) have considered aspects of process design of cases where gas absorption is accompanied by chemical reaction and both gas- and liquid-film resistances are important.

(*b*) *Trickle-Bed Reactors*

There are some industrial processes where a relatively large quantity of a liquid is contacted with gas in the presence of a catalyst (see Chapter 13 and Section 14.4). Both cocurrent and countercurrent modes of operation can be adopted but cocurrent downflow is preferred because it forestalls flooding. A typical example is the hydrodesulfurization of petroleum fractions with hydrogen, using cobalt–molybdenum or nickel–tungsten catalysts (van Deemter, 1965; Satterfield, 1975). Trickle-bed reactors (Figure 14.1*c*) are also used in the petroleum industry for hydrocracking and hydrotreating. Here, the liquid flows as a thin film in a column packed with catalyst particles, and since the liquid flow over the packing is rather slow, this mode of operation is referred to as trickle flow. An important advantage of the trickle-bed reactor as compared to a slurry reactor is that there is no need to separate the product from catalyst particles. Further (unlike the case of slurry reactor, where there is substantial backmixing in the gas phase when mechanically agitated contactors are used), the reactor approaches plug flow behavior. In the case of trickle-bed reactors, the ratio of the amount of catalyst to the amount of reactant is relatively high as compared to slurry reactors and therefore the resulting high reaction rate minimizes the cost of the expensive reactor, particularly for high-pressure operation. Thus, trickle-bed reactors are expected to be even more useful for operations requiring relatively high flow rates of the liquid and very low gas flow rates. However, the reaction should be reasonably fast, since the residence time of the liquid in the trickle-bed reactor is very limited. Various aspects of slurry and trickle-bed reactors were discussed in Section 13.2. There is, however, very limited information in the literature on $k_L a$ and a values provided by trickle-bed reactors. Mahajani and Sharma (1979) have reported some values of a and $k_L a$ for activated carbon pellets and granules for aqueous and nonaqueous systems.

Trickle-bed reactors can also be used for systems where solid particles react with the gas and the liquid. Typical examples are the production of calcium bisulfite (Østergaard, 1968), copper sulfate, and the like.

(c) *Thin-Film Reactors*

There are a number of industrially important reactions that involve viscous heat-sensitive substances and where a large quantity of heat is evolved. For such systems a thin-film reactor could be advantageously used. It consists of a cylindrical or conical vessel, and the liquid film is agitated by means of blades fixed onto a central shaft. There is a close clearance between the blade and the wall of the vessel. Thus highly viscous liquids can also be agitated efficiently. Further, the vessel can be jacketed and a heating or cooling medium can be circulated through the jacket. Because of efficient agitation of the liquid film, high heat and mass transfer rates can be attained (Mützenberg, 1965; Fischer, 1965; Mützenberg and Giger, 1968), and therefore highly exothermic reactions involving heat-sensitive substances can be handled. The equipment can be operated continuously, which ensures consistent product yield and quality. There is practically no backmixing in the liquid phase, and by modifying the design of the apparatus the residence time of the liquid can be accurately controlled. Further, by using an alternative rotor design, slurries can also be handled.

(d) *Disk Reactors*

A large number of disks made out of suitable plastic materials or from steel or alloy steels can be mounted on a horizontal shaft and housed in a vessel where the disks partially dip in the liquid (Murakami et al., 1972). (see Figure 14.1*d*). In the case of plastic disks corrugations can be incorporated to improve turbulence and to nominally increase the interfacial area. The rate of surface renewal can be increased by increasing the speed of agitation. The gas-side pressure drop will be very small in such contactors. The literature contains very limited information on the mass transfer characteristics of such contactors. Ravetkar and Kale (1981) have made a study in a 20-cm-i.d. contactor and have reported values of k_L in the range of $4\text{–}8 \times 10^{-3}$ cm/sec. With a close spacing of disks and with a contactor half filled with a liquid we may be able to obtain a as large as 1.25 cm^2/cm^3 of contactor volume. This type of contactor has been suggested for the treatment of wastewater (some blood oxygenators have a design akin to this type of contactor).

14.1.2. Contactors with Dispersion of Gas into Liquids

(a) *Plate Columns*

Plate columns (Figure 14.2*a*) are used in practice because of their ability to handle wide variations in gas and liquid flow rates, as also for situations where gas rate is very high but the liquid flow rate is inordinately low. The performance of plate columns with downcomers is only slightly affected by the liquid flow rate, unlike the case of a packed column, where it is important. It is thus possible to vary the residence time of the liquid in the column over a wide range. Further, if necessary, heat can be supplied or removed from each plate. Thus, for instance, in the manufacture of HNO_3 by the absorption of NO_2 in water, a large quantity of heat is evolved and it is desirable to remove this heat in order to obtain higher concentrations of HNO_3. In all plate columns, the gas phase essentially moves in the plug flow.

Plate columns without downcomers are simpler and cheaper in construction and can handle relatively large gas and liquid rates as compared to plates with downcomers. Further, these are useful for slurries or systems where the solids are generated *in situ*. However, the scale-up of plate columns without downcomers poses serious problems (Kaji, 1971). Raymond (1978) has suggested a new design of an inclined perforated plate (without downcomer) column; with it, k_L values as high as 0.07 cm/sec have been reported. Further work is necessary in this area. In general, plate columns without downcomers are not very flexible and should not be considered.

A variety of plate designs are available but the most common designs are bubble caps and sieve plates, the latter design being considerably cheaper than the former. In recent years, valve trays have gained a lot of importance and it seems that most new columns are provided with sieve or valve trays. Union Carbide of the United States has modified the conventional sieve plate and they call their version Linde tray. The modified design improves the flexibility and hydraulic characteristics of the sieve plate (Frank et al., 1969).

Plate columns offer relatively high values of k_L as compared to those offered by the packed columns. In general, the superficial gas velocities used in plate columns are significantly higher than those used in packed columns. The values of effective interfacial area per unit volume of dispersion in the plate columns are also generally higher than the values of effective interfacial area per unit of packed volume. In the case of bubble cap plate columns the value of a is primarily dependent on the superficial gas flow rate and the liquid submergence. The physical properties of the liquid, like viscosity, surface tension, and ionic strength, exercise very little influence on the values of a (Sharma et al., 1969; Stichlmair and Mersmann, 1978). The comparison between the plate and packed columns should, however, be made on the basis of the column volume, which in the case of the plate column depends on the plate spacing. In the old practice a very liberal plate spacing was provided but in modern practice, provided the systems are clean, the plate spacing is usually kept in the range of 15–25 cm unless maintenance considerations require larger plate spacing. It is necessary to make a detailed cost analysis before a final selection is made.

If the plates have to be made of rather expensive materials, then they may prove less economical to use than other contactors, such as bubble or packed bubble columns. Recently, the Koch Engineering Co. of the United States introduced a Venturi(valve)-type plate of plastic construction that allows gases laden with dust particles to be absorbed in the desired absorbent at low liquid circulation rates. These plates also have a good flexibility.

There are some industrial applications (e.g., absorption of a relatively small percentage of Cl_2 in air in aqueous Na_2CO_3 or NaOH solutions, absorption of a lean $COCl_2$–air mixture or lean HCN/CO_2–air mixture in aqueous NaOH solution, etc.) where the gas rate may be very high but the liquid flow rate is very low. In these circumstances, packed columns may work very inefficiently and it may become necessary to use plate columns or bubble columns. In some cases, however, it may be possible to overcome this difficulty in packed columns by working at higher liquid flow rates and continuously bleeding out a small quantity of liquid. Further, new regular packings made out of gauze (metal or plastic) appear to work well at relatively low liquid flow rates.

In some practical situations a wide variation in the gas flow rate may have to be considered, and in such cases plate columns are not well suited. Recently, however, a new design has been suggested that divides the plate column scrubber into either two or four sections with an internal damper on all but one section. (An automatic control for the damper can also be used that will be based on the pressure drop across the tray.) Thus even one-eighth of the design load can be successfully handled. This design can also handle particulate matter (Figure 14.2*b*; *Chem. Eng.*, 1977).

When a distillation column is used as a reactor (e.g., for the esterification of butanol with acetic acid; the esterification of phthalic anhydride with methanol, ethanol, and butanol; reaction between acetone and HCN to give acetone cyanohydrin) and if the reaction is relatively slow, then it becomes necessary to provide for large residence time for the liquid. Further, the distillation operation usually requires some finite number of plates. In these circumstances it becomes very attractive to use plate columns with high submergence on each plate so that a high residence time of the liquid can be conveniently provided. In the larger columns the submergence may be as high as 100 cm. Haug (1976) has shown that in such high-submergence sieve-plate columns the abnormal liquid flow patterns associated with oscillation and/or slashing and rotation of the liquid may be observed. Oscillation of the liquid is highly undesirable. These abnormalities are observed because of nonuniform gas distribution. Haug has shown, on the basis of experiments on a 100-cm-diameter tray with submergence as high as 100 cm, that uniform gas distribution can be achieved when the combinations of the gas flow rate and hole area are such that the pressure drop is above some critical value. The critical pressure drop was reckoned as 2 cm of liquid, which corresponds to a hole F factor (superficial velocity through hole $\times \sqrt{\text{gas density}}$) of 14 (m/sec) $(kg/m^3)^{1/2}$. In practice the operating hole F factor should be twice this value.

There are some specific cases in which plate columns offer higher selectivity with respect to the desired component when the system has more than one solute gas. Danckwerts and Sharma (1966) have shown how in the case of the absorption of CO_2 and ammonia in water, for instance, better selectivity with respect to ammonia can be realized in a plate column than in a packed column (see Chapter 6). An important drawback of the conventional plates is that the pressure drop is relatively high and the liquid residence time is also high. However, in the case of multidowncomer tray (MDT) designed by the Union Carbide Corporation (Delnicki and Wagner, 1970) the pressure drop is considerably lower than in the case of (say) a sieve plate, and the liquid residence time is also short.

The MDT is also very useful for large-diameter trays where for single-pass trays maldistribution of the liquid (and even the vapor) occurs. It is known that liquid maldistribution and channeling can substantially reduce the plate efficiency. In view of these advantages, MDT are frequently specified for large-diameter trays. It is important to ensure that the liquid and/or vapor ratio in all the passes is equal, so that optimal results are realized. This can probably be achieved by ensuring that all the passes have equal areas and that within each pass the bubbling area is the same. Further, inlet weir may be employed. In addition, the configuration of the outlet weir can also be modified (e.g., by employing a picket fence configuration where the weir height is staggered between two elevations; Bolles, 1976).

In the case of sieve-plate or modified sieve-plate columns it may be useful to consider the relative merits of operating the distillation at a reduced pressure in different flow regimes. The distinct advantages of operating in the spray regime (see Figure 14.3*b*) may be realized for some types of systems. Broadly, two types of systems are encountered: surface tension positive and surface tension negative (Fell and Pinczewski, 1977).

In some cases it may be advantageous to consider plate columns where just above the weir a pad of regular packing, such as multifilament gauze or Sulzer packing, is kept. This is expected to improve the performance of the column on a unit volume basis, since a substantial contribution to mass transfer will be provided by the pad.

In some absorption and/or stripping duties where dirty liquids are handled and solid particles are formed or where slurries are used, it may be helpful to use hollow polypropylene spheres on plates, which may improve the contacting efficiency as well as reduce the extent of scale formation. In the case of the Solvay soda ash plant the regeneration of ammonia from the aqueous solution of ammonium chloride is accomplished by reaction with a slurry of hydrated lime, and plate columns are used for such duties. Here it has been claimed that the use of 38-mm hollow polypropylene balls prevent scale formation (Shiraki et al., 1979).

Controlled-Cycle Contactors. In recent years a new method of contacting two (immiscible) phases has been introduced and is referred to as controlled-cycle operation. This type of contactor was first suggested by Cannon (1961). In this method only one phase flows at a time for a controlled interval. In the case of plate columns, both phases flow through the same openings and hence weirs and downcomers can be avoided. This alternate one-way flow should be desirable for two reasons: First, it is expected to overcome the tendency of phases to channel and thus would be expected to improve contacting efficiency. Second, a greater concentration gradient should be obtained in this contactor as compared to that obtained in the analogous conventional flow system. It is also likely that the throughput of the contactor will increase when this mode of operation is adopted, since the problem of flooding will be less severe. There is sufficient information in the literature to substantiate these expectations (Szabo, et al., 1964; Schrödt, 1965; Schrödt et al., 1967). Controlled-cycle operation is distinctly different from pulsed columns where kinetic energy is added to one or both phases without stoppage of flow, and which employs much shorter cycle times than the 2- to 10-sec cycle used in controlled-cycle contactors. Robinson and Engel (1967) have reported results obtained from a 10-cm-i.d. sieve-plate absorption column operated with controlled cycling. It is clear from their results that controlled-cycle operation offers substantially higher mass transfer coefficient values as compared to conventional units. These authors are of the opinion that this type of contactor should be very useful for aerobic fermentors. However, the utility of this type of contactor of industrial sizes is yet to be demonstrated.

(*b*) *Mechanically Agitated Contactors*

Mechanically agitated contactors (Figure 14.2*c*; Valentine 1967; Mehta and Sharma, 1971; van't Riet, 1979; Joshi et al, 1982) offer a number of advantages, such as the ease with which the residence time of the liquid can be varied, the ease with which heat can be removed or supplied, and the ease with which the intensity of agitation can be varied. The true k_L values in a mechanically agitated contactor are quite high and comparable to those provided by plate columns in their normal range of operation. The values of the effective interfacial area provided by mechanically agitated contactors are generally relatively high. At high tip speeds it is possible to get a values as high as 10–15 cm^2/cm^3 for liquids like water at superficial gas velocities lower than 0.5 cm/sec.

A variety of agitators can be employed, but the most common type is a turbine with straight or inclined blades. (A modified version called an axial flow turbine is considered to be good, particularly from the point of view of power consumption.) If the agitator tip speed is reasonably good (say $> 12{,}000$ cm/min for liquids like water), then it is not necessary to introduce the gas at the eye of the impeller; instead, gas can be simply introduced from one of the top openings. Here the speed of agitation is so good that the dispersion is caused by "sucking" the gas from the head space. The performance characteristics of the contactor in the two cases will be practically the same. It would, therefore, be desirable to introduce the gas just above the liquid surface, particularly when the gas is available at atmospheric or a little more than atmospheric pressure. A considerable saving in the cost associated with the compression of the gas can be realized (Boerma and Lankester, 1968; Mehta and Sharma, 1971).

At agitation speeds greater than the critical speed, the gas velocity has practically no influence on the performance of the contactor. Hence, when the gas is to be almost completely absorbed, the mechanically agitated contactors have an edge over other contactors. Such cases are encountered in some addition chlorination reactions, the hydrogenation of unsaturated compounds, and the like.

The performance of a mechanically agitated contactor depends on such physical properties of the liquids as viscosity, surface tension, and the presence of electrolytes. Even adventitious impurities could make a substantial difference to the values of k_La or a. It does not appear to be practical to have any generalized correlation to predict the values of k_La and a. However, experiments with the desired system can be made in a geometrically similar small contactor whose inside diameter is 20–30 cm, and the data so obtained can be used for the larger-scale contactor. It appears that an equal ratio of impeller tip speed to the tank diameter could be used as a satisfactory criterion for equal values of k_La and a (Mehta and Sharma, 1971; Juvekar, 1976).

The principal disadvantage of a mechanically agitated contactor is that the liquid phase is completely backmixed and the gas phase is almost completely backmixed at higher impeller tip speeds. If the system conforms to regime 2, then the backmixing in the liquid phase is unimportant. Further, if a pure gas is used (as in the hydrogenation of organic compounds) and provided no gaseous products are formed, then the backmixing in the gas phase is also unimportant. In a large number of cases encountered in industrial practice, however, at least the backmixing in the gas phase is important. Bubble columns offer an important advantage in that the gas phase essentially moves in the plug flow manner. For the sake of illustration, we may consider an example where 99% of the solute gas diluted with an inert gas has to be absorbed in a system that is first order with respect to the solute gas and is unaffected by the backmixing in the liquid phase. From the charts given by Levenspiel (1967) it appears that the ratio of the contactor volume for a mechanically agitated contactor (assuming complete backmixing in the gas phase) and a bubble column (assuming no backmixing in the gas phase) will be about 21.

In relatively large mechanically agitated absorbers the impeller tip speed is usually below the critical speed and the mass transfer characteristics are dependent on both the gas flow rate and the impeller speed. Further, when the height-to-diameter ratio is greater than 2, and horizontal baffles at suitable locations are also employed, then the extent of backmixing in the liquid phase may not be severe. It appears that for higher height-to-diameter ratios and relatively lower impeller speeds the gas moves essentially in the plug flow (Sullivan and Treybal, 1970). It would therefore appear to be attractive to employ mechanically agitated contactors with height-to-diameter ratios of 3–7. One impeller should be provided for a height equal to the diameter of the column. (Hitherto the general practice has been to employ a height-to-diameter ratio of about 1.2–1.5.) Whenever a reaction has to be carried out under pressure, the use of a higher height-to-diameter ratio for the same volume of liquid will result in decreasing the thickness of the shell.

It has been observed that in the presence of fine solid particles in the liquid phase, the gas phase tends to move in the plug flow manner even at a relatively high speed of agitation (Juvekar and Sharma, 1973; Komiyama and Smith, 1975).

When mass transfer is the controlling factor, then

the output of a mechanically agitated contactor can possibly be increased by increasing the speed of agitation provided there are no other limiting factors. The upper limit of the agitation speed will be governed by a number of mechanical factors and economic considerations. In some cases it may not be desirable to employ a higher agitation speed, since the latter results in the formation of smaller bubbles. It is well known that the k_L value provided by small bubbles (say less than 2 mm in diameter) is substantially lower than that provided by large bubbles (say more than 3 mm in diameter). Lower k_L values will matter when the system conforms to the regime between 3 and 4. Further, the selectivity in a consecutive reaction may be adversely affected when small bubbles are present (see Chapter 4). In addition, if the product of the reaction has an undesirable influence on the rate and selectivity of a reaction, it will be desirable to employ conditions that give relatively large bubbles and hence a higher k_L value. A higher k_L value will ensure that the product of the reaction is transferred to the bulk at a higher rate. This problem is encountered in a number of air oxidation reactions (see, e.g., Steeman et al., 1961, and Section 3.4). In such systems it may be desirable to consider other contactors, such as bubble, packed bubble, and sectionalized bubble columns.

In many operations in practice the once-through passage of the gas may be inadequate and it becomes necessary to recycle the gas into the contactor through an external loop using a compressor. Such a situation may arise when the speed of agitation is below the critical speed and the solute gas is diluted with an inert gas. The use of an external loop, particularly for high-pressure and toxic systems, is not very attractive. Martin (1972) has suggested a technique of recycling gas from a gas cap without the use of an external loop and a recycle compressor. Here the sparger consists of a hollow shaft connected to a hollow impeller. This type of impeller is referred to as a *gas-inducing impeller*. An orifice is provided in the shaft above the liquid level to allow the gas to enter and another orifice (or orifices) is (are) provided in the hollow impeller to allow the gas to leave. It is reported that reactors whose capacity ranges from about 1000 to 5000 liters employing this principle are in commercial operation. Martin has discussed the design aspects of this type of contactor and has suggested a procedure for scale-up. Some mass transfer studies for a gas-inducing impeller have been made by Topiwala and Hammer (1974) and by Joshi and Sharma (1977).

(c) Bubble Columns

Bubble columns (Figure 14.2*d*) are commonly used in industrial practice. The gas is dispersed in the liquid phase at the bottom by a suitable distributor. Since the liquid holdup is large and the liquid residence time can be varied over a wide range, bubble columns may be used as reactors, absorbers, or strippers. They may be operated in a semibatch, countercurrent, or cocurrent manner.

The absence of moving parts, smaller floor space, large interfacial area, and high heat and mass transfer coefficients are some of the advantages that bubble columns offer. In high-pressure large contactors the stirrer seals may pose serious problems, and in such cases bubble columns can often be advantageously employed. Bubble columns, with or without sectionalization, can be used for stripping operations, particularly when solid particles are formed. It has been reported that in hydrometallurgical operations the stripping of ammonia could be successfully carried out in bubble columns, whereas bubble cap plates gave operational problems. However, backmixing in the liquid phase, some backmixing in the gas phase, and a rapid decrease of effective interfacial area at high height-to-diameter ratios (say, > 15) are some of the disadvantages of bubble columns.

A number of papers have covered the hydrodynamic behavior, mixing characteristics, and mass and heat transfer aspects of bubble columns (Sharma and Mashelkar, 1968; Mashelkar and Sharma, 1970; Mashelkar, 1970; Deckwer, 1977a, b; Mersmann, 1977). Schumpe and Deckwer (1978) and Gerstenberg (1979) have considered various aspects pertaining to the effective utilization of bubble columns as reactors.

From the studies reported, it appears that an increase in the superficial gas velocity increases the gas holdup, the effective interfacial area, and the overall mass transfer coefficient. The true mass transfer coefficients, however, are unaffected by the superficial gas velocity. The height-to-diameter ratio seems unimportant in the range of 4–10. The sparger design appears to be unimportant for superficial gas velocities greater than 5–10 cm/sec. The physical properties of the gas phase have no effect on the performance of the column. However, the physical properties of the liquid phase have a profound effect on the performance of the column. Thus, an increase in the viscosity, or a decrease in the surface tension, increases the effective interfacial area. The nature and concentration of electrolytes seem to be important in so far as the effective interfacial area is concerned. The electrolyte solutions give smaller bubble size and consequently higher gas holdup and higher effective interfacial area. Schumpe et al. (1979) have considered various aspects of the utilization of bubble columns as reactors. They refer to the flow regime at lower superficial gas velocities (< 5 cm/sec for aqueous system) as pseudohomogeneous; at higher superficial gas velocities (> 5 cm/sec for aqueous system) the flow regime is referred to as heterogeneous. They have recommended that for a system falling between regimes 1 and 2 the operation in the pseudohomogeneous flow regime is favorable, since we can realize higher conversion of the solute gas and the space-time yield passes through a maximum. Even for systems falling in the fast pseudo-mth-order reaction regime it is better to operate in the pseudohomogeneous flow regime; at higher superficial gas velocities the attainable conversions of the solute gas are low and the space-time yield, at best, increases only marginally. It is recommended that superficial gas velocities higher than 10 cm/sec should not be chosen, and we should design our reactor with this background. It is possible to work out an optimal value of the superficial gas velocity for a specified set of conditions.

In tall bubble columns for a system conforming to regime 1 or to the regime between 1 and 2, where we have a finite concentration of A in the bulk B phase, we may get some desorption of dissolved A at a certain height from the base of the column. This situation arises because of extensive backmixing in the liquid phase and a pressure variation in the column due to the variation in the hydrostatic head. Care should be exercised in the design of such systems to avoid any wastage of column volume.

It does not appear possible to have generalized correlation for predicting a, k_L, and k_G. However, model experiments on small-scale apparatus (say, 10- to 20-cm-i.d. columns) can be carried out with the desired system at the same superficial gas velocity as envisaged in industrial practice. The values of a and k_La or k_Ga so obtained can be used for the large-scale design.

The studies on mixing in the liquid phase and gas phase indicate that there is a considerable amount of backmixing in the liquid phase, whereas the gas flows essentially in the plug flow manner (Mashelkar, 1970). When the liquid concentration gradients in the column are important from the point of view of yield and selectivity in the column, the liquid backmixing can be minimized by using packed bubble columns or by using sectionalization (with dual-flow sieve trays, horizontal baffles, or bubble cap trays; Mashelkar, 1970; see below). It appears that in large-diameter columns, the backmixing in the gas phase may also become substantial (Deckwer, 1976b). Joshi and Sharma (1978, 1979b) and Joshi (1980) have given correlations that can be conveniently used for calculating the liquid-phase axial dispersion coefficient.

In some cases it may be desirable to have substantial backmixing, even though from a reaction rate point of view it has a detrimental effect. Such situations arise in the air oxidation of organic compounds, such as acetaldehyde, where the designer may like to ensure that no buildup of peroxide, an intermediate in the oxidation reaction, occurs at any location in the reactor, since this may be dangerous. By contrast, in other cases we might like to have plug flow behavior in a reactor, since this might give a more attractive product distribution. In the liquid-phase oxidation of n-butane the ratio of methyl ethyl ketone to acetic acid in the product varies very substantially as we change over from backmixed to plug flow behavior; the plug flow reactor gives a very high yield of methyl ethyl ketone (see Section 3.2.3). Similarly, in the air oxidation of liquid isobutane to *tert*-butyl hydroperoxide, where *tert*-butanol is obtained as an undesirable by-product, a sectionalized bubble column would be expected to give more favorable yields of the hydroperoxide.

The published work on heat transfer in bubble columns indicates that the bubble action provides sufficient agitation in the liquid film at the heating surface to give high heat transfer coefficients, which are comparable to those in mechanically agitated contactors. Further, because of good liquid backmixing, the contents of the vessel are kept uniform in temperature. Thus, heat removal problems in such contactors are relatively simple, and these contactors may be conveniently used for exothermic reactions (Mehta, 1970; Joshi et al., 1980).

The mode of operation of the column will depend on the particular set of conditions. If the reaction is relatively slow, then it may be operated in a semibatch manner—that is, a batch of liquid is taken and the appropriate gas is passed continuously through the column. For a reaction that is moderately fast, both cocurrent and countercurrent operation may be employed.

In some situations we may have relatively high values of the superficial liquid velocity (say, greater than 30 cm/sec) and low values of the superficial gas velocity (~ 1–3 cm/sec); in these cases it may be advantageous to use a cocurrent downflow column. Herbrechtsmeier and Steiner (1978) has reported some operating characteristics of this type of contactor.

In certain cases, where the reaction of a gas results in the formation of another gas on a mole-to-mole basis and the exothermic heat of reaction is removed by vaporization of the liquid, a situation can arise where the superficial velocity of the gas increases substantially as the gas traverses up the column (e.g., the chlorination of benzene, where heat of 23.1 kcal/mol HCl is liberated and this is sufficient to vaporize about 3 mol of benzene). (A part of this increase will be due to decreasing hydrostatic head of the liquid.) In other cases there may be a drastic fall in the superficial gas velocity as it traverses the column (e.g., the alkylation of benzene with C_2H_4 in the presence of $AlCl_3$ as catalyst). Deckwer (1976a) has considered some aspects of gas expansion and shrinkage on axial mixing in the liquid phase and has shown that serious error may result if we neglect gas expansion and shrinkage even under isobaric conditions. Such factors should be carefully considered while designing the columns.

The performance of bubble columns can be improved by pulsations. Baird and Garstang (1967, 1972) have studied the effect of very low-frequency high-amplitude pulsations in a bubble column. They used an air-pulsed system that operated with two vertical columns in tandem, on the "push–pull" principle. In the lower range of the superficial velocity of gas (0.8–2.4 cm/sec) the value of $k_L a$ increased by a factor as high as 3 when the column was pulsed.

The performance of bubble columns can also be improved by using fluidized packings (Douglas et al., 1963; Douglas, 1964; Blyakher et al., 1967; Chen and Douglas, 1968; Kitu et al., 1976; Østergaard, 1977). Packings with relatively low density such as hollow polypropylene spheres, foamed polystyrene spheres, or hollow glass spheres,are recommended (Figure 14.2*e*). A considerable improvement in the values of the liquid-side mass transfer coefficient and effective interfacial area has been reported. Values of a as high as 12 cm^2/cm^3 have been reported. In this type of contactor, however, the superficial gas velocity has to be relatively high (generally 200–600 cm/sec).

The principal disadvantages of the bubble column arise out of the extensive backmixing in the liquid phase and relatively high pressure drop of the gas due to the high static head of the liquid. The backmixing in the liquid phase can be substantially reduced by using packings (Figure 14.2*f*) or inserting perforated or grid plates at various locations in the column (Figure 14.2*g*).

In some cases, where the pressure drop in the gas phase is important and reaction belongs to regime 1 or 2 it may be desirable to consider the use of horizontal sparged vessels, where the height of the liquid is relatively very small (see Figure 14.2*h*). There is a lack of design data for such contactors. Zuiderweg and Bruinzeel (1968) and Joshi and Sharma (1978) have reported some data on backmixing characteristics of the liquid phase. Joshi and Sharma (1976*a*) have also reported mass transfer characteristics of such contactors and have suggested a criterion for scale-up. It appears that these types of contactors offer reasonably good values of a, $k_L a$, and $k_G a$. The performance of this type of contactor can be further improved by providing suitable mechanical stirrers. It is likely that systems that show pronounced foaming in bubble columns and mechanically agitated contactors may be successfully handled in this type of contactor. Sasaki (1971) has reported some limited mass transfer data obtained from horizontal contactors provided with various designs of impellers. The air oxidation of sodium sulfite was used as a model system and $k_L a$ values of the order of about 0.07 sec^{-1} have been reported. These $k_L a$ values compare favorably with those provided by bubble columns operated at a superficial gas velocity in the range of 5–15 cm/sec. Andou et al. (1971) have provided some data on power consumption in such contactors. Joshi and Sharma (1976*b*) have obtained some data on a, $k_G a$, and $k_L a$ and have suggested a criterion for scale-up.

In recent years the need to design very large bubble columns has arisen in the manufacture of proteins from methanol and/or ethanol and in wastewater treatment. Further, it is necessary to have very high water circulation rates in order to allow high heat transfer coefficients as well as to keep solid particles suspended. In addition, at relatively lower values of the superficial gas velocity, mass transfer coefficients will increase because of the high liquid circulation rates. Designs based on an external loop as well as on an internal loop (i.e., with downcomers) have been suggested. These reactors can be above ground, as in the case of fermenters (for ease of cleaning), or below ground, as for wastewater treatment. The latter reactors are referred to as deep-shaft aerators and may have depths up to 300 m. In this design the desorption of the product gas, CO_2, is facilitated. Kubota et al. (1978) have given a mathematical model of a deep-shaft aerator and have brought out the condition of air supply to maintain a stable liquid circulation in the shaft. The selection of the air sparger location is important and the level of oxygen demand affects the optimization.

(*d*) *Packed Bubble Columns*

It can be visualized that the introduction of packings in a bubble column (Figure 14.2*f*) will tend to reduce the coalescence of bubbles as well as the extent of liquid backmixing in the column. Packed bubble columns will be particularly suitable where liquid backmixing is undesirable.

From the available data reported in the literature, it appears that the gas holdup depends on the packing type and size and is higher than that in the case of unpacked bubble columns. Also, the introduction of packing produces little extra pressure drop, and if the higher gas holdup is taken into account, the pressure drop per unit of gas holdup across it is actually lower than that across an unpacked bubble column. The effective interfacial area is about 15–80% higher than that in an unpacked bubble column, although the true mass transfer coefficient is practically the same as in an unpacked bubble column (Mashelkar and Sharma, 1970; Sahay and Sharma, 1973; Sawant et al., 1979). There is a considerable reduction in the spread of residence time in the gas as well as the liquid phase (Carleton et al., 1967). Mashelkar and Sharma (1970) have shown that packed bubble columns are likely to be useful for systems where a considerable gas shrinkage occurs as a result of a chemical reaction.

It should be possible in some cases to employ for the packing a construction material that catalyzes the reaction. For instance, in the case of the substitution chlorination of benzene, packed bubble columns are likely to be useful and mild steel Raschig rings may be used as a packing. A very small quantity of iron in the packing will be progressively converted to $FeCl_3$, which is known to catalyze the chlorination of benzene.

In some cases it may be considered desirable to have high circulation rates for the liquid phase. The Koch Company in the United States has suggested a packed-bubble-column reactor design provided with regular packings (e.g., Sulzer packing in metal or plastic) where a downcomer arrangement exists so that high liquid flow rates are realized (Figure 14.2*i*).

(*e*) *Sectionalized Bubble Columns*

When backmixing in the liquid phase is important and where relatively fine solid particles are present as catalyst or reactant and where removal or supply of heat is necessary, then packed bubble columns are unlikely to be useful. In such cases it may be desirable to consider a sectionalized bubble column (Figure 14.2*g*). Perforated plates or grids can be used at various heights in the column. The use of sectionalized bubble columns has also been considered for aerobic fermenters (Kitai and Ozaki, 1969; Kitai et al., 1969; Kats and Genin, 1967). It is evident from the work of Kitai et al. (1969) on the residence time distribution of liquids that backmixing in the liquid is substantially reduced by the introduction of perforated plates. Further, in smaller columns, where the height of each section equals the diameter, the column may be approximated as a number of stirred units in series with little intermixing in between the sections (the number of well-mixed units may be considered to be the same as the number of sections). It appears that at relatively high superficial gas velocities (say, greater than 10–15 cm/sec) the intermixing between the sections is insignificant. Kaji (1971) has shown that the values of $k_L a$ and a in sectionalized bubble columns are slightly higher than in the case of a bubble column at any specified superficial gas velocity. There are no published data on backmixing in the liquid phase in large sectionalized bubble columns (say, with a diameter greater than 100 cm). Joshi and Sharma (1979a) have given a rationale for deciding the hole diameter and spacing of radial baffles in a sectionalized bubble column. The hole diameter should be 0.72 times the diameter and the spacing should be 0.81 times the diameter of the column.

The packed and sectionalized bubble columns may be operated cocurrently or countercurrently. If the liquid is nonvolatile it would be desirable to use countercurrent operation, since this would usually ensure maximum utilization of the solute gas. By contrast, if the liquid reactant is volatile, it may be desirable to operate the column in a cocurrent manner. For example, a variety of substitution organic chlorination reactions can be carried out in packed and sectionalized bubble columns. If the organic liquid is very volatile (e.g., benzene, toluene), then the losses of the liquid may be very high if countercurrent operation is adopted. It may become necessary to modify the ancillary equipment to recover the raw material lost in the product gas. However, when cocurrent operation is adopted the chlorine utilization will probably be affected if the rate of chlorination of the raw material is very much greater than that of the intermediate product (e.g., benzene or chlorobenzene). It is necessary to carefully consider these factors before a final selection is made for the mode of operation of the column.

A cocurrent bed contactor consisting of a deep sieve plate filled with knitted mesh packing has also been suggested. With an air–water type of system values of a as high as 13 cm^2/cm^3 have been reported (Wynn, 1978). Pulsed columns sectionalized with sieve plates have shown a very high efficiency in wastewater treatment (Brauer and Sucker, 1979).

(*f*) *Two-Phase Horizontal Cocurrent Contactors*

When absorption is accompanied by an irreversible reaction, then as pointed out elsewhere, the mode of operation of the unit (i.e., cocurrent or countercurrent) is immaterial in so far as its effect on the driving force is concerned. In these circumstances, it may be desirable in some cases to consider the horizontal cocurrent contactor.

The use of horizontal pipeline chemical reactors for heterogeneous flow systems is advantageous from the point of view of good heat transfer, very wide ranges of operating temperature and pressure, and the use of high volumetric flow rates to prevent settling of the slurries and caking of the precipitated reaction products. This type of contactor is also well suited for photochemical reactions (e.g., chlorination of molten polyethylene; sulfooxidation of hydrocarbon). Bubble columns and mechanically agitated contactors can also be employed for such reactions. However, the diameter of the bubble column or mechanically agitated contactor cannot be made large, since then the efficiency of utilization of light energy becomes low. Recently it has been suggested that this type of contactor may be useful for secondary sewage and industrial wastewater treatment. Apparently the idea in the case of sewage is the use of sewer pipe itself as a pipeline contactor (Russell, 1972; Characklis and Busch, 1972; Buley, 1973). It has also been suggested that the oxidation of black liquor in the paper industry can be advantageously carried out with pure O_2 in pipeline contactors (Galeano and Amsden, 1970; Cooper and Rossano, 1973). If the outlet from the pipe reactor contains some free dissolved oxygen, then a holding tank for the liquor can provide enough residence time for the dissolved O_2 to react with the unreacted Na_2S. The alkylation of aluminum triethyl with ethylene can also be advantageously carried out in a pipeline reactor.

An outstanding feature of two-phase cocurrent flow is that a variety of flow patterns are possible, ranging between the two extremes of a small quantity of gas dispersed as bubbles in a continuous liquid medium and a small amount of liquid dispersed as droplets in a continuous gas stream (see Figure 14.2*j*). The type of flow regime that can be obtained depends on the flow rates of the two phases, the physical properties of the system, and the geometry of the contactor (i.e., pipe diameter, entrance arrangement, etc.).

Although a great deal of work has been published about heat and momentum transfer in such units, relatively little is known about the mass transfer coefficients in these contactors. Some mass transfer data in plug or bubble flow (Scott and Hayduk, 1966; Lamont and Scott, 1966; Shah and Sharma, 1975), froth flow, (Heuss et al., 1965) and annular, spray, or dispersed flow (Wales, 1966) have been reported.

It appears that very high interfacial areas and mass transfer rates can be obtained by working in a two-phase horizontal contactor. In general, an increase in the gas and/or liquid rate increases the interfacial area as well as the overall mass transfer coefficient. Gas properties have been found to be unimportant when the contactor is operated at the same superficial gas velocity. The highest rates of transfer are obtainable in the dispersed flow regime, where the liquid flows as small droplets, thus providing very large values of interfacial area. If the situation demands, pipelines of varying diameter can also be employed. The performance of pipeline contactors can be further improved by incorporating inside the pipe, elements that will improve the dispersion characteristics (e.g., Static Mixer of the Kenics Corporation; see Section 14.2.2). Static mixers have gained considerable importance, particularly for wastewater (aerobic) treatment.

Jepsen (1970) has proposed a correlation that can be used for predicting the $k_L a$ values in pipeline contactors up to a diameter of 10 cm.

A modified form of horizontal contactor has been suggested that employs a bank of horizontal reactors. Thus a parallel feed arrangement is made and reactants circulate at high velocity through a centrally located horizontal draft tube; a propeller agitator is used to obtain high circulation velocities. Bundles of U-tubes are used inside the draft tube to remove heat. This type of reactor has been recommended for the alkylation of toulene with acetylene in the presence of 95% sulfuric acid containing mercuric sulfate as a catalyst. Here three phases are involved (*Chem. Eng.*, 1956).

(*g*) *Coiled Reactors*

The use of a coil in place of a pipe has the added advantage of compactness. Banerjee et al. (1970) have determined the values of the overall liquid-side mass transfer coefficient and the effective interfacial area in helical coils of various diameters. The data for the overall liquid-side mass transfer coefficient were correlated with the pressure drop in the test section, whereas those for the interfacial area were related to the energy dissipation in the test section. It appears that the $k_L a$ values were much higher than those obtained in the case of a pipeline contactor. Thus, in a typical case under comparable conditions, the $k_L a$ value was 0.5 sec^{-1} in a coil contactor as against 0.17 sec^{-1} for a pipeline contactor. The interfacial area, however, was found to be much lower, possibly because of lower entrainment. Thus, values of a were found to be 2–6.2 cm^2/cm^3 in the case of a coiled reactor as against 3–25 cm^2/cm^3 for a pipeline contactor.

(*h*) *Plunging Jet Reactor; Jet Reactors*

Here, a coherent liquid jet plunges through a reactive gaseous atmosphere into a batch of jet liquid. This type of reactor is representative of LD steel converters (here gas jets are used). Burgess et al. (1972) have made a study of this type of reactor and have reported interfacial area values of 1.5–6.0 cm^2/cm^3. van de Sande and Smith (1975) have also studied some aspects of this type of contactor and have indicated that the treatment of wastewater may be carried out in this type of contactor. Recently Shigelschi and Suciu (1977) have measured liquid-side mass transfer coefficients in this type of contactor.

Jet Reactors. A variety of jet reactors have been designed (also see Section 14.3)—for example, a self-priming injector nozzle. Alternatively, the two phases can be introduced together, from below, into the reactor through an annular nozzle (Weisweiler and Rösch, 1978). A number of papers on this type of reactor have been published by Nagel and co-workers (see, e.g., Nagel et al., 1972). These reactors offer fairly high values of a and $k_L a$. It has been claimed that such reactors are useful not only in wastewater treatment but also in the oxidation of a variety of hydrocarbons (e.g., cyclohexane). In an ejector contactor design suggested by Wynn (1978), where on each stage gas is expanded through nozzles and liquid is sucked into the high-velocity gas stream, remarkably high values of a of 60 cm^2/cm^3 have been reported. Because this value of a is unusually high, further work is necessary to check the performance with a variety of systems.

(*i*) *Vortex Reactors (Cyclo Reactors)*

The vortex reactor is a special type of reactor in which a fine dispersion of a gas into a liquid is created without using mechanical devices in the contactor. Figure 14.2*k* gives the pertinent details. Here a high-speed radial flow vortex is created at the bottom of the reactor and the intense shear forces in the core of the vortex promote intimate mixing of the gas and the liquid. Such a reactor has been suggested by the Ashbrook Company of the United States for, among other tasks, the air oxidation of black liquor. Such a reactor can handle highly viscous absorbent with or without solid particles. The values of a provided by this type of contactor for an air–water system range from 1 to 2.5 cm^2/cm^3 and the $k_L a$ values range from 0.05 to 0.15 sec^{-1} (Virkar, 1974; Hon, 1977; Gopal and Sharma, 1980). It appears that a considerable improvement in mass transfer characteristics can be realized by introducing inserts in the inner concentric tubes and values of a as high as 9 cm^2/cm^3 have been obtained with an air–water system (Hon, 1977; Gopal and Sharma, 1980). The vortex reactor is unlikely to have a very high flexibility.

14.1.3. Contactors Where Liquid Is Dispersed in the Continuous Gas Phase

(*a*) *Spray Columns*

There are some instances where the gas contains some solid impurities and/or where the product is solid and the gas is available at pressures slightly greater than atmospheric pressure. In such cases a spray column (Figure 14.3*a*) or a grid column may prove useful. (In a grid column, part of the liquid flows as a film and part in the form of drops.) The pressure drop in the gas phase is relatively low compared to that in (say) packed columns. There is no danger of clogging. In the manufacture of superphosphate fertilizer by the treatment of phosphate rock with sulfuric acid, HF and SiF_4 are generated and the gas carries a lot of suspended phosphate rock particles. It is common practice to absorb this gas in a spray column (SiF_4 hydrolyzes to give fluosilicic acid particles).

A spray absorber/dryer has been suggested for the manufacture of sodium carbonate from aqueous caustic soda solutions (*Chem. Process Eng.*, 1970). Here the aqueous caustic liquor is sprayed through suitably designed nozzles, and hot flue gas containing CO_2 is passed through the unit. The sensible heat of the flue gases and the heat of the reaction are advantageously employed for the evaporation of water, and a solid product is withdrawn from the unit.

If spraying is done with a solid cone type of nozzle (which gives an excellent spray), the liquid has to be pumped to give a sufficient head—of the order of 10–15 m of water—for the successful operation of the nozzle. On the other hand, for a grid column, a trough-type distributor may be used.

Typical values of true k_L in spray columns are comparable to those obtained in packed columns. However, the values of a in the spray column, in general, are substantially lower than those obtained in the case of (say) a packed column (Mehta and Sharma, 1970). There is a considerable amount of backmixing in the gas phase, particularly at superficial gas velocities less than 10 cm/sec, which drastically reduces the effective driving force unless the gas is pure. In those operations where the solute content has to be reduced to a very low value, the spray column may prove unsatisfactory. On the whole, the spray column is a relatively inefficient contactor and its use is justifiable only in limited cases.

Recently Edwards and Huang (1977) have suggested a new design for a cross-flow horizontal spray absorber (Figure 14.3*c*). Here the pressure drop in the gas phase is low and the extent of backmixing in the gas phase is greatly reduced. Further, the capacity of the plant can be simply increased by increasing the number of banks. This new design, called the Kellog–Weir Air Quality Control System, has been successfully employed to remove SO_2 from the stack gases of power plants by absorption in a soluble magnesium compound. A slurry tank is provided right below the absorber where lime or limestone is added; 97% removal of SO_2 has been claimed.

Rotating spray reactors have also been suggested for the purification of waste gases containing Cl_2, HCl, SO_2, and the like.

(*b*) *Venturi Scrubbers*

Venturi scrubbers (Figure 14.3*d*) offer a number of advantages associated with the relatively simple mechanical design, low first cost of equipment, ability to handle large flow rates of gas in relatively small equipment, and ability to handle a slurry absorbent. Further, in dust-laden gases the collection efficiency of fine particles is very high. The venturi scrubbers are well suited for situations where fine solid particles have to be handled and the pressure drop on the gas side should be low (e.g., absorption of lean SO_2 from off-gases in a suspension of lime, limestone, MgO, etc.; Kerr, 1974). Two modes of operation can be applied: Pease–Antony, where the liquid is introduced into the throat of the venturi; the wet approach, where the liquid is introduced in such a manner that the entire convergent section is wet by the liquid phase. The wet approach offers low pressure drops as compared to the Pease–Antony mode, and values of a and $k_L a$ for the two modes of operation are comparable (Virkar and Sharma 1975; Hon, 1977). In particular, it may be mentioned that k_L values as high as 0.11 cm/sec can be realized.

Beenackers and van Swaaij (1976) have reported mass transfer characteristics of a new type of cyclone reactor where the gas was introduced through the wall, which was made of porous stainless steel. Values of a as high as 45 cm^2/cm^3 of the contactor volume corresponding to the height of the porous cylinder were found. Further, remarkably high k_L values—of the order of 0.3 cm/sec—have been reported. Further work is desirable to assess its practical utility.

14.1.4. Foaming Problems

When a gas is finely dispersed in a relatively deep pool of liquid it may show a tendency to foam. Thus, in the type of contactor where this type of dispersion is found, as in bubble and modified bubble columns and mechanically agitated contactors, operational problems associated with foaming of the liquid may be encountered. It is generally not possible to predict a priori whether foaming will occur under conditions of mass transfer. In some cases even adventitious impurities may cause foaming. It may sometimes be possible to use a suitable antifoaming agent, which will supress foaming. However, this may be undesirable in many practical systems, since it will introduce a foreign substance into the system, which may be unacceptable. The problem of foaming is usually not encountered in film contactors (Section 14.1.1) and contactors where liquid is dispersed in the continuous gas phase (Section 14.1.3), and it would be desirable to consider such contactors for industrial practice. In some specific cases mechanical foam breakers are installed on top of the bubble column to overcome the operational problems of foaming. For instance, when bubble columns are used for the air oxidation of black liquor—a system that shows a pronounced tendency to foam—mechanical foam breakers are installed at the top of the column (Murray, 1968). In contrast, where the height of dispersion is relatively low and dispersion is coarse, it is expected that the foaming problem will be less severe (e.g., in horizontal sparged contactors). Foaming systems can be conveniently handled in pipeline contactors.

14.1.5. Contactors for Non-Newtonian Fluids

We have already considered some aspects of mass transfer with chemical reaction in non-Newtonian systems (see Chapter 8). The common examples where mass transfer with chemical reaction is encountered in such type of fluids are polycondensation reactions, polyamide formation, aerobic fermentation, treatment of effluents, including those involving dissolved polymeric substances, reactions in slurries, and the like. In this section we shall consider some aspects of equipment that is used for these systems. Mashelkar (1976) has discussed this matter in a comprehensive review. The rheological complexities of non-Newtonian fluids have been discussed at length in the literature (see, e.g., the book by Astarita and Marrucci, 1974). The fluid behavior of non-Newtonian fluids can be classified into three broad categories: (1) time-independent viscoinelastic fluids; (2) time-dependent viscoinelastic fluids; (3) viscoelastic fluids. We shall very briefly cover the salient characteristics of these categories of non-Newtonian fluids so that special problems associated with mass transfer in such fluids can be properly understood. In the case of time-independent viscoinelastic fluids, the viscosity of the fluid can be a decreasing function of the shear rate, and in such cases these fluids are referred to as *pseudoplastic* or *shear-thinning* fluids. Some common examples of pseudoplastic fluids are polymer solutions and/or melts, blood, and the like. In some cases the fluids show yield stresses, and these are referred to as *Bingham plastic*. Some fermentation broths and liquid effluents show such characteristics.

For time-dependent viscoinelastic fluids the stresses depend on both the strain rate and the strain rate history. The materials belonging to this category are commonly described as thixotropic or rheopectic and are substantially free of elastic effects. Such fluids do not return to their original configuration when an applied stress is released. Slurries and colloidal aggregates sometimes exhibit this behavior.

Viscoelastic fluids develop pronounced normal or elastic stresses even under conditions of laminar shearing flow. Further, these fluids also exhibit the phenomena of stress relaxation and strain recovery.

The dispersion characteristics may be profoundly affected by the fluid behavior. It is possible that the conventional mass transfer equipment used for low-viscosity Newtonian fluids may prove to be practically useless for non-Newtonian fluids. Further, the scale-up of contactors will pose problems in view of the rheological complexities. Consider the case of the polymerization of caprolactam to polyamide nylon-6. The viscosity of the nylon-6 melt at the 245°C temperature at which the desorption of water is carried out is above 40 P. In such a case a small-area high-speed agitator for generating a high interfacial area will be completely unsatisfactory because of the low inertia levels in the contactor. Further, in conventional mechanically agitated contactors there is a nonuniform shear distribution. For fluids where the shear viscosity varies with the shear rate, the shear rates will be highest near the tip of the impeller and will decay rapidly as the contactor wall is approached. Thus, gas will have a strong tendency to channel through the impeller region in view of the low viscosity in this region, and the dispersion characteristics will be very poor. Loucaides and McManamey (1973) have reported this type of behavior in the case of a fermentation broth that exhibited pseudoplastic behavior.

In the case of Bingham-plastic-type fluids, if the yield stress is higher than the characteristic shear stress in the contactor, the gas bubbles may not have any relative motion with respect to the rest of the fluid, resulting in serious repurcussions. In addition to the foregoing factors, the elasticity of the fluids may result in a situation where instead of the fluid's being thrown away from the impeller, it is sucked in toward the impeller. Although these observations have been made in unaerated vessels at low rotational speeds and only under laminar conditions, it is conceivable that such drastic changes in overall flow patterns may significantly alter the dispersion characteristics. Further, studies in idealized flow situations have shown that the processes of bubble deformation and breakup are severely hampered in elastic liquids. The experimental observations of poor dispersions and low interfacial areas in elastic liquids reported by Yagi and Yoshida (1975) are probably due to this phenomenon. In practice, the agitated vessels will be operated under turbulent conditions. Even moderately elastic liquids are known to severely dampen the turbulence, which in turn will adversely affect the dispersion characteristics. Walstra (1974) has reported that the addition of certain long-chain water soluble polymers caused an increase in drop size by about 200%.

In practical cases situations are also encountered where the viscosity of the fluid changes drastically during the course of the reaction. For instance, during glucamylose fermentation, the pseudoplasticity index changes from 0.9 to 0.3 (Taguchi and Miyamoto, 1966). Further, during the manufacture of polysaccharides the apparent viscosity of the medium may rise from a few centipoise to about 250 P and then drop again to the initial value (Leday et al., 1974).

For aerobic fermentation we may be required to maintain agitation in such a way that in no part of the fermentor the oxygen supply is less than the demand, since otherwise this will lead to the death of microorganisms. Further, dead spaces in the contactor may be highly undesirable for thermally unstable polymers or for situations where infusible material may be produced.

These factors clearly bring out the complexities in non-Newtonian systems that make the situation very different from that encountered in Newtonian fluids. There is limited information in the published literature on mass transfer in non-Newtonian systems (Loucaides and McManamey, 1973; Perez and Sandall, 1974). Further work on the mass transfer characteristics of contactors with fluids comparable to those that are used in practice is urgently needed. Two types of contactors are commonly used in practice: (1) interfacial surface generators; and (2) mechanically agitated thin-film contactors.

In the interfacial surface generators a thin film of material is produced on a continuously moving surface. This can be achieved by, for instance, mounting a large number of disks on a horizontal shaft and partially dipping these disks in the liquid [see Section 14.1.1(d)]. The speed of rotation is carefully selected. It appears that very limited information on mass transfer in such contactors is available in the published literature. Murakami et al. (1972) have studied some aspects of the liquid holdup, power consumption, mixing time, dead space, and surface renewal rates with corn syrup solutions whose viscosity ranged from 50 to 5000 cP.

We have already covered some systems of mechanically agitated thin-film contactors [see Section 14.1.1(c)]. Simple wetted-wall column reactors are most unlikely to be useful, since very high film thickness will be encountered with high-viscosity materials, resulting in very poor mass transfer coefficient values. It therefore becomes necessary to agitate the film. The gap between the rotor blade and the wall is kept small ($\approx$ 1 mm) and the blades may be either straight or slightly pitched. Since the distance between the rotor blade and the wall controls the mean film thickness, it becomes essentially independent of the viscosity of the fluid. The pitched-blade rotor shows superior performance, particularly for higher-viscosity materials.

Widmer (1973) has reported very useful data on the final stage of the polycondensation step in the manufacture of polyesters. These data were obtained from a freely falling film reactor as well as an agitated thin-film reactor and show clearly that much higher rates of condensation were realized in the agitated-film reactors.

Todd and Irving (1969) have suggested that a double-screw extruder reactor can be employed for polycondensation. These authors have developed a rotor design that provides very good surface renewal rates and at the same time limits the axial dispersion.

14.2. LIQUID–LIQUID CONTACTORS

A variety of contactors can be used for bringing two liquid phases into contact. The basic objective is to create a fairly high specific area of contact and at the same time ensure that the phase separation also takes place readily. Usually the interfacial tension for liquid–liquid systems is low as compared to that for gas–liquid systems. Consequently, it is relatively easy to obtain high values of specific interfacial area in the case of liquid–liquid systems as compared to those for gas–liquid systems (see Tables 14.1 and 14.2). The difference in the density of the two phases is very small in the case of liquid–liquid contactors as compared to the case of gas–liquid contactors. While this condition of small difference in density in itself is favorable for creating more interfacial area, too small a density difference is detrimental to the quick separation of the two phases and this may lead to operational difficulties. In some cases, "haze" formation occurs that may require an unusually long time to settle. It should be ensured that the efficient contact between the two liquid phases does not result in emulsification.

TABLE 14.2. Continuous-Phase Mass Transfer Coefficient and Effective Interfacial Area in Liquid–Liquid Contactors[a]

Type of Equipment	RTD Dispersed Phase	RTD Continuous Phase	ϵ_D	R_C	$k_L \times 10^2$ (cm/sec)	a (cm^2/cm^3)	$k_L a \times 10^2$ (sec^{-1})
Spray columns	P	M	0.05–0.1	Limited	0.1–1	1–10	0.1–10
Packed columns	P	P	0.05–0.1	Limited	0.3–1	1–10	0.3–10
Mechanically agitated contactors	PM	M	0.05–0.4	Can be varied over a wide range	0.3–1	1–800	0.3–800
Air-agitated liquid–liquid contactors	PM	M	0.05–0.3	Can be varied over a wide range	0.1–0.3	10–100	1.0–30
Two-phase cocurrent (horizontal) contactors	P	P	0.05–0.2	Limited	0.1–1.0	1–25	0.1–25

[a]The continuous phase is aqueous solutions. Notation used in the table is the same as in Table 14.1 except that ϵ_D is the fractional dispersed-phase holdup and R_C is the residence time of the continuous phase.

Table 14.2 gives typical values of continuous-phase mass transfer coefficient (continuous phase: aqueous solutions) and interfacial area that are provided by some contactors. Table 14.2 also gives an indication of the residence time distribution of the continuous and dispersed phases.

Pilhofer (1979) has considered the load diagram for all types of countercurrently operated extraction columns. In practically all types of columns, the dispersed phase is transported through the continuous phase by volume forces (buoyancy and gravity) acting on the drops. Columns with free drop motion (spray and unpulsed sieve-plate columns; see below) exhibit relatively very high throughputs. In the case of columns where external energy is supplied, the reciprocating-plate column stands out as regards throughputs, since the whole cross-section can be utilized for drop motion (Pilhofer, 1979).

There is limited discussion in the literature on the criterion for the selection of a contactor for reacting systems. Because of the great importance of reacting systems in the solvent extraction of metals and earlier in nuclear energy programs, some literature has appeared that qualitatively discusses some important points. Laddha and Degaleesan (1976) have discussed the design aspects of different types of liquid–liquid contactors. Brandt et al. (1978) and Reissinger and Schröeter (1978) have surveyed different types of liquid–liquid extractors and have suggested criteria for selection. A rule-of-thumb procedure through a selection chart has been suggested by Reissinger and Schröeter. Marr (1978) has discussed this matter with reference to extractors with rotating agitators. Most extractors behave very differently with respect to the different liquid properties, and even trace adventitious impurities can make considerable difference in the performance of the equipment. Thus great caution has to be exercised in selecting an extractor and often pilot-plant and/or laboratory-scale experiments with actual solutions are highly desirable, if not necessary.

For reacting systems we will have to consider problems associated with residence time requirements of one or both phases, levels of conversions of species A and B, supply or removal of heat, inventory of phases in the column, presence of solid particles or mucky materials, and the like.

The available equipment may be classified in the following manner (adapted from Treybal, 1963; Warwick, 1973):

1. Gravity-operated extractors
   a. No mechanically operated moving parts:
      (i) spray columns
      (ii) packed columns
      (iii) sieve-plate columns
      (iv) controlled-cycle columns
   b. Mechanically agitated contactors:
      (i) mixer–settlers; inert-gas-agitated contactors
      (ii) columns agitated with rotating stirrers
      (iii) pulsed columns: liquid contents hydraulically pulsed; reciprocating plates; air pulsed

2. Pipeline contactors; static mixer contactor
3. Centrifugal extractors

14.2.1. Gravity-Operated Extractors

Figures 14.4–14.7 show the salient features of the contactors discussed here.

(a) No Mechanically Operated Moving Parts

(i) ***Spray Columns.*** The spray column is probably the simplest and cheapest type of extraction column (Figure 14.4*a*). It can conveniently handle solid impurities in the system. The column can also be cleaned very easily. The true mass transfer coefficient values in this column are comparable to those in isked and sieve-plate columns. However, the effective interfacial area values are significantly lower than those in (say) packed columns.

The most important disadvantage of a spray column arises out of substantial backmixing in the continuous phase, which reduces the driving force drastically. (The dispersed phase moves essentially in plug flow except at flooding, when some backmixing occurs in the dispersed phase.) Consequently, the spray column is not recommended for operations requiring more than two stages. The situation is, however, quite different when the continuous phase consists of a pure material, since then backmixing in the continuous phase will be irrelevant. Further, if the system conforms to regime 2, then the concentration of reactive species B becomes unimportant. Backmixing in the B phase will be important if the system conforms to regimes 1, 3, and 4. There are some examples of industrial importance where a pure organic material is contacted with the B phase. It would be then desirable to make the organic phase the continuous phase. If the viscosity of the organic phase is relatively high, it may offer an added advantage, since the effective interfacial area generally increases with an increase in the viscosity of the continuous phase.

Spray columns can be conveniently adopted if it is necessary to remove or supply heat to the system.

A recent innovation in the operation of the spray column concerns the dense packing of drops. (In the normal mode of operation dispersed packing of drops is obtained.) The information available in the literature suggests that the column can be operated satisfactorily in the regime of dense packing of drops. Very high values of the effective interfacial area are obtained. In a typical case Puranik and Sharma

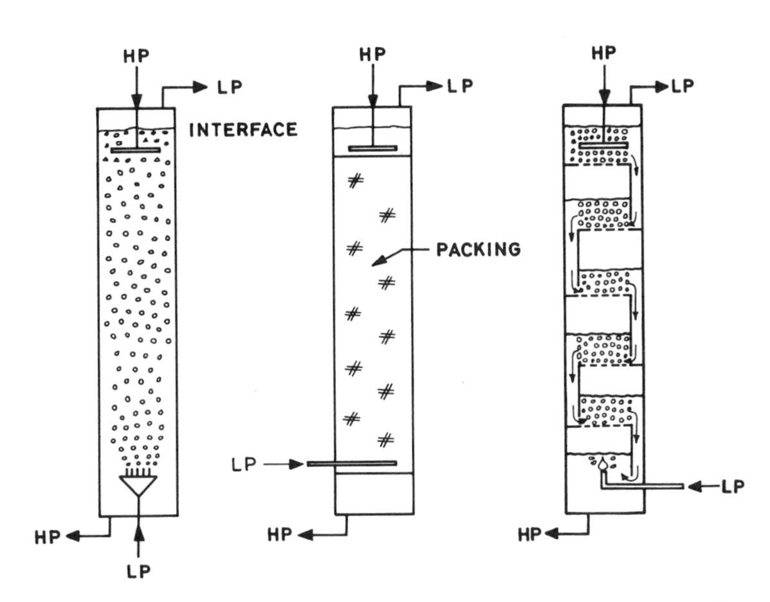

Figure 14.4. Gravity-operated extractors (no mechanically operated moving parts). (*a*) spray column; (*b*) packed column; (*c*) sieve-plate column.

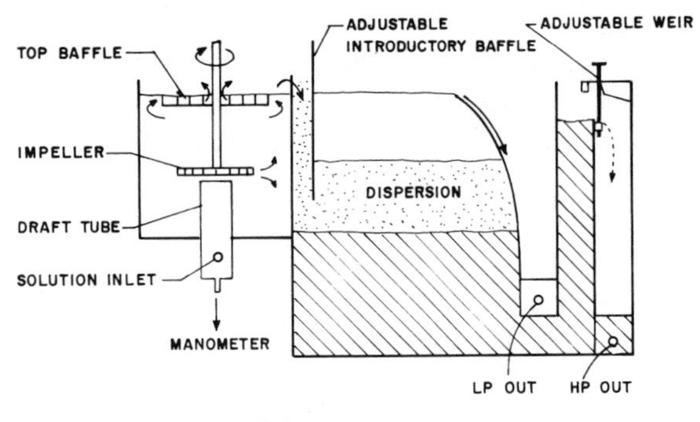

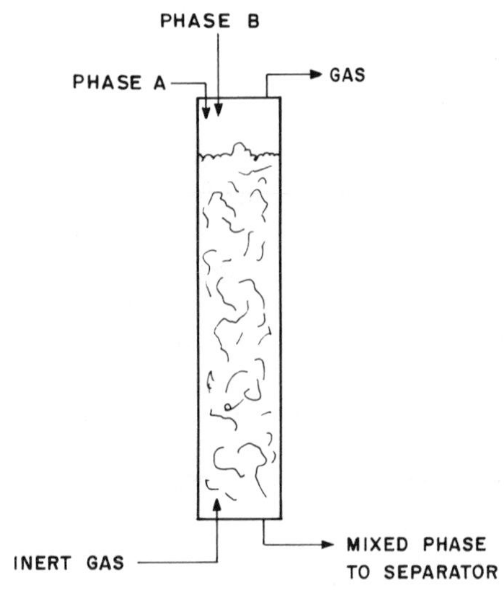

(1970a) found that for the same flow rates of the continuous and dispersed phases (for 2-ethyl butyl formate transfer into aqueous NaOH; organic phase dispersed) the interfacial area values were 10 and 0.5 cm^2/cm^3 for the dense and dispersed packing of drops, respectively. Further exploration of the potential uses of spray columns operated in the dense packing regime should be done. There is, however, some backmixing in the dispersed phase when the spray column is operated in the regime of dense packing of drops.

There may be some advantages in introducing an inert gas into spray columns when nonvolatile reactants are involved (Steiner, 1978).

Spray columns are rarely used as reactors in practice except in the case of dirty systems—for example, in the high-pressure hydrolysis of vegetable and animal fat for the manufacture of fatty acids and glycerin (Jeffreys et al., 1961; Donders et al., 1968). Sometimes these columns are used to carry out neutralizations and for situations where direct contact heat transfer is advantageous.

(*ii*) ***Packed Columns.*** The packed column (Figure 14.4*b*) is a very versatile, simple, and cheap contactor. The presence of packing in the column increases the local velocities, helps in the dispersion of the dispersed phase, and markedly reduces the backmixing in the continuous phase. Thus the main disadvantage of a spray column can be eliminated by

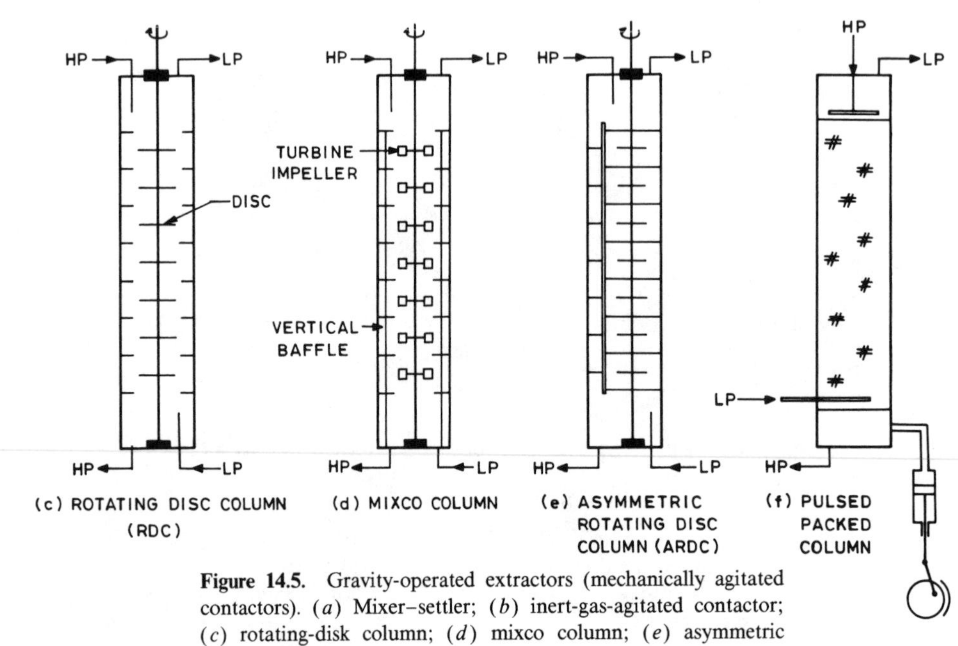

Figure 14.5. Gravity-operated extractors (mechanically agitated contactors). (*a*) Mixer–settler; (*b*) inert-gas-agitated contactor; (*c*) rotating-disk column; (*d*) mixco column; (*e*) asymmetric rotating-disk column; (*f*) pulsed packed column.

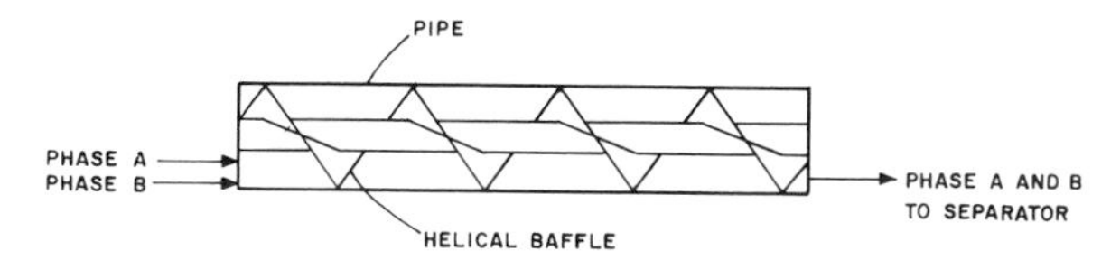

Figure 14.6*a*. Horizontal pipeline mixer (static mixer).

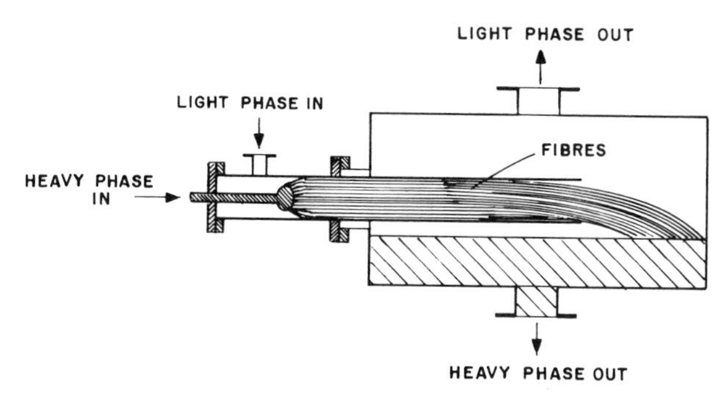

Figure 14.6*b*. Fiber film contactor.

introducing packings in the column. The prediction of the mass transfer coefficient for packed columns is also probably more reliable than that for other contactors. This arises out of the observation that droplet size becomes independent of the packing size above a critical size of the packing. For common systems the critical size of the packing for Raschig rings is around 1 cm. The dispersed phase should not preferentially wet the packing, since otherwise the dispersed phase will flow as a film and relatively low mass transfer coefficient values will be obtained. In recent years, plastic packings of various designs have been made available and these packings can withstand a variety of organic materials. Most of the data reported in the literature are confined to 6.25-, 10-, 12.5-, and 25-mm ($\frac{1}{4}$-, $\frac{3}{8}$-, $\frac{1}{2}$-, and 1-in.) Raschig rings and Berl saddles. Newer types of packings such as Intalox saddles and Pall rings are expected to be attractive. Nemunaitis et al. (1971) have reported that 6.25-, 20-, and 25-mm ($\frac{1}{2}$-, $\frac{3}{4}$-, and 1-in.) ceramic Intalox saddles and 16- and 25-mm ($\frac{5}{8}$- and 1-in.) copper Pall rings can handle higher flow rates of the dispersed phase than the corresponding ceramic Raschig rings. The newer packings were also found to be more efficient than Raschig rings. Multifilament gauze packings, Sulzer-type packings, and the like in metals and plastics also merit consideration.

Verma and Sharma (1975) have found that the overall (continuous-phase) mass transfer coefficient and effective interfacial area offered by the same nominal size Intalox saddles and Pall rings, under otherwise uniform conditions, are only about 10 and 35% higher than those provided by the Raschig rings. However, the flooding velocities for the newer packings are as much as 80% higher than those for the conventional packings. Thus it should be possible to operate the columns with newer packings at relatively higher dispersed- and continuous-phase velocities. The values of the effective interfacial area vary almost linearly with the dispersed-phase velocity at any specified continuous-phase velocity (Puranik and Sharma, 1970b; Verma and Sharma, 1975).

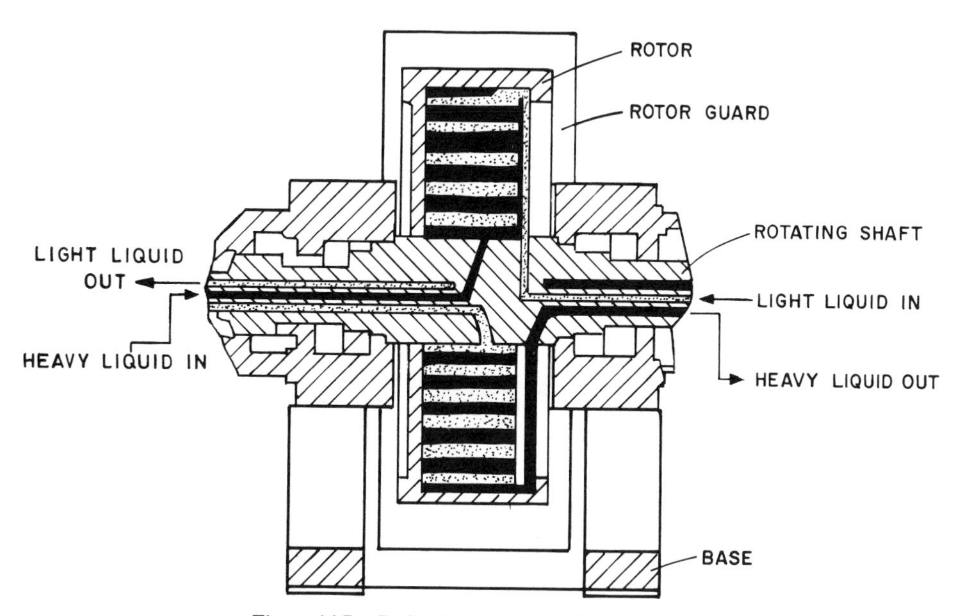

Figure 14.7. Podbielniak centrifugal extractor.

Houlihan and Landau (1974) have reviewed the available equations for predicting the flooding velocities and have made specific recommendations. In general, the lowest value of the height equivalent to the theoretical stage will be about 30 cm; values of 60–120 cm are common. Nemunaitis et al. (1971) have recommended that the industrial columns should be designed on the basis of only 20% of the flooding velocity. This is somewhat surprising, since the general recommendation is that the column should be designed at 40–50% of the flooding velocity. Eckert (1976) has also discussed some general aspects of the design of packed extraction columns.

The presence of solids or adventitious solid impurities is detrimental to the operation of packed columns. Further, the efficiency of packed columns is relatively low as compared to that of mechanically agitated contactors. The problem of channeling in the liquid probably becomes important with an increase in the size of the column. Packed columns are generally not recommended when more than 7–8 theoretical stages are required.

(iii) Sieve-Plate Columns. The sieve-plate column (Figure 14.4*c*) is also a simple contactor, and it offers relatively high efficiencies even in large-diameter columns. The sieve-plate column is basically a modification of the spray column. A number of plates perforated with small holes (the most common diameter is 2 mm) are introduced in a vertical column. The throughput of this type of column depends on the density difference between the two phases and the height of the backup layer under the plates. Backmixing is thus restricted to any single stage. The repeated coalescence and dispersion also leads to better mass transfer rates. There are, however, certain limitations to the use of sieve-plate columns. The flexibility of the column is rather poor—that is, it offers good efficiency only in a narrow range of operating conditions. Further, there is a danger that solid impurities, if present, will clog the holes.

In the case of relatively large columns, as in the case of gas–liquid systems, multiple downcomer columns can be advantageously used.

(iv) Controlled-Cycle Extraction Columns. For fluid–fluid contactors the principle of controlled cycling was discussed in Section 14.1.2. Szabo et al. (1964) have shown that controlled-cycle packed and sieve-plate extraction columns show substantially better results than those shown by the conventional flow system. Darsi and Feick (1971) have also reported that controlled-cycle sieve-plate extraction columns give higher efficiencies than the conventional sieve-plate column. In a specific case of water–acetic acid–methyl isobutyl ketone (encountered in the acetate rayon industry) they found at least 100% improvement in efficiency and about a 50% increase in the handling capacity. They have also proposed a model that accounts for the observed increase in efficiency. Schrödt (1965) has reported some data pertaining to the purification of chlorinated phenols. It appears that in conventional extractors serious problems associated with emulsification due to the presence of sodium chlorophenate have been encountered. However, the use of a controlled-cycle extractor obviated these difficulties.

(b) Mechanically Agitated Contactors

(i) Mixer–Settlers. A mixer–settler unit (Figure 14.5*a*) is a simple, highly flexible, and versatile contactor. Any ratio of the two phases can be handled, and there is no hydrodynamic limitation imposed with respect to flooding as in the case with (say) the spray or the packed column. It can be used for batchwise or continuous operation and maintenance is very easy. The agitation conditions can be varied from stage to stage to suit specific requirements. The unit can be designed to give very high efficiencies, irrespective of the characteristics of the liquids being treated, and scale-up can be done satisfactorily on the basis of experiments on a small-scale apparatus. We can easily incorporate additional stages in existing systems. Suspended solid particles can also be handled in this equipment. A variety of industrially important processes are carried out in mixer–settler units. For instance, the removal of free fatty acids from fats is usually carried out by treatment with aqueous or alcoholic caustic soda in the mixer–settler type of contactor. In many organic substitution chlorination reactions, some dissolved HCl is usually present in the final product at the end of the chlorination reaction. This dissolved HCl is removed by extraction into aqueous soda ash or caustic soda solutions. These operations require only one theoretical stage. Batch nitrations and sulfonations are often carried out in this type of contactor. In the case of batch nitration with mixed acid it would be desirable to contact the aromatic substance, such as toluene or chlorobenzene, and sulfuric acid effectively and add nitric acid at predetermined intervals. This will ensure high selectivity with respect to the mononitrated product. Should we decide to operate by adding the aromatic substance to the mixed acid, we would get a lower yield of the monoproduct, since by this procedure we allow a much higher ratio of the concentration of nitric acid to that of the aromatic substance to prevail.

A mixer–settler unit is approximately equivalent to one theoretical stage. Consequently when any operation requires a relatively large number of stages (say > 5), then the corresponding number of stages have to be used and this requires a lot of space. However, new designs based on the box configuration have been suggested that require less space. Some doubts have been expressed about the efficiency in individual stages of the box unit, and it is suspected that the efficiency may be as low as 50%. Further, pumps will be required for the transfer of liquid from one stage to the next one, and the overall power consumption is relatively high. If radioactive material has to be handled, a mixer–settler arrangement is unsatisfactory because the holdup is relatively large. The residence time of the phases is long and consequently for costly and sensitive materials such a contactor may prove unsatisfactory. Further, in some systems a number of undesirable side reactions might occur because of the long residence time.

In recent years in the vegetable oil industry, for a variety of reactions (e.g., the removal of free fatty acids or coloring matter) a combination of a jet mixer and a centrifugal separator has been suggested.

The mode of operation of a multistage mixer–settler system will depend on circumstances. Thus Albright and Hanson (1969) have reported that for the nitration of aromatic compounds it would be desirable, from the point of view of heat and mass transfer considerations, to use countercurrent rather than cocurrent operation. The choice of continuous phase sometimes depends on circumstances. In the petroleum industry, in the case of alkylation reactions (e.g., the alkylation of isobutane with isobutylene or butene) that use sulfuric acid as the catalyst, a continuous emulsion of sulfuric acid will produce a much better quality alkylate for gasoline than that produced under identical operating conditions with a continuous hydrocarbon emulsion (Albright, 1966). Further, the consumption of sulfuric acid is also less for the acid–continuous operation.

In principle it is possible to design the multistage mixer–settler system in such a way that external pumping is avoided by using impellers that have pumping characteristics. This design is particularly relevant where the recycle of one phase within a stage is required. Figure 14.5*a* shows the design conceived by the Power Gas Company of England incorporating these features (Warwick, 1973). The flow from one stage to the next one can also be induced by the hydrostatic head created by the difference in the densities caused by mixing.

The Lurgi Company of West Germany has evolved yet another type of multistage contactor: It consists of stacked settler units, and thus results in a marked reduction in the floor-space requirement. A centrifugal stirrer is attached to the side of the settling column. This mixer is responsible for mixing, mass transfer, and pumping. The flow of liquid is guided by a complex arrangement of baffles to be useful only for fast-reacting systems, since the residence time in each mixing stage is of the order of 0.5 sec. Further, the efficiency of each stage is adversely affected by entrainment. One motor can be used to drive three to five mixer pumps.

Although mixer pumps have been suggested by some companies, doubts have been expressed about their utility. The optimal speed for mixing often differs from that for pumping, and the combination of mixer and pump may not give the optimal results (Reissinger and Schröter, 1978).

Settlers. Horizontal vessels are usually used as settlers, since it has been shown that the separating efficiency is proportional to the area of the phase interface. It is generally necessary to conduct experiments to ascertain the coalescence rate.

The settling area can usually be reduced by the use of coalescing aids such as mesh and metal swarf. In recent years attempts have been made to use an electrostatic field as a coalescence aid. Apparently the Lurgi column employs an electrostatic field for promoting coalescence. Mumford and Thomas (1972) and Jeffreys and Mumford (1974) have described various methods for reducing the overall size of the settlers. A particular reference may be made to woven packings made of two different materials such as metals and alloys and plastics. Thus we have high- as well as low-energy surfaces. Such packings are referred to as differential contact (DC) packings. It has been claimed that these packings act as excellent coalescence aids.

In settlers having a diameter of more than 1 m, due to recirculating flow caused by the density gradient in the flow direction within the heavy phase we are likely to encounter uncontrolled backmixing. This problem can be circumvented to a considerable extent by increasing the length of the settler; settling aids can be used only downstream of this zone.

Graesser Contactor. In the Graesser contactor a cylinder rotating with a horizontal axis is used and vertical partitions are provided. The dispersion and mixing are achieved by using dippers. The throughput of this type of contactor is relatively low.

Inert-Gas-Agitated Contactors. Inert-gas-agitated liquid–liquid contactors (Figure 14.5*b*) offer certain advantages, such as the absence of moving parts and the little maintenance that is required for these types of contactors. The liquids to be contacted, however, should have a low vapor pressure at the operating temperature; otherwise the losses of the phases to be contacted with the outgoing inert gas will be excessively high. It has been reported that purification of crude naphthalene with H_2SO_4 at 100°C (10% by weight of naphthalene) can be carried out with air bubbling. In some cases the process involves two liquid phases and a gas phase. Thus, in the manufacture of protein from suitable petroleum fractions the system consists of hydrocarbon and the aqueous phase, and air is sparged through the system for the oxygen supply to the microorganisms. Further, the O_2 requirements are relatively high and hence the superficial air velocity is fairly high.

Fernandes and Sharma (1968) have studied some aspects of mass transfer in such contactors. Both the effective interfacial area and the liquid-side mass transfer coefficient increased with increasing gas velocity as well as the increasing fraction of the dispersed phase in the column. The ratio of dispersion height to contactor diameter had no influence on the value of a when it exceeded 3, and the design of the gas distributor was found to be unimportant. An increase in interfacial tension reduced the value of a. At any given superficial gas velocity, the value of a was independent of the column diameter.

It is not possible to predict a priori the values of a in air-agitated liquid–liquid contactors, but it should be possible to scale-up on the basis of experiments on a small-scale apparatus with the desired system and at the same superficial gas velocity as in the larger column.

In some pyrometallurgical operations, such as open-hearth steel making and continuous lead softening, two liquid phases have to be brought into contact. Because of the high values of the interfacial tension between the two phases it becomes very difficult to disperse one phase into another. In the examples cited, agitation is provided by large bubbles but no dispersion occurs. It is known that mass transfer plays an important role in these operations (Szekely, 1967).

(ii) Columns Agitated with Rotating Stirrers. The mass transfer coefficient values offered by spray, packed, and sieve-plate columns are relatively low, and consequently tall columns have to be used. The mass transfer coefficient values can be considerably improved by providing agitation through impellers. Reman introduced the rotating-disk contactor (RDC, Figure 14.5*c*) in 1951. Another design was suggested by Oldshue and Rushton in 1952; it is referred to as the Mixco column (Figure 14.5*d*). In the case of the RDC, the impellers are disks with a diameter of 0.3–0.6 times the diameter of the contactor, and horizontal baffles are provided. The ratio of the diameter of the contactor to the height of the compartment is kept between 2 and 8. In the Mixco column, turbine-type agitators are provided and both horizontal and vertical baffles are used.

These types of columns are particularly useful when systems showing high interfacial tension values have to be handled and the overall driving force is relatively small. There are a number of industrially important organic reactions in which the interfacial tension of the system is relatively high. The height equivalent to a theoretical stage in an RDC varies from 100 to 200 cm. An RDC is well suited for high throughputs at low separation performance. In the case of an RDC, a suitable increase in the rotor speed makes it possible to handle as much as 50% of the design capacity without a loss in efficiency. An RDC is well suited for dirty systems. RDCs have been built of different materials, including fiberglass-reinforced plastics, and with diameters of up to 6–8 m but with a height of only 10–12 m. The height is restricted because the shaft should be continuous, and if intermediate bearings are employed, these provide centers for flooding. The problem of the residence time distribution in both phases and the importance of the droplet size distribution should be carefully considered when the scale-up is carried out (Olney, 1964; Bibaud and Treybal, 1966; Landau and Houlihan, 1974; Laddha et al., 1978; Marr, 1978).

Mechanically agitated contactors like the RDC and Oldshue–Rushton column have many attractive features. However, there is a considerable amount of backmixing in the two phases, and this poses scale-up problems. For this reason attempts have been made to devise columns that closely approximate the mixer–settler. A modified form of the RDC, called the *asymmetric rotating-disk contactor* (ARDC), has been found attractive (see Figure 14.5*e*). In this design the shaft with agitator disks is located asymmetrically to the column axis, and nonperforated plates are used to separate the agitating zones. The height equivalent to a theoretical stage (HETS) in an ARDC varies from about 35 to 100 cm and is thus superior to that of an RDC. Further, unlike the RDC, the rotor shaft can be made with couplings and so taller columns can be used. Multiple agitators can also be employed. However, an ARDC is a relatively expensive contactor.

Kuehni Column. Here centrifugal agitators are used and stator disks are perforated and their free cross-sectional area can be adopted to suit the specific requirements. It is remarkable that an HETS value as low as 10 cm has been reported. It has been claimed that this type of column extractor is well suited for reacting systems and for extreme phase ratios.

(iii) Pulsed Column. In some practical cases it becomes necessary to contact two liquid phases that have relatively high interfacial tension values. Under normal conditions of operation with a spray or packed column, very tall columns may be required for the desired duty. Mechanically agitated contactors, as stated earlier, can substantially reduce the height. However, in certain specific operations, such as the extraction of metals from radioactive solutions (produced in atomic energy operations), mechanical agitation may be highly undesirable because of health hazards. In these circumstances, pulsed columns can be satisfactorily used. The pulsations can be introduced in a number of ways. For instance, in a perforated column the plate assembly can be mechanically moved up and down while the liquids pass through the contactor. Alternatively, liquids can be "pulsed" by an outside mechanism. Various devices are described in the literature (Treybal, 1963; Reissinger and Schröter, 1978). One such unit is shown in Figure 14.5*f*.

Baird et al. (1968) have suggested a new design by which liquid pulsations are produced without the need for any mechanical moving parts. An air column is used to provide pulsation, and by ensuring operation under conditions of resonant frequency, the power requirement can be reduced significantly. The resonant pulsing apparatus includes a solenoid valve for the air supply and exhaust linked to a liquid level switch or a pressure switch. However, further work is necessary to establish the industrial utility of this design.

In the case of packed columns the efficiency can be improved by a factor of 2 through the introduction of pulsation. Bender et al. (1979) have discussed the operating characteristics of pulsed packed columns. Raschig rings are not recommended, since the droplets of the dispersed phase are likely to adhere to the packings. Pulsed columns work well in situations where the liquid properties do not change substantially in the column. On the whole, a pulsed packed column is not a very efficient column, and it requires that the density difference between the two phases be more than 0.08 g/cm^3.

Pulsed sieve-plate columns have shown good efficiencies, particularly when these are operated at frequencies between 60 and 150 strokes/min and amplitudes under 1 cm. In general, a plate spacing of 10 cm is considered most favorable. However, these columns operate well in a limited load range and are also susceptible to fouling, particularly with sticky products. To some extent the reduction in efficiency at underload can be compensated by changing the pulsation characteristics; the load can also be artificially increased by recycling the raffinate. One of the attractive designs is that of the Karr column, where sieve plates with perforated areas of 50–60% are used and columns up to 100 cm in diameter are in operation (see below).

Reciprocating Sieve-Plate Column. Reciprocating sieve-plate columns, where the plate assembly is imparted a reciprocating motion, have also received attention (Karr and Lo, 1976); the reciprocation speed can be varied over a wide range, and a baffle plate can be employed to minimize axial mixing. Karr and Lo have discussed procedures for scale-up on the basis of data obtained from a column approximately 7.5 cm in diameter and have tested this with up to 90-cm-diameter columns. It appears that there is an optimal value of the reciprocation speed, at which the HETS value decreases and beyond the optimal value it increases. Further, the HETS value increases substantially with an increase in the column diameter [HETS $\propto$ (column diameter)$^{0.38}$], and for columns 90 cm in diameter we may have an HETS value of around 50 cm for a system like *o*-xylene–acetic acid–water.

Pulsed columns are generally not used when diameters are more than about 180 cm, since mechanical support problems arise and pulse generation becomes difficult. Moreover, uncertainties due to backmixing become important in such cases. Small pulsed columns have been successfully used for the extraction of metals from slurries (Warwick, 1973).

Vibrating-Plate Extractors. Instead of pulsed sieve-plate columns, vibrating-plate extractors have been suggested (Rod, 1976). Rod has reported results on the oximation of cyclohexanone and pointed out some advantages of this type of contactor.

14.2.2. Pipeline Contactors

Horizontal pipeline contactors offer a number of advantages, such as the simplicity of the apparatus, the wide range of flow rates that can be successfully handled, and relatively high values of the overall mass transfer coefficient. The various flow regimes that have been observed are essentially similar to those that have been observed in the corresponding gas–liquid contactors: drop, plug, stratified, wavy, annular, and dispersed (see Figure 14.2*k*). The range of flow rates that probably covers all the flow regimes for common liquids of moderate viscosities is from 3 to 120 cm/sec for both phases. The flow regime depends mainly on the ratio of the flow rates of the two phases, the viscosities of the phases, and the flow geometry. Unlike gas–liquid systems, here an additional factor associated with the density difference between the two phases also becomes important. It is usually necessary to have a unit for the separation of the two phases after the fluids come out of the contactor.

There is some information in the literature concerning the hydrodynamics of the system, but the data on mass transfer are scarce. Watkinson and Cavers (1967) have reported continuous-phase mass transfer coefficient values in the range of $5–15 \times 10^{-3}$ sec^{-1} for the dispersed flow regime for *n*-butanol–water (*n*-butanol is the continuous phase). Shah and Sharma (1971) have reported physical mass transfer coefficient values and effective interfacial area values for the drop and plug flow regimes for a variety of systems. The typical values of a are in the range of 0.5–4.5 cm^2/cm^3 for this regime for the system *n*-butyl formate–aqueous solutions. This type of contactor is likely to be satisfactory for a variety of reactions.

A considerable improvement in $k_L a$ and a values can be achieved by using coiled units, although at the expense of a higher pressure drop (Shah and Sharma, 1973). It has been claimed that for the manufacture of ethylenediamine by the reaction between ethylene dichloride and aqueous ammonia, a coil reactor can be advantageously used. Here, ethylenedichloride is sparingly soluble in the aqueous phase and the reaction is carried out under pressure (Zbigniew et al. 1967). For high-pressure operation smaller-diameter pipes require less thick metal. It appears that in some commercial designs of continuous nitrators for benzene, toluene, and the like a coil reactor is used.

A modified form of horizontal contactor that uses a bank of tubes has also been suggested [see Section 14.1.2(f), pipeline contactors]. Such a reactor has been recommended for the alkylation of xylenes with acetaldehyde in the presence of sulfuric acid (a two-phase system) to give dixylyl ethane (*Chem. Eng.*, 1956).

Static Mixer. It is possible to modify pipeline contactors by incorporating inside the pipe elements that will promote mixing and thus cause better dispersion (Figure 14.6*a*). For instance, the Kenics Corporation has a patented design called *Static Mixer* that consists of a series of helical elements—flat planes twisted 180°, aligned axially end to end, each at 90° angles to the preceding element, alternating right- and left-hand twists. It is claimed that such a unit can handle liquids of very high viscosities and that a narrow drop size distribution is obtained. This type of contactor may be useful for the manufacture of cyclohexanone oxime, which is made by the reaction between cyclohexanone and aqueous hydroxylamine sulfate. Static mixers should be useful for the removal of acidic substances in hydrocarbons with aqueous caustic soda solutions.

Fiber Film Contactor. Norris (1975) has suggested the use of cocurrent contactor that contains a bundle of long continuous small-diameter solid fibers (Figure 14.6*b*). The fiber material is selected to ensure wetting by the smaller-volume phase. Thus, effectively it becomes a film type of contactor and a large area of contact is established. In this type of contactor phase separation is quite easy. This kind of contactor has been successfully used for the removal of mercaptans from gasolines by treatment with aqueous caustic soda and can also be used for the extraction of COS from C_3 and other liquid streams.

14.2.3. Centrifugal Extractors

When liquids having a very small difference in densities and/or very low interfacial tension have to be handled, the use of gravity-operated contactors may become extremely difficult since such systems tend to form an emulsionlike dispersion that may take very long time to separate. This will drastically reduce the handling capacity of the equipment. Further, for some specific processes the operating conditions might demand a short residence time of the substance to avoid degradation of the desired species (e.g., the extraction of penicillin). In addition, in some cases both phases may be so viscous that gravity operation becomes quite difficult. Under these conditions centrifugal extractors (see Figure 14.7) have proven attractive. Here, the gravity force is replaced by a large centrifugal force that may be a few thousand times greater than the gravity force. The handling capacity of such equipment would be expected to be very large, and consequently the residence time of the sensitive substance can be kept low. Further, the inventory is also low, which may be an advantage for expensive substances. In addition, the floor-space requirements are relatively low. The Podbielniak extractor is a typical centrifugal extractor that is widely used. In some respects this unit can be referred to as a *rotating sieve-tray extractor*, since it contains a number of concentric sieve trays located around a horizontal axis through which the two liquid phases flow in a countercurrent pattern. Each extractor can provide three to five theoretical stages and throughputs of the order of 130,000 liters/hr can be handled. However, this extractor is not suitable for emulsions and requires that the density difference between the two phases be greater than 0.05 g/cm^3 (Reissinger and Schröter, 1978).

In the recovery of vanadium by a hydrometallurgical route, vanadic acid anion is extracted by a tertiary amine that is insoluble in water. In this case it is desirable to have a relatively short contact period between the two phases; otherwise, vanadic acid (a strong oxidizing agent) will attack the amine. The tertiary amines used for this extraction are very expensive and their losses must be kept to a minimum. Rosenbaum et al. (1971) have reported that centrifugal extractors are used for the foregoing operation. Centrifugal extractors have been considered for the treatment of waste liquors from nuclear energy systems.

Centrifugal extractors are rather expensive in capital as well as recurring costs as compared to other types of extractors. The maintenance of the equipment also requires close attention. It may be necessary to remove solid particles from the feed in order to minimize maintenance problems. Use of centrifugal extractors is therefore restricted to special operations.

14.3. GAS–LIQUID–SOLID CONTACTORS (SOLIDS AS REACTANTS)

Bubble columns, grid columns, and mechanically agitated contactors can satisfactorily handle gas–liquid systems involving solids (see Section 14.1.2). Some aspects of the selection of contactors where solid particles are used as a catalyst will be discussed in the next section (Section 14.4). In the case of bubble columns, the gas must be available at higher pressures, which must be at least equal to the ambient pressure plus the pressure drop through the absorption unit. For systems where a slow reaction that requires a long residence time for the liquid occurs, the mechanically agitated contactor appears to be very satisfactory.

When the gas and liquid flow rates are relatively high, then a horizontal pipeline contactor can also be employed. Typical examples are the aerobic treatment of wastewater containing suspended solids, delignification of pulp with O_2, and leaching of minerals.

When the pressure drop through the contactor is important and the reaction is reasonably fast, grid columns can be used. For small-diameter columns, a new type of contactor—the bowl and cone contactor developed by Kaji and Sharma (1969)—may be considered. As the name implies, this type of contactor consists of a series of bowl and cone cascades. The liquid coming from the top passes down over the inside surface of the cone and falls on the hemispherical bowl below. The liquid gets distributed over the outside surface of the bowl and falls on the inside surface of the section cone immediately beneath it.

In some cases, particularly hydrometallurgical operations, the solid is a reactant and its dissolution may be slow, and consequently the residence time of solid particles becomes important. It is also important to make sure that all the solid particles are kept in suspension. In some cases the solid particles have a high density although the particle size is relatively small ($\simeq$ 100 mesh). It thus becomes imperative to have either relatively high gas velocities in the case of the bubble column (which may require recirculation of the gas if the solute gas is expensive), or to use a mechanically agitated contactor. If because of the high system pressure it becomes necessary to use vessels with a high height-to-diameter ratio, then a number of agitators will be required (approximately one for a height equal to the diameter of the vessel).

In recent years, bubble columns containing

fluidized packings have gained importance. It is reported that in the paper industry, columns up to 3 m in diameter containing fluidized packings are used for the absorption of SO_2 [Douglas et al., 1963; Douglas, 1964; Chen and Douglas, 1969; Østergaard, 1977; see also Section 14.1.2(c)]. It is necessary to use packings that have a low density. Hollow polypropylene spheres, foamed polystyrene spheres, and hollow glass spheres are some of the materials that have been successfully used. This type of contactor involves relatively high superficial gas velocities (generally 200–600 cm/sec).

In some examples of industrial importance where reaction between a gas, a liquid, and a solid is involved, it may be advantageous to use a three-phase fluidized-bed reactor. Consider the example of the manufacture of calcium bisulfite by the reaction between SO_2, water, and calcium carbonate. In conventional practice a trickle-bed reactor is used (i.e., a column is packed with calcium carbonate particles, and water and SO_2 flow countercurrently. These towers are generally referred to as Jenssen towers). Jenssen towers suffer from a number of disadvantages associated with uneven distribution of the liquid, choking in the tower, a low production capacity per unit volume, and the like. Østergaard (1968) has reviewed the work in this field and considered the use of a fluidized-bed reactor. With finely divided calcium carbonate (25–30 mesh) particles, it was found that the mass transfer coefficient values in the fluidized-bed reactor were about 25 times higher than in the fixed-bed reactor.

Volpicelli and Massimilla (1970) have pointed out that Jenssen towers may be unsuitable for poor-quality limestones, which contain a fairly high percentage of inerts and are friable. They have suggested the use of a three-phase bubble-fluidized bed. Here the superficial velocity of the gas will have to be greater than 50 cm/sec. Their experimental data show that the suggested type of contactor can be successfully used, and that rates of limestone dissolution per unit volume of the contactor are about two orders of magnitude greater than those obtained in the Jenssen tower. However, in the bubble-agitated fluidized-bed contactor the SO_2 recoveries are not comparable to those realized in Jenssen towers, primarily because of extensive backmixing in the liquid phase.

It is likely that in certain circumstances aqueous slurries containing a fairly high percentage of solids, and sometimes exhibiting thixotropic behavior, can be conveniently and advantageously contacted with a gas in vortex-type (cyclo reactor) scrubbers. A number of variations in the design are possible (see Figure 14.2*l*; Gopal and Sharma, 1980). It has been claimed that the oxidation of black liquor (obtained in the kraft process for making pulp), which may contain up to 65% solids and which at higher levels of solids concentrations exhibits a pronounced thixotropic effect, can be advantageously treated with air in the vortex scrubbers (the reaction is $2Na_2S + 2O_2 + H_2O \rightarrow Na_2S_2O_3 + 2NaOH$). Another related situation where vortex scrubbers are likely to be attractive is the chlorination of certain types of pulps.

The utility of conventional and new designs of spray absorbers, where slurries are used as the absorbent, was brought out in Section 14.1.3.

Venturi scrubbers have been recommended for the absorption of very dilute SO_2 in aqueous suspensions of MgO. A very large quantity of such a gas comes out of power stations using fuels containing sulfur and from sulfuric acid plants, and because of air pollution laws it is becoming increasingly important to reduce SO_2 content to less than 250 ppm (Kerr, 1974; see Section 14.1.3).

In the treatment of wastewater by the activated sludge process, the system contains solid particles and the air pressure drop is important. A variety of sparged contactors have been considered for such operations (also see Section 14.1.5).

14.4. GAS–LIQUID–SOLID CONTACTORS (SOLIDS AS CATALYSTS)

It can be seen from Chapter 13 and Table 1.7, which gives examples of industrial importance where solid particles are used as catalyst in gas–liquid reactors, that the hydrogenation and hydrocracking of organic compounds are by far the most important reactions in this category; we shall therefore confine our attention essentially to hydrogenation reactions. The rates of hydrogenation of a majority of substances over conventional catalysts are usually low, and hence semibatch reactors are used for these hydrogenations. In some specific cases where the hydrogenation reaction is reasonably fast (e.g., the hydrogenation of some unsaturated fats, Fischer–Tropsch reactions) and where the scale of operation is rather large, continuous multistage slurry reactors are employed. Likewise, continuous trickle-bed reactors are also employed [e.g., in the hydrogenation of butynediol to butenediol, BIOS 367 (1945)]. Albright (1973) has reported that in the case of the hydrogenation of unsaturated fats a saving of about 9–13¢ (American currency) per kilogram of hydrogenated oil may be realized for a plant having a capacity of about 45,000 ton/yr. It is important to ensure that the mixing of the liquid phase is such that no polyunsaturated fat leaves the hydrogenator unreacted. It appears that a number of continuous units for the partial and complete hydrogenation of unsaturated fats are now in operation. An important advantage of continuous reactors is that a substantial part of the heat required for preheating the oil can be recovered from the hot oil leaving the reactor through a heat exchanger. Probably the most important advantage is that with a constant feedstock, product with more constant characteristics can be obtained than in batch operation. It is likely that with a proper choice of operating variables hydrogenated fats having more desirable properties can be obtained in continuous hydrogenators. Multistage contactors of various designs are used in practice (see Albright, 1973).

The main disadvantage of a continuous unit is that it is rather inflexible. A changeover to a different feedstock or a different end product would require approximately three times the residence time in the system, and during this period material of off-standard specifications will be obtained. Further, because of a residence time distribution in the continuous reactor, selectivity will be lowered (Coenen, 1976).

In the case of slurry reactors, bubble columns (gas sparged), mechanically agitated contactors, and jet-loop systems can be used. (The relevant details of these contactors have been covered in Section 14.1.2.) In the case of bubble columns a high flow rate of hydrogen will have to be maintained in order to keep the solid particles completely suspended and to maintain a uniform concentration of catalyst throughout the column; Hammer (1979) has considered this problem. Since the hydrogen consumption is low, it will become necessary, for economic reasons, to recirculate the hydrogen gas. By contrast, in the case of mechanically agitated contactors we can work with very low flow rates of H_2 and in fact hydrogenation can be conducted in a "dead-end hydrogenator" where hydrogen is introduced at a rate commensurate with its consumption provided no volatile product is formed. The agitation characteristics can be further improved by using the gas-inducing type of agitator [see Section 14.1.2(b)]. However, the usefulness of gas-inducing agitators may not be attractive for very large-scale units, since gas induction then becomes difficult because of the high hydrostatic head of the liquid. In some designs two stirrers, one above the other, are employed; the upper one is located just below the surface and sucks the gas by producing small vortices, and the gas is drawn into the bulk liquid through the second stirrer. If desired, gas from the top of the vessel can be recycled to the bottom through an external circulation pump system. The makeup required can be supplied in the loop. For large-scale operation under pressure, problems of sealing of the stirrer shaft and catalyst attrition might arise in mechanically agitated slurry reactors, and in such cases it may be advantageous to employ gas-sparged slurry reactors. van Goolen (1976) has recommended the use of gas-sparged slurry reactors for the large-scale manufacture of hydroxylamine phosphate by the hydrogenation of an ammonium nitrate solution in the presence of a noble metal (Pd) on carbon catalyst (see Example 4 in Section 13.1.8).

Lemcoff and Jameson (1975a, b) have brought out the advantages of employing a vibrating slurry reactor, which in principle works like a resonant bubble column [see Section 14.1.2(c)]. Because of bubble cycling the k_{SL} value can increase by as much as a factor of 10 compared to the values realized in mechanically agitated contactors at the same levels of energy input per unit volume.

Waller (1970) has described a new type of contactor that can perhaps be categorized as a sectionalized bubble column containing suspended catalyst particles in each section. The unit may be operated cocurrently and the liquid rate may be sufficient to keep the catalyst particles in suspension. The catalyst particles do not move from one section to other, and in view of this design feature, different catalyst particles can be used in various sections. Further, in each section an additional amount of gas can be introduced. If exothermic reactions are involved, then cold feed may be introduced in various section. Alternatively, cooling coils can be provided in each section. The design can be made sufficiently flexible to remove a part of the catalyst for regeneration or replacement. It is claimed by Waller (Shell International Research) that this type of contactor is likely to be useful for the hydrogenation of unsaturated fats, and the hydrodesulfurization, hydrodenitrogenation, and hydrocracking of petroleum fractions, and the like.

Pruden and Weber (1970) have suggested that a transport reactor, where the catalyst–gas–liquid mixture is conveyed through the reactor, may be employed in order to avoid the problems associated with the recirculation of the gas in the case of bubble columns. Here the solid particles would be kept in suspension by the conveying action. The liquid superficial velocity can be of the order of 4 cm/sec. Further work is necessary before a recommendation can be made about this type of reactor.

The gas-sparged reactor can be modified to have a downcomer so that the liquid and gas are carried upward with the catalyst and this mixture returns through the downcomer. (In principle this unit is equivalent to a draft-tube gas-sparged reactor; Kürten and Zehner, 1979).

In gas-sparged upflow reactors it should be possible to use an internal pump in the reactor with the desired liquid recirculation rate. Here also the catalyst in the reactor can be withdrawn and fresh catalyst can be introduced. Because of the high liquid recirculation rates temperature can be controlled very well.

In principle, the solid particles can be kept in suspension by using an external pump. It appears that in the French process (IFP process) for the hydrogenation of benzene to cyclohexane, in the presence of nickel catalyst, an external pump is used (Dufau et al., 1964). Similarly, in the IFP's process for the total hydrogenation of unsaturated liquid hydrocarbons obtained in the steam cracking of naphtha the heat removal is accomplished by pumping the reaction medium through a heat exchanger. It would be desirable to fit the circulation pump at the highest point of the circuit, which implies that the slip ring seal would be located in the gas space, thereby eliminating problems associated with the solids.

In some hydrogenation reactions the heat load may be relatively high, and even a mechanically agitated contactor might not be adequate. In such cases we may consider tubular reactors, where the material to be hydrogenated, along with the suspended catalyst particles (which should be of relatively fine size), flows inside the tube and the heat transfer medium is circulated on the jacket side (Figure 14.8). Hodossy (1968) and Haidegger et al. (1971) have reported the use of this reactor for the hydrogenation of furfural. However, it is likely that by using an external pump and a shell-and-tube exchanger we can accommodate high heat loads in mechanically agitated contactors. Multitubular reactors with catalyst in the form of particles packed in the tubes, have also been considered (e.g., reaction between isobutylene and methanol to give methyl *tert*-butyl ether; *Chem. Eng.*, 1979; Figure 14.9).

Alternatively, a loop reactor consisting of the reactor, pump, and mixing nozzle can be employed. A self-priming injector nozzle is employed, and therefore the hydrogen gas in the upper part of the reactor is dispersed automatically as a result of the energy of the propulsion liquid. Only makeup has to be introduced into the reactor in the head space (Figure 14.10). It has been claimed that this type of reactor should be very useful for carrying out a variety of reactions where H_2 is used, including those where a selectivity problem is encountered (Leuteritz, 1973; Leuteritz et al., 1976; Kürten and Zehner, 1979). Loop reactors have also been suggested for situations where powdered ion-exchange resins are used as a catalyst (Martinola, 1980). An external heat exchanger is used and the reactor can also be provided

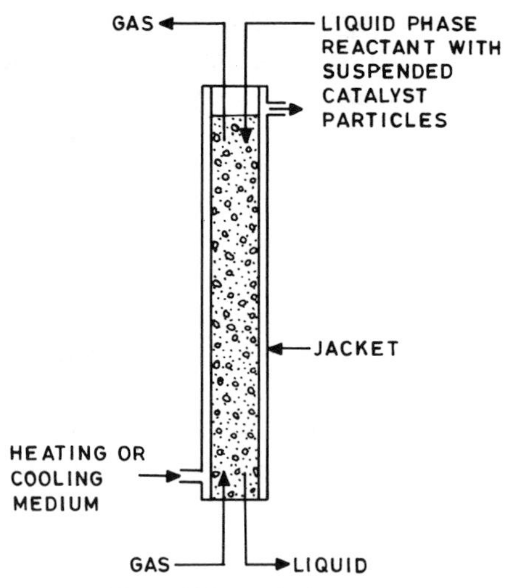

Figure 14.8. Tubular reactor.

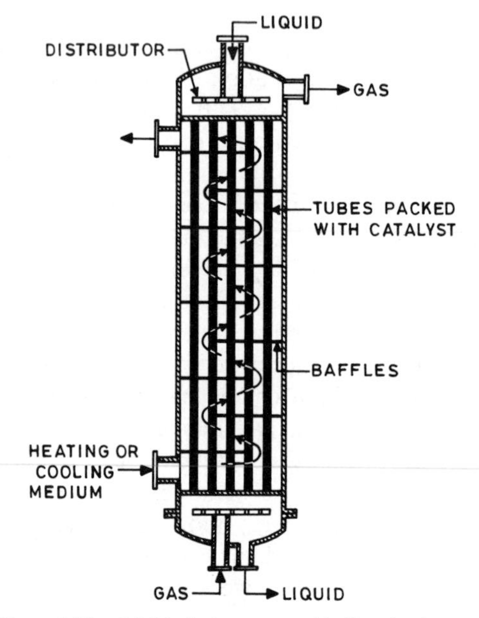

Figure 14.9. Multitubular reactor (shell-and-tube type).

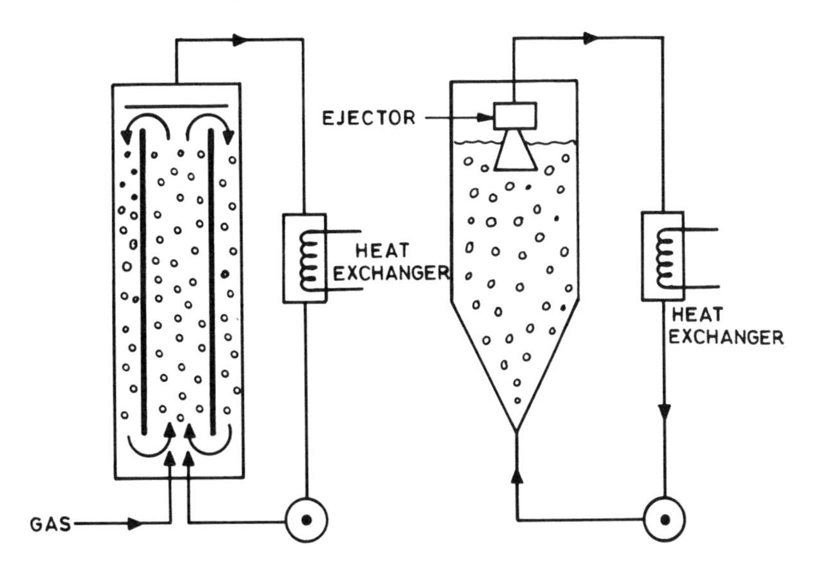

Figure 14.10. Jet-loop reactor: (*a*) Self-aeration; (*b*) pressure aeration.

with a Limpet coil. The handling capacity of the recirculating pump is relatively high, and a large increase in the pressure is required (Figure 14.10*a*). These duties cannot be satisfactorily provided by propeller pumps. Kürten and Zehner (1979) have discussed the hydrodynamic aspects of loop reactors. A special pump having a double mechanical seal and that can withstand slurries has to be employed. Figure 14.10*b* shows a pressure-aerated jet-loop reactor.

Slurry reactors offer a number of advantages over trickle-bed (fixed-bed) reactors (Sherwood and Farkas, 1966; Kürten and Zehner, 1979).

1. Since the reactor contents are well mixed, a uniform temperature can be maintained. By contrast, in trickle-bed reactors, which are operated adiabatically, temperature may vary substantially and hot spots may be encountered.
2. The removal of heat can be easily ensured because of the high heat transfer coefficient values offered by such reactors. Further, the presence of a large amount of liquid provides a built-in capacity for preventing wide fluctuations in the temperature.
3. In general, powdered catalysts are cheaper than pelleted catalysts. Further, the internal diffusional resistance is likely to be absent in slurry reactors (i.e., the effectiveness factor is unity). By contrast, in the trickle-bed reactor the effectiveness factor may be 0.1–0.2 for common sizes of pellets. In addition, the catalyst can be easily regenerated by continuous withdrawal of a slip-stream.
4. In many applications the pressure can be considerably reduced—by as much as an order of magnitude compared to the trickle-bed reactor.

The main disadvantage of the slurry reactor involves the filtration of the catalyst from the product stream. The filtration may prove to be unsatisfactory in some cases and in other cases may result in the loss of valuable materials, particularly when the catalyst is based on noble metals. For mechanically agitated slurry reactors we may face abrasion and erosion in the impeller. Further, for a very large-scale operation, for a reaction carried out under pressure slurry reactors may prove very expensive. Typical examples are the hydrodesulfurization and hydrotreating of petroleum fractions, where units with a capacity of the order of 1 million tonne/year are in operation. For these types of reactions where the scale of operation is very large and the hydrogen consumption relatively low, trickle-bed reactors are ideally suited. Here, there is no problem associated with the filtration of the catalyst. Further, the backmixing in the gas and liquid phases is limited and the performance of the reactor is practically independent of the hydrogen flow rate in the lower range of H_2 flow rates. (In the slurry reactor the liquid phase is backmixed and the gas phase may also be substantially backmixed.) Actually, a nearly stoichiometric amount of the gas may be employed in some cases, which will also avoid expensive recirculation of the gas. In addition, the ratio of the amount of the catalyst to that of the liquid reactant present in the reactor is very high as compared to the slurry reactor, and hence higher reaction rates should be realized in trickle-bed reactors. This implies that the size of the reactor will be smaller in the case of trickle-bed reactors than in slurry reactors. Thus, for high-pressure applications, trickle-bed reactors should prove more attractive. Further, if the liquid-phase reactant has a finite vapor pressure at the operating temperature, and where the catalyst pellets are not completely wet, then a substantial part of the reaction may occur on the dry portions of the catalysts and thus the overall rate per unit amount of the catalyst will increase.

When expensive catalysts are employed, such as those based on Pd, Pt, and the like, and the controlling resistance is due to gas–liquid or solid–liquid mass transfer, then a considerable saving in catalyst inventory cost can be realized by replacing active catalyst particles with inactive catalyst support particles. Further, if the wetting characteristics of the original support particles are poor, then inactive catalyst particles of the same external dimensions, but of a material that withstands the operating conditions and is more wettable, should be used. This will result in an improvement in the performance of the reactor, since better liquid distribution will be realized, giving higher $k_L a$ and $k_{SL} a$ values (Enright and Chuang, 1978).

In some cases cocurrent upflow trickle-bed reactors may show superior performance compared to downflow reactors. Ternan and Whalley (1976) have cited some work on the hydrodesulfurization and hydrodenitrogenation of high-boiling-point hydrocarbon feedstocks where it was found that upflow reactors were superior to downflow reactors. This difference is caused by the higher-boiling-point components in upflow reactors having a longer residence time as compared to downflow reactors under otherwise comparable conditions. In the case of the upflow reactor the low-boiling-point compounds vaporize and flow up through the catalyst particles quickly with hydrogen. Montagna and Shah (1975) have studied the removal of vanadium and sulfur from residual oil in a cocurrent downflow and a cocurrent upflow reactor. These authors found significant improvements in the removal of vanadium and sulfur in upflow reactors compared to downflow reactors. We have already emphasized that the flow regime can change greatly when we change over from downflow to upflow reactors under otherwise similar conditions. At lower liquid flow rates the upflow reactor will operate essentially as a packed bubble column reactor, and this will be expected to give higher $k_L a$ values. Further, a liquid-filled bed will largely eliminate the liquid maldistribution that may occur in downflow trickle-bed operation.

A recent development in the design of trickle-bed reactors consists of the gradual replacement of catalyst by introducing fresh catalyst at the top and withdrawing used catalyst at the bottom. This type of reactor has been referred to as the *Bunker flow reactor* (Weekman, 1976).

The main limitation of trickle-bed reactors is that the liquid residence time is low, and hence the reaction must be reasonably fast to be handled in these units. Further, if the catalyst is not properly wetted and the reaction is highly exothermic, then hot spots may develop, leading to undesirable effects. In the specific case of the hydrogenation of unsaturated fats the trickle-bed reactor with a pelleted catalyst is not likely to be useful. It was pointed out in Example 2, Section 13.1.8, that the transport of bulky triglyceride into the pores of the catalyst may affect the selectivity adversely. In pelleted catalysts pore diffusional factors are expected to be much more important than with the powdered catalysts used in slurry reactors, and hence the selectivity will be poor in the former case (Coenen, 1976).

The temperature in trickle-bed reactors can be controlled to a considerable extent by the recirculation of the gas and/or liquid product after cooling outside the reactor. In some specific cases where a large excess of gas is desirable (e.g., H_2 in hydrocracking) then the recycling of gas becomes attractive. In some cases it may be possible to control the temperature by the evaporation of liquid provided the liquid has a reasonably good value of vapor pressure at the temperature of operation. This is particularly attractive in the case of aqueous solutions in view of the high value of the heat of vaporization of water.

There is scope for optimization of trickle-bed reactors when a nonvolatile intermediate liquid quench is used to control the temperature of the reactors. Shah et al. (1976) have reported a dynamic analysis of a hydrodesulfurization reactor with varying catalyst activity. For a given set of reactor conditions, the decline in catalyst activity is counterbalanced by an increase in the inlet temperature required to maintain the desired desulfurization level. Proper location of the quench is shown to result in a maximum cycle life. The cycle life has been determined when the temperature anywhere in the reactor exceeds a certain value.

In some special cases a three-phase fluidized-bed reactor may merit consideration [see Sections 14.3 and 14.1.2(c)]. Consider the case of the conversion of a mixture of CO and H_2 to methanol where normally a fixed-bed reactor is employed. A suggestion has also been made for the use of a fluidized-bed reactor. Sherwin and Frank (1976) have pointed out the advantages of using a three-phase fluidized-bed reactor for this reaction. Here the phase separation between solid, liquid, and vapor occurs at the top so that the catalyst remains in the reactor and the problems associated with the separation of catalyst particles do not arise. Because of excellent temperature control, higher conversions per pass can be realized compared to fixed-bed reactors, since in this case thermodynamic limitations are severe and conversion decreases with an increase in temperature. In this case the liquid hydrocarbon medium acts as a heat sink, and since the methanol is immiscible with the hydrocarbon, separation of the methanol becomes very simple. In this type of reactor attrition of the catalyst particles is expected to be much less than in the case of the gas-phase fluidized-bed reactor. Further, the extent of backmixing in the gas phase will be smaller in the three-phase fluidized-bed reactor than in the gas-phase fluidized-bed reactor. Sherwin and Frank have claimed that the three-phase reactor system is more attractive than the conventional process when overall energy consumption is taken as the basis.

Recently van Landeghem (1980) has considered salient features of different types of multiphase reactors (gas–liquid, liquid–liquid, and gas–liquid–solid reactors).

REFERENCES

Albright, L. F. (1966), *Chem. Eng.*, **73**(18), 119.

Albright, L. F. (1973), *J. Am. Oil Chem. Soc.*, **50**, 255.

Albright, L. F., and Hanson, C. (1969), *Loss Prev.*, **3**, 26.

Andou, K., Hara, H., and Endoh, K. (1971), *Kagaku Kogaku*, **35**, 1379.

Ashbrook Corporation, Texas, Bulletin on Kinetic Reactor.

Astarita, G., and Marrucci, G. (1974), *Principles of Non-Newtonian Fluid Mechanics*, McGraw-Hill, New York.

Baird, M. H. I., and Garstang, J. H. (1967), *Chem. Eng. Sci.*, **22**, 1663.

Baird, M. H. I., and Garstang, J. H. (1972), *Chem. Eng. Sci.*, **27**, 823.

Baird, M. H. I., Glovne, A. R., and Meghani, M. A. N. (1968), *Can. J. Chem. Eng.*, **46**, 249.

Banerjee, S., Scott, D. S., and Rhodes, E. (1970), *Can. J. Chem. Eng.*, **48**, 542.

Beenackers, A. A. C. M., and van Swaaij, W. P. M. (1976), *Proc. 4th Intern./6th European Symp. Chem. React. Eng.*, p. 260.

Bender, E., Berger, R., Leuckel, W., and Wolf, D. (1979), *Chem. Ing.-Tech.*, **51**, 192.

Bibaud, R. E., and Treybal, R. E. (1966), *AIChE J.*, **12**, 472.

Billet, R. (1969), *J. Chem. Eng. Japan*, **2**, 107.

Billet, R., Machowiak, J., and Suder, S. (1978), *Ger. Chem. Eng.*, **1**, 226.

Blyakher, I. G., Zhivaikin, L. Ya., and Yurovskaya, N. A. (1967), *Int. Chem. Eng.*, **7**, 485.

Boerma, H., and Lankester, J. H. (1968), *Chem. Eng. Sci.*, **23**, 799.

Bolles, W. L. (1976), *AIChE J.*, **22**, 153.

Bomio, P. (1977), *Chem. Ing.-Tech.*, **49**, 895.

Bomio, P. (1979), *Sulzer Tech. Rev.*, **61**(2), 62.

Brandt, H. W., Reissinger, K.-H., and Schröter, J. (1978), *Chem. Ing.- Tech.*, **50**, 345.

Brauer, H., and Sucker, D. (1979), *Ger. Chem. Eng.*, **2**, 77.

BIOS Final Rept. No. 367, Manufacture of 1,4-Butynediol at I. G. Ludwigshafen (1945).

Buley, V. F. (1973), *Tappi*, **56**(7), 101.

Burgess, J. M., Molloy, N. A., and McCarthy, M. J. (1972), *Chem. Eng. Sci.*, **27**, 442.

Cannon, M. R. (1961), *Ind. Eng. Chem.*, **53**, 629.

Carleton, A. J., Flain, R. J., Rennie, J., and Valentin, F. H. H. (1967), *Chem. Eng. Sci.*, **22**, 1839.

Characklis, W. G., and Busch, A. W. (1972), *Chem. Eng.*, **79**(10), 61.

Chem. Eng. (1956), **63**(9), 118.

Chem. Eng. (1977), **84**(24), 65.

Chem. Eng. (1979), **86**(8), 73.

Chem. Process Eng., (1970), **51**(6), 139.

Chem. Pro Equipment Corporation, Bulletin 700 on Saddelox Tower Packing, Fairfield, New Jersey.

Chen, B. H., and Douglas, W. J. M. (1968), *Can. J. Chem. Eng.*, **46**, 245.

Chen, B. H., and Douglas, W. J. M. (1969), *Can. J. Chem. Eng.*, **47**, 113.

Coenen, J. W. E. (1976), *J. Am. Oil Chem. Soc.*, **53**, 382.

Collins, T. T. (1962), *Paper Trade J.*, **146**(July 23), 39.

Cooper, H. B. H., Jr., and Rossano, A. T., Jr. (1973), *Tappi*, **56**(6), 100.

Danckwerts, P. V. (1970), *Gas–Liquid Reactions*, McGraw-Hill, New York.

Danckwerts, P. V., and Sharma, M. M. (1966), *Chem. Eng., Inst. Chem. Eng.*, No. 202, CE244.

Danckwerts, P. V., and Rizvi, S. F. (1971), *Trans. Inst. Chem. Eng.*, **49**, 124.

Darsi, C. R., and Feick, J. E. (1971), *Can. J. Chem. Eng.*, **49**, 95, 101.

Deckwer, W. D. (1976a), *J. Chem. Eng. Data*, **21**, 176.

Deckwer, W. D. (1976b), *Chem. Eng. Sci.*, **31**, 309.

Deckwer, W. D. (1977a), *Chem. Eng. Sci.*, **32**, 51.

Deckwer, W. D. (1977b), *Chem. Ing.-Tech.*, **49**, 213.

Delnicki, W. V., and Wagner, J. L. (1970), *Chem. Eng. Prog.*, **66**(3), 50.

Dodds, W. S., Stutzman, L. F., Sollami, B. J., and McCarter, R. J. (1960), *AIChE J.*, **6**, 390.

Donders, A. J. M., Wijffels, J. B., and Rietema, K. (1968), *Proc. 4th European Symp. Chem. React. Eng.* p. 159 (Suppl. to *Chem. Eng. Sci.*).

Douglas, W. J. M. (1964), *Chem. Eng. Prog.*, **60**(7), 66.

Douglas, H. R., Snider, I. W. A., and Tomlinson, G. H. (1963), *Chem. Eng. Prog.*, **59**(12), 85.

Dufau, F. A., Eschard, F., Haddad, A. C., and Thonon, C. H. (1964), *Chem. Eng. Prog.*, **60**(9), 43.

Eckert, J. S. (1970), *Chem. Eng. Prog.*, **66**(3), 39.

Eckert, J. S. (1976), *Hydrocarbon Process. Petrol. Refiner*, **72**(3), 117.

Edwards, W. M., and Huang, P. (1977), *Chem. Eng. Prog.*, **73**(8), 64.

Enright, J. T., and Chuang, T. T. (1978), *Can. J. Chem. Eng.*, **56**, 246.

Fell, C. J. D., and Pinczewski, W. V. (1977), *Chem. Eng. (London)*, No. 316, 45.

Fernandes, J. B., and Sharma, M. M. (1968), *Chem. Eng. Sci.*, **23**, 9.

Fischer, R. (1965), *Chem. Eng.*, **72**(19), 186.

Frank, J. C., Geyer, G. R., and Kehde, H. (1969), *Chem. Eng. Prog.*, **65**(2), 79.

Fukushima, S., and Kusaka, K. (1977a), *J. Chem. Eng. Japan*, **10**, 461.

Fukushima, S., and Kusaka, K. (1977b), *J. Chem. Eng. Japan*, **10**, 468.

Galeano, S. F., and Amsden, C. D. (1970), *Tappi*, **53**(11), 2142.

Gerstenberg, H. (1979), *Chem. Ing.-Tech.*, **51**, 208.

Gianetto, A., Baldi, G., and Specchia, V. (1970), *Ing. Chim. Ital.*, **6**, 125.

Gianetto, A., Specehia, V., and Baldi, G. (1973), *AIChE J.*, **19**, 916.

Gopal, J. S., and Sharma, M. M. (1980), *Can. J. Chem. Eng.*, **58**, 538.

Haidegger, E., Hodossy, L., Kriza, D., and Peter, I. (1971), *Chem. Process Eng.*, **52**(8), 39.

Hammer, H. (1979), *Chem. Ing.-Tech.*, **51**, 295.

Haug, H. F. (1976), *Chem. Eng. Sci.*, **31**, 295.

Hayashi, Y., Hirai, E., and Higashi, S. (1978), *J. Chem. Eng. Japan*, **11**, 270.

Herbrechtsmeier, P., and Steiner, R. (1978), *Chem. Ing.-Tech.*, **50**, 944.

Heuss, J. M., King, G. G., and Wilke, C. R. (1965), *AIChE J.*, **11**, 866.

Hochman, J. M., and Effron, E. (1969), *Ind. Eng. Chem. Fundam.*, **8**, 63.

Hodossy, L. (1968), *Brit. Chem. Eng.*, **13**, 1277.

Hon, H. C. (1977), Studies in Mass Transfer: Mass Transfer Characteristics of Venturi Scrubbers, Vortex Reactors and Packed Columns Operated Concurrently, Ph.D. thesis, University of Bombay.

Houlihan, R., and Landau, J. (1974), *Can. J. Chem. Eng.*, **52**, 758.

Huber, M., and Meier, W. (1975), *Sulzer Tech. Rev.*, **1**, 1.

Jeffreys, G. V., and Mumford, C. J. (1974), *Process Eng.*, **11**, 73.

Jeffreys, G. V., Jenson, V. G., and Miles, F. R. (1961), *Trans. Inst. Chem. Eng.*, **39**, 389.

Jepsen, J. C. (1970), *AIChE J.*, **16**, 705.

Joshi, J. B. (1980), *Trans. Inst. Chem. Eng.*, **58**, 155.

Joshi, J. B., and Sharma, M. M. (1976a), *Trans. Inst. Chem. Eng.*, **54**, 42.

Joshi, J. B., and Sharma, M. M. (1976b), *Can. J. Chem. Eng.*, **54**, 560.

Joshi, J. B., and Sharma, M. M. (1977), *Can. J. Chem. Eng.*, **55**, 683.

Joshi, J. B., and Sharma, M. M. (1978), *Can. J. Chem. Eng.*, **56**, 116.

Joshi, J. B., and Sharma, M. M. (1979a), *Can. J. Chem. Eng.*, **57**, 375.

Joshi, J. B., and Sharma, M. M. (1979b), *Trans. Inst. Chem. Eng.*, **57**, 244.

Joshi, J. B., Pandit, A. B., and Sharma, M. M. (1982), *Chem. Eng Sci.*, **37**, 813.

Joshi, J. B., Sharma, M. M., Shah, Y. T., Singh, C. P. P., Ally, M., and Klinzing, G. E. (1980), *Chem. Eng. Commun.*, **6**, 257.

Juvekar, V. A. (1976), Studies in Mass Transfer in Gas–Liquid and Gas–Liquid–Solid Systems, Ph.D. (Tech.) thesis, University of Bombay.

Juvekar, V. A., and Sharma, M. M. (1973), *Chem. Eng. Sci.*, **28**, 825.

Kaji, A. T. (1971), Studies in Mass Transfer: Rod Plate without Downcomer, Sectionalized Bubble Column and Bowl and Cone Contactor, Ph.D. (Tech.) thesis, University of Bombay.

Kaji, A. T., and Sharma, M. M. (1969), *Brit. Chem. Eng.*, **14**, 1416.

Karr, A. E., and Lo, T. C. (1976), *Chem. Eng. Prog.*, **72**(11), 68.

Kats, M. B., and Genin, L. S. (1967), *Int. Chem. Eng.*, **7**, 246.

Kenics Corporation Bulletin KB471, 1 South Side Road, Danvers, Massachusetts.

Kerr, C. P. (1974), *Ind. Eng. Chem. Process Design Dev.*, **13**, 222.

Kitai, A., and Ozaki, A. (1969), *J. Ferment. Technol. (Japan)*, **47**, 527.

Kitai, A., Goto, S., and Ozaki, A. (1969), *J. Ferment. Technol. (Japan)*, **47**, 340.

Kitu, M., Shimada, M., Sakai, T., Sugiyama, S., and Wen, C. Y. (1976), in Keairns, D. L. (Ed.), *Fluidization Technology* (Proc. Int. Fluidization Cong., June 1975), Vol. 1, Hemisphere, Washington, D.C., p. 411.

Koch Engineering Co., Flexipac, Bulletin KFP-1, North Wichita, Kansas.

Kolev, N. (1974), *Verfahrenstechnik*, **8**, 145.

Komiyama, H., and Smith, J. M. (1975), *AIChE J.*, **21**, 664; 670.

Kubota, H., Hosono, Y., and Fujie, K. (1978), *J. Chem. Eng. Japan*, **11**(4), 319.

Kürten, H., and Zehner, P. (1979), *Ger. Chem. Eng.*, **2**, 220.

Laddha, G. S., and Degaleesan, T. E. (1976), *Transport Phenomena in Liquid Extraction*, Tata McGraw-Hill, New Delhi.

Laddha, G. S., Degaleesan, T. E., and Kannappan, R. (1978), *Can. J. Chem. Eng.*, **56**, 137.

Lamont, J. C., and Scott, D. S. (1966), *Can. J. Chem. Eng.*, **44**, 201.

Landau, J., and Houlihan, R. (1974), *Can. J. Chem. Eng.*, **52**, 338.

Leday, A., Marsan, A. A., and Coupal, B. (1974), *Biotechnol. Bioeng.*, **16**, 61.

Lemcoff, N. O., and Jameson, G. J. (1975a), *Chem. Eng. Sci.*, **30**, 363.

Lemcoff, N. O., and Jameson, G. J. (1975b), *AIChE J.*, **21**, 730.

Leuteritz, G. M. (1973), *Process Eng.*, No. 12, 62.

Leuteritz, G. M., Reimann, P., and Vergeres, P. (1976), *Hydrocarbon Process. Petrol. Refiner*, **55**(6), 99.

Levenspiel, O. (1967), *Chemical Reaction Engineering*, 2nd ed., Wiley, New York.

Linek, V., Soty, V., Machon, V., and Krivsky, Z. (1974), *Chem. Eng. Sci.*, **29**, 1955.

Linek, V., Krivsky, Z., and Hudec, P. (1977), *Chem. Eng. Sci.*, **32**, 323.

Loucaides, R., and McManamey, W. J. (1973), *Chem. Eng. Sci.*, **28**, 2165.

Mahajani, V. V., and Sharma, M. M. (1979), *Chem. Eng. Sci.*, **34**, 1425.

Mahajani, V. V., and Sharma, M. M. (1980), *Chem. Eng. Sci.*, **35**, 941.

Marr, R. (1978), *Chem. Ing.-Tech.*, **50**, 337.

Martin, G. Q. (1972), *Ind. Eng. Chem. Process Design Dev.*, **11**, 397.

Martinola, F. (1980), *Ger. Chem. Eng.*, **3**, 79.

Mashelkar, R. A. (1970), *Brit. Chem. Eng.*, **15**, 1297.

Mashelkar, R. A. (1976), *Chem. Ind. Dev.*, **10**(9), 17.

Mashelkar, R. A., Sharma, M. M. (1970), *Trans. Inst. Chem. Eng.*, **48**, T162.

Mass Transfer Ltd. (124 Highgate, Kendal, England), Bulletin on Cascade Mini-Rings.

Mehta, K. C. (1970), Mass Transfer and/or Heat Transfer in Columns, Ph.D. (Tech.) thesis, University of Bombay.

Mehta, K. C., and Sharma, M. M. (1970), *Brit. Chem. Eng.*, **15**, 1440, 1556.

Mehta, V. D., and Sharma, M. M. (1971), *Chem. Eng. Sci.*, **26**, 461.

Mersmann, A. (1977), *Chem. Ing.-Tech.*, **49**, 679.

Montagna, A. A., and Shah, Y. T. (1975), *Ind. Eng. Chem. Process Design Dev.*, **14**, 479.

Mumford, C. J., and Thomas, R. J. (1972), *Process Eng.*, **12**, 54, 57.

Murakami, Y., Fujimato, K., Kakimoto, K., and Sekiho, M. (1972), *J. Chem. Eng. Japan*, **5**, 257.

Murray, F. E. (1968), *Pulp Paper Mag. Can.*, **69**(January 5), 3.

Mützenburg, A. B. (1965), *Chem. Eng.*, **72**(19), 175.

Mützenburg, A. B., and Giger, A. (1968), *Trans. Inst. Chem. Eng.*, **46**, T187.

Nagel, O., Hegner, B., and Kürten, H. (1978), *Chem. Ing.-Tech.*, **50**, 934.

Nagel, O., Kürten, H., and Sinn, R. (1972), *Chem. Ing.-Tech.*, **44**, 367.

Nemunaitis, R. R., Eckert, J. S., Foote, E. H., and Rollison, L. R. (1971), *Chem. Eng. Prog.*, **7**(11), 60.

Norris, B. E. (1975), *Hydrocarbon Process. Petrol. Refiner* **54**(9), 127.

Oldshue, J. Y., and Rushton, J. H. (1952), *Chem. Eng. Prog.*, **48**, 297.

Olney, R. B. (1964), *AIChE J.*, **10**, 827.

Østergaard, K. (1968), *Adv. Chem. Eng.*, **7**, 71.

Østergaard, K. (1977), Three-phase Fluidization Studies of Hold-up Mass Transfer, and Mixing, Chemical Engineering with Per Sol'toft, Tekniskforlag a-5, Copenhagen, Denmark, p. 119.

Patil, V. K., and Sharma, M. M. (1981), *Can. J. Chem. Eng.*, **59**, 606.

Perez, J. F., and Sandall, O. C. (1974), *AIChE J.*, **20**, 770.

Pilhofer, Th. (1979), *Chem. Ing.-Tech.*, **51**, 231.

Pruden, B. B., and Weber, M. E. (1970), *Can. J. Chem. Eng.*, **48**, 162.

Puranik, S. A., and Sharma, M. M. (1970a), *Indian Chem. Eng. (Trans.)*, **12**, 49.

Puranik, S. A., and Sharma, M. M. (1970b), *Chem. Eng. Sci.*, **25**, 257.

Ravetkar, D. D., and Kale, D. D. (1981), *Chem. Eng. Sci.*, **36**, 399.

Raymond, B. (1978), *Chem. Eng. Sci.*, **33**, 1157.

Reiss, L. P. (1967), *Ind. Eng. Chem. Process Design Dev.*, **6**, 486.

Reissinger, K. H., and Schröter, J. (1978), *Chem. Eng.*, **85**(25), 109.

Robinson, R. G., and Engel, A. J. (1967), *Ing. Eng. Chem.*, **59**(3), 22.

Rod, V. (1976), *Proc. 4th Int./6th European Symp. Chem. React. Eng.*, p. 271.

Rosenbaum, J. B., George, D. R., and May, J. T. (1971), U.S. Department of the Interior, Bureau of Mines Information Circular 8502.

Russell, T. W. F. (1972), *Can. J. Chem. Eng.*, **50**, 179.

Sahay, B. N., and Sharma, M. M. (1973), *Chem. Eng. Sci.*, **28**, 2245.

Sasaki, E. (1971), *Kogyo Kagaku Zasshi*, **74**, 799.

Satterfield, C. N. (1975), *AIChE J.*, **21**, 209.

Sawant, S. B., Joshi, J. B., and Pangarkar, V. G. (1979), *Chem. Eng. J.*, **18**, 143.

Schrödt, V. N. (1965), *Ind. Eng. Chem. Fundam.*, **4**, 108.

Schrödt, V. N., Sommerfield, J. T., Martin, O. R., and Chien, H. H. (1967), *Chem. Eng. Sci.*, **22**, 759.

Schumpe, A., and Deckwer, W.-D. (1978), *Chem. Ing.-Tech.*, **50**, 630.

Schumpe, A., Serpemen, Y., and Deckwer, W. -D. (1979), *Ger. Chem. Eng.*, **2**, 234.

Scott, D. S., and Hayduk, W. (1966), *Can. J. Chem. Eng.*, **44**, 130.

Shah, A. K., and Sharma, M. M. (1971), *Can. J. Chem. Eng.*, **49**, 596.

Shah, A. K., and Sharma, M. M. (1973), *Can. J. Chem. Eng.*, **51**, 772.

Shah, A. K., and Sharma, M. M. (1975), *Can. J. Chem. Eng.*, **53**, 572.

Shah, Y. T., Stiegel, G. J., and Sharma, M. M. (1978), *AIChE J.*, **24**, 369.

Shah, Y. T., Mhaskar, R. D., and Paraskos, J. A. (1976), *Ind. Eng. Chem. Process Design Dev.*, **15**, 400.

Sharma, M. M., and Mashelkar, R. A. (1968), *Proc. Symp. Tripartite Chem. Eng. Conf.* (Montreal), p. 10.

Sharma, M. M., Mashelkar, R. A., and Mehta, V. D. (1969), *Brit. Chem. Eng.*, **14**, 70.

Shende, B. W., and Sharma, M. M. (1974), *Chem. Eng. Sci.*, **29**, 1763.

Sherwin, M. B., and Frank, M. E. (1976), *Hydrocarbon Process. Petrol. Refiner*, **55**(11), 122.

Sherwood, T. K., and Farkas, E. J. (1966), *Chem. Eng. Sci.*, **21**, 573.

Shigelschi, O., and Suciu, G. D. (1977), *Chem. Eng. Sci.*, **32**, 889.

Shiraki, Y., Adachi, K., and Nomura, T. (1979), Jpn. Kokai Tokkyo Koho 78, 100, 200, *Chem. Abstr.* (1979), **90**, 106561.

Steeman, J. W. M., Kaarsemaker, S., and Hoftyzer, P. J. (1961), *Chem. Eng. Sci.*, **14**, 139.

Steiner, L. (1978), *Chem. Ing. -Tech.*, **50**, 389.

Stichlmair, J., and Mersmann, A. (1978), *Int. Chem. Eng.*, **18**, 223.

Strigle, R. F., and Rukovena, F. (1979), *Chem. Eng. Prog.*, **75**(3), 86.

Sullivan, G. A., and Treybal, R. E. (1970), *Chem. Eng. J.*, **1**, 302.

Sweeney, D. E. (1967), *AIChE J.*, **13**, 663.

Szabo, T. T., Lloyd, W. A., Cannon, M. R., and Speaker, S. S. (1964), *Chem. Eng. Prog.*, **60**(1), 66.

Szekely, J. (1967), *Chem. Eng.* (*London*), No. 206, CE41.

Taguchi, H., and Miyamoto, S. (1966), *Biotechnol. Bioeng.*, **8**, 43.

Ternan, M., and Whalley, M. J. (1976), *Can. J. Chem. Eng.*, **54**, 642.

Todd, D. B., and Irving, H. F. (1969), *Chem. Eng. Prog.*, **65**(9), 84.

Topiwala, H. H., and Hammer, G. (1974), *Trans. Inst. Chem. Eng.*, **52**, 113.

Treybal, R. E. (1963), *Liquid Extraction*, 2nd ed., McGraw-Hill, New York.

Turpin, J. L., and Huntington, R. L. (1967), *AIChE J.*, **13**, 1196.

Valentine, F. H. H. (1967), *Absorption in Gas-Liquid Dispersions*, Spon, London.

van Deemter, J. J. (1965), *Chem. Eng. Sci.*, **20** (Special Suppl.), 215.

van de Sande, E., and Smith, J. M. (1975), *Chem. Eng. J.*, **10**, 225.

van Goolen, J. T. J. (1976), *Proc. 4th Int./6th European Symp. Chem. React. Eng.*, IX-399.

van Krevelen, D. W. (1950), *Research*, **3**, 106.

van Landeghem, H. (1980), *Chem. Eng. Sci.*, **35**, 1912.

van't Riet, K. (1979), *Ind. Eng. Chem. Process Design Dev.*, **18**, 357.

Verma, R. P., and Sharma, M. M. (1975), *Chem. Eng. Sci.*, **30**, 279.

Virkar, P. D. (1974), Gas-Liquid Contactors, M. Chem. Eng. thesis, University of Bombay.

Virkar, P. D., and Sharma, M. M. (1975), *Can. J. Chem. Eng.*, **53**, 512.

Volpicelli, G., and Massimilla, L. (1970), *Chem. Eng. Sci.*, **25**, 1361.

Wales, C. E. (1966), *AIChE J.*, **12**, 1166.

Waller, J. (1970), Ger., 193, 38, 98 (to Shell International Research Maatschappij N.V.).

Walstra, P. (1974), *Chem. Eng. Sci.*, **29**, 882.

Warwick, G. C. I. (1973), *Chem. Ind.*, 5 May, 403.

Watkinson, A. P., and Cavers, S. D. (1967), *Can. J. Chem. Eng.*, **45**, 258.

Weekman, V. W., Jr. (1976), *Proc. 4th Int./6th European Symp. Chem. React. Eng.*, p. 615.

Weisweiler, W., and Rösch, S. (1978), *Ger. Chem. Eng.*, **1**, 212.

Widmer, F. (1973), *Adv. Chem. Ser.*, **128**, 51.

Wnek, W. J., and Snow, R. H. (1972), *Ind. Eng. Chem., Process Design Dev.*, **11**, 343.

Wynn, N. P. (1978), *Sulzer Tech. Rev.* **60**(4), 162.

Yagi, H., and Yoshida, F. (1975), *Ind. Eng. Chem. Process Design Dev.*, **14**, 488.

Zbigniew, L., Jan, K., Aleksander, P., and Wlodzimierz, B. (1967), *Przemysl Chem.*, **46**(4), 210 (in Polish); *Chem. Abstr.* (1967), **67**, 32273.

Zuiderweg, F. J., and Bruinzeel, C. (1968), *Proc. 4th European Symp. Chem. React. Eng.* (Suppl. to *Chem. Eng. Sci.*), p. 183.

Author Index

Abramzon, A. A., 57
Acres, G. J. K., 9, 10, 281, 292, 294
Adams, C. T., 104
Ai, M., 142
Alagy, J ., 200, 209
Albright, L. F., 3, 5, 9, 57
Ali, M. E. A. R., 313
Allenbach, U., 76
Alper, E., 38, 71, 152, 156, 176, 225, 226, 229, 277, 286, 301
Ameno, T., 222
Amsden, C. D., 335
Anderson, R. F., 96
Ando, M., 156
Andou, K., 333
Andrew, S. P. S., 69, 195, 200, 226, 228, 270
Anwar, M. M., 6, 178, 180, 181
Arpe, H. J., 5, 11, 12
Asai, S., 23, 28, 30, 31, 97, 126, 138, 152, 163, 260
Asinger, F., 4, 101
Astarita, G., 27, 70, 97, 159, 166, 169, 194, 198, 338
Atkinson, B., 313
Augugliaro, V., 77

Baans, C. M. E., 2, 88, 105, 159
Bailes, P. J., 6, 92, 93, 186, 195
Baird, M. H. I., 333, 347
Bakhshi, N. N., 9, 274
Bakker, C. A. P., 112
Balasubramanian, S. N., 4, 160, 176
Baldi, G., 249, 251
Balyanski, G. V., 78
Banerjee, S., 336
Barker, J. J., 234, 241
Barona, N., 2, 3, 5, 55
Barron, C. H., 64, 69, 70, 71
Bartholome, E., 3, 101
Baveja, K. K., 65, 73, 200
Beaverstock, M. C., 137
Beek, W. J., 71
Beenackers, A. A. C. M., 89, 222, 337
Begley, J. N., 299
Bekhli, E. Yu., 95
Bell, R. P., 80
Beman, F. L., 11
Bender, E., 347
Bender, M. L., 95
Bengtsson, S., 71
Bennett, G. E., 11
Bennett, M. R., 10, 277, 297
Berbé, Fr., 178
Bern, L., 290
Beutler, J. A., 35, 36
Bhargava, R. K., 48, 64, 175, 206, 222
Bhatia, S., 7, 249
Bhatia, S. P., 11
Bhave, R. R., 6, 51, 66, 250
Bibaud, R. E., 346
Bidner, M. S., 66
Bill, W., 10
Billet, R., 321, 326
Bird, A. J., 279, 297
Bishnoi, P. R., 47
Bizhanov, F. B., 289
Bjerle, I., 9, 28, 34, 71
Bliss, H., 200
Blyakher, I. G., 333
Bobaleck, E. G., 9, 274
Bochner, M. B., 255
Boerma, H., 330
Bolles, W. L., 329
Bomio, P., 323
Bondi, A., 301
Boon-Long, S., 243, 244
Booth, F. B., 2
Boozer, C. E., 49
Bossier, J. A., 2, 79
Bourne, J. R., 111
Boussoulengas, A. V., 278
Brahme, P. H., 10
Brandt, H. W., 340
Bratchley, R., 65, 68
Brauer, H., 335
Brennan, J. P., 210
Breuer, M. M., 7, 253
Brian, P. L. T., 31, 36, 64, 97, 105, 106, 111, 112, 137, 205, 206, 243, 245
Bridge, A. G., 312
Britton, E. C., 11
Brooks, B. W., 2
Broström, A., 89
Bruinzeel, C., 333
Brown, D. E., 234
Brown, H. C., 2, 52, 79
Buley, V. F., 335
Bunton, C. A., 250
Burgess, J. M., 336
Burkin, A. R., 8, 9
Burmakin, N. M., 3
Busch, A. W., 335

Calderbank, P. H., 234, 241, 244, 294
Caldin, E. F., 63
Camahort, J. L., 100, 101
Cannon, M. R., 329

Carberry, J. J., 109
Carleton, A. J., 2, 47, 334
Carlson, K. D., 2, 78
Carr, N. L., 88
Carraher, C. E., Jr., 52, 95
Cavers, S. D., 348
Cerfontain, H., 89
Chandalia, S. B., 2, 46–48, 107, 160, 200
Chandrasekaran, K., 1, 2, 11, 61, 65, 77, 279, 296
Chang, P., 84
Chapman, J. W., 66, 85
Characklis, W. G., 335
Charest, F., 277
Charpentier, J. C., 225, 226, 301
Chaudhari, R. V., 1, 49, 175, 223, 266, 277, 286
Chauvin, Y., 50
Chavan, V. V., 237, 248
Chen, B. H., 333, 350
Chen, T. I., 71
Chhabria, M. C., 65, 67, 68
Chiang, S. H., 110
Chilton, C. H., 195
Chock, P. E., 80
Chornet, E., 277
Chou, T. S., 237, 302
Chu, C., 222
Chua, Y. H., 3, 4, 120, 121, 134, 160, 176, 177, 222
Chuang, T. T., 10, 308, 314, 354
Clarke, A., 289
Clarke, J. K. A., 64
Clegg, G. T., 109
Clippinger, E., 58
Coenen, J. W. E., 90, 290, 291, 351, 354
Coffey, R. S., 79
Coggan, G. C., 111
Coldiron, D. C., 101, 104
Collins, T. T., 2, 325, 326
Cook, A. E., 109
Coombes, R. G., 57
Cooper, B. J., 9, 281, 292
Cooper, H. B. H., Jr., 2, 335
Cordova, W. A., 291
Cornils, B., 178
Coughanowr, D. R., 4, 159
Coughlin, R. W., 11, 295, 314
Coulson, J. M., 234
Counce, R. M., 69
Cowdrey, W. A., 89
Cox, P. R., 5, 50, 57, 66, 85, 106
Crine, M., 304, 312
Crynes, B. L., 3, 89
Cutter, L. A., 244
Cvetanovic, K., 78

Damronglerd, S., 237
Danckwerts, P. V., 1, 24, 27, 28, 36–39, 49, 55, 57, 63, 64, 66, 70, 84–87, 91, 98, 105, 108–110, 112, 142, 156, 167, 169, 171, 176, 195, 208, 225, 226, 229, 317, 323, 329
Darsi, C. R., 344
Da Silva, A. T., 86, 87, 108, 110, 112, 171, 226
Datta, R. L., 80
Davidsohn, A., 195
Davies, D. S., 89
Davis, H. S., 159, 169, 279
Dean, D. N., 300
Deckwer, W.-D., 60, 75, 76, 277, 331–333
Degaleesan, T. E., 340
Dehmlow, E. V., 53
Dehmlow, S. S., 53
Delnicki, W. V., 329
De Santiago, M., 66
De Waal, K. J. A., 64, 70
De Wilt, H. G. J., 11
Ding, J. S. Y., 112, 113
Dingman, J. C., 159, 169
Dixon, J. K., 5, 82
Dodds, W. S., 325
Domask, W. G., 3
Donders, A. J. M., 5, 342
Doraiswamy, L. K., 1, 9, 10, 49, 175, 266
Douglas, H. R., 333, 350
Douglas, W. J. M., 333, 350
Dovell, F. S., 9, 292
Dufau, F. A., 9, 352

Eckert, J. S., 324, 344
Edwards, W. M., 322, 337
Effron, E., 325
Eigen, M., 89
Eleazer, A. E., 10
Ellis, S. R. M., 181
Emig, G., 69
Emmert, R. E., 97
Engel, A. J., 11, 295, 329
Enright, J. T., 10, 308, 314, 354
Epstein, N., 9, 275
Ertl, G., 275
Eustace, D. J., 90

Falk, J. C., 9, 12, 248
Farkas, E. J., 9, 277, 280, 288, 353
Favier, M., 301
Feick, J. E., 344
Fell, C. J. D., 329
Fendler, E. J., 53
Fendler, J. H., 53
Fern, A. S., 7, 253
Fernandes, J. B., 230, 346
Ferrari, G., 10, 287
Finkelstein, N. P., 94
Fischer, R., 327
Fischer, R. H., 8
Fisher, M., 216
Fleming, C. A., 94
Flett, D. S., 94
Flores-Fernandez, G., 216
Floyd, M. B., 49
Fogler, H. S., 8, 270
Foster, R. L., 195, 209
Frank, J. C., 328
Frank, M. E., 10, 355
Frantz, J. F., 3
Freifelder, M., 9, 10
Friedlander, S. K., 249, 289
Friedman, H. M., 8
Friend, L., 3, 160

Frost, A. A., 120
Fuji, H., 170
Fujinawa, K., 111
Fukushima, S., 68, 325
Furmer, Yu. V., 111
Furusawa, T., 235
Furzer, I. A., 39

Galeano, S. F., 335
Ganguli, K. L., 79
Garbei, A., 10, 287
Garnell, F. H., 159, 169
Garrett, H. E., 8
Garstang, J. H., 333
Gates, B. C., 11, 312
Gehlawat, J. K., 3, 5, 40, 47, 65, 72, 75, 76, 104, 120, 121, 134, 142, 159, 162, 169
Genin, L. S., 334
Germain, A. H., 9, 301, 310, 311
Gerstenberg, H., 331
Ghorpade, A. K., 4, 65, 101, 102
Gianetto, A., 301, 307, 325
Gibbon, J. D., 181
Giger, A., 3, 327
Gilbert, J. B., 11, 312
Gillham, A. J., 66, 226
Gilliland, E. R., 88
Gioia, F., 159, 169
Glass, K. I., 3
Glastonbury, J. R., 234, 240, 243, 247
Glueck, A. R., 4, 101, 102
Goar, B. G., 160
Godfrey, J. H., 38
Goettler, L. A., 159, 163, 166
Gokel, G. W., 250
Goldstein, R. F., 2, 5, 121, 200
Golovin, A. I., 12
Gomezplata, A., 235, 243
Gopal, J. S., 336, 350
Gopalrao, M., 255
Gorin, E., 103
Goto, S., 11, 236, 281, 296, 301, 307, 309, 313, 314
Green, D. C., 312
Green, M., 65, 68
Greenfield, H., 79, 288
Gregory, D. P., 58
Griskey, R. G., 6, 95
Grobler, A., 79
Groggins, P. H., 3, 5–8, 186
Groothuis, H., 5, 57, 107
Grummitt, O., 79
Gunn, D. J., 4, 159
Gunstone, F. D., 5
Gupta, D. V., 10, 297
Gupta, R. K., 8, 64, 200
Guterbock, H., 121

Haase, D. J., 2, 88, 195
Habashi, F., 8, 9, 195, 273
Hague, D. N., 7, 63
Hahn, A. Y., 160
Haideggar, E., 10, 352
Hales, H. B., 243, 245
Halpem, J., 80
Halt, B. W., 101, 103
Hammer, G., 331
Hammer, H., 280, 351
Hancock, E. G., 5, 81
Hancock, M. D., 113
Hansen, F. K., 6
Hanson, C., 5, 57, 66, 83, 85, 92, 94, 107, 186, 345
Hanson, D., 69, 200
Harada, M., 92
Hardwick, T. J., 4
Hardwick, W. H., 6. 92, 195
Harnisch, H., 6, 58, 233
Harriott, P., 5, 82, 120, 234, 241, 243, 291
Hart, D. R., 62
Hartley, G. S., 96
Hartman, M., 11, 295, 314
Haselden, G. G., 208
Hashimoto, K., 9, 291
Hatch, L. F., 2, 160
Hatch, T. F., 4, 160, 176
Hatcher, W. J., 62
Hatt, B. W., 101, 103
Haug, H. F., 328
Hawkins, P. A., 3
Hayashi, Y., 326
Hayduk, W., 335
Hegner, B., 160, 177
Helfferich, F., 254, 255
Henry, H. C., 11, 312
Herbrechtsmeier, P., 333
Herskowitz, M., 311
Heuss, J. M., 335
Hikita, H., 23, 28, 30, 31, 63, 68, 73, 97, 105, 106, 111, 126, 138, 152, 163, 222, 260
Hirose, T., 235–237
Hjortkjaer, J., 2, 49
Hobbs, C. C., 55, 214
Hochman, J. M., 325
Hodossy, L., 10, 352
Hoffman, L. A., 112, 113
Hoffman, U., 69
Hofmann, H., 10, 52, 237, 301, 307
Hoftyzer, P. J., 3, 195, 198, 203, 208, 209
Holroyd, F. P. B., 4, 101, 102
Holy, N. L., 290
Hon, H. C., 336, 337
Horak, M., 8, 272
Horie, T., 3
Houlihan, R., 344, 346
Hsu, S. H., 11, 297
Huang, C. J., 34, 35, 222
Huang, P., 322, 337
Hubbard, W. D., 235
Huber, M., 324
Huff, G. A., Jr., 294
Hughes, M. A., 6, 92, 94, 195
Hugo, P., 251
Hulme, P., 3, 200
Hussien, M., 271
Hutington, R. L., 325

Ichikawa, Y., 249
Ido, T., 284

Ikemizu, K., 110
Imaishi, N., 111
Inoue, H., 48, 69, 70, 121
Irving, H. F., 339
Ismail, H. A. M., 5, 66, 83, 170

Jagirdar, G. C., 6, 92, 180, 182
Jahan, S., 65, 68
James, B. R., 2, 79
Jameson, G. J., 351
Jeffreys, G. V., 3, 5, 186, 342, 345
Jensen, V. W., 2, 49
Jepson, J. C., 335
Jernigan, E. C., 5
Jhaveri, A. S., 55, 65, 67, 68, 98, 143, 152, 226
Johnson, A. I., 7, 241, 249
Johnson, G. R., 3, 89
Johnson, P. R., 5
Jones, S. J. R., 234, 241
Jones, J. M., 95
Joosten, G. E. H., 80, 216, 223
Jordan, D. G., 3, 160
Joshi, J. B., 329, 331–334
Juvekar, V. A., 8, 64, 175, 213, 230, 234, 240, 265, 280, 296, 330

Kafarov, V. V., 180
Kaji, A. T., 327, 334, 349
Kakovsky, I. A., 272
Kaldi, P., 9, 248, 274
Kale, D. D., 327
Kaloshin, V. M., 92
Kalra, H., 105, 106
Kameoka, Y., 69, 74, 156
Kane, P. G., 65, 68
Karlsson, H. T., 28, 34
Karr, A. E., 347
Karter, E. M., 9, 274
Kastanek, F., 72
Kataoka, T., 92
Kats, M. B., 334
Katz, M., 96
Kawakami, K., 285, 289, 300
Kawamura, K., 239
Kawazoe, K., 283
Kekre, S. Y., 255
Kelmers, A. D., 10, 277, 297
Kenney, C. N., 4, 9, 49, 100–102, 113, 114, 171, 223, 283, 295, 310
Kerr, C. P., 337, 350
Kerridge, D. H., 101, 103
Kholmanskikh, Yu. B., 272
Kiff, B. W., 56
Kikkaw, S., 103
Kingsley, H. A., 200
Kirk, R. E., 2–4, 9, 121
Kirk, R. S., 11
Kiseleva, E. N., 181
Kishinevskii, M. Kh., 97
Kitai, A., 334
Kitu, M., 333
Klanica, A. J., 210
Klassen, J., 11
Kobayashi, O., 249
Kobayashi, T., 121, 239
Kobe, K. A., 3
Kohl, A. L., 110
Kohn, P. M., 11
Kölbel, H., 294
Kolev, N., 323
Komasawa, I., 51
Komiyama, H., 11, 48, 69, 277, 296, 330
Kondo, K., 66, 99
Konstantinov, I. I., 7, 252
Korsorotov, V. I., 200
Kothari, P. J., 5, 66, 81, 89
Kramers, H., 65, 69, 84
Krause, F. E., 4, 159
Krause, R. L., 9
Kremers, F. J., 3
Krueger, K. H., 73
Kubota, H., 334
Kulkarni, A. A., 55
Kumar, S., 236, 248
Kumazawa, H., 223
Kuo, C. H., 34, 35, 78, 222
Kürten, H., 352
Kusaka, K., 325
Kustin, K., 89, 106
Kusunoki, K., 289

Laddha, G. S., 340, 346
Laddha, S. S., 7, 181, 182, 252
Ladhabhoy, M. E., 2, 40, 65, 74, 109
La Force, R. C., 172
Lahiri, R. N., 65, 73, 200, 210
Lamont, J. C., 335
Landau, J., 344, 346
Langley, P. E., 208
Lankester, J. H., 330
Larson, R. A., 80
Laudry, J. E., 88
Laurent, A., 71, 225, 230
Lawless, J. J., 1, 77
Le, H., 61
Lechev, P., 9
Leday, A., 339
Leder, F., 142
Lee, E. S., 192
Lee, L. M., 82
Lee, Y. Y., 286
Lefebvre, G., 90
Lefers, J. B., 74, 223
Lemay, Y., 234, 237
Lemcoff, N. O., 351
Leszezynski, A., 6, 121
Leuteritz, G. M., 352
Levec, J., 11, 306, 313
Levenson, G. I. P., 8
Levenspiel, O., 38, 120, 330
Levins, D. M., 234, 240, 243, 247
Leznoff, C. C., 233, 277
Li, K. Y., 223
Lightfoot, E. N., 235
Linek, V., 60, 64, 70, 323
Liotta, C., 250

Lira, E. P., 96
Lites, I. L., 170
Livbjerg, H., 11
Lo, T. C., 347
Lobo, P. A., 248
Loucaides, R., 338
Low, D. I. R., 55
Lowndes, M. R., 2
Lund, K., 8, 270

McGreavy, C., 11, 277
McIver, R. G., 4
McKillop, A., 233, 278
McLachlan, C. N. S., 208
McManamey, W. J., 338
McNeil, K. M., 66
Madden, A. G., 5
Mahajani, V. V., 11, 216, 265, 297, 306, 325, 327
Manecke, G., 277, 278
Mann, R., 109, 213, 216, 222
Manning, F. S., 7, 271
Manogue, W. H., 59, 64, 159
Mansoori, G. A., 5
Marangozis, J., 7, 241, 248, 249, 290
Margolin, E. D., 4, 103
Marr, R., 346
Marrucci, G., 159, 169, 338
Martin, G. Q., 331
Martinola, F., 233, 254, 352
Martynov, Yu. M., 199
Maslan, F., 4
Mashelkar, R. A., 60, 64, 66, 134, 176, 230, 237, 248, 331, 334, 338
Massimilla, L., 9, 350
Matsui, T., 237, 308, 310
Mayrhoferwa, J., 70
Mears, D. E., 307
Mehta, K. C., 332, 337
Mehta, V. D., 64, 230, 329
Meier, W., 324
Melnyk, P. B., 78
Menger, F. M., 53, 54
Merrill, R. P., 299
Mersmann, A., 328, 331
Meyerink, E. S., 249
Mhaskar, R. D., 190–192, 223
Midoux, N., 302
Midwilsky, B. M., 195
Miles, D., 234, 240, 241, 243, 245
Miller, D. N., 234
Miller, J., 5
Miller, R. E., 11
Miller, S. A., 3, 5
Millich, F., 52
Mills, J. F., 200, 210
Milnes, M. H., 181
Mirviss, S. B., 79
Mishra, G. C., 72
Misic, D. M., 277, 280
Mitchell, L. C., 10
Mitter, H. K., 80
Miyamoto, S., 339
Miyauchi, T., 3
Mochizuki, S., 237, 308, 310
Moden, M. M., 10
Molzahn, M., 160, 177
Montagna, A. A., 312, 354
Moo-Young, M. B., 244
Moore, E., 109
Moore, T. F., 159, 169
Morgan, J. P., 61
Morgan, P. W., 6, 95, 186
Morita, S., 308, 310
Morita, Z., 7, 253
Morrel, C. E., 88, 105
Morsi, B. I., 301, 302
Mosby, J. F., 5
Motomura, H., 7, 253
Mukherjee, K. D., 9
Mulder, A. J., 107
Mumford, C. J., 345
Murakami, Y., 327, 339
Murray, F. E., 2, 61, 337
Mützenberg, A. B., 3, 327

Nagata, S., 241, 248, 249
Nagel, O., 317, 336
Nakao, K., 120, 121, 136
Nanda, A. K., 5, 66, 81, 99, 108, 186, 192, 230
Nardhani, K. M., 46
Naworski, J. S., 5, 82
Neelkantan, J., 72
Nelemans, J., 10, 293
Nelson, A. L., 8
Nemunaitis, R. R., 343
Nene, S. A., 4
Newman, M. S., 12, 288
Nicholl, E. McK., 112
Nienow, A. W., 234, 240, 241, 243–246
Niiyama, H., 235
Nijsing, R. A. T. O., 64, 97, 98
Nikonov, V. Z., 95, 157
Ninomiya, K., 170
Nishikawa, M., 238
Norris, B. E., 324, 348
Nyvlt, V., 72

Oblad, A. G., 2
Ohashi, Y., 283
O'Hern, H. A., 70
Ohi, T., 142
Ohnishi, R., 12
Oishi, T., 98
Okeson, J. C., 64, 70
Olander, D. R., 37, 38, 100, 101, 191, 197
Oldenkamp, R. D., 4, 103
Oldshue, J. Y., 346
Olivier, K. L., 2
Olney, R. B., 346
Oloman, C., 169
Onda, K., 35, 70, 163, 171, 222
Onoue, Y., 10
Osborn, J. A., 79
Østergaard, K., 327, 333, 350
Ostrovskit, M. V., 57
Othmer, D. F., 2–4, 9, 121

Otto, F. D., 105, 106
Ouwerkerk, C., 159, 166, 169
Owens, R. M., 53
Ozaki, A., 334
Özel, F., 310

Pal, S. K., 1, 2, 11, 286, 297
Palko, A. A., 56
Pangarkar, V. G., 4, 32, 64, 120, 121, 123, 125, 127, 135, 176, 177, 188, 195, 200, 202, 204, 210
Paraskos, J. A., 312
Parshall, G. W., 104
Patil, V. K., 239, 243, 326
Paulik, F. E., 10
Pearson, R. G., 120
Pepper, K. W., 8, 271, 272
Perez, J. F., 339
Perona, J. J., 10, 69, 306, 308, 310
Perry, J. H., 246
Perry, R. H., 195
Peters, R. H., 7, 8, 253, 269
Pexidr, V., 289
Phadtare, P. G., 9, 266
Pigford, R. L., 4, 59, 64, 69, 74, 97, 156, 158–160, 163, 166, 176, 195
Pilhofer, Th., 340
Pinczewski, W. V., 329
Piret, E. L., 52
Pittman, C. U., 10
Pocker, Y., 48
Pogrebnaya, U. L., 74
Pohorecki, R., 66
Polyakov, A. A., 178
Popovic, M., 75, 76
Potter, O. E., 84
Pratt, M. W. T., 180
Prengle, H. W., 2, 3, 5, 55, 216
Preston, C., 7, 253
Pruden, B. B., 9, 61, 351
Pryde, E. H., 2, 78, 200
Puranik, S. A., 57, 62, 341, 343
Puri, P. S., 295
Puxbaumer, H. H., 60

Raghuram, S., 112, 113
Ramachandran, P. A., 1, 4, 8, 87, 90, 105, 138, 142, 158, 159, 163, 166, 167, 171–173, 175, 176, 200, 204, 235, 258, 264, 266, 277, 286
Rase, H. F., 51
Ratcliffe, J. S., 3, 4, 120, 121, 134, 160, 176, 177, 222
Rattee, I. D., 7, 253
Raval, R. P., 11, 298
Ravetkar, D. D., 327
Raymond, B., 327
Razumovskii, S. D., 77, 78
Regen, S. L., 250, 256
Reichert, K. H., 300
Reilly, I. G., 9, 273
Reiss, L. P., 325
Reissinger, K. H., 340, 345, 347, 349
Reith, T., 71
Repas, M., 178
Richards, G. M., 66
Richardson, F. D., 5, 56, 57, 90, 200
Richardson, J. A., 51
Riegel, H., 4, 101, 103
Riemenschneider, W., 2
Riesenfeld, F. C., 110
Rizvi, S. F., 70, 323
Rizzuti, L., 65, 77
Roberts, D., 64
Roberts, G. W., 277, 282, 307
Robinson, R. G., 329
Rockwell, A. L., 80
Rod, V., 5, 94, 186, 192, 223, 348
Rodiguin, N. M., 120
Rodiguina, E. N., 120
Roper, G. H., 166, 175
Rösch, S., 336
Rosenbaum, J. B., 2. 92, 93, 195, 349
Rosenwald, R. H., 2
Rosenzweig, M. D., 2, 10
Rossano, A. T., Jr., 2, 335
Rossi, P. P., 78
Rossi-Bernardi, L., 91
Roth, J. F., 49
Roughton, F. J. W., 90, 91
Rowe, P. N., 238
Rozen, A. M., 186
Rozhdestvenskava, I. D., 10
Rueggeberg, W. H. C., 7
Ruether, J. A., 11, 236, 237, 295, 297
Rukovena, F., 320
Rushton, J. H., 336, 346
Russell, T. W. F., 335
Ruthven, D. M., 4, 100, 101
Ryan, J. M., 249
Rychnovsky, L., 94
Rylander, P. N., 2, 79
Rys, P., 136

Sada, E., 8, 64, 73, 74, 111, 169, 170, 175, 192, 222, 223, 261, 264–266, 286
Sadasivan, K., 249
Sadek, S. E., 160, 177
Saeki, G., 3, 142, 155
Sahay, B. N., 230, 323, 334
Saito, H., 239
Saleem, A., 4, 159
Sandall, O. C., 339
Sankholkar, D. S., 5, 40, 65, 66, 75, 162, 170, 195, 209
Sano, T., 209
Sasaki, E., 333
Sastri, N. V. S., 9, 275
Sato, Y., 301
Satterfield, C. N., 9, 236, 237, 277, 289, 294, 301, 309, 310, 312, 326
Satyamurthy, N., 72
Sauchel, V., 1
Saunby, J. B., 56
Sanders, K. W., 5, 82
Savage, D. W., 194, 198
Sawant, S. B., 334
Sawicki, J. E., 64, 69, 71
Schaper, W., 251
Scher, M., 48

Schmeal, W. R., 11, 299
Schmidt, A., 160
Schmitz, P., 73
Schneider, J. A., 200, 210
Schöön, N. H., 290
Schorr, V., 216
Schreiner, W. C., 200
Schrödt, Y. N., 329, 344
Schröter, J., 340, 345, 347, 349
Schuit, G. C. A., 11, 312
Schuler, R., 159, 169
Schumpe, A., 331, 332
Schwartz, J. G., 302, 307
Schwartzberg, H. G., 241
Schwind, R. A., 1
Scibona, G., 5
Scott, D. S., 9, 273, 335
Scriven, L. E., 185, 190, 192
Seaburn, J. T., 11, 295
Searle, H. T., 1, 77
Secor, R. M., 3, 35, 36, 199
Sedriks, W., 9, 283, 295, 310
Seebold, J. E., 88
Seif, S., 271
Selke, W. A., 234
Shaffer, D. L., 76
Shah, A. K., 5, 335, 348
Shah, Y. T., 88, 109, 112, 114, 171, 194, 197, 206, 210, 223, 277, 301, 307, 312, 317, 354, 355
Sharma, M. M., 1–8, 11, 36, 38–40, 47, 48, 51, 53–55, 57, 60–68, 74–77, 80, 81, 83–89, 91, 92, 98, 99, 105, 108, 114, 120, 121, 123, 125, 134, 135, 142, 157–159, 163, 166, 167, 169–172, 175–177, 180–182, 186, 190–192, 194, 195, 197, 200, 204, 209, 216, 225–227, 230, 239, 240, 250–252, 258, 264–266, 279, 280, 296, 306, 323, 325–337, 341, 343, 346, 348–350
Sharma, R. C., 7, 66, 106, 251
Sharma, S., 112
Sheldon, R. A., 11, 298
Shende, B. W., 325
Sheng, M. N., 11
Sherwin, M. B., 10, 355
Sherwood, T. K., 9, 69, 158, 195, 236, 249, 277, 280, 288, 353
Sheth, M. N., 64, 142, 222
Shiao, D. D. F., 7, 252
Shigelschi, O., 336
Shima, T., 209
Shimizu, Y., 312
Shingu, H., 11
Shiraki, Y., 329
Shrier, A. L., 142
Shropshire, J. A., 90
Sicardi, S., 301, 303, 306
Sim, M. T., 213
Singh, D., 68, 299
Sirotkin, G. D., 3
Sittig, M., 2–4, 11
Slesser, C. G. M., 280
Slizovskaya, L. V., 1
Smith, C. S., 3
Smith, J. M., 11, 235, 236, 277, 280, 296, 306, 308–310, 313, 314, 330, 336
Smith, R. M., 2
Smithson, G. L., 9, 274
Snider, J. W., 10, 306, 308, 310
Snow, R. H., 326
Snowdon, C. B., 235, 255
Sobotka, M., 60
Sohrabi, M., 62
Sokolov, L. B., 95, 96, 157
Specchia, V., 249, 251
Sprow, F. B., 5, 82
Sridharan, K., 38, 64, 65, 68, 87, 88
Srivastava, R. D., 70, 72
Starks, C. M., 53, 250
Stasinevich, D. S., 200, 211
Steeman, J. W. M., 33, 209, 331
Steiner, L., 342
Steiner, R., 333
Sternburg, H. W., 8
Stichlmair, J., 328
Storck, W., 277, 278
Strachan, A. N., 5, 50, 57, 66, 85, 106
Street, J. R., 11, 299
Strigle, R. F., 320
Subba Rao, D., 244
Subramanian, K. N., 5, 56
Suciu, G. D., 336
Sucker, D., 335
Sukhdev, 11
Sullivan, G. A., 330
Summer, H. H., 253
Sundermeyer, W., 100
Sundstrom, D. W., 9, 274
Suzuki, M., 283
Sweeney, D. E., 325
Sykes, P., 235, 243
Sylvester, N. D., 281
Szabo, M., 9, 248, 278
Szabo, T. T., 329, 344
Szekely, J., 5, 57, 90, 346
Szonyi, G., 4, 101, 102

Taguchi, H., 339
Takeuchi, H., 65, 74, 98, 156, 170
Talmor, E., 301
Tamhankar, S. S., 266
Taneja, V. K., 244
Taylor, M. D., 159, 170
Taylor, R. F., 100
Teramoto, M., 65, 73, 75, 120, 121, 134, 135, 160, 174, 176
Tarasawa, M., 278, 290
Ternan, M., 354
Teshima, H., 283
Themelis, N. J., 90
Thomas, R. J., 345
Thomas, W. J., 39, 88, 112
Throckmorton, P. E., 2, 78, 200
Tiwari, R. K., 5, 51, 55
Todd, D. B., 339
Tong, S. B., 293
Toor, H. L., 110
Topiwala, H. H., 331
Tournie, P., 238
Trambouze, P., 52
Treybal, R. E., 158, 195, 234, 241, 330, 340, 346
Tripathi, G., 236, 238

Trushanov, V. N., 72
Tsao, G. T., 222, 280, 286
Tsigin, B. M., 7, 252
Turpin, J. L., 325
Turek, F., 283
Turner, J. C. R., 195, 235, 255
Turner, P. E., 3, 200
Twitchett, H. J., 7, 8, 252

Uchida, S., 8, 262, 266
Ugelstad, J., 6
Upadhyay, S. N., 236, 238

Valentine, F. H. H., 329
Van Deemter, J. J., 11, 311, 326
Van den Berg, H. J., 79
Van der Baan, H. S., 11
Van de Sande, E., 336
Van de Vusse, J. G., 120, 121, 134
Van Dijk, C. P., 200
Van Direndonck, L., 4, 10, 101, 102, 293
Van Dongen, R. H., 308
Van Goolen, J. T. J., 10, 294, 351
Van Klinken, J., 308
Van Krevelen, D. W., 2, 3, 31, 34, 88, 105, 159, 195, 198, 203, 209, 317
Van Landeghem, H., 355
Van Ling, G., 10
Van Swaaij, W. P. M., 89, 222, 337
Van't Hoog, A. C., 64, 70
Van't Riet, K., 329
Vasudevan, T. V., 83
Venkataraman, K., 7
Verma, R. P., 343
Vieth, W. R., 249
Villadson, J., 11
Virkar, P. D., 336, 337
Vlugter, J. C., 10
Volpicelli, G., 9, 350
Von Kutepow, N., 2

Wace, P. F., 6, 92, 195
Waddams, A. L., 2, 5, 121, 200
Wadekar, V. V., 6, 7, 180–182, 252
Wagner, J. L., 329
Waker, D. G., 2, 88, 195
Wales, C. E., 335
Wallace, T. J., 2
Waller, J., 351
Walstra, P., 339
Warwick, G. C. I., 340, 348
Watkinson, A. P., 348
Weber, M. E., 9, 351
Weber, W. P., 250
Weekman, V. W., Jr., 312, 354
Weinrotter, F., 4
Weissermel, K., 5, 11, 12
Weisweiler, W., 336
Wen, C. P., 78
Wesselingh, J. A., 64, 70
West, T. F., 96
Westerterp, K. R., 64
Weston, C. D., 253
Whalley, M. J., 354
Whewell, R. J., 6, 94
White, D. E., 310
Whiteway, S. G., 5, 90
Whitt, F. R., 3
Widmer, F., 209, 339
Wiewiorowski, T. K., 160
Wielgosz, Z., 6, 96
Wild, J. D., 84
Wilke, C. R., 84
Williams, B. B., 270
Williams, D. E., 178
Williamson, D. G., 78
Wise, W. S., 178
Wisniak, J., 10, 295
Wittbecker, E. L., 96
Wnek, W. J., 326
Wojtowicz, J. A., 210
Wyatt, M., 314
Wynn, N. P., 335, 336
Wystrach, V. P., 12

Yadav, G. D., 3, 7, 38, 53, 64, 80, 157, 250, 265
Yagi, H., 338
Yagi, S., 70
Yagodin, G. Ya., 92
Yahikozawa, K., 297
Yakushkin, M. I., 92
Yamanaka, Y., 74, 170
Yang, W. C., 7, 271
Yano, T., 65, 76
Yates, K., 80
Yokoyama, H., 209
Yoshida, F., 338
Yoshitome, H., 239
Young, D. W., 233, 278

Zabor, R. C., 11
Zaidi, A., 10, 280, 294
Zajacek, J. G., 11
Zbigniew, L., 348
Zehner, P., 352
Zhavoronkov, N. M., 199
Zuiderweg, F. J., 333
Zwietering, T. N., 241, 246

Subject Index

Absorption:
  accompanied by chemical reaction(s):
    of acetylene, 83, 266
    of ammonia, 145, 176
    autocatalytic, 213
    of carbon dioxide, 55, 60, 63, 66, 87, 91, 97, 105, 144, 145, 148, 150, 154, 156, 163, 168, 170, 172, 173, 176, 265, 274, 300
    of carbon monoxide, 49, 88, 91, 173, 178
    of carbonyl sulfide, 66, 163
    of C_4 fractions, 47, 75, 161, 169
    of chlorine, 47, 80, 81, 88, 103, 106, 123, 127, 134, 136, 157, 177, 216, 274
    consecutive, 120
    of hydrogen cyanide, 170
    of hydrogen sulfide, 88,105, 167, 168, 173, 178
    irreversible, 17
    of isobutylene, 47, 75, 134, 161, 169
    of mercaptans, 57, 88, 170
    of NO_x gases, 69, 156, 170, 266
    of oxygen, 47, 55, 61, 67, 68, 70, 74, 90, 98, 172, 173, 272, 274
    of ozone, 75, 77, 216
    of phosphine, 48, 77
    photochemical, 216
    reversible, 34
    simultaneous:
      with desorption, 199
      of two gases, 158, 171, 174
    in solid (catalytic)-liquid systems, 277
    in solid (reacting)-liquid systems, 258
    of sulfur dioxide, 103, 170, 172, 177, 265, 274
    two-step, 136
  of one gas in two reactants:
    depletion regime, 152
    examples, 142, 155
    fast reactions, 143
    instantaneous reactions, 147
    kinetics of, 155
    one reaction instantaneous, other between regmine 2 and 3, 149
    regime between 2 and 3, 143
    slow rections, 143
    very slow reactions, 142
Acetic acid:
  absorption of isobutylene in, 47
  from carbonylation of methanol, 49
Acetylene:
  absorption in cuprous chloride slurry, 266
  alkylation of toluene and xylenes with, 83
Acidization of dolomite, calcite and feldspar, 270
Acidulation of phosphate rock, 270
Alkylation:
  of benzene with straight chain olefins, 51
  of isobutane with butenes, 82
  of phenols with isobutylene, consecutive reactions, 134
  of toluene with acetaldehyde/acetylene, 82
  of toluene and xylenes with acetadehyde, 82
Autocatalytic reactions:
  chlorination of cylcohexanone, effect of volatile intermediate, 216
  in gas absorption, 213
  radical multiplying chain reaction, 216

Bubble column reactors:
  for gas-liquid systems, 331
  for solid-liquid systems, mass transfer in, 238, 239

Carbon dioxide:
  absorption:
    in aqueous amines, 144, 148, 150, 154, 156
    in aqueous amines and alkalies, reversible, 105
    in aqueous buffer containing carbonic anhydrase, 300
    in aqueous diethanolamine solutions, 63
    in aqueous monoethanolamine solutions, 87, 98
    in aqueous sodium hydroxide/potassium hydroxide, 63, 98
    in calcium hydroxide slurries, 265
    in carbonate buffer solutions, 55, 60, 66
      hypochlorite catalyzed, 94
    in hemoglobin, 91
    in magnesium hydroxide slurries, 265
    in magnesium oxide suspensions, 274
  desorption from hot potassium carbonate-bicarbonate solutions, 207
  simultaneous absorption:
    with ammonia, 145, 176
    with carbon monoxide, 173
    with carbonyl sulfide, 163
    with hydrogen cyanide, 170
    with hydrogen sulfide, 167, 168, 173
    with mercaptans, 170
    with phosgene, 172
    with sulfur dioxide, 172
  simultaneous absorption-desorption, 210
Carbon disulfide, reaction with amines, 81
Carbon monoxide:
  absorption:
    in aqueous cuprous ammonium chloride, 88
    in cuprous aluminum complex solutions, 88
    in hemoglobin, 91
    in methanol, 49
  simultaneous absorption:
    with carbon dioxide, 173
    with oxygen, 172, 173
    with hydrogen, for hydroformylation, 178
Carbonyl sulfide, absorption:
  in aqueous alkalies, 66

Carbonyl sulfide, absorption (*Continued*)
in aqueous amines, 66
simultaneous, with carbon dioxide, 88
C_4 fractions, absorption:
in acetic acid, 47
in aqueous sulfuric acid, 47, 75, 161, 169
in bubble columns, 76
in ionic thalium (III) solutions, 76
in trifluoroacetic acid, 76
Chlorination:
of acetylene, 177
of aqueous buffer solution of phenols, 157
of *p*-cresol, 123, 127, 134
of cyclohexanone, 216
of *n*-decane, 134
of 1,2-dichloroethane, 134
of ethylene, 177
in melts, 103
of phenol, 136
of wood pulp, 274
Chlorine, absorption:
in acetone, 80
in aqueous dithiocarbamate, 89
in aqueous phenolic solutions, 80, 157
in aqueous sodium carbonate and hydroxide, desorption of hypochlorous acid, 88
in chlorobenzene, 47
in cyclohexanone, 81
in water, reversible, 106
Complex reactions:
in absorption with autocatalytic reactions, 213
in absorption with photochemical reactions, 216
glossary of, 222
in sumultaneous absorption of two gases, 171
Consecutive reactions:
both in depletion regime, 125
both fast reactions, 124
both slow or very slow reactions, 121
effect of mass transfer coefficient on selectivity, 131
effect of temperature on selectivity, 133
examples, 121, 134
first step in regime 3 or between regimes 2 and 3 and second step slow, 122
first step instantaneous, 128
selectivity index in, 126, 130, 136
Contractors:
for gas-liquid systems, 317
for gas-liquid-solid (catalytic) systems, 350
for gas-liquid-solid (reacting) systems, 349
for liquid-liuid systems, 339
simulation and design, 225
Controlling mechanism, procedure for discerning:
by the effect of temperature, 42
examples, 42
for irreversible reactions:
gas-liquid, 38
liquid-liquid, 42
with jet apparatus, 38
with mechanically agitated contactor, 41, 42
in packed bubble column reactors, 308
in slurry reactors, 280
with stirred cell, 40
with stirred contactor, 41
in trickle-bed reactors, 307, 309
Cyclohexanone:
chlorination, 216
oximation, 192

Dehydrogenation of secondary alcohols in slurry reactors, 298
Desorption:
physical, 195
preceded by chemical reaction, 195
simultaneous absorption-desorption, 205
with reaction, 199
Desorption preceded by chemical reaction:
in nonpolymeric systems, 195
examples, 195, 207
fast reactions, 196
instantaneously reversible reactions, 197
slow reactions, 196
in polymeric systems, 198
Dissociation extraction:
of *N*-alkylanilines and *N*-alkyltoluidines, 182
of carboxylic acids, 182
of chlorocresols, 181
of chlorophenols, 181
of chloroxylenols, 182, 252
of cresols, 181
of cresols and 2,6-xylenol, 181
of isomeric chlorobenzoic acids, 252
of isomeric xylidines, 182
of piperidine and *N*-methyl piperidine, 180
of substituted anilines, 182
theory, 178
Dissolution with reaction:
of copper and cupric sulfide in aqueous ammonia, 272
of esters and acetals, 251
of phthalic anhydride, 251
of silver halides, 252
theory, 248, 258
Dyeing of cellulosic fabrics, 252

Enhancement factor:
asymptotic, 27, 127, 150, 264
for desorption, 198
effect of diffusivity ratio in depletion regime, 31
for gas absorption, 23, 161
for solid dissolution, 264
Epoxidation of olefins and styrene in slurry reactors, 298
Esters:
alkaline hydrolysis:
in liquid-liquid systems, 50, 53, 57, 62, 81
in solid-liquid systems, 251
manufacture, using ion exchange resins, 255
phosphate esters of alcohols, synthesis in solid-liquid systems, 251
Ethylene chlorohydrin, manufacture, 155
Extraction accompanied by chemical reaction:
of beryllium cation with 2-ethyl hexyl phosphoric acid, 93
of borates, 93
in both liquid phases, 185
of copper:
with alkylated 8-hydroxyquinoline, 94
with hydroxyoximes, 94, 99
of copper sulfate from aqueous solutions, 94
examples, 5, 50, 56, 62, 81, 91, 99
of free fatty acids from glycerides, 91

of metals, 83, 92
simultaneous nitration of benzene and toluene, 170
simultaneous, of two solutes, 178
theory, *see* Mass transfer, in fluid-fluid systems
of uranium anions with tertiary amines, 92
Extractive reactions:
in acid hydrolysis of pentosans, 52
in dichromate oxidation of secondary alcohols, 52
in slurry reactors, 288

Fast reactions:
effect of temperature on mass transfer, 108
effect of temperature rise at interface, 109
examples, 63
with gas side resistance, 63
theory, 20
Film type contactors:
disk reactors, 327
packed columns, 318
thin-film reactors, 327
trickle-bed reactors, 326
Fischer-Tropsch reaction in slurry reactors, 294
Fixed-bed reactors, 301
discerning controlling mechanism, 307
effect of temperature, 307
examples, 309
flow regimes, 301
mass transfer in, 301
use of inert particles in, 307
Fluid-fluid-solid (catalytic) systems:
contactors for, 350
examples, 9
see also Mass transfer, in fluid-fluid-solid (catalytic) systems
Fluid-fluid-solid (reacting) systems:
contactors for, 349
examples, 8, 9
see also Mass transfer, in fluid-fluid-solid (reacting) systems

Gas-dispersed contactors;
bubble columns, 331
coiled reactors, 336
controlled cycle contactors, 329
horizontal cocurrent contactors, 335
jet reactors, 336
mechanically agitated contactors, 329
packed bubble columns, 334
plate columns, 327
plunging jet reactors, 336
sectionalized bubble columns, 334
vortex reactors, 336
Gas-liquid contactors:
foaming in, 337
gas-dispersed, 327
liquid as film, 318
liquid-dispersed, 336
for non-Newtonian fluids, 338
salient features, 323
selection, 317
simulation and design, 225
Gas-liquid reactions:
contactors for, 317
controlling mechanism, procedure for discerning, 38
examples, 1, 46, 55, 59, 63, 87, 97
in pyrometallurgy, 90
theory, *see* Mass transfer, in fluid-fluid reactions
Gas-liquid-solid:
contactors:
solids as catalysts, 350
as reactants, 349
reactions, 8, 9, 272
Gravity operated extractors:
controlled cycle columns, 344
Graesser contactor, 346
inert-gas-agitated contactor, 346
Kuehni column, 347
mixer-settlers, 344
packed column, 342
pulsed column, 347
reciprocating sieve-plate column, 347
sieve plate column, 344
spray column, 341
vibrating-plate extractor, 348
Grignard reagents, manufacture in solid-liquid systems, 272

Hydrochlorination of olefins, 48
Hydrodemetallization of residual oils in fixed-bed reactors, 312
Hydrodesulfurization of petroleum fractions in fixed-bed reactors, 311
Hydroformylation of isobutylene, 178
Hydrogen sulfide, absorption:
in amines, 88
reversible, in amines and alkalies, 105
simultaneous:
with carbon dioxide, 167, 168, 173
with ethylene oxide, 178
Hydrogenation:
in manufacture of alkali metal hydrides, 274
in packed bubble columns:
of d-methyl styrene, 309
of phenyl acetylene, 309
in slurry reactors:
of allyl alcohols, 295
of crotonaldehyde, 295
of fatty oils, 290
of fumaric acid, 295
and hydrocracking of α-cellulose, 297
of α-methyl styrene, 288
of nitroaromatics, 292
of olefinic compounds, 290
of phenyl acetylene, 289
simultaneous, of ethylene and propylene, 300
of xylose, 295
in trickle-bed reactors:
of benzene, 310
of crotonaldehyde, 310
of α-methyl styrene, 309, 310, 311
of phenyl acetylene, 309
Hydrolysis, alkaline:
of acetate esters, 50, 57, 62, 81
of benzyl chloride, 50
of C_5 chlorides, 50
of esters and acetals in solid-liquid systems, 251
of formate esters, 81
of *p*-nitrophenyl laurate, effect of surfactants, 53
of phthalic anhydride/maleic anhydride in solid-liquid systems, 249
of α,α,α-trichlorotoluene, use of emulsifiers, 54

Instantaneous reactions:
  contribution of gas-side resistance, 87
  effect of diffusivity ratio, 86
  effect of temperaure, 109
  effect of temperature rise at surface, 110
  examples, 86
  theory, 26
Interfacial area:
  chemical method for measuring, 63
  from Danckwerts' plot, 84
  emulsifiers for enhancing, 54
  in gas-liquid contactors, 323
  in liquid-liquid contactors, 340
Interfacial polycondensation:
  involving copolycondensation, 157
  nylon 6-10, manufacture, 95
  polycarbonates, manufacture, 96
  reaction in both phases, 193
Interfacial reactions, 53
Interfacial turbulence:
  effect on extraction, 112
  effect on gas absorption, 111
Ion exchange resins:
  in esterification reactions, 255
  manufacture, 271
  mass transfer in systems involving, 254
  Nernst-Planck model for reaction rates involving, 255
  triphase catalysis, 256
Irreversible reactions, rate expressions for mass transfer:
  depletion regime:
    film theory solution, 28
    effect of diffusivity ratio, 31
    penetration theory solution, 30
  fast reactions:
    film theory solution, 20, 22
    various values of *m* and *n*, 22
  instantaneous reactions:
    film theory solution, 27
    with gas side resistance, 33
    penetration theory solution, 27
  regime between 1 and 2, 18
  regime overlapping 1, 2 and 3:
    Danckwerts' surface renewal theory solution, 26
    film theory solution, 24
  regime between 2 and 3:
    Danckwerts' surface renewal theory solution, 24
    film theory solution, 21
    penetration theory solution, 23
  slow reactions, 17
  very slow reactions, 17
  volatile liquid-phase reactant, 31
Isobutylene, absorption
  in acetic acid, 47
  in ionic thallium (III) solutions, 76
  in sulfuric acid, 75, 161, 169
  in trifluoroacetic acid, 76
Isocyanates, manufacture in solid-liquid systems, 252
Isomerisation of epoxides in slurry reactors, 299
Isotopes:
  manufacture of, 106
  preparation of C-13, 56

Kinetically controlled reactions, *see* Very slow reactions
Kinetics:
  of gas-liquid reactions, examples, 46, 63, 64, 70
  of liquid-liquid reactions, examples, 50, 66, 81
  from theory of mass transfer with chemical reaction, 59, 62, 83

Liquid-dispersed contactors:
  spray columns, 336
  venturi scrubbers, 230, 337
Liquid-liquid contactors:
  centrifugal extractors, 348
  gravity operated extractors, 341
  pipeline contactors, 348
  salient features, 340
  selection, 339
  simulation and design, 230
Liquid-liquid reactions:
  contactors for, 339
  controlling mechanism, procedure for discerning, 42
  examples, 5, 50, 56, 62, 81, 91, 99
  in pesticide manufacture, 96
  phase transfer catalysis in, 52
  in purification of phosphorus, 58
  in pyrometallurgy, 56, 90
  use of emulsifiers in, 54
  see also Mass transfer, in fluid-fluid systems

Marangoni effect, 111. *See also* Interfacial turbulence
Mass transfer:
  in fluid-fluid systems:
    absorption-desorption with reaction, 199
    absorption of one gas into two reactants, 142
    absorption, simultaneous of two gases:
      in non-reacting media, 158
      that react with each other, 174
      in a reacting media, 158, 168
    autocatalytic reactions, 213
    complex reactions in simultaneous absorption of two gases, 171
    contactors:
      for gas-liquid, 317
      for liquid-liquid, 339
    consecutive reactions, 120
    desorption preceded by reactions, 195
    gas-liquid reactions, examples, 1
    irreversible reactions, 17
    liquid-liquid reactions, examples, 5
    photochemical reactions, 216
    physical absorption-desorption, criteria for supersaturation, 205
    physical desorption, 195
    reaction in both phases, 185
    reversible reactions, 34
    simulation and design of contactors, 225
    two-step reactions, 136
  in fluid-fluid-solid (catalytic) systems, 277
    contactors for, 350
    examples, 9
    fixed-bed reactors, 301
    packed bubble column reactors, 306
    slurry reactors, 279
    trickle-bed reactors, 326
  in fluid-fluid-solid (reacting) systems:

absorption, simultaneous of two gases, 265
contactors for, 349
examples, 8, 9, 265, 269
insoluble particles:
of changing size, 268
of constant size, 267
sparingly soluble particles:
negligible dissolution in film, 258
significant dissolution in film, 260
in solid-liquid systems:
bubble column reactors, 238
horizontal pipeline reactors, 248
with ion-exchange resins, 254
liquid fluidized-bed reactors, 237
mechanically agitated reactors, 240
non-Newtonian systems, 248
packed bubble columns reactors, 237
pulsing flow reactors, 237
shrinking and transpiration effects in, 244
spouted-bed reactors, 238
in stagnant media, 236
mass transfer coefficient, measurement, 234
reaction of insoluble solids, 8, 266
reaction of sparingly soluble solids, 7, 248
Mass transfer coefficient:
in fluid-fluid systems:
from Danckwerts' plot, 84
in gas-liquid contactors, 323
gas-side, measurement, 63
in liquid-liquid contactors, 340
liquid-side, measurement, 59
in solid-liquid systems, measurement techniques:
chemical method, 235
electrochemical method, 235
solids dissolution, 234
use of ion exchange, 234
use of solid catalytic particles, 235
moment analysis of dynamic data, 235
Mass transfer with chemical reaction:
determination of rate constant, 59, 62, 83
effect of diffusivity ratio, 86
effect of temperature, 106
estimation of diffusivity, 87
measurement:
of gas-side mass transfer coefficient, 63
of holdup, 54
of interfacial area, 63, 84
of liquid-side mass transfer coefficient, 59
of solubility in reacting systems, 59
Mechanically agitated contactors:
correlations for solid-liquid mass transfer coefficient, 240
calculation of solid-liquid mass transfer coefficient, 245
effect of operating variables on solid-liquid mass transfer coefficient, 245
for gas-liquid systems, 329
for liquid-liquid systems, 344
scale-up, 230
theories of solid-liquid mass transfer in, 240
Melts, in gas-liquid reactions:
butadine with molten maleic anhydride, 104
carbonylation of ethylene, 103
chlorination:
of methane, 103
of methyl cyclohexane, 103
coupling of hydrocarbons, 104
examples, 99, 101
fluorination of carbon tetrachloride, 100
hydrogenation of olefins, 104
nitration of propane, 104
oxidation:
of benzoic acid, 102
of hydrogen chloride, 100
of sulfur dioxide, 102
of tetravalent vanadium, 102
oxidative dehydrogenation of hydrocarbons, 104
oxychlorination of ethane and ethylene, 103
processing of spent fuels in nuclear reactors, 100
recovery of sulfur dioxide/sulfur trioxide, 103
Mercaptans, absorption in caustic soda, 88
Methanation in trickle-bed reactors, 314
Micellar catalysis, 53
Model contactors:
gas-liquid systems, 38
jet apparatus, 38, 230
mechanically agitated contactor, 41
salient features, 227
stirred cell, 40
stirred contactor, 41
use in simulation and design, 226
liquid-liquid systems, 42

Nitration:
of aromatic compounds, 57, 85, 251
of chlorobenzene, 50
of 1-dodecene, 58
of phenol, 92
of propane in molten nitrates, 104
of toluene, 57, 83, 85
simultaneous, of benzene and toluene, 170
Nitric oxide, absorption:
in aqueous nitric acid, 74
in concentrated nitric acid, gas phase reaction, 74
in lime slurries containing sodium chlorite, 73, 266
reversible, in aqueous solutions of ferrous sulphate, 106
Nitrogen dioxide/nitrogen tetroxide, absorption:
Nitrogen dioxide and nitric oxide/nitrogen dioxide, absorption:
simultaneous, 170
with sulfur dioxide, 170
in weak alkaline solutions, 69
Nitrogen dioxide and nitric oxide/nitrogen dioxide, absorption:
in aqueous alkaline solutions of sodium sulfite, 156
in water, 69
NO_x gases, absorption:
in aqueous alkaline sodium dithionite, 73
in aqueous alkaline sodium chlorite and sodium hydroxide, 73
in aqueous alkaline sodium hypochlorite, 73
in aqueous alkaline solutions with and without sodium sulfite, 74
in aqueous potassium permanganate solutions containing sodium hydroxide, 73
in aqueous sodium carbonate, 74
in aqueous sodium hydroxide, 74
in aqueous sodium sulfide, 73

NO_x gases, absorption (*Continued*)
in aqueous sodium sulfite containing Fe(III)-EDTA-sodium and ferric sulfate, 74
in hydrogen peroxide, 73
in water, reaction between dissolved nitric oxide and oxygen, 69

Olefins:
absorption in cuprous ammonium compounds, 88
dimerisation of, 50
hydrochlorination of, 48
Wacker processes, 48
Oligomerization of butene-1, 82
Oxidation:
by air:
of aqueous sodium sulfide, 61, 296
of benzoic acid in melts, 102
of black liquor, 61
of butane, 56
of *n*-butyraldehyde, 74, 75
of cumene, 55
of cyclohexane/cyclododecane, desorption of water, 209
of ethyl benzene, 46
of 2-ethylhexaldehyde, 74
of hydrogen chloride in cuprous chloride melts, 100
of hydrogen sulfide, 61
of mercaptans, 61
of *p*-nitrotoluene sulfonic acid, 47
of paraffinic hydrocarbons, 47
of sulfur dioxide, 171
of sulfur dioxide over melts, 101
of tributyl phosphine, 49
of tributyl phosphite, 49
of *o*-xylene, 55
by oxygen/ozone mixture:
of aluminum trialkyls, 79
of aqueous alkaline potassium cyanide solutions, 78
of tri-*n*-butylboron, 79
of cyclododecatriene, 78
of formaldehyde, 78
of formic acid, 78
of methanol, 78
of methyl oleate and methyl soyate, 78
of 1-(*p*-nitrophenyl) 2-acetylamino-1,3 propanediol, 78
of sulfides, 78
in slurry reactors:
of alcohols, 297
of aqueous sodium sulfide, 296
of sulfur dioxide, 295
in trickle bed reactors:
of dilute formic acid and acetic acid, 312
of sulfur dioxide, 314
wet air:
of effluent liquors, 61
of nylon-66, 276
Oximation of cyclohexanone, 81
Oxychlorination of ethylene, 171
Oxygen, absorption:
in alkaline sodium dithionite, 68, 98
in alkaline solutions containing the sodium salt of 1,4-naphthaquinone-2-sulfonic acid, 98
in aqueous acidic cuprous chloride, 55, 67
in aqueous sodium sulfite, 68, 98
in aqueous sodium sulfite, kinetics of, 70
in *n*-butyraldehyde, 75
in cuprous amine complexes in polar solvents, 67
in cuprous and cobaltous amine complexes, 67, 68
in *n*-ethylhexaldehyde, 74
in hemoglobin, 90
in silver cyanide solutions, 272
simultaneous, with carbon monoxide, 172, 173
Ozone, absorption:
in aldehydes, 75
in alkaline solutions, 77
in aqueous phenol, 77
for colour removal, 78
in wastewater treatment, 77
simultaneous, with oxygen, 78

Packed bubble column:
carbon dioxide absorption in carbonate buffer, 60
discerning controlling mechanism, 308
for gas-liquid systems, 334
scaleup, 231
solid-liquid systems, mass transfer in, 237
use of inert particles, 307
Packed column:
carbon dioxide absorption in carbonate buffer, 60
cocurrent *vs*. countercurrent, 325
cross flow, 326
for gas-liquid systems, 318
for liquid-liquid systems, 342
simulation and design, 229
stacked *vs*. random packing, 325
tube type, 326
Phase transfer catalysis:
in liquid-liquid systems, 52
manufacture of benzyl esters, 250
polymer supported, 256
Phosphine, absorption:
in aqueous formaldehyde and hydrochloric acid, 48
in aqueous sodium hypochlorite, 77
in aqueous sulfuric acid, 77
Photochemical reaction, in gas absorption, 216
Pipeline contactors:
fiber film, 348
static mixer, 348
Plate column:
for gas-liquid systems, 327
for liquid-liquid systems, 344
Polyethylene terephthalate, synthesis in solid-liquid systems, 249

Reaction in both (liquid) phases:
examples, 192
fast reactions, 188
instantaneous reactions, 190
reactions in depletion regime, 192
reaction in single phase, 188
very slow reactions, 186
Reaction schemes, glossary of, 219
Reduction:
of ammonium nitrite/nitrate in slurry reactors, 294
of aromatic nitrocompounds with sodium sulfide/sodium disulfide, 51, 250
of molten dinitrochlorobenzene, 57
of uranium (V) in slurry reactors, 297
of vat dyes in solid-liquid systems, 269

Regimes of mass transfer with reaction, theory and examples:
fast reactions (regime 3), 20, 62
fast reactions with gas side resistance, 33, 63, 87
instantaneous reactions (regime 4), 26, 86
regime between 1 and 2, 18, 59
regime between 2 and 3, 21, 83
regime between 3 and 4, 28, 97
regime overlapping between 1, 2 and 3, 24, 85
slow reactions (regime 2), 17, 55
very slow reactions, 17, 46
Removal/Recovery:
of aliphatic acids from aqueous streams, 91
of bromine from lean aqueous bromides, 89
of hydrochloric acid and hydrofluoric acid from aqueous solutions, 91
of mercaptans from petroleum fractions, 57
of carbonyl sulfide from C_3/C_4 streams, 66
of sulfur dioxide and sulfur trioxide from emissions, 103
Reversible reactions:
examples, 105
rate expression for mass transfer:
fast reactions with depletion in film, 36
fast reactions without depletion in film, 34
instantaneous reactions, 37

Scaleup:
fast reactions, 83
instantaneous reactions, 97
regime between fast and instantaneous reactions, 99
regime between very slow and slow reactions, 62
packed columns, 229
packed bubble columns, 231
mechanically agitated contactors, 230
slow reactions, 59
very slow reactions, 54
Selectivity Index:
in consecutive reactions, 126, 130
effect of liquid side mass transfer coefficient, 131
effect of temperature, 133
in homogeneous systems, 136
Separation:
by dissociation extraction, 178
of *n*-paraffins from isoparaffins, 271
see also Dissociation extraction
Simulation and design of fluid-fluid reactors:
absorption in model apparatus, 226
complications due to additional reactions in bulk, 227
gas-liquid systems, 225
integral modeling, 228
laminar jet apparatus for, 230
packed columns, 229
point modeling, 225
liquid-liquid systems, 230
model contactors, salient features, 227
small scale apparatus for, 230
small scale contactor for, 227
Simultaneous absorption of two gases:
in a non-reacting medium, 158
in a reacting medium, 158, 168
ammonia and carbon dioxide, 145
carbon dioxide and carbonyl sulfide, 163
depletion regime, 160, 162
examples, 159, 161, 163, 167, 168
fast reactions, 159, 161
gas film controlled, of one gas, 167
hydrogen cyanide and carbon dioxide, 170
hydrogen sulfide and carbon dioxide, 167, 168
instantaneous reactions, 161, 166
instantaneous reaction for one gas, 160, 165
isobutylene and butene-2, 161, 169
mercaptans and carbon dioxide, 170
nitrogen dioxide and nitric oxide, 170
nitric oxide/nitrogen dioxide and sulfur dioxide, 170
reaction in bulk, 168
followed by complex reactions:
carbon dioxide and phosgene, 172
carbon monoxide and carbon dioxide, 173
carbon monoxide and oxygen, 172
hydrogen sulfide and carbon dioxide, 173
oxygen and carbon monoxide, 173
product of first gas as reactant for second gas, 171
reaction of first gas resulting in formation of second gas, 172
reversible, 173
sulfur dioxide and carbon dioxide, 172
sulfur dioxide and oxygen, 171
gases reacting with each other:
ammonia and carbon dioxide, 176
carbon dioxide and hydrogen, 178
chlorine and acetylene, 177
chlorine and ethylene, 177
chlorine and sulfur dioxide, 177
examples, 160
gases introduced separately, 175
gases in a mixture, 174
Simultaneous absorption-desorption with reaction:
chlorine in aqueous sodium hydroxide, desorption of hypochlorous acid, 210
examples, 200, 209
fast reactions, 202
instantaneous reactions, 204
liquid-phase-controlled desorption, 204
slow reactions, 200, 202
sulfur dioxide in aqueous carbonate buffers, desorption of carbon dioxide, 210
supersaturation during, 206
very slow reactions, 201
Slow reactions:
examples, 55
effect of temperature, 107
theory, 17
Solid-liquid reactions:
examples:
solids insoluble, 8
solids slightly soluble, 7
Stability of gas-liquid reactors:
multiple steady states, 113
two steady states in hydrogenation, 311
Spray column:
gas-liquid operation, 336
liquid-liquid operation, 341
Sulfonation:
of aromatics with sulfur trioxide, 89
of aromatics with sulfuric acid, 62
Sulfur dioxide, absorption:
in calcium hydroxide/magnesium hydroxide slurries, 265
in manufacture of dithionites, 274

Sulfur dioxide, absorption (*Continued*)
oxidation of, 171
in slurry reactors, 295
in trickle-bed reactors, 314
recovery from emissions, 103
simultaneous:
with carbon dioxide, 172
with chlorine, 177
with NO_x gases, 170
Supersaturation:
effect on mass transfer rates, 206
in absorption-desorption with reaction, 206
in physical absorption-desorption, 205

Temperature, effect on mass transfer with chemical reaction:
fast reactions, 108
instantaneous reactions, 109
slow reactions, 107
very slow reactions, 106
Temperature rise at interface:
for fast reactions, 109
for instantaneous reactions, 110
Transcat process, 103
Trickle-bed reactors:
backmixing in, 307
controlling mechanism, procedure for discerning, 307, 309
examples, 309
for gas-liquid systems, 326
for solid-liquid systems, mass transfer in, 236
for wastewater treatment, 312, 313
use of inert particles in, 307
Triphase catalysis, 256
Two-step reactions:
in depletion regime, 138
fast to instantaneous, 137
instantaneous, 140

Venturi jet scrubber, simulation, 230
Very slow reactions:
effect of temperature, 106
examples, 46
theory, 17

Wacker processes, 48, 67, 171

Zieglar-Natta catalysts:
characteristics, 299
diffusional factors in, 300
models for, 299, 300
narrow molecular weight distributions, methods for obtaining, 300
slurry polymerization with, 299